Probability of Independent Events: $P(A \cap B) = P(A) \times P(B)$

Factorial Notation: $n! = n \times (n-1) \times (n-2) \times \ldots \times 2 \times 1$

Permutations: $P(n, r) = \frac{n!}{(n-r)!}$

Permutations with a, b, and c Like Objects $= \frac{n!}{a!b!c!\ldots}$

Combinations: $C(n, r) = \frac{n!}{(n-r)!r!}$

Odds in Favour of A: $P(A):1 - P(A)$

Chapter 5

Expected Value of a Discrete Random Variable:

$$E(X) = \sum_{i=1}^{n} x_i P(X = x_i)$$

Binomial Theorem: $(a+b)^n = \sum_{r=0}^{n} \binom{n}{r} a^{n-r} b$

Pascal's Identity: $\binom{n}{r} + \binom{n}{r+1} = \binom{n+1}{r+1}$

General Term of a Binomial Expansion: $t_{r+1} = \binom{n}{r} a^{n-r} b^r$

Binomial Probability Distribution: $P(X = k) = \binom{n}{k} (p)^k (1-p)^{n-k}$

Expected Value of a Binomial Probability Distribution: $E(X) = np$

Normal Approximation of a Binomial Probability Distribution:

$$x = np \qquad \sigma = \sqrt{np(1-p)}$$

NELSON

Mathematics of Data Management

Authors

David Zimmer
Gordon Cooke
Stewart Craven
Beverly Farahani
Thomas Steinke
Chris Kirkpatrick

THOMSON NELSON™

Australia Canada Mexico Singapore Spain United Kingdom United States

Mathematics of Data Management

David Zimmer
Gordon Cooke
Stewart Craven
Beverly Farahani
Thomas Steinke
Chris Kirkpatrick

Director of Publishing
David Steele

Publisher, Mathematics
Cheryl Turner

Program Manager
Colin Garnham

Project Manager
Debbie Davies-Wright

Developmental Editors
Noel Walker, Mary Steele

Editorial Assistant
Vanessa Davison

Senior Managing Editor
Nicola Balfour

Editors
Evelyn Maksimovich, Margot Miller, Laurel Sparrow, Dave Wright

Senior Production Coordinator
Sharon Latta Paterson

Creative Director
Angela Cluer

Interior Design
Katherine Strain

Cover Design
Katherine Strain, Peter Papayanakis

Composition
Nelson Gonzalez

Photo Research and Permissions
Paula Joiner

Creative Art/Technical Art
Debra Crowle, Peter Papayanakis, Anthony de Ridder

Printer
Transcontinental Printing Inc.

The authors wish to express their thanks to Jan and Barry Scully.

Printed and bound in Canada
3 4 5 6 08 07 06 05

For more information contact Nelson, 1120 Birchmount Road, Toronto, Ontario, M1K 5G4. Or you can visit our Internet site at http://www.nelson.com

National Library of Canada Cataloguing in Publication Data

Main entry under title:
Mathematics of data management

Ontario ed.
Includes index
ISBN 0-17-615779-4

1. Mathematics statistics.
I. Cooke, Gord

QA273.M37 2002 519.5
C2002-900790-9

Advisory Panel

Alison Gibbs
Assistant Professor
York University

Jacqueline Hill
Port Perry High School
Durham District School Board

Mary Howe
Coordinator of Mathematics, Science and Technology
London District Catholic School Board

Don McLeish
Professor
University of Waterloo

Mike Neill
Opeongo High School
Renfrew County District School Board

Silvanna F. Simone
Instructional Leader for Mathematics
Toronto District School Board

Reviewer Panel

Alexandra Belloni
Mother Teresa High School
Ottawa-Carleton Catholic Secondary School Board

Louise Brighton
Mother Teresa Catholic Secondary School
Toronto Catholic District School Board

Karen Bryan
North Dundas District High School
Upper Canada District School Board

Angela Con
St. Elizabeth Catholic Elementary School
Peterborough Victoria Northumberland Clarington CDSB

Frank DiPietro
Consultant
Windsor-Essex District School Board

Bob Fleischauer
Centre Wellington District High School
Upper Grand District School Board

Bonnie Fraser
Retired
Formerly Greater Essex County District School Board

Patricia Kehoe
Mother Teresa High School
Ottawa-Carleton Catholic School Board

Elizabeth Pattison
Westlane Secondary School
Niagara District School Board

Kathy Pilon
St. John Catholic High School
Catholic District School Board of Eastern Ontario

Greg Pyke
Richview Collegiate
Toronto District School Board

Peter Wei
North Toronto Collegiate Institute
Toronto District School Board

Betsy Wimbs
SATEC @ W.A. Porter
Toronto District School Board

Contents

Part 3
Making Sense of the Data

Part 4
Making the Case and Evaluating the Conclusions

Introduction to Nelson Mathematics of Data Management

Nelson Mathematics of Data Management is designed to help you develop skills in finding, using, and making sense of data. You may have already experienced first hand the challenge facing researchers in recent years: too much data, much of which is biased, incomplete, or inadequate. *Nelson Mathematics of Data Management* is intended to prepare you to deal with the increasing need to "locate, organize, analyze, and use accurate information effectively."

In real-world applications, data are used to guide decisions, explain events, predict future courses of action, or provide the basis for a solution to a problem. Data are never collected without a specific purpose. This course emphasizes

- strategies and methods for finding, organizing, and analyzing large amounts of data; and
- applying these strategies to solving problems and exploring significant issues.

Statistical methods and probability theory are included in the course to provide the mathematical background and technical tools needed to support the management of data for solving significant problems.

The Culminating Project

In line with the focus on the application of data management to problem solving, you will be asked to present a final course project. You will be expected to demonstrate your understanding of the concepts of the course by completing "a culminating project on a topic or issue of significance that requires the integration and application of the expectations of the course." In addition, you will "present this project to an audience and critique the projects of others." The *Ontario Curriculum Guideline* for the Mathematics of Data Management course states the following expectations related to your course project.

Carrying Out a Culminating Project

By the end of this course, students will

- pose a significant problem whose solution would require the organization and analysis of a large amount of data;
- select and apply the tools of the course (e.g., methods for organizing data, methods for calculating and interpreting measures of probability and statistics, methods for data collection) to design and carry out a study of the problem;
- compile a clear, well-organized, and fully justified report of the investigation and its findings.

Presenting and Critiquing Projects

By the end of this course, students will

- create a summary of a project to present within a restricted length of time, using communications technology effectively;
- answer questions about a project, fully justifying mathematical reasoning;
- critique the mathematical work of others in a constructive fashion.

The Culminating Project and This Textbook

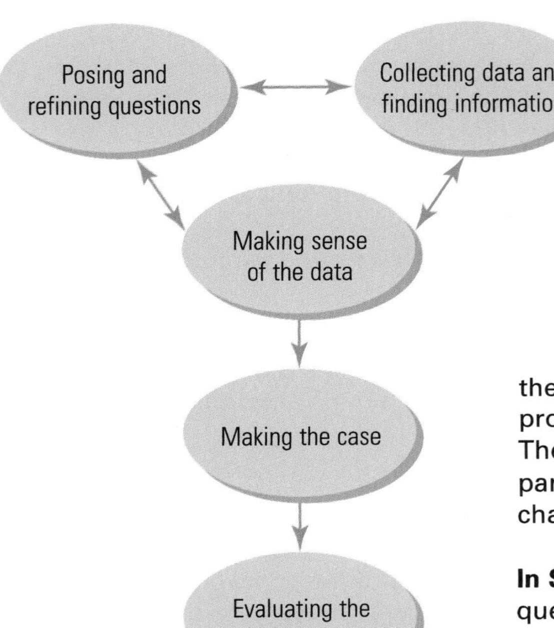

The sequence in which the course topics are presented in this textbook reflects the Data-Driven Problem Solving process presented in the flow chart shown to the left. The key components of the process are as follows:

- Posing and Refining Questions
- Collecting Data and Finding Information
- Making Sense of the Data
- Making the Case
- Evaluating the Conclusions

The topics in this textbook are sequenced to follow the steps of this process so that you can work on your project as you complete your study of the course material. The relevant steps of the process being presented in any particular chapter are highlighted in the process flow chart on the first page of each chapter.

Chapter 1: The Power of Information and **Chapter 2: In Search of Good Data** focus on posing and refining questions and on collecting data and finding information. **Sections 6.1** and **6.2** of Chapter 6 provide diagramming techniques that will help you organize your thoughts and explore relationships among data.

Chapter 3: Tools for Analyzing Data provides the statistical tools you will need to organize and analyze the data you have collected. **Sections 6.3** and **6.4** of Chapter 6 present matrix methods for working with certain types of data that can also be used to help you organize and analyze your data.

Chapter 4: Dealing with Uncertainty—An Introduction to Probability and **Chapter 5: Probability Distributions and Predictions** develop the theory and applications of probability and provide the mathematical background for the development and future study of statistics. These chapters also present techniques for building and evaluating simulations when it is not possible to theoretically determine the actual characteristics of a population. As you work through this textbook, you will be able to develop your course project in small, manageable steps, and use data to solve problems drawn from realistic situations.

Getting Started on the Culminating Project

A. **Ask the Right Question**
The most important, and most difficult, step in any research project is the *selection of a topic*. If the topic is too broad, you will not be able to complete the project in the time available. By narrowing your focus, you increase your chances of making in-depth analysis with your project. However, if your topic is too narrow, you risk spending too much time on a minor issue of no statistical interest. If you can *state your topic as a question*, you increase the likelihood of finding relevant data to help answer your question.

For example, suppose you were interested in discovering the impact a part-time job has on the academic achievement of a high school student. You might pose a question such as, *What effect does the number of hours a student works have on her or his science marks?* This narrows the focus of your research by forcing you to answer a relatively specific question. Without a specific question to define your problem, your research efforts could span a wide variety of topics and issues.

B. **Develop Your Topic**
The process of developing your topic will take time, as will collecting and analyzing data in terms of your question. *If you can't find the answer in your research, you may need to narrow or broaden your question.*

Narrow your question if
- you can't find reliable data or the amount of data available is overwhelming;
- you can't reach specific conclusions; or
- you can't make specific recommendations.

Broaden your question if
- you seem to be spending a lot of time on a minor aspect;
- you discover there are major aspects or issues you haven't considered; or
- you can't find information on your topic.

C. **Revise Your Question (If Necessary)**
As you become more knowledgeable about the topic and are able to make better sense of the data you have collected, you may need to modify your question. Your research may even require you to refine or modify your question several times before you finalize it. If you find that you are headed down the wrong path, consider completely revising your question.

Here are some specific suggestions for deciding whether to modify or revise your question:
- **Develop a working knowledge of your topic as soon as possible.** You should be able to talk about your topic with someone else for at least a few minutes. This will mean you know enough of the basic ideas and issues to begin formulating questions for further inquiry.

If not, more research or a narrowing of your question may be needed.

- **Choose an aspect of your topic that is specific and distinct.** You will know this is the case if you can ask a reasonably specific question and find information with which you can really work. If not, modify or revise your question.
- **You should be personally interested in the topic.** A personal interest in the topic will make the time and energy required to do a good job on the final project less of a burden. If this is not the case, revise your topic and question.
- **Find controversies or questions related to your narrowed topic.** Read the literature, examine the news media, and search the Internet to find current and interesting data. This will help you to identify significant issues associated with your topic and to see what research has already been carried out.
- **Look for data in a variety of places.** Be cautious about using the Internet as your only source of information. Data that appear there are not always trustworthy. An Internet search may be useful in providing you with a list of other places to look for credible information. Try to locate sources of information in which the data have been validated, such as research journals. These publications use professional researchers to check the accuracy of the reported information and validate the analyses.

D. Sources of Information

Here is a partial list of sources of information you might explore:

Source	Comments
• Subject-related research journals • Subject-specific encyclopedias • Databases like those provided by Statistics Canada	• provide specific information on the subject • provide refereed data and analysis • identify researchers and other reliable sources of information
• Newspapers and magazines • Radios and television reports	• most likely to identify contemporary issues, controversies, or questions associated with the subject • may provide pointers to sources of data, special interest groups, or experts in the subject
• Interview of researchers in the field of interest • Government publications	• may provide current or unpublished data • can provide insight into current research in the field of interest • may provide leads to experts or sources of information • most likely to lead to contemporary information on the subject
• Internet search engines	• may provide leads to experts or sources of information • may identify contemporary issues, controversies, or questions associated with the subject • may provide pointers to other sources of data, special interest groups, or individuals interested in the subject

E. **Researching Your Project**

Start off by *looking for general background information* on your topic. Once you've found relevant background information on your topic, you should be able to finalize your question. Then you can begin to look for more specific and more recent information. *Make your question more specific as you find out more about your topic.*

Collecting too much information too early can be counterproductive. If everything you find seems relevant to your research question, then your question is probably too *general*. Although some of the information will be directly usable in your final presentation, much of it will not. Don't accumulate so much information that you can't figure out where to begin.

As part of your final project presentation, you will have to provide a bibliography of all your information sources. In order to credit the original source of any data you use, remember to keep detailed records of where and when you found the information.

F. **Scheduling Your Project**

You will have a deadline for your completed project and your presentation. Consult your teacher and follow these guidelines:

- *Divide the project into a series of separate tasks, each with its own target date.* This will enable you to plan each task in advance.
- *Schedule your time conservatively.* Allow more time for a task rather than less.
- *Consult with your teacher.* Work with your teacher to set up a series of deadlines so that you can monitor your progress. Inform your teacher whenever you have to change your plans.
- *Use a calendar to schedule all the work that has to be completed.* Don't overwhelm yourself with too much to do near the due date.

G. **A Task List**

Here's a suggested **task list** to help you get started. Copy it into your notebook and use it to begin planning your project.

Task	Earliest Possible Start Date	Related Chapters
1. **Identify an area of interest** to be researched.		1
2. Initial research stage—begin to accumulate **general background knowledge** and attempt to state the initial broad research question.		1, 2
3. Second research stage—**narrow the focus** of the research and attempt to refine the research question.		2
4. Third research stage—**locate and accumulate information and data** specific to the research question. This may involve original research on your part or it may involve finding data in a database.		2
5. Plan how you will analyze the data. Determine which **statistical tools** and **technology** you will use to analyze the data.		3
6. **Conduct the data analysis.** Make sure that the data, the analysis methods, and the conclusions are consistent with your research question.		3, 4, 5, 6

The following tasks should begin as soon as you are ready. You may be ready to work on them as soon as you begin working on Chapter 4 or 5. The material in Chapter 6 may be useful for the completion of your project as well.

Task	Earliest Possible Start Date	Related Chapters
7. Write the first draft of your report.		
8. Plan your presentation. You should expect to require no more than 10–15 min. • Determine any technology required for your presentation. • Create graphical representations for the data. • Create handout notes for the audience.		
9. Finalize your report.		
10. Finalize your presentation.		

H. Preparing and Organizing Presentations

You will need to decide on the format for your final product and presentation. Be prepared to give a presentation of at least 10 min in length, although the duration may vary.

For your presentation, state the question to be answered. Research results must be recorded in an organized manner, analyzed, and synthesized. Conclusions should be clearly communicated, justified, and follow naturally from the information that is presented.

There are a number of ways in which your presentation can be prepared and readied for the class. For example:

- Record the research on cue cards and then arrange the cards in a logical order.
- Use presentation software to create a slide show. This will visually reinforce your material, as well as keep you on track.
- Write an outline for the presentation.
- Have others in the class edit your presentation before you give it.
- Read your research to others and discuss the conclusions.

Checklist for Preparing and Organizing Oral Presentations

All good presentations follow a similar basic format. What follows is a checklist you can use when preparing your presentation.

Getting Ready to Speak

Identify your purpose. Decide what you want your audience to believe, remember, or do when you finish. Aim all parts of your presentation toward this purpose.

Know your audience. Consider how to create your presentation (its organization, appeals, and examples) so that it is most useful to the knowledge and needs of your audience.

Organizing the Introduction

Get the audience involved. Get the audience's attention by opening with a promise, story, startling fact, question, quote, relevant problem, or joke.

Establish yourself. Demonstrate your credibility by identifying your position, expertise, knowledge, or qualifications.

Preview your main points. Introduce your topic and summarize its principal parts.

Organizing the Body

Develop two to four main points. Streamline your topic so that you can concentrate on its major issues.

Arrange the points logically. Sequence your points chronologically, from most important to least important, by comparison and contrast, or by some other strategy.

Prepare transitions. Between each major point write "bridge" statements that connect the previous item to the next one. Use transitional expressions as verbal signposts. For example, words such as *first, second, then, however, consequently, on the contrary,* and so on, are good bridging words.

Have extra material ready. Be prepared with more information and visuals in case you have additional time to fill.

Organizing the Conclusion

Review your main points. Emphasize your main ideas in your closing so that your audience will remember them.

Provide a final focus. Tell how your audience can use this information, why you have spoken, or what you might want them to do.

Designing Visual Aids

Select your medium carefully. Consider the size of your audience, degree of formality desired, cost and ease of preparation, and potential effectiveness.

Highlight main ideas. Use visual aids to illustrate major concepts only. Keep them brief and simple.

Use aids carefully. Talk to the audience, not to the visuals. Paraphrase their contents.

Developing Electronic Presentations

Learn to use your software program. Study template and slide layout designs to see how you can adapt them for your purposes.

Select a pleasing colour palette. Work with five or fewer colours for your presentation.

Use bulleted points for major headings. Make sure your points are all parallel and never have more than seven points on a slide.

Make speaker's notes. Jot down the narrative supporting each slide and use these notes to practise your presentation.

Maintain control. Don't let your slides upstage you. Use a pointer to connect you to the slides and your audience.

Remember that it is perfectly natural and acceptable to be nervous. Your audience will forgive mistakes made along the way as long as you go back and correct them before continuing.

I. Bibliographies

While doing your research, you will use sources of information that you did not collect firsthand. The information may come from a book, an encyclopedia, an anthology, a CD-ROM, a film, a speech, or any one of a number of sources, and each one must be correctly documented in your bibliography.

The American Psychological Association (APA) developed a style of documentation that your teachers may want you to follow. Here are some examples of APA citations for a bibliography, based on the *Publication Manual of the American Psychological Association,* Fourth Edition, 1994.

In a bibliography using APA style, indent the first line of each entry and begin subsequent lines flush with the left margin. Invert all authors' names, giving surnames and initials, regardless of the number of authors. Use an ampersand (&) rather than the word "and" before the last author. Do not invert personal names that are not in the author position. Capitalize only the first word of the title and subtitle and any proper names. Shorten the publisher's name. Write out the names of associations, corporations, and university presses, but omit unnecessary terms such as *Publisher, Co.,* and *Inc.* Retain the words *Books* and *Press.*

A book by a single author

Include the author's name, the date of publication, the title of the book, the place of publication, and the publisher. You will find this information on the copyright page.

Garner, J. F. (1994). Politically correct bedtime stories: Modern tales for our life and times. Rockland, MA: Wheeler.

A book by two or more authors

Aker, D., & Hodgkinson, D. (2002). Language & writing 11. Toronto: Nelson.

A work in an anthology

King, T. (1998). Borders. In J. C. Stott, R. E. Jones, & R. Bowers (Eds.), The Harbrace anthology of literature (pp. 1163–1171). Toronto: Harcourt.

A reference book

If the article is signed by an author, begin the entry with the author's name. Otherwise, begin with the title of the article itself.

McGlathery, J. M. (1998). Grimm's fairy tales. In The world book encyclopedia. Chicago: World Book.

October Crisis. (1999). In The Canadian encyclopedia. Toronto: McClelland & Stewart.

A leaflet, brochure, or pamphlet

Canadian Authors Association. (1996). Writers helping writers [Leaflet]. Campbellford, ON: Author.

A newspaper or magazine article

Always show the date of the newspaper article along with the section and page number. Precede page numbers for newspaper articles with "p." or "pp."

York, G. (2000, August 21). Divers open sub's hatch. The Globe and Mail, pp. A1, A7.

Atwood, M. (1996, March–April). Why I write poetry. This Magazine, pp. 44–48.

A CD–ROM

Langley, C. (2000). Small-business basics [CD-ROM]. Red Deer, AB: Databurst Publishing.

A Web site

Include the date you retrieved the information.

Browning, R. (1849). My last duchess. In Dramatic romances and lyrics [Online]. Available December 10, 2000: http://www.library.utoronto.ca/utel/rp/ poems/browning1.html

A speech, lecture, or address

Clarkson, A. (1999, October 7). Installation speech. Rideau Hall, Ottawa.

A film or video

Kashiwabara, H., & Mimura, W. (Writers), & Okawara, T. (Director). (2000). Godzilla 2000 [Film]. Columbia Pictures.

J. Critiquing the Presentations of Others

Learning Mathematics from the Presentations of Other Students

Your presentation will be critiqued by the rest of the class as well as by your teacher. The assessment form that follows contains questions that will help you to effectively critique the presentations of others as well as the mathematics involved.

Assessment Criteria	**Rating**
1. Rate the overall presentation. *Comments:*	1 2 3 4 5
2. Rate the product. *Comments:*	1 2 3 4 5
3. The presenter appeared to be well-prepared. *Comments:*	1 2 3 4 5
4. The conclusions reached were reasonable and valid. *Comments:*	1 2 3 4 5
5. The presentation was interesting and informative. *Comments:*	1 2 3 4 5

6. If this had been my presentation, what might I have done differently? Explain.

7. Describe the topic of the presentation.

8. Summarize the presentation.

9. Describe the mathematics presented, giving examples.

10. Describe the conclusions reached. Do you agree with them? Why?

Special Features of Nelson Mathematics of Data Management

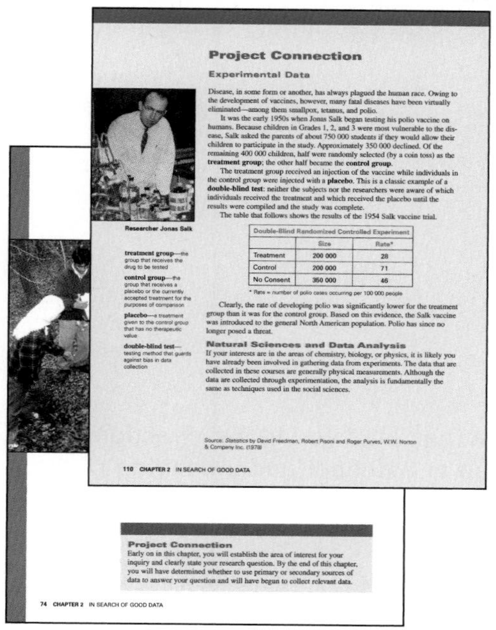

Project Connection

Experimental Data

Disease, in some form or another, has always plagued the human race. Owing to the development of vaccines, however, many fatal diseases have been virtually eliminated—among them smallpox, tetanus, and polio.

It was the early 1950s when Jonas Salk began testing his polio vaccine on humans. Because children in Grades 1, 2, and 3 were most vulnerable to the disease, Salk asked the parents of about 750 000 students if they would allow their children to participate in the study. Approximately 350 000 declined. Of the remaining 400 000 children, half were randomly selected (by a coin toss) as the **treatment group**; the other half became the **control group**.

The treatment group received an injection of the vaccine while individuals in the control group were injected with a **placebo**. This is a classic example of a **double-blind test**: neither the subjects nor the researchers were aware of which individuals received the treatment and which received the placebo until the results were compiled and the study was complete.

The table that follows shows the results of the 1954 Salk vaccine trial.

Researcher Jonas Salk

treatment group—the group that receives the drug to be tested

control group—the group that receives a placebo or the currently accepted treatment for the purposes of comparison

placebo—a treatment given to the control group that has no therapeutic value

double-blind test—testing method that guards against bias in data collection

Double-Blind Randomized Controlled Experiment

	Size	Rate*
Treatment	200 000	28
Control	200 000	71
No Consent	350 000	46

* Rate = number of polio cases occurring per 100 000 people

Clearly, the rate of developing polio was significantly lower for the treatment group than it was for the control group. Based on this evidence, the Salk vaccine was introduced to the general North American population. Polio has since no longer posed a threat.

Natural Sciences and Data Analysis

If your interests are in the areas of chemistry, biology, or physics, it is likely you have already been involved in gathering data from experiments. The data that are collected in these courses are generally physical measurements. Although the data are collected through experimentation, the analysis is fundamentally the same as techniques used in the social sciences.

Source: *Statistics* by David Freedman, Robert Pisoni and Roger Purves, W.W. Norton & Company Inc. (1978)

110 CHAPTER 2 IN SEARCH OF GOOD DATA

Project Connection

Early on in this chapter, you will establish the area of interest for your inquiry and clearly state your research question. By the end of this chapter, you will have determined whether to use primary or secondary sources of data to answer your question and will have begun to collect relevant data.

74 CHAPTER 2 IN SEARCH OF GOOD DATA

This textbook has a number of useful features that make it a valuable learning tool.

Help with Your Final Project

Project Connection is a feature that appears throughout the text as either a full-page insert or a margin note to suggest how recently presented material can be applied to your project. In addition, the second page of each chapter describes how the chapters will contribute to your project's research and development.

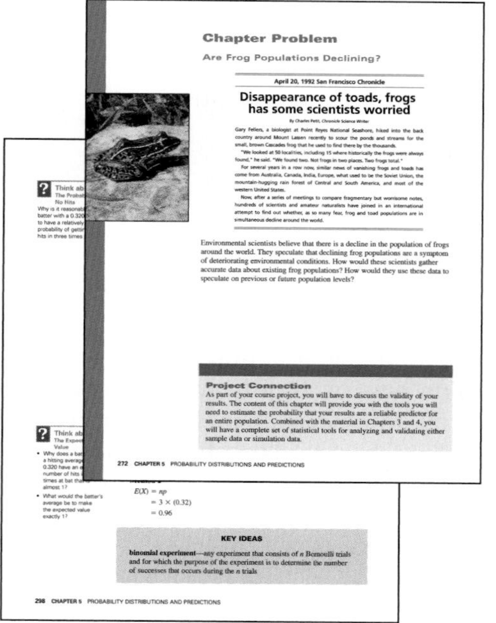

Chapter Problem

Are Frog Populations Declining?

April 20, 1992 San Francisco Chronicle

Disappearance of toads, frogs has some scientists worried

By Charles Petit, Chronicle Science Writer

Gary Fellers, a biologist at Point Reyes National Seashore, hiked into the back country around Mount Lassen recently to scour the ponds and streams for the small, brown Cascades frog that he used to find there by the thousands.

"We looked at 50 localities, including 15 where historically the frogs were always found," he said. "We found two. Not frogs in two places. Two frogs total."

For several years in a row now, similar news of vanishing frogs and toads has come from Australia, Canada, India, Europe, what used to be the Soviet Union, the mountain-hugging rain forest of Central and South America, and most of the western United States.

Now, after a series of meetings to compare fragmentary but worrisome notes, hundreds of scientists and amateur naturalists have joined in an international attempt to find out whether, as so many fear, frog and toad populations are in simultaneous decline around the world.

Environmental scientists believe that there is a decline in the population of frogs around the world. They speculate that declining frog populations are a symptom of deteriorating environmental conditions. How would these scientists gather accurate data about existing frog populations? How would they use these data to speculate on previous or future population levels?

Project Connection

As part of your course project, you will have to discuss the validity of your results. The content of this chapter will provide you with the tools you will need to estimate the probability that your results are a reliable predictor for an entire population. Combined with the material in Chapters 3 and 4, you will have a complete set of statistical tools for analyzing and validating either sample data or simulation data.

272 CHAPTER 5 PROBABILITY DISTRIBUTIONS AND PREDICTIONS

$E(X) = np$
$= 3 \times (0.32)$
$= 0.96$

KEY IDEAS

binomial experiment—any experiment that consists of n Bernoulli trials and for which the purpose of the experiment is to determine the number of successes that occurs during the n trials

298 CHAPTER 5 PROBABILITY DISTRIBUTIONS AND PREDICTIONS

Making Connections

Mathematics is an integral part of daily life and may be a determining factor in your choice of career. At the start of each chapter, there is a chapter problem that applies the mathematics of Data Management to various real-world situations.

Variety of Approaches

The lessons in *Mathematics of Data Management* provide the opportunity to work on your own or with others to explore concepts. Some lessons feature several solved examples to help you build an understanding of a concept; others guide you through the investigation of a concept.

Concept Lessons

Concepts and ideas are presented using solved examples. The skills taught are then reinforced in Key Ideas and Exercises. Exercises provide opportunities to practise and consolidate your understanding.

Investigations

Investigations provide hands-on experience with concepts and ideas, building on your understanding and further developing your skills. They can be completed on your own, either in class or at home; with a small group; or as a class, with your teacher acting as a guide. Key Ideas provide a summary of the important concepts discussed.

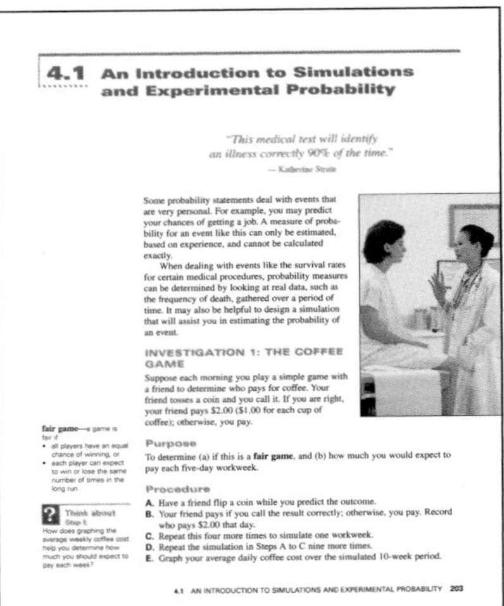

4.1 An Introduction to Simulations and Experimental Probability

"This medical test will identify an illness correctly 90% of the time."
— Katherine Strain

Some probability statements deal with events that are very personal. For example, you may predict your chances of getting a job. A measure of probability for an event like this can only be estimated, based on experience, and cannot be calculated exactly.

When dealing with events like the survival rates for certain medical procedures, probability measures can be determined by looking at real data, such as the frequency of death, gathered over a period of time. It may also be helpful to design a simulation that will assist you in estimating the probability of an event.

INVESTIGATION 1: THE COFFEE GAME

Suppose each morning you play a simple game with a friend to determine who pays for coffee. Your friend tosses a coin and you call it. If you are right, your friend pays $2.00 ($1.00 for each cup of coffee); otherwise, you pay.

fair game—a game is fair if
- all players have an equal chance of winning, or
- each player can expect to win or lose the same number of times in the long run

Purpose

To determine (a) if this is a **fair game**, and (b) how much you would expect to pay each five-day workweek.

Procedure

A. Have a friend flip a coin while you predict the outcome.
B. Your friend pays if you call the result correctly; otherwise, you pay. Record who pays $2.00 that day.
C. Repeat this four more times to simulate one workweek.
D. Repeat the simulation in Steps A to C nine more times.
E. Graph your average daily coffee cost over the simulated 10-week period.

Think about Step E
How does graphing the average weekly coffee cost help you determine how much you should expect to pay each week?

4.1 AN INTRODUCTION TO SIMULATIONS AND EXPERIMENTAL PROBABILITY 203

Think about

Questions or information that may lead you in the direction of another interesting application or a deeper understanding of the material you are studying are provided in the Think about feature.

Technolink

These two icons identify a chance to use technology.

You will use graphing technology or the Internet.

You will use the CD accompanying the textbook.

Definitions

New terms introduced in the text are often defined in the margin. This feature is useful for review purposes when studying for tests or exams.

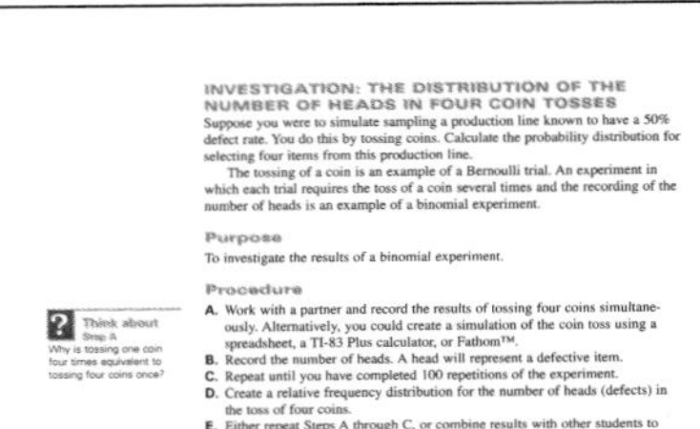

INVESTIGATION: THE DISTRIBUTION OF THE NUMBER OF HEADS IN FOUR COIN TOSSES

Suppose you were to simulate sampling a production line known to have a 50% defect rate. You do this by tossing coins. Calculate the probability distribution for selecting four items from this production line.

The tossing of a coin is an example of a Bernoulli trial. An experiment in which each trial requires the toss of a coin several times and the recording of the number of heads is an example of a binomial experiment.

Purpose

To investigate the results of a binomial experiment.

Procedure

A. Work with a partner and record the results of tossing four coins simultaneously. Alternatively, you could create a simulation of the coin toss using a spreadsheet, a TI-83 Plus calculator, or Fathom™.
B. Record the number of heads. A head will represent a defective item.
C. Repeat until you have completed 100 repetitions of the experiment.
D. Create a relative frequency distribution for the number of heads (defects) in the toss of four coins.
E. Either repeat Steps A through C, or combine results with other students to increase the number of trials.
F. Create a new relative frequency distribution using the larger data set.

Think about Step A
Why is tossing one coin four times equivalent to tossing four coins once?

Discussion Questions

1. How did increasing the number of repetitions of the experiment affect the shape of the distribution?
2. Why is tossing a single coin once a trial?
3. Why is each trial a Bernoulli trial?
4. Why is the number of heads obtained in each repetition a discrete random variable?

Technolink
Using technology to record your data and generate a histogram will save time.

THE PROBABILITY DISTRIBUTION FOR A DIE-ROLL SIMULATION

In a binomial experiment, the number of successes in n repeated Bernoulli trials is a discrete random variable, usually represented by the letter X. X is termed a **binomial random variable** and its probability distribution is called a **binomial distribution**.

binomial random variable—the number of successes in n repeated trials of a binomial experiment

binomial distribution—the probability distribution of a binomial random variable

Rolling a Die

Suppose a cereal company puts one of six possible prizes in each cereal box. You can use a simulation involving rolling a six-sided die to determine the probability distribution for getting a particular prize in four purchased boxes of cereal.

5.3 BINOMIAL DISTRIBUTIONS 293

Additional Achievement Chart Questions

Each chapter contains exercises labelled *Knowledge and Understanding; Application; Thinking, Inquiry, Problem Solving;* or *Communication*. These are the four achievement chart categories that your teacher uses to assess your understanding. You can use these exercises to help determine your strengths and weaknesses and, with the help of your teacher, to develop a plan for improving your achievement. Each chapter also concludes with a feature titled Additional Achievement Chart Questions, which can be used for review in these categories.

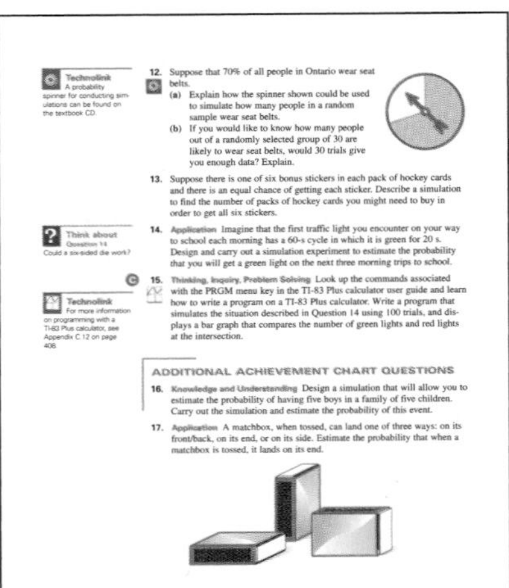

Technolink
A probability spinner for conducting simulations can be found on the textbook CD.

12. Suppose that 70% of all people in Ontario wear seat belts.
    (a) Explain how the spinner shown could be used to simulate how many people in a random sample wear seat belts.
    (b) If you would like to know how many people out of a randomly selected group of 30 are likely to wear seat belts, would 30 trials give you enough data? Explain.
13. Suppose there is one of six bonus stickers in each pack of hockey cards and there is an equal chance of getting each sticker. Describe a simulation to find the number of packs of hockey cards you might need to buy in order to get all six stickers.
14. Application Imagine that the first traffic light you encounter on your way to school each morning has a 60-s cycle in which it is green for 20 s. Design and carry out a simulation experiment to estimate the probability that you will get a green light on the next three morning trips to school.
15. Thinking, Inquiry, Problem Solving Look up the commands associated with the PRGM menu key in the TI-83 Plus calculator user guide and learn how to write a program on a TI-83 Plus calculator. Write a program that simulates the situation described in Question 14 using 100 trials, and displays a bar graph that compares the number of green lights and red lights at the intersection.

Think about Question 14
Could a six-sided die work?

Technolink
For more information on programming with a TI-83 Plus calculator, see Appendix C.12 on page 408.

ADDITIONAL ACHIEVEMENT CHART QUESTIONS

16. Knowledge and Understanding Design a simulation that will allow you to estimate the probability of having five boys in a family of five children. Carry out the simulation and estimate the probability of this event.
17. Application A matchbox, when tossed, can land one of three ways: on its front/back, on its end, or on its side. Estimate the probability that when a matchbox is tossed, it lands on its end.

212 CHAPTER 4 DEALING WITH UNCERTAINTY—AN INTRODUCTION TO PROBABILITY

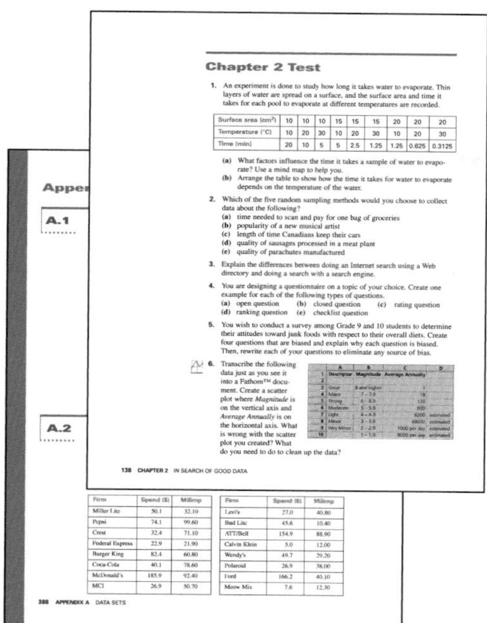

Chapter 2 Test

1. An experiment is done to study how long it takes water to evaporate. Thin layers of water are spread on a surface, and the surface area and time it takes for each pool to evaporate at different temperatures are recorded.

Surface area (cm²)	10	10	10	15	15	15	20	20	20
Temperature (°C)	10	20	30	10	20	30	10	20	30
Time (min)	20	10	5	5	2.5	1.25	1.25	0.625	0.3125

(a) What factors influence the time it takes a sample of water to evaporate? Use a mind map to help you.
(b) Arrange the table to show how the time it takes for water to evaporate depends on the temperature of the water.

2. Which of the five random sampling methods would you choose to collect data about the following?
(a) time needed to scan and pay for one bag of groceries
(b) popularity of a new musical artist
(c) length of time Canadians keep their cars
(d) quality of sausages processed in a meat plant
(e) quality of parachutes manufactured

3. Explain the differences between doing an Internet search using a Web directory and doing a search with a search engine.

4. You are designing a questionnaire on a topic of your choice. Create one example for each of the following types of questions.
(a) open question (b) closed question (c) rating question
(d) ranking question (e) checklist question

5. You wish to conduct a survey among Grade 9 and 10 students to determine their attitudes toward junk foods with respect to their overall diets. Create four questions that are biased and explain why each question is biased. Then, rewrite each of your questions to eliminate any source of bias.

6. Transcribe the following data just as you see it into a Fathom™ document. Create a scatter plot where *Magnitude* is on the vertical axis and *Average Annually* is on the horizontal axis. What is wrong with the scatter plot you created? What do you need to do to clean up the data?

138 CHAPTER 2 IN SEARCH OF GOOD DATA

Firm	Spend ($)	Millimp
Miller Lite	50.1	32.10
Pepsi	74.1	99.60
Crest	32.4	71.10
Federal Express	22.9	21.90
Burger King	82.4	60.80

Firm	Spend ($)	Millimp
Levi's	27.0	40.80
Bud Lite	45.6	10.40
ATT/Bell	154.9	88.90
Calvin Klein	5.0	12.00
Wendy's	49.7	29.20

Chapter Wrap-Up

This feature provides the opportunity to reinforce your understanding of the concepts and skills you have developed. Refer to Key Ideas and solved examples when answering these questions. These questions can also be used for review and study.

Chapter Test

This test can be used for the purpose of review and to determine if you are ready for a test or exam.

Appendix A: Data Sets

This appendix includes nine data samples that can be used as a starting point for your course project or during class discussions.

Appendix B: Tables

Included here is a z-score table and a random number table to be used in constructing manual simulations.

Appendix C: How to Use a TI-83 Plus Calculator

This appendix lists 19 demonstrations with examples on how to complete different tasks with a TI-83 Plus graphing calculator. This textbook includes links in the margin that tell you when to turn to this appendix. You may also choose to browse through it to brush up on your skills.

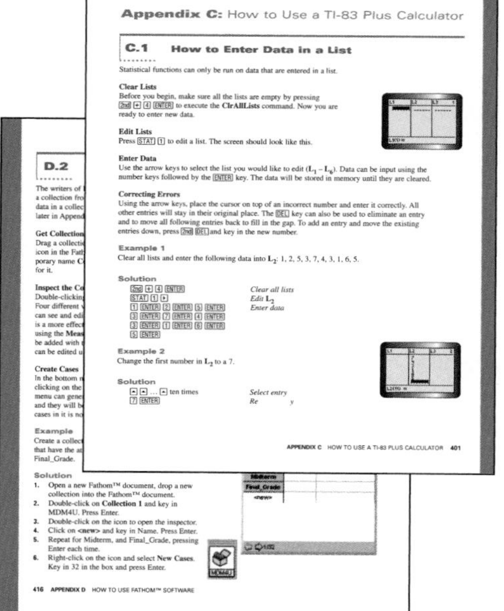

Appendix C: How to Use a TI-83 Plus Calculator

C.1 How to Enter Data in a List

Statistical functions can only be run on data that are entered in a list.

Clear Lists
Before you begin, make sure all the lists are empty by pressing [2nd] [+] [4] [ENTER] to execute the **ClrAllLists** command. Now you are ready to enter new data.

Edit Lists
Press [STAT] [1] to edit a list. The screen should look like this.

Enter Data
Use the arrow keys to select the list you would like to edit ($L_1 - L_6$). Data can be input using the number keys followed by the [ENTER] key. The data will be stored in memory until they are cleared.

Correcting Errors
Using the arrow keys, place the cursor on top of an incorrect number and enter it correctly. All other entries will stay in their original place. The [DEL] key can also be used to eliminate an entry and to move all following entries back to fill in the gap. To add an entry and move the existing entries down, press [2nd] [DEL] and key in the new number.

Example 1
Clear all lists and enter the following data into L_2: 1, 2, 5, 3, 7, 4, 3, 1, 6, 5.

Solution
[2nd] [+] [4] [ENTER] *Clear all lists*
[STAT] [1] [▸] *Edit L_2*
[1] [ENTER] [2] [ENTER] [5] [ENTER] *Enter data*
[3] [ENTER] [7] [ENTER] [4] [ENTER]
[3] [ENTER] [1] [ENTER] [6] [ENTER]
[5] [ENTER]

Example 2
Change the first number in L_2 to a 7.

Solution
[▴] [▴] … [▴] ten times *Select entry*
[7] [ENTER]

APPENDIX C HOW TO USE A TI-83 PLUS CALCULATOR 401

Appendix D: How to Use Fathom™ Software

Similar to Appendix C, this resource describes how to complete nine simple tasks using the power of Fathom™ software. Solved examples are included in each demonstration. Margin links in the textbook tell you when to turn to this appendix, or you may choose to use it to learn the power of this tool on your own.

Appendix E: How to Use Spreadsheet Software

This appendix contains five demonstrations, with examples, of how to use spreadsheet software, to manage, analyze, and get meaning out of data. Margin links direct you to this appendix, but you may choose to go through it on your own to improve your data management skills.

1 The Power of Information

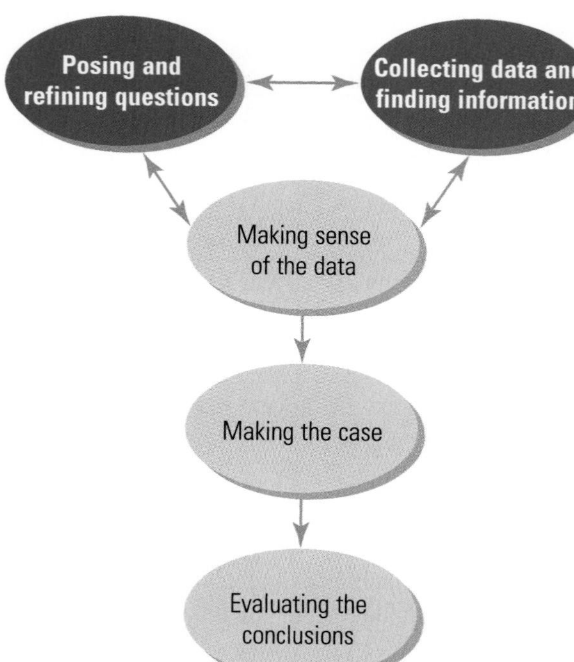

People who own stocks or mutual funds often will check their performance in newspapers or on the Internet. The types of information they might be interested in obtaining include

- the highest and lowest price paid
- volume traded
- profit per share

Similarly, people who bet on the outcome of a horserace will look at all the published data contained in a racing form. The racing form includes information about each horse's most recent race times, heritage, performance in previous races, and so on. Bettors then use these data, in conjunction with racing conditions such as weather, to select the horse they think is most likely to win the race.

In this chapter, you will learn how to make data more meaningful and how to use it to inform both yourself and others.

In this chapter, you will

- develop significant conclusions about a data set
- state, support, and refute conclusions based on data
- explore some of the misuses of data
- use the correlation coefficient and scatter plots to describe the relationship between two variables

Chapter Problem

Trends in Canada's Population

Canada is the world's second-largest country (9 093 507 km^2); yet, its current population is less than the population of the state of California. Canada's population and its structure have changed significantly since it became a country in 1867. The table below shows the percent of the population for various age groups since 1851.

Age Structure of the Population[1]

Year	Total (000s)	% Under 5 Years	% 5–19 Years	% 20–44 Years	% 45–64 Years	% 65+ Years
1851	2 346	18.51	37.81	31.65	9.40	2.67
1861	3 230	16.81	37.21	32.66	10.15	3.03
1871	3 689	14.67	38.03	32.28	11.14	3.66
1881	4 325	13.85	36.02	33.94	12.14	4.12
1891	4 833	12.64	34.49	35.40	12.91	4.55
1901	5 371	12.03	32.73	36.19	14.00	5.05
1911	7 207	12.35	30.15	38.81	14.06	4.66
1921	8 788	12.05	31.51	36.63	15.02	4.78
1931	10 377	10.36	31.29	36.07	16.74	5.55
1941	11 507	9.14	28.39	37.19	18.61	6.67
1951	14 009	12.29	25.60	36.63	17.74	7.75
1961	18 238	12.37	29.44	33.19	17.37	7.63
1971	21 568	8.42	30.97	33.87	18.66	8.09
1981	24 343	7.32	24.70	39.14	19.13	9.70
1991	27 297	6.99	20.42	41.33	19.66	11.61
1996	28 847	6.65	20.60	39.03	21.49	12.23
1998[2]	30 300	6.26	20.26	38.97	22.18	12.33

Source: Census of Canada, Statistics Canada
(1) Total percent for census years may not equal 100 due to rounding.
(2) Preliminary numbers.

What trends are visible in the table above? What are some contributing factors that could account for these trends? As you proceed through this chapter, you will investigate the data above as part of the chapter problem.

Project Connection

In this chapter, you will work with a wide variety of contexts and establish the topic for your final project. In subsequent chapters, you will develop the tools needed to help you collect and analyze data relevant to your final project.

1.1 Constructing and Interpreting Visual Displays of Data

"More people are born in the spring than in the fall."

In order to draw general conclusions, such as the one above, information must be gathered, organized, and displayed clearly.

When information is gathered from all people in a **population**, the activity is called a census. For example, every five years, Statistics Canada takes a census of the population. The first census of the millennium was on May 15, 2001. The results from that census were released beginning in the spring of 2002.

A poll (or opinion survey) is a method of collecting **data** from a **sample** of a population by asking people to give their answers to a set of questions. Once collected, the data are then organized in a meaningful way so that valid conclusions can be made.

population—refers to the entire group about which data are being collected

data—information providing the basis of a discussion from which conclusions may be drawn; data often take the form of numbers that can be displayed graphically or in a table

sample—part of a population that is selected to gain information about the whole population

frequency—the number of times an event occurs or the number of items in a given category

frequency table—a table listing a variable together with the frequency of each value

---

Example 1 Organizing Data: Frequency Tables

The members of a Grade 12 class were asked on what day of the week they were born. The results were as follows:

Monday, Tuesday, Wednesday, Thursday, Monday, Friday, Friday, Tuesday, Thursday, Wednesday, Saturday, Friday, Tuesday, Wednesday, Saturday, Monday, Wednesday, Wednesday, Thursday, Thursday, Tuesday, Wednesday, Tuesday, Thursday, Tuesday, Thursday, Saturday, Tuesday, Sunday, Monday

(a) Organize the data in a **frequency table**.

(b) How many students responded to the question?

(c) What percent of the students were born on weekends?

Solution

(a)

Day	Tally	Frequency
Monday	||||	4
Tuesday	~~||||~~ ||	7
Wednesday	~~||||~~ |	6
Thursday	~~||||~~ |	6
Friday	|||	3
Saturday	|||	3
Sunday	|	1

(b) Total number of students $= 4 + 7 + 6 + 6 + 3 + 3 + 1$
$= 30$

(c) Percent born on a weekend $= \frac{\text{number born on weekend}}{\text{total number of students}}$

$= \frac{4}{30} \times 100\%$

$\doteq 13.3\%$

Example 2 Organizing Data: Frequency Tables and Stem-and-Leaf Plots

The heights of the members of two high school classes were measured in centimetres. The results were as follows:

136, 156, 172, 160, 175, 186, 187, 122, 186, 157, 153, 130, 164, 143, 181, 186, 176, 184, 193, 136, 122, 120, 184, 186, 176, 181, 167, 164, 149, 186, 155, 192, 174, 184, 156, 164, 181, 186, 172, 181, 163, 190, 188, 182, 174, 157, 152, 183, 171, 156

stem-and-leaf plot—
a way of organizing and presenting a collection of numbers

(a) Display the data using a **stem-and-leaf plot**.

(b) Use your answer to part (a) to set up a frequency table using class intervals.

(c) How is the frequency table in part (b) different from the stem-and-leaf plot?

(d) Explain why class intervals are more useful than individual measurements.

Solution

(a) The set of numbers is rewritten, with each of the hundreds and tens digits becoming a stem and the units digits becoming the leaves. The leaves are entered in numerical order to produce a stem-and-leaf plot.

Stem	Leaf
12	0 2 2
13	0 6 6
14	3 9
15	2 3 5 6 6 6 7 7
16	0 3 4 4 4 7
17	1 2 2 4 4 5 6 6
18	1 1 1 1 2 3 4 4 4 6 6 6 6 6 6 7 8
19	0 2 3

This branch represents the numbers 143 and 149.

The hundreds and tens digits are called the **stems**.

The units digits are called the **leaves**.

class interval—a category or division used for grouping a set of observations

(b) A reasonable **class interval** for this data is a spread of 10 units. Given that the smallest value is 120 and the largest value is 193, the intervals to best display this data are 120–129, 130–139, and so on.

Class Interval	Frequency
120–129	3
130–139	3
140–149	2
150–159	8
160–169	6
170–179	8
180–189	17
190–199	3

(c) In the stem-and-leaf plot, individual items were listed. In the frequency table in part (b), items were grouped into class intervals.

(d) Using individual items would create a table with the data so spread out that it would become difficult to view any trends.

DISPLAYING DATA

Tables are used to organize data; however, graphs are used to display data in a more meaningful way. A *bar graph* consists of parallel bars of equal widths with lengths proportional to the frequency of the variables they represent. A bar graph is used to represent nominal data, such as days of the week. Typically, bar graphs are used for discrete data. Look at the example on the top of the next page.

Project Connection
Give thoughtful consideration to the type of graph that will best display your data.

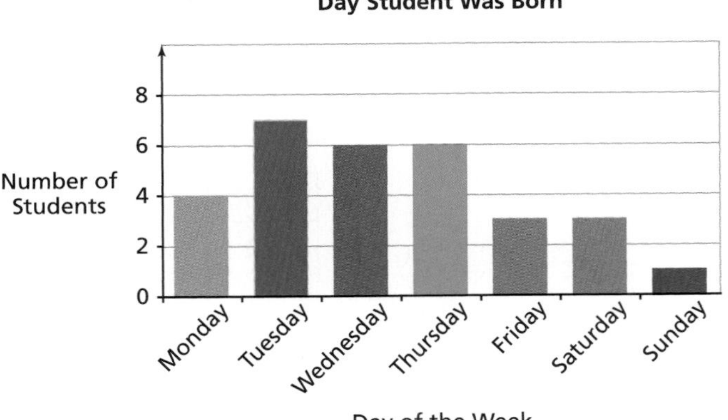

frequency distribution—a set of values of a variable, together with the frequency of each value

A *histogram* is a **frequency distribution** where the horizontal axis is divided into equal class intervals into which data have been divided. The heights of the rectangles represent the frequencies associated with the corresponding intervals. A histogram is used to represent data that are organized into class intervals, such as student heights. It is important that each interval have the same width. Typically, histograms are used for continuous data. The following is an example.

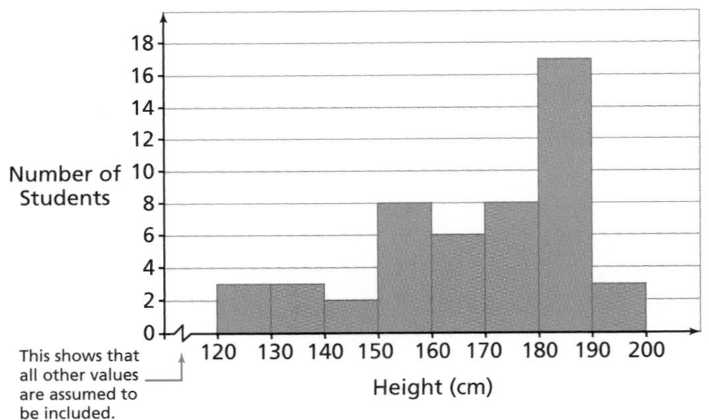

A *pictograph* is a symbolic representation of data. The following pictograph displays the number of participants (aged 15 and older) in the five most popular sports activities in Canada.

Sport Activity	Number of Participants
Golf	🧍🧍🧍🧍🧍🧍🧍🧍🧍🧍🧍🧍🧍🧍🧍🧍🧍🧍
Ice Hockey	🧍🧍🧍🧍🧍🧍🧍🧍🧍🧍🧍🧍🧍🧍🧍
Baseball	🧍🧍🧍🧍🧍🧍🧍🧍🧍🧍🧍🧍
Swimming	🧍🧍🧍🧍🧍🧍🧍🧍🧍🧍🧍
Basketball	🧍🧍🧍🧍🧍🧍🧍

Legend: 🧍 represents 100 000 people

Source: Statistics Canada, General Social Survey, 1998.

central angle—a measure of proportion in a pie chart. It is calculated as follows: central angle = percent of data for a category × 360°

A *circle graph* (or *pie chart*) is a circle divided into sectors whose areas are proportional to the quantities represented. The size of each piece of a pie chart is determined by the **central angle**. It is calculated by multiplying the percent of data for each category by 360°. For example, in the following table and pie chart, which display the television viewing habits of Canadians, Sports represents 4.7% of the data, or $0.047 \times 360° \doteq 17°$.

Programming Type	Percent of Viewing Time
News and Public Affairs	31.8
Documentary	2.7
Instruction	3.7
Religion	0.3
Sports	4.7
Variety and Games	13.2
Music and Dance	0.8
Comedy	8.8
Drama	28.7
Other	5.3

Source: Statistics Canada

? Think about TV Viewing Habits
What would the results from your class look like? How would you collect these data?

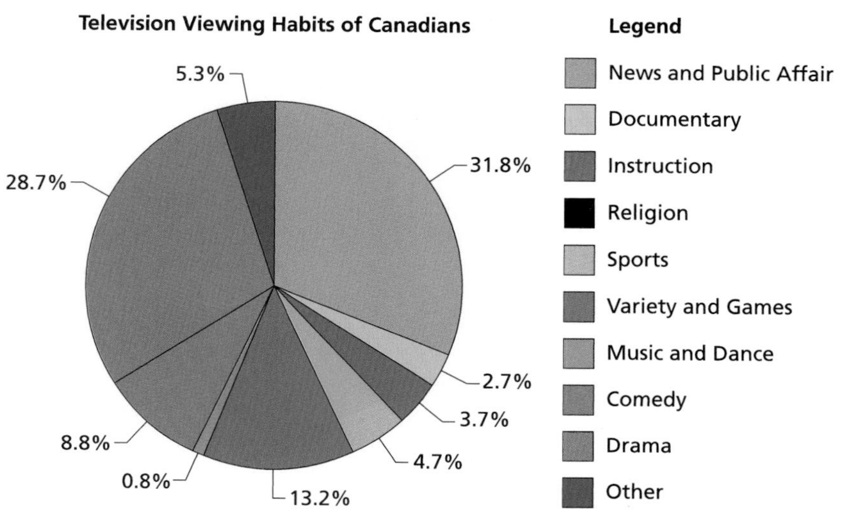

Example 3 Displaying Data

A survey conducted in a math class asked students what mode of transportation they normally use to get to school. The results were as follows:

Bike	10
Walk	15
Bus	9
Car	6

Construct a circle graph to display these data.

Solution

Calculate the angle for each sector, as shown in the following table.

Mode of Transportation	Number of Students	Central Angle
Bike	10	$\frac{10}{40} \times 360° = 90°$
Walk	15	135°
Bus	9	81°
Car	6	54°
Total	40	360°

Use the sector angles and a protractor to construct the circle graph.

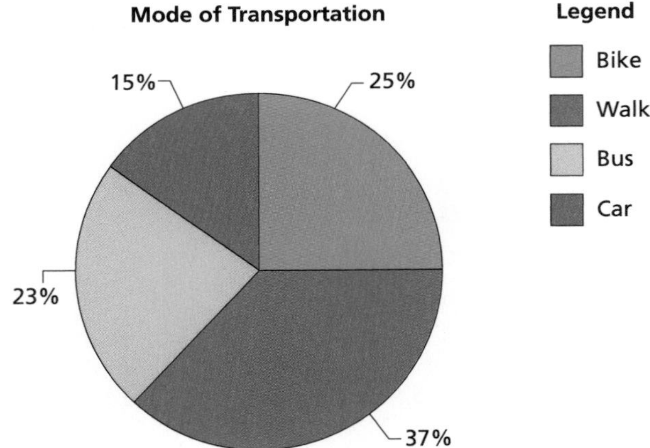

Graphs for Examining the Spread of Data

box-and-whisker plot—a horizontal representation of the spread of a distribution of data

median—the middle value in a frequency distribution

In a **box-and-whisker plot**, the box contains the **median** of the data and its width represents the middle half of the data. From the sides of the box, horizontal lines are drawn extending to the smallest and largest values of the data. The following box-and-whisker plot displays the spread of the heights of a group of high school students.

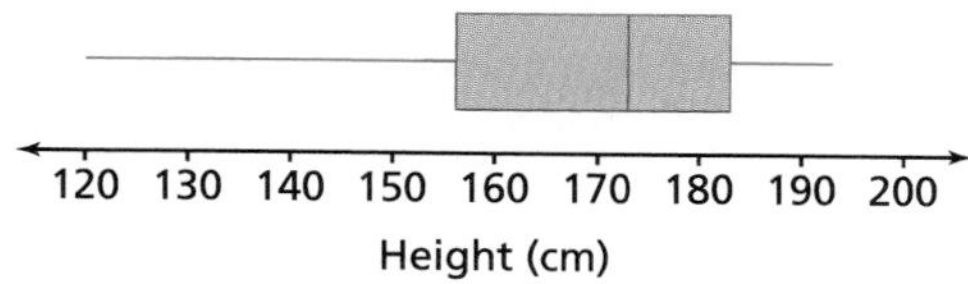

To find the median, the heights are listed in ascending order (smallest to largest). The middle value (or the average of the middle two values if there is an even number of items in the data set) is the median. The median for this data set is 173.

The medians of the upper half and the lower half of the data are calculated to find the upper and lower limits of the box. In this data set, these values are 184 and 156, respectively.

To construct the box-and-whisker plot, the data are plotted on a number line, and the three calculated values are indicated. A box is drawn around the central half of the data, and then lines are drawn extending to the smallest and largest values of the distribution to create the whiskers.

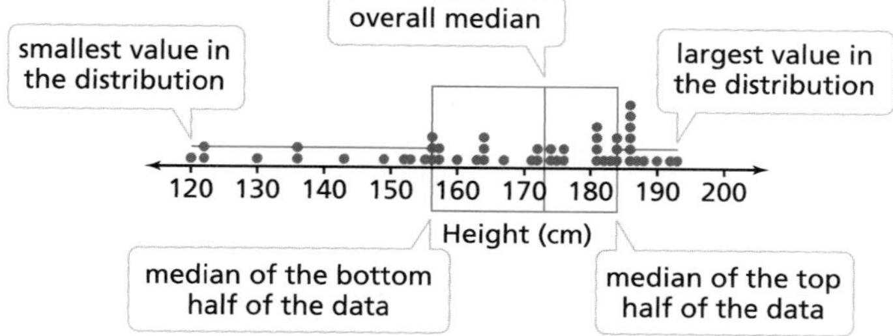

Graphs for Examining Trends

A **broken-line graph** is a graph created by joining data points with line segments. The following is an example. Notice that all graphs must include a title and the axes must be labelled. Pie charts and pictographs must also have legends.

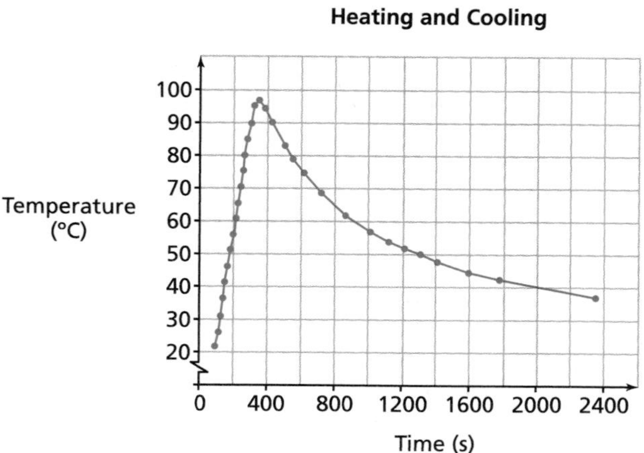

KEY IDEAS

population—refers to the entire group about which data are being collected

data—information providing the basis of a discussion from which conclusions may be drawn; data often take the form of numbers that can be displayed graphically or in a table

sample—part of a population selected so as to gain information about the whole population

frequency—the number of times an event occurs or the number of items in a given category

stem-and-leaf plot—a way of organizing and presenting a collection of numbers

class interval—a category or division used for grouping a set of observations

bar graph—a visual display of data in which quantities are represented by bars of equal width; typically used with discrete data

frequency distribution—a set of values of a variable, together with the number of occurrences (frequency) of each value

histogram—a visual display of data that have been organized into equal class intervals, which appear on the horizontal axis. The heights of the rectangles are proportional to the frequencies they represent. Typically used with continuous data.

pictograph—a graph that uses pictures or symbols to represent variable quantities

circle graph (pie chart)—a circle divided into sectors whose areas are proportional to the variables represented

median—the middle term in a frequency distribution

box-and-whisker plot—a horizontal representation of the spread of a distribution

broken-line graph—a graph created by joining data points with line segments

1.1 Exercises

A

1. The number of goals scored by the top four players on the school soccer team are displayed. Jared has 14 goals.

   (a) What information is missing from the graph? Provide it.
   (b) How many goals does each player have?
   (c) What are the advantages and disadvantages of using a pictograph?

2. Some students were asked to name the four Beatles. Their responses are displayed below.

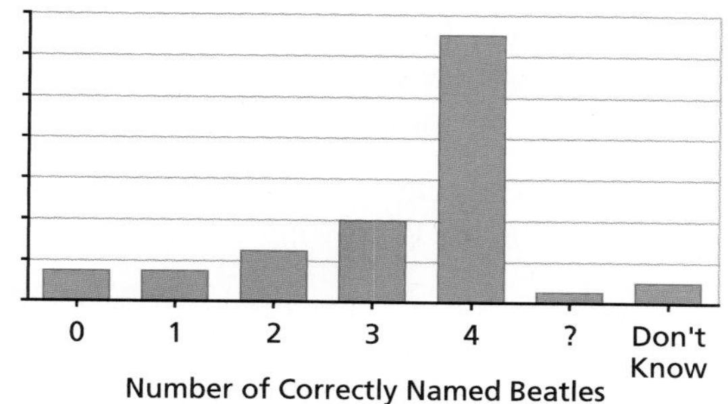

   (a) The vertical scale is missing. If seven students knew the names of three of the Beatles, what would the scale be?
   (b) How can the scale be altered, yet still display the same meaning?
   (c) If these data represent the response of 1000 students at a local high school, how many would be able to name all four Beatles?

3. Some Grade 12 students were asked to estimate the number of hours of television they watch each day. These are their responses:

   1, 1, 0.5, 1, 1, 0, 3, 2, 1.5, 0.5, 1, 1, 2, 2, 2, 5, 1, 0.5, 0.5, 2, 1, 0.5, 1, 0, 0.5, 3

   (a) Construct a tally and frequency table.
   (b) Use the information to produce a graph.
   (c) How many hours of television per day do you watch?
   (d) Investigate the average daily television watching time for Canadians. Compare this information with that from the class. Draw conclusion(s) from your comparison. Give reasons for your answer.

4. The stride lengths, in centimetres, of a group of Grade 12 students are displayed in the following histogram.

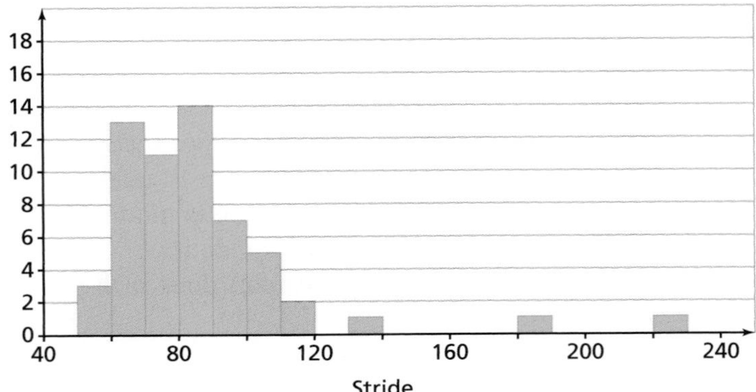

(a) What information is missing?
(b) In what ways are bar graphs and histograms similar?
(c) In what ways are they different?
(d) When is a histogram more appropriate than a bar graph? Give reasons for your answer.

5. The school library has received a donation and will purchase books based on the borrowing patterns of the students.

Library Borrowing Patterns

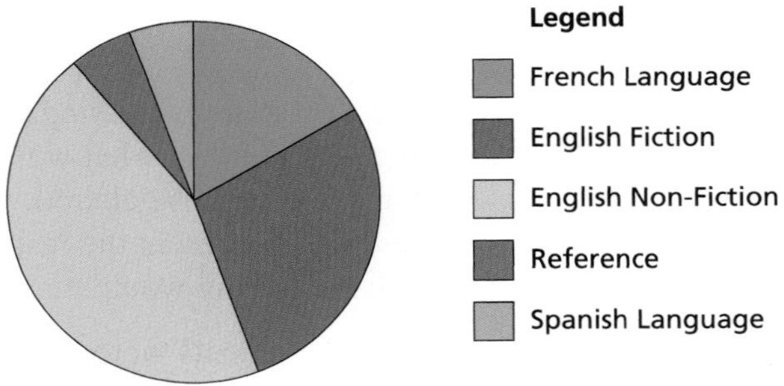

(a) Based on the graph, estimate what percent of the money should be spent on each book type.
(b) If the library received a donation of $125 000, estimate how much money should be spent on each book type.

6. Thirty people were asked to state their favourite sport. The responses are listed below.

Tennis	6
Football	8
Swimming	10
Badminton	3
Volleyball	3

Construct a circle graph to display this information.

7. **Knowledge and Understanding** The lengths of the songs on a CD compilation set are given in minutes and seconds below.

3:44	3:40	4:57	4:08	4:02	4:47
4:08	2:39	4:04	4:06	3:24	4:48
4:27	3:03	4:13	4:05	4:16	4:01
3:40	3:53	3:02	3:43	5:13	3:49
4:38	5:21	4:01	4:32	3:45	3:59
4:00	3:29	4:05	4:06		

What percent of the songs are less than 5 min in length?

(a) First, use a 30-s class interval to construct a frequency table.
(b) Then, use the table constructed in part (a) to answer the question.
(c) Explain why the table was more helpful than the list in answering the question.
(d) Which type of graph should be used to display these data? Construct it.

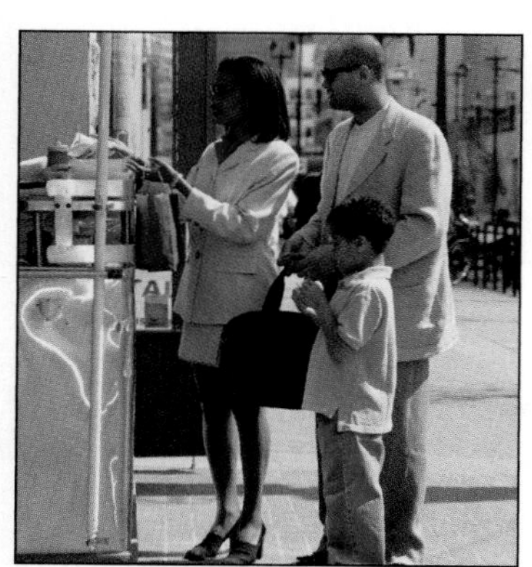

8. The number of hot dogs sold by a street vendor for each day in the month of June is recorded below.

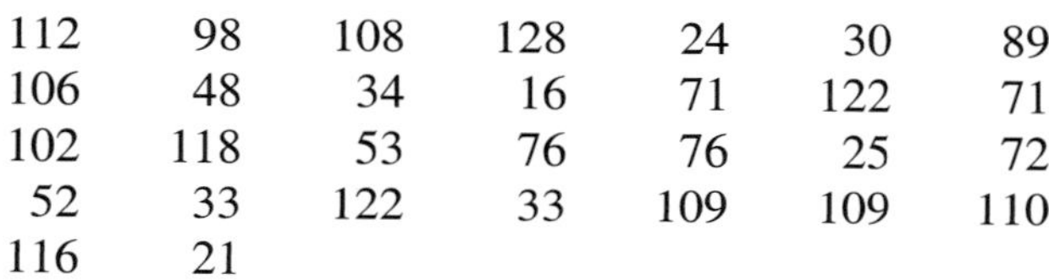

112	98	108	128	24	30	89
106	48	34	16	71	122	71
102	118	53	76	76	25	72
52	33	122	33	109	109	110
116	21					

(a) Construct a stem-and-leaf plot to display the data.
(b) Use the plot to determine the number of days when fewer than 80 hot dogs were sold.
(c) On what percent of the days were more than 100 hot dogs sold?

9. The members of a Grade 9 class and a Grade 12 class were given a list of five animals: cat, dog, bird, fish, and iguana. From the list, they were asked to pick the animal they would want as a pet. The results were as follows:

Pet	Grade 9	Grade 12
Cat	2	7
Dog	4	6
Bird	9	3
Fish	10	6
Iguana	5	8

(a) Construct a pictograph for both classes.
(b) What percent of students did not choose a cat or dog?
(c) Compare your answer in part (b) to the percent of Grade 9 students who did not choose a cat or dog. Show your work.

10. **Application** For each of the following, determine the type of graph that would best represent the data collected. Explain.
   (a) What portion of the general population reads a newspaper on a daily basis? On Saturday only?
   (b) How does your heart rate change when doing each of the following activities: sleeping, walking slowly, jogging, running?
   (c) Which type of vacation do people prefer: camping, tropical holiday, cruise, cottage, or visiting relatives?
   (d) How do high school students spend a typical Saturday?
   (e) How do students spend a typical weekday during the school year?

B

11. **Communication** For Question 12, below, write a plan explaining how you would carry out the investigation. List all the steps clearly and reference specific resources. For example, if you plan to use the Internet, list specific Web-site addresses.

12. Investigate the breakdown of blood types in Canada.
   (a) Use your findings to construct a circle graph.
   (b) If 750 people attended a high school basketball game, calculate the number that you would expect to have blood type A.

C

13. Choose five pop stars. Conduct a survey of students to determine their favourite pop star.
   (a) Organize the data in a frequency table.
   (b) Construct a bar graph to display the data.
   (c) Create a question about your graph. Have someone in the class answer your question and provide an explanation for his or her answer.

14. Investigate the breakdown of enrolment in each of the Grade 12 math courses in your school.
   (a) Construct an appropriate display of the data.
   (b) Give reasons for your choice of display.
   (c) Draw conclusions from your data. Give reasons for your answer.

15. **Thinking, Inquiry, Problem Solving**
   (a) Conduct a survey of students that asks one or more of the questions that follow.
      (i) How many hours per week do you spend at your part-time job?
      (ii) How much money per month do you spend on entertainment (e.g., CDs, concerts, movies, etc.)?
      (iii) How tall are you in centimetres?
      (iv) How many hours of television do you watch each week?
      (v) List all the sports that you have participated in during the last four weeks.
   (b) Display your results in graphical form.
   (c) Draw any conclusions that arise from the data. Explain.
   (d) Reflect on how you conducted the survey. Explain any improvements that you would make if you were to conduct the survey with a different group of students.

ADDITIONAL ACHIEVEMENT CHART QUESTIONS

16. **Knowledge and Understanding** The 1996 Census of Canada reports the following composition of Canadian families. Create two different displays of these data.

Number of Children	Number of Families (in thousands)
Without children at home	2730
With one child	2106
With two children	2047
With three children	729
With four children	175
With five or more children	51
Total families	7838

Source: Statistics Canada

17. **Application**

(a) Choose a topic that interests you and survey your classmates to find their responses.
(b) Organize your data in a frequency table.
(c) Create the most appropriate graph to display your data.
(d) Use the table and your graph to draw a conclusion about your class.

18. **Thinking, Inquiry, Problem Solving**

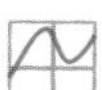

(a) Use the Internet to find data that show a trend over time.
(b) Use the most appropriate graph to display your data.
(c) Use the graph to make a prediction. Give reasons for your answer.

19. **Communication** Explain the difference between histograms and bar graphs, and provide an example of a set of data that is best suited for each of these types of graphs.

Chapter Problem

Trends in Canada's Population

Use the data given in the chapter problem on page 2 to answer these questions.

CP1. Create three different types of graphs that can be used to compare the structure of Canada's population in 1996.

CP2. Of the three graphs you created, which graph best displays the similarities and differences in the structure of the population? Explain.

1.2 Conclusions and Issues

"Female students like school more than male students do."

What does the statement above mean? Do you agree with it? How do people make statements like this with confidence?

An important step in coming to this conclusion is gathering data. In this case, the data about male and female opinions of school were gathered using a survey and the data were then recorded in a table like the one shown here.

	A	B
1	Ontario Youths	
2	Gender	How do you feel about school?
3	F	3. I like school a bit.
4	F	1. I hate school.
5	F	4. I like school quite a bit.
6	F	5. I like school very much.
7	M	5. I like school very much.
8	F	1. I hate school.
9	M	2. I don't like school very much.
10	M	3. I like school a bit.
11	F	2. I don't like school very much.

Example 1 Do Female Students Like School More Than Male Students Do?

What follows is a **split-bar graph** showing the distribution of the responses to the question *How do you feel about school?* with each bar split by gender. Based on these data, do females like school more than males do?

split-bar graph—a visual way of comparing information in which two different quantities are represented by the lengths of bars

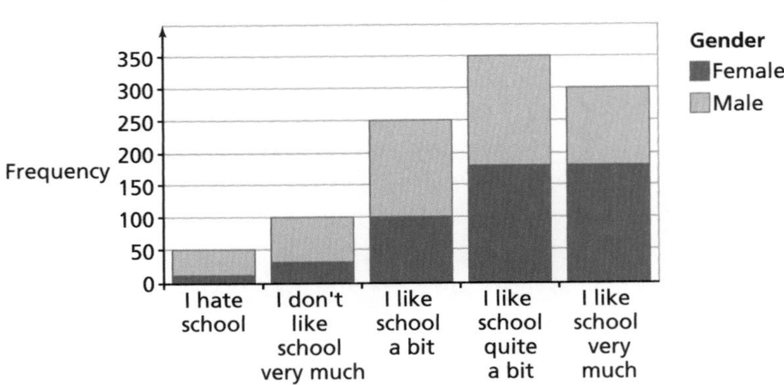

Technolink
The data shown in the split-bar graph and the table above were taken from the full data set on the textbook CD.

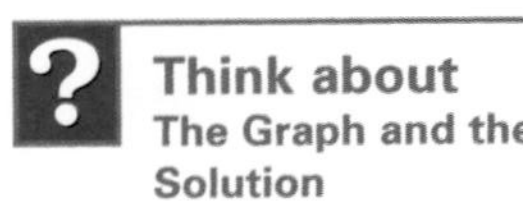

Think about The Graph and the Solution
The analysis used the first and fifth bars to arrive at the conclusion that females like school more than males do. Do the other bars also support this conclusion? Why or why not?

Solution

From the split-bar graph it is clear that

- about three times as many males chose "I hate school" than did females
- more females chose "I like school very much" than did males

Based on this analysis, it seems reasonable to conclude that, compared with males, females like school more.

The conclusion in Example 1, that females like school more than males do, raises some interesting issues. One issue is the possible reasons for the results; that is, why do females like school more than males do?

One theory is that students who hated school often were not doing well in school. The students who were asked whether they liked school were also asked how well they were doing in school. The results were added to the table, which follows.

Project Connection

With any conclusion, it is interesting to ask *Why is this the case?* If in Example 1, the answer for the results is found, then action might be taken to ensure that males and females like school equally as well.

	A	B	C
1	Ontario Youths		
2	Gender	How do you feel about school?	How well are you doing in school?
3	F	3. I like school a bit.	Average
4	F	1. I hate school.	Poorly
5	F	4. I like school quite a bit.	Well
6	F	5. I like school very much.	Very well
7	M	5. I like school very much.	Very well
8	F	1. I hate school.	Average
9	M	2. I don't like school very much.	Average
10	M	3. I like school a bit.	Very well
11	F	2. I don't like school very much.	Average
12	M	3. I like school a bit.	Average
13	F	5. I like school very much.	Well
14	M	5. I like school very much.	Very well
15	M	1. I hate school.	Well
16	F	4. I like school quite a bit.	Well
17	F	5. I like school very much.	Average
18	F	5. I like school very much.	Very well
19	M	4. I like school quite a bit.	Well
20	M	2. I don't like school very much.	Very well
21	M	1. I hate school.	Average
22	F	4. I like school quite a bit.	Well
23	F	5. I like school very much.	Very well
24	M	3. I like school a bit.	Very well
25	F	2. I don't like school very much.	Very well
26	M	5. I like school very much.	Very well
27	F	5. I like school very much.	Very well

Example 2 Performance at School

It seems reasonable to expect that students who are not doing well would not like school. Does the data support this conclusion? How confident are you in the results?

Solution

From the data above, the following observations can be made:

- Most students answered "Very well" when asked how well they were doing in school.
- There is only one student who selected "Poorly" when asked how well she was doing in school.
- Of the four students who answered "I hate school," one claimed he was doing well.

Based on these data, one might conclude that students hate school because they are not doing well. This is, however, a very small sample to say with confidence that a relationship exists between performance at school and feelings about school. More data are needed to draw conclusions with more confidence. (**Note:** There were 1046 students interviewed in this survey and the results are provided on the textbook CD.)

Example 3 Large Amounts of Data to Justify Conclusions: Sample Size

The following graphs were created to show the data from 1046 students. Does the data from the population support the conclusion drawn from the sample?

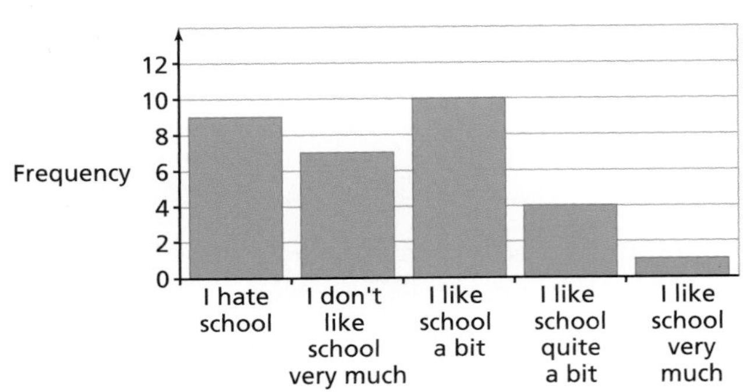

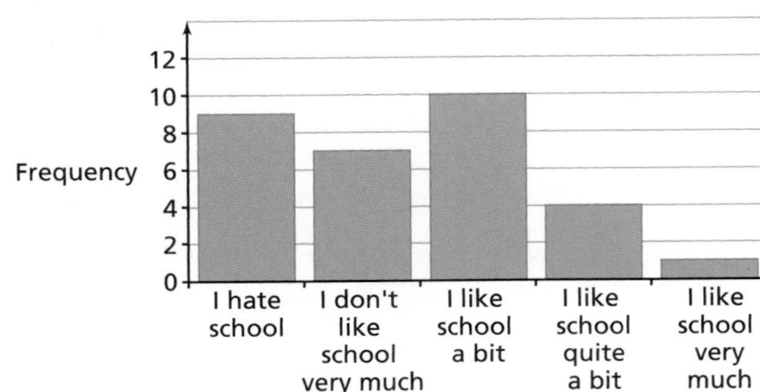

Technolink
For assistance performing this analysis in Fathom™, see Appendix D starting on page 415.

Students Who Do Well

Frequency: 0, 50, 100, 150, 200

I hate school | I don't like school very much | I like school a bit | I like school quite a bit | I like school very much

How Do You Feel About School?

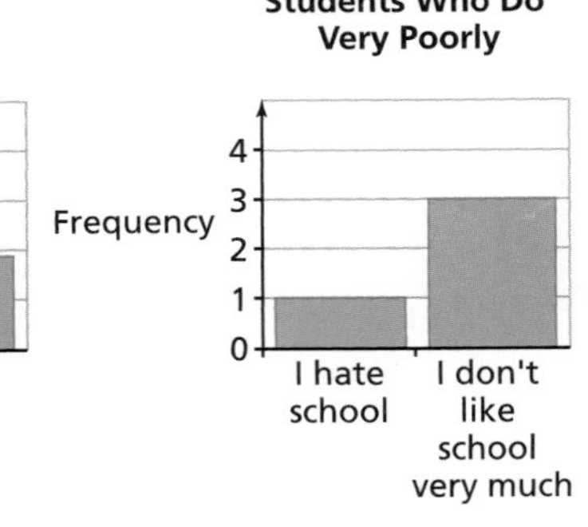

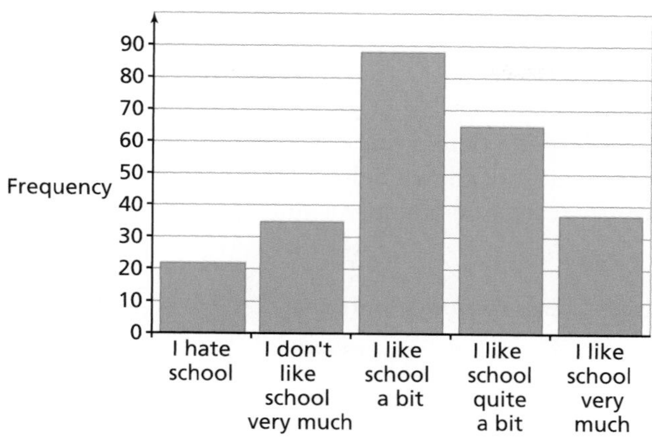

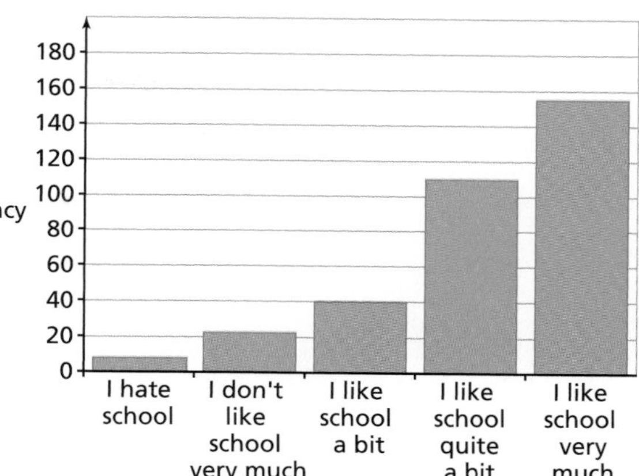

Solution

From the data, the following conclusions can be made:

- All students who responded "Very poorly" also responded "I hate school" or "I don't like school very much."
- A larger proportion of students who responded "Poorly" also responded "I hate school" or "I don't like school very much."

causal relationship—where one variable directly affects another

As a result, it seems reasonable to conclude that a relationship exists between a student's performance in school and his or her feelings about school; however, it is not possible to determine if a **causal relationship** exists without further in-depth study.

Technolink
For more data that imply causal relationships, see pages 388, 391, and 396 of Appendix A.

KEY IDEAS

sample—part of a population selected so as to gain information about the whole population

causal relationship—where one variable directly affects another. Proving a causal relationship is the result of an in-depth study.

1.2 Exercises

A

1. **Knowledge and Understanding** Students were asked if they possess a valid driver's licence. The results are shown below, broken down by gender. Does gender have any effect on whether a student has a licence or not? Explain.

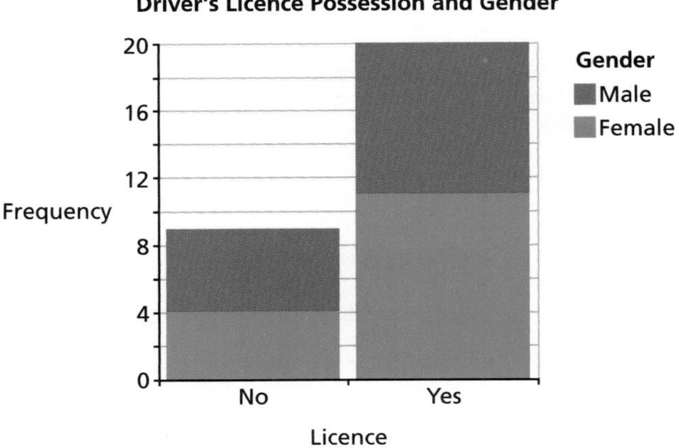

2. Students were asked whether they are able to wiggle their ears as well as whether they know the words to the national anthem. Are students who know the words to the national anthem more likely to be able to wiggle their ears? Explain.

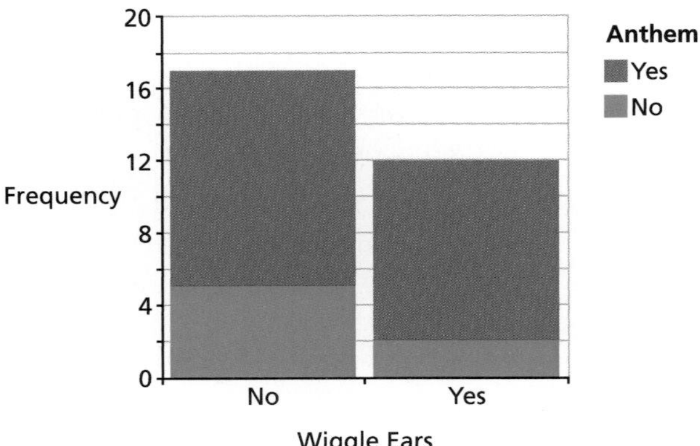

3. Students were asked to identify their dominant hand. Are females or males more likely to be ambidextrous? Explain.

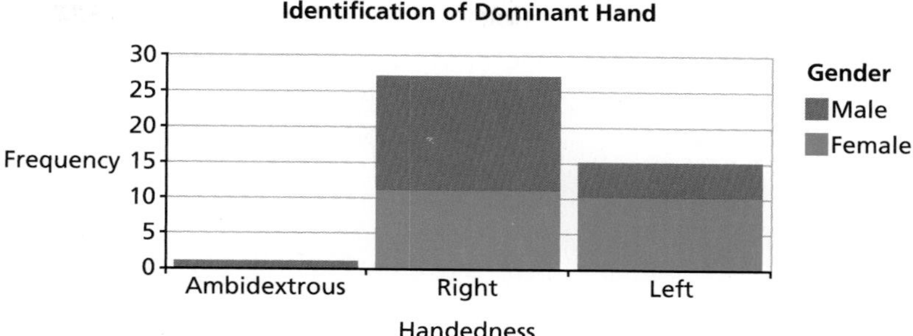

4. Students were asked in which direction they prefer the toilet paper to come off the roll: *don't care* (DC), *over the top of the roll* (O), or *from under the bottom of the roll* (U). The responses are broken down by gender. Do males or females care less about how the paper comes off the roll? Explain.

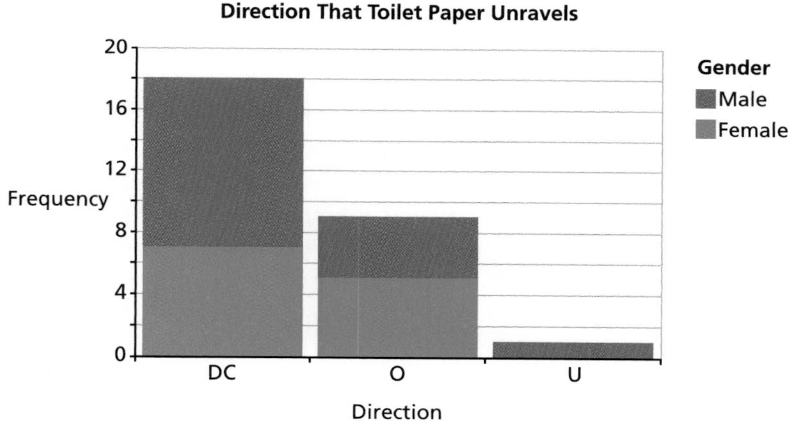

5. Students were asked if they know the words to the national anthem. Do more females than males know the words to the national anthem? Explain.

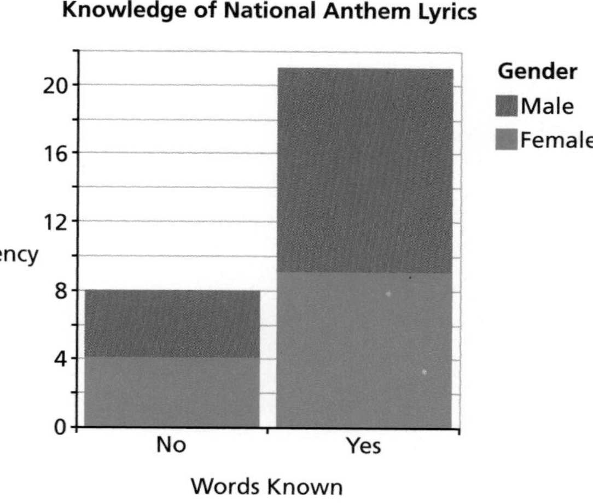

6. Students were asked if they wear corrective lenses. The graph shows the responses. Do more females or more males wear corrective lenses? Explain.

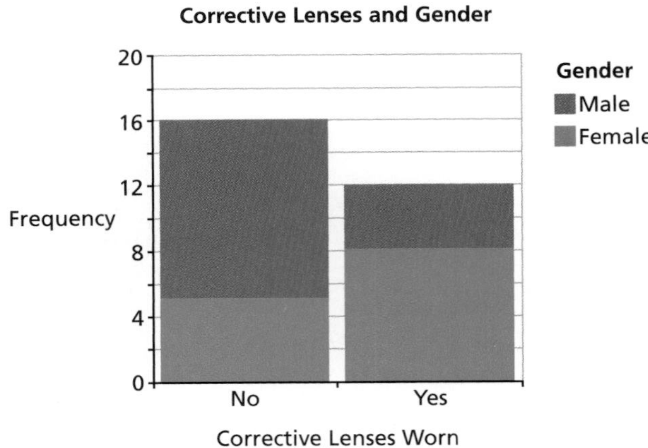

7. In addition to being asked if they wear corrective lenses, students were asked if they had ever worn braces. The graph shows the responses. Do more students who have worn braces wear corrective lenses than students who have not? Explain.

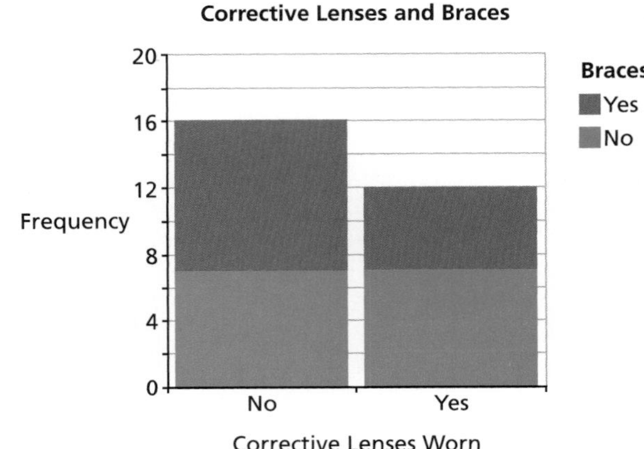

8. Responses to *In which direction does a hurricane spin in Canada?* are shown below, broken down by gender. Do more females or more males know the direction in which a hurricane spins in Canada? Explain.

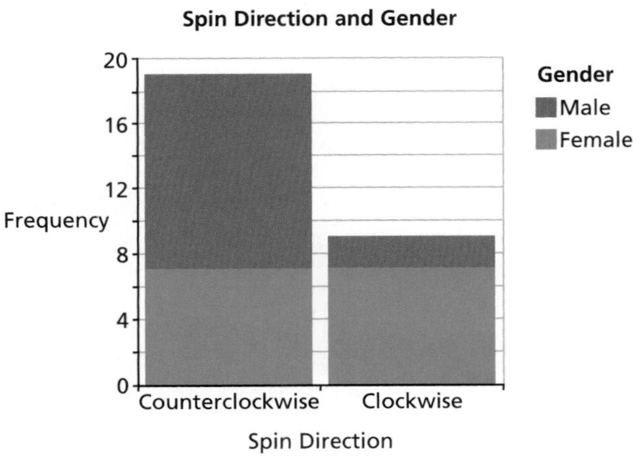

B

9. Communication In a recent poll at a local high school, a sample of 200 students was asked a number of questions. The results of two of the questions are shown below.

How well would you say you get along with your parents/guardians?

	Very Well	Fairly Well	Not At All Well	No Opinion
Males	55%	41%	3%	1%
Females	61%	35%	4%	0%
Overall	58%	38%	4%	0%

How serious do you consider the following offences—shoplifting, cheating on exams, public profanity?

	Very Serious	Somewhat Serious	A Little Serious	Not Serious	No Opinion
Shoplifting	91%	4%	2%	2%	1%
Cheating on Exams	56%	31%	7%	6%	0%
Public Profanity	41%	44%	13%	1%	1%

Write a brief article for the school newspaper summarizing the results of these two questions.

10. You have been asked to conduct a survey to analyze the shopping habits of the people in your community.

(a) Compose 5 to 10 questions that you would ask in the survey.

(b) List the steps that you would follow to choose a sample of the population.

(c) How would you display your results? Give reasons for your answer.

11. The teacher sponsoring this year's ski trip has said that 55% of the student body must be in favour of the trip or it will be cancelled. The student council distributed a questionnaire to a sample of the student body and the results are summarized below.

	Number of Students Responded
I definitely will go on the ski trip.	18
I probably will go on the ski trip.	25
I may go on the ski trip.	11
I probably will not go on the ski trip.	4
I definitely will not go on the ski trip.	27

(a) Is there enough interest to hold this year's ski trip? Explain.

(b) To improve the appearance of the results, explain how the student council should present the findings of the questionnaire.

12. A survey of students asked, among other questions, *How much do you enjoy math?* and *What level of school will you complete?* The responses are shown in the graphs below. Consider the conclusion *The level of enjoyment in math will affect the level of education a student will complete.*

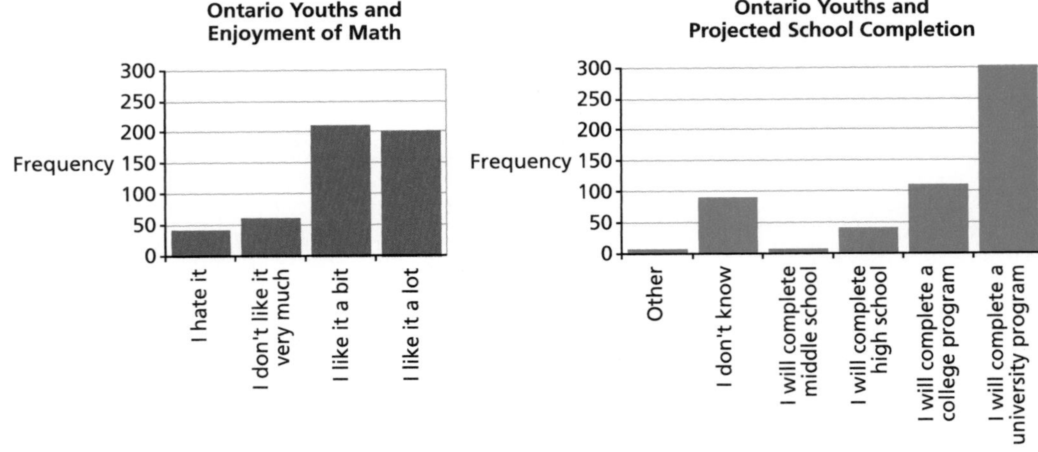

(a) Do the data allow you to support or refute the conclusion? Give reasons for your answer.

(b) Describe how you would organize the data to help you decide whether to accept or reject the hypothesis.

(c) Is there enough data for you to be confident in supporting or refuting the hypothesis? Explain.

13. Application The following graphs show Canadian population data from 1948 to 1997.

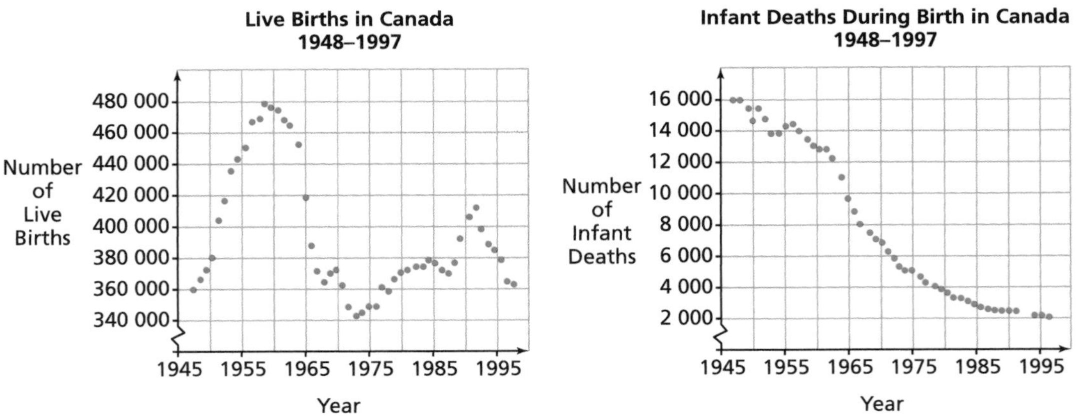

Source: Data have been extracted from Fathom Dynamic Statistics™, Key Curriculum Press.

(a) State a conclusion based on the graphs. Give reasons for your answer.

(b) What issue would require further exploration based on the conclusion you have drawn? Give reasons for your answer.

14. The following graphs were created from temperatures taken at the South Pole in 1957 and 1987.

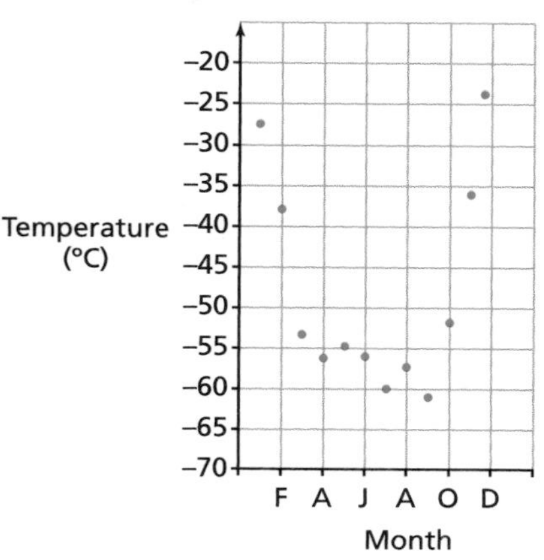

South Pole Temperature, 1987

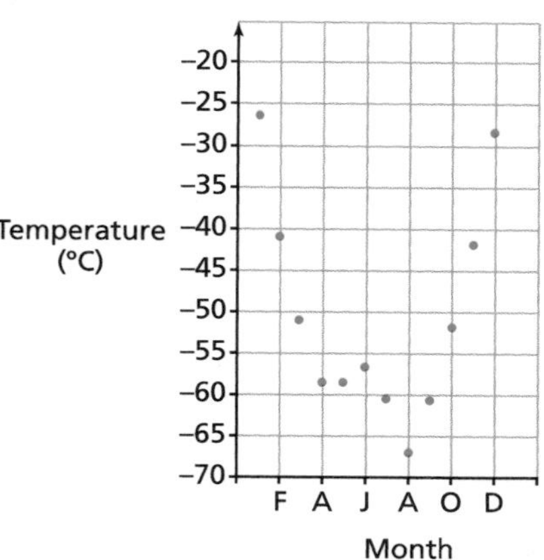

Source: Data have been extracted from Fathom Dynamic Statistics™, Key Curriculum Press.

(a) State a conclusion based on the graphs. Give reasons for your answer.

(b) What issue would require further exploration based on the conclusion you have drawn? Give reasons for your answer.

(c) What is the relationship between the sample size and the degree of confidence you may have in a conclusion you have drawn based on the sample? Explain.

15. On June 21, 2001, COMPAS Inc. issued a report outlining the results of a survey of Canadians in which participants were asked to respond to 10 questions taken from the citizenship test. Some of the results are shown in the tables that follow.

(a) State a conclusion based on the information in Table 1. Give reasons for your answer.

(b) How would you display the data in Table 2 (on page 26) more clearly?

(c) State a conclusion based on the information in Table 2. Give reasons for your answer.

Table 1: Citizenship Test Report Card

Number of Questions Correctly Answered	0	1	2	3	4	5	6	7	8	9	10
Percent of Respondents	14	14	15	12	15	13	8	4	3	2	0

Source: COMPAS Inc.

Table 2: Correct Response in Percent by Education

	High School	College	University	Post-Grad/ Law/Medicine
What important trade or commerce did the Hudson's Bay Company control during the early settlement of Canada?	60	69	83	90
Which group of people played a major role in physically building the Canadian Pacific Railway across the West?	33	56	55	54
Who are the Métis? From whom are they descended?	34	51	54	56
Parliament created a new territory in Canada's North. What is the name of the new territory?	29	52	58	62
What does one call a law before it is passed?	23	51	49	71
What does one call the Queen's representative in the provinces and territories?	12	28	35	50
Which four provinces first formed the Confederation?	12	16	33	38
Which province is the only bilingual province?	11	18	31	23
When did the British North America Act come into effect?	9	20	23	37
How many electoral districts are there in Canada?	0	4	5	4

Source: COMPAS Inc.

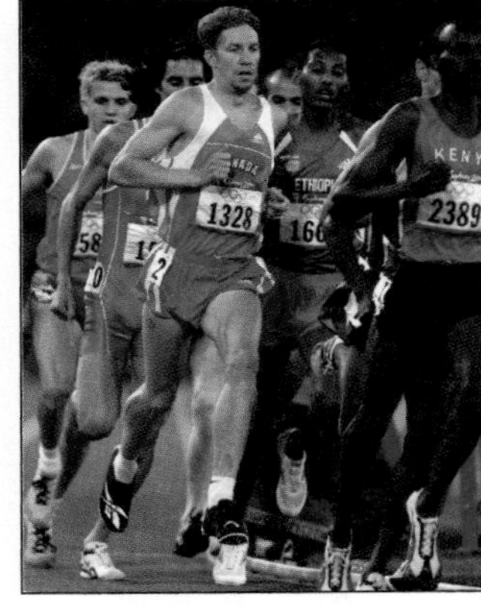

16. **Thinking, Inquiry, Problem Solving** Television networks bid for the right to televise the Olympic games. Using Fathom™ and the data in the Olympics–Cost file on the textbook CD, consider the issue of the cost of hosting the Olympics. Write a report that includes

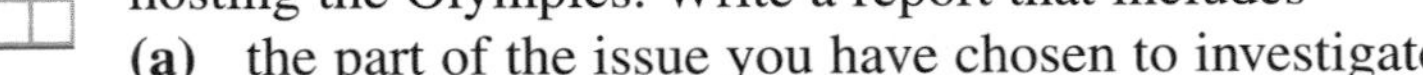

(a) the part of the issue you have chosen to investigate;
(b) your hypothesis based on the data;
(c) an analysis of how the data supports your hypothesis; and
(d) any modifications you would make to your original hypothesis.

17. With a small group of students, brainstorm some issues that are of interest.
(a) Choose two of the issues from your list and state a hypothesis for each.

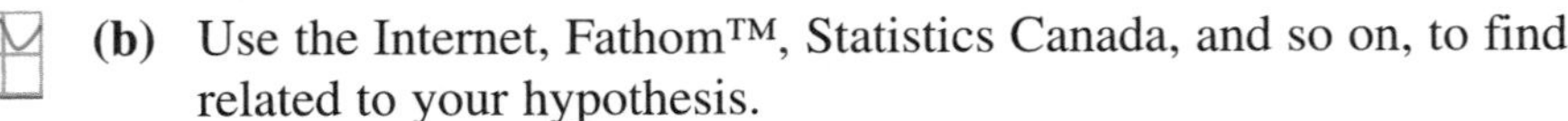

(b) Use the Internet, Fathom™, Statistics Canada, and so on, to find data related to your hypothesis.
(c) Does the data support or refute your hypothesis?
(d) What other issues arise from the data?

ADDITIONAL ACHIEVEMENT CHART QUESTIONS

Examples 1, 2, and 3 investigated two possible factors (namely gender and academic performance) that influence students' feelings about school. Another factor that can be explored is unkind treatment by other students. The following data were gathered.

	A	B	C
1		Ontario Youths	
2	**Gender**	**How do you feel about school?**	**Are you treated unkindly?**
3	F	3. I like school a bit.	Never
4	F	1. I hate school.	Some of the time
5	F	4. I like school quite a bit.	Rarely
6	F	5. I like school very much.	Some of the time
7	M	5. I like school very much.	Rarely
8	F	1. I hate school.	Never
9	M	2. I don't like school very much.	Rarely
10	M	3. I like school a bit.	Rarely
11	F	2. I don't like school very much.	Some of the time
12	M	3. I like school a bit.	Rarely
13	F	5. I like school very much.	Never
14	M	5. I like school very much.	Rarely
15	M	1. I hate school.	All the time
16	F	4. I like school quite a bit.	Never
17	F	5. I like school very much.	Never
18	F	5. I like school very much.	Most of the time
19	M	4. I like school quite a bit.	Never
20	M	2. I don't like school very much.	Never
21	M	1. I hate school.	Never
22	F	4. I like school quite a bit.	Never
23	F	5. I like school very much.	Never
24	M	3. I like school a bit.	Some of the time
25	F	2. I don't like school very much.	Some of the time
26	M	5. I like school very much.	Never
27	F	5. I like school very much.	Rarely

Consider the hypothesis: *Unkind treatment by other children causes students to dislike school.*

18. Knowledge and Understanding
- **(a)** What is the sample in this study?
- **(b)** What is the population that the sample represents? Explain.
- **(c)** Is there enough data for you to be confident in supporting or refuting the hypothesis? Explain.

19. Application Organize the data so that it can be analyzed more easily.

20. Thinking, Inquiry, Problem Solving Use the data to support or refute the hypothesis. Give reasons for your answer.

21. Communication Describe how you would present these data to convince an audience of your hypothesis.

Chapter Problem

Trends in Canada's Population

Below is a graph of the age classes from the data provided in the table on page 2.

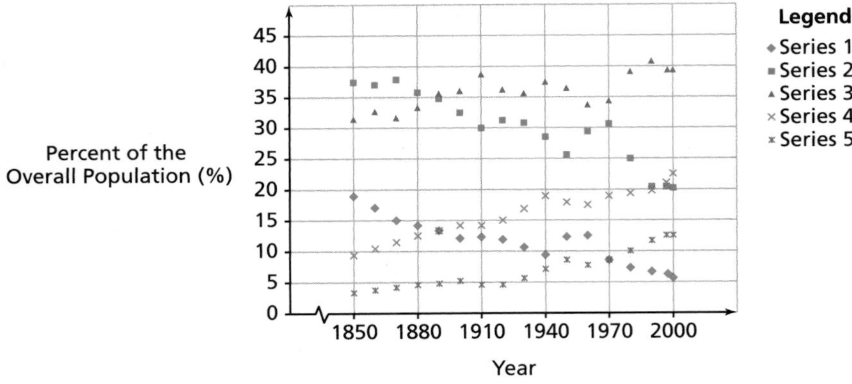

CP3. Identify which series belongs to each age class.

CP4. State a conclusion for each age class based on the graph.

CP5. Identify some issues that would be worth further exploration based on your conclusions. Give reasons for your answer.

CP6. What is the relationship between the sample size and the degree of confidence you may have in a conclusion you have drawn based on these data? Explain.

Project Connection

The Action Plan

Deadlines are an inescapable part of life, and completing projects on time is just as important in the workplace as it is in school. So, how will you avoid having to rush through all parts of your project at the last minute? The answer is simple: Develop a formal action plan.

Featured on the next page is a list of stages through which a major research project must successfully pass. Completing this action plan will help you organize your time and give you attainable goals and deadlines.

Set aside an hour to complete the action plan. Note that the times listed for each stage of the project are only a guide. Adjust the time you spend on each phase in accordance with the scope of your project, your personal situation, and the issues affecting you.

Issues Affecting Project Completion

Consider the issues that may interfere with your completing the project in a time-efficient manner. For example:

- part-time job
- after-school sports activities
- homework
- other assignments
- tests in other courses
- driving school
- access to research/technology
- being with friends
- school dances/parties
- family commitments

What other issues might you add to this list? Confer with your teacher throughout all phases of your project (about 5–10 min per conference) to ensure that you are on track.

Project Action Plan

1. Select the topic you would like to explore.

Suggested time length: 1 d to 3 d

Your probable time length:

Finish date:

2. Create the topic question that you would like to answer.

Suggested time length: 1 d to 3 d

Your probable time length:

Finish date:

3. (a) Find the data.

Suggested time length: 5 d to 10 d

Your probable time length:

Finish date:

(b) Analyze the data.

Suggested time length: 5 d to 10 d

Your probable time length:

Finish date:

4. Create a presentation outline.

Suggested time length: 2 d to 4 d

Your probable time length:

Finish date:

5. Prepare a first draft.

Suggested time length: 3 d to 10 d

Your probable time length:

Finish date:

6. Revise, edit, and proofread.

Suggested time length: 3 d to 5 d

Your probable time length:

Finish date:

7. Prepare and practise the presentation.

Suggested time length: 3 d to 5 d

Your probable time length:

Finish date:

8. Buffer room (time during which unplanned issues are dealt with).

Suggested time length: 3 d to 7 d

Your probable time length:

Finish date:

1.3 The Power of Visualizing Data—Trends

The data in Section 1.2 helped you determine if the issues raised were supported or not supported by the data. Data like these represent the moment in time when they were collected. Once you have identified a pattern at one moment in time, you might find it useful to look at the data over a longer period. Looking at data collected over a longer period of time may show trends and allow you to make predictions about future events. One effective way to predict these events is to create a visual display of the data in the form of a scatter plot.

scatter plot—a graphical method of showing the joint distribution of two variables in which each point on the graph represents a pair of values

independent variable—a variable whose values are arbitrarily chosen

dependent variable—a variable whose values depend on the independent variable

Example 1 Creating a Scatter Plot

Many people (especially insurance agents and driving instructors) are interested in the relationship between the **independent variable** (driver age) and the **dependent variable** (the number of fatal driving accidents per year). The number of fatal accidents over a three-year period and involving 18- to 25-year-olds is given below. Use a scatter plot of the data to determine if there is a relationship.

Age	Number of Fatal Accidents		
	Year 1	Year 2	Year 3
18	8	4	2
19	7	7	6
20	1	7	1
21	6	2	10
22	3	10	4
23	1	9	8
24	10	3	3
25	10	2	9

Solution

Typically, the independent variable is on the horizontal axis and the dependent variable is on the vertical axis. Each piece of data is then plotted as an individual point. A legend is used to differentiate points from one year to the next.

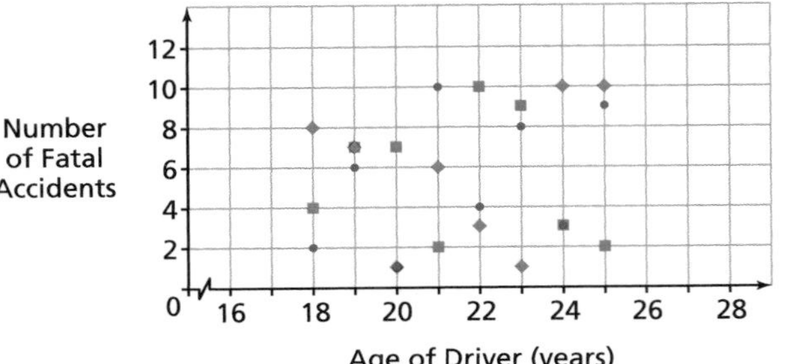

The plotted points appear to be randomly placed; no relationship is clearly evident.

INVESTIGATION: TUITION FEES—WILL I BE ABLE TO AFFORD THEM?

Purpose

To determine whether a table or a graph is more effective in predicting how much one might expect to pay in tuition fees when entering college or university.

Canadian Tuition Consumer Price Index 1975–2000

Year	Relative Cost ($)
1975	29.6
1976	29.9
1977	31.0
1978	33.4
1979	34.2
1980	36.1
1981	39.6
1982	41.5
1983	49.7
1984	50.2
1985	52.0
1986	57.4
1987	60.1

Year	Relative Cost ($)
1988	68.3
1989	70.2
1990	75.0
1991	87.3
1992	100.0
1993	111.3
1994	123.8
1995	126.5
1996	140.1
1997	161.9
1998	171.4
1999	184.3
2000	198.6

Source: Statistics Canada

Procedure

The above table shows a comparison of tuition fees based on assigning $100 as the value of the fees in 1992. The other fees are determined relative to the fees in 1992 using the consumer price index (CPI).

trend—a pattern of average behaviour that occurs over time

line of best fit—a straight-line graph that best represents a set of data

A. Make a scatter plot of the data shown in the table. Describe any patterns that you observe in the graph that you did not notice in the table.
B. In what year(s) does the relative cost increase the most? The least?
C. Which of the following words would you use to describe the **trend** of the data: *steady growth*, *steady decline*, *irregular growth*, or *irregular decline*? Justify your choice.
D. Predict the cost of tuition when you enter college or university relative to the cost in 1992.
E. Draw a **line of best fit**. Was it easier to use the table or the scatter plot to make your prediction? Give reasons for your answer.

Discussion Questions

1. Explain how you arrived at your prediction in Step D. Compare your prediction with those of your classmates.
2. Copy the following *confidence scale* into your notebook.

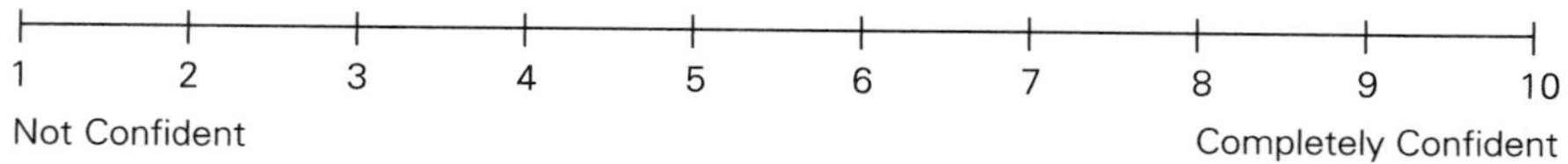

Place a dot on the scale to show your confidence in your prediction. Give reasons for your answer.

3. Do you think you can afford to go to college or university? Why or why not?

DETERMINING RELATIONSHIPS: CORRELATION

A scatter plot helps reveal a relationship by showing a general trend in the data. The arrangement of points helps determine the type and strength of the relationship. Consider the following scatter plots.

Use the graphs to answer the Think about questions on page 34.

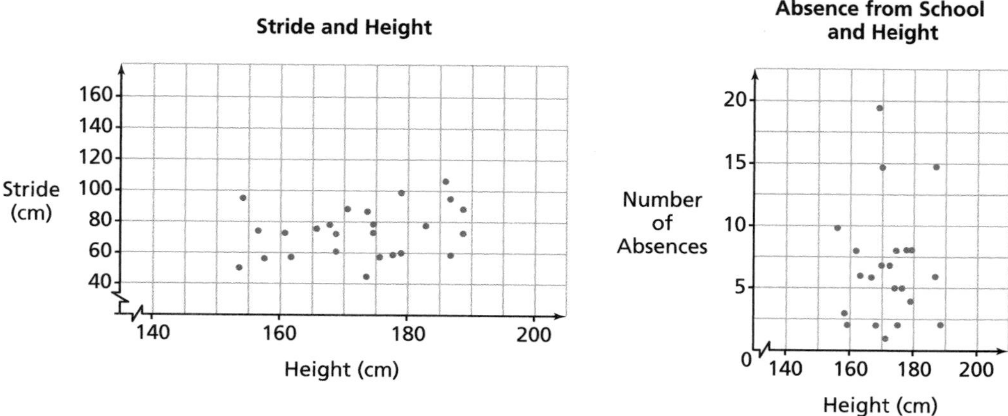

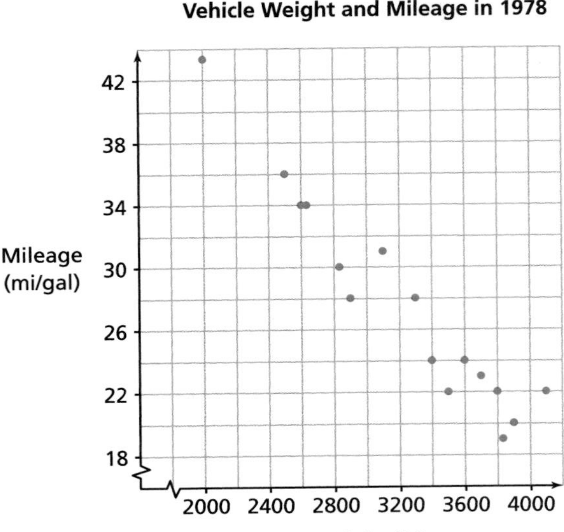

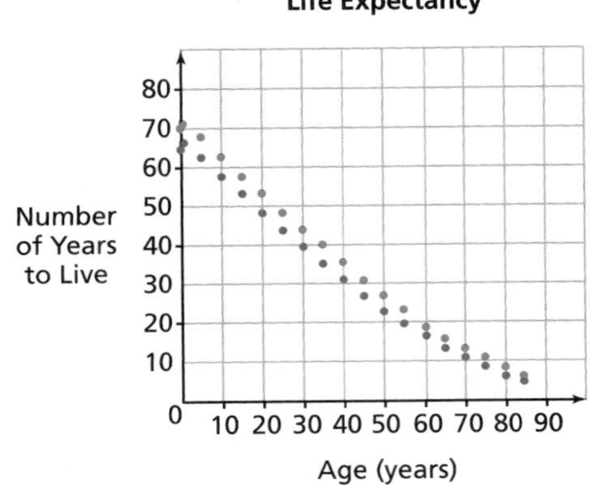

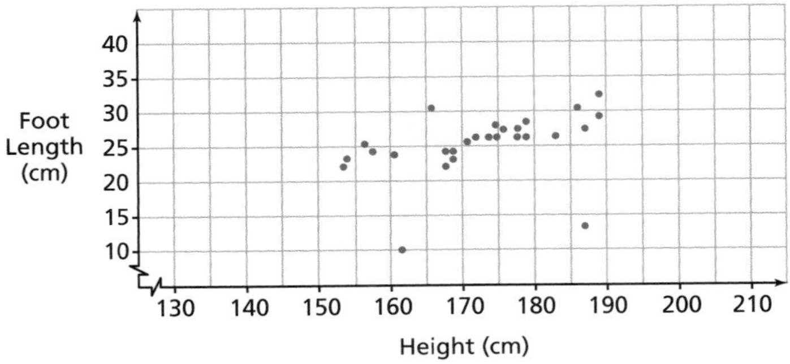

Think about The Scatter Plots

- Which of the scatter plots indicate the strongest trend? Give reasons for your answers.
- Which of the scatter plots do not indicate a trend? Give reasons for your answer.
- If a line of best fit were drawn on each of the scatter plots that show a trend, describe the slope of each line.

correlation—the apparent relation between two variables

There appears to be no relationship between absences and height; the dots are scattered randomly. The strongest relationship appears to be in life expectancy. A very clear trend is evident from the data.

The scatter plot showing a strong trend and having a line of best fit with a positive slope is said to have a strong positive **correlation**. The scatter plot showing a trend that is not strong and that has a line of best fit with a positive slope is said to have a weak positive correlation.The scatter plot showing no trend is said to have no correlation.

Negative correlation occurs in scatter plots where a line of best fit has a negative slope.

Think about Negative Correlation

Write a definition for a strong negative correlation and a weak negative correlation.

median–median line—a linear model used to fit a line to a data set. The line is fit only to key points calculated using medians.

Example 2 The Median–Median Line

The environment club is interested in the relationship between the number of canned drinks sold in the cafeteria and the number of cans that are recycled. The data they collected are listed below.

Number of Canned Drinks Sold	15	18	23	25	28	30	30	36
Number of Cans Recycled	6	2	4	1	6	8	4	10

(a) Draw a scatter plot for this information.

(b) Observe the trend in the data and identify the type of correlation.

(c) Draw a median–median line for the line of best fit.

(d) Use the line drawn in part (c) to determine the number of cans that will likely be found in the recycling box if 35 canned drinks are sold.

Solution

(a)

Recycling Habits of Students

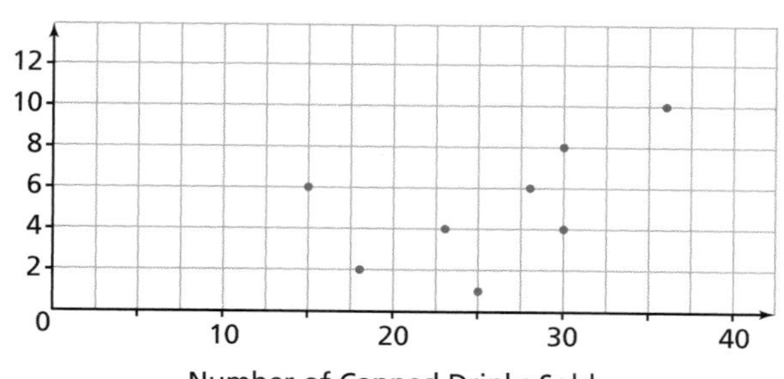

Number of Canned Drinks Sold

(b) The trend has a weak positive correlation because the data points are fairly spread out; yet, they suggest a line with positive slope.

(c) To draw the median–median line, the data are broken up into three vertical sections. As much as possible, each section contains an equal number of data points.

Recycling Habits of Students

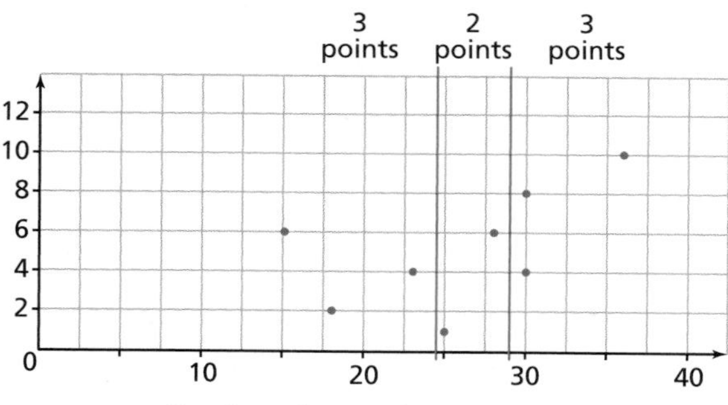

Number of Canned Drinks Sold

Find the median of the x-coordinates (x-median) and the median of the y-coordinates (y-median) in each section. In the first section, the x-median of 15, 18, and 23 is 18, and the y-median of 6, 2, and 4 is 4. Plot the median point (18, 4). The median point is indicated on the graph that follows by a Δ. Repeat the process for the other two sections. Place the edge of a ruler along the line joining the first and third median points. If the second point is not on this line, slide the ruler about a third of the way toward the second point. Ensure that the slope of the line has not changed. Draw the median–median line along the edge of the ruler.

Technolink
More data for trend analysis are available in Appendix A starting on page 388.

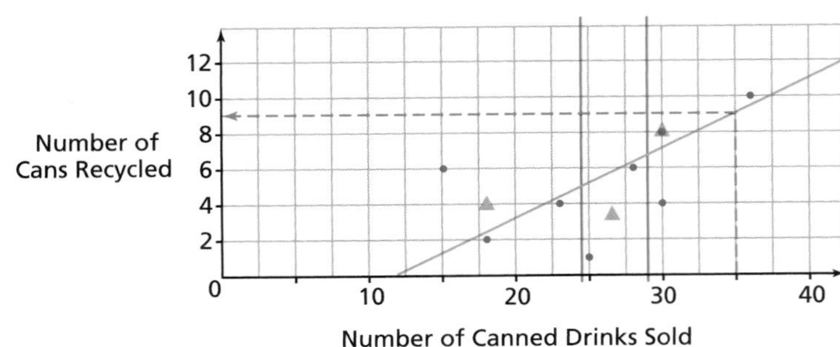

(d) They would expect to find nine cans in the recycling box.

KEY IDEAS

scatter plot—a graphical method of showing the joint distribution of two variables in which each point on the graph represents a pair of values

independent variable—a variable whose value is arbitrarily chosen

dependent variable—a variable whose value depends on the independent variable

trend—a pattern of average behaviour that occurs over time

line of best fit—a straight-line graph that best represents a set of data

correlation—the apparent relation between two variables

strong linear correlation—occurs if the two variables vary at similar rates

weak linear correlation—occurs if the two variables vary at rates that are not similar

positive linear correlation—occurs if the slope of the line of best fit or median–median line is positive

negative linear correlation—occurs if the slope of the line of best fit or median–median line is negative

median–median line—a linear model used to fit a line to a data set; the line is fit only to key points calculated using medians

1.3 Exercises

A

1. **Knowledge and Understanding** Make a scatter plot to display the data in each of the following tables.

(a)

Planet	Time of One Revolution (year)	Mean Distance from the Sun (AU)
Mercury	0.24	0.39
Venus	0.61	0.72
Earth	1.00	1.00
Mars	1.88	1.52
Jupiter	11.86	5.20
Saturn	29.46	9.54
Uranus	84.07	19.19
Neptune	164.82	30.06
Pluto	247.68	39.53

Note: AU ≐ 150 million km

(b) Students posing for yearbook photos have several package options.

Number of Photos	44	30	24	15
Total Cost ($)	18.00	16.00	13.00	10.00

(c) The number of available seats and the average speed of a variety of planes are listed below (the data are taken from Fathom™).

Plane	Seats	Average Speed (km/h)
B747-400	396	538
B747-100	447	520
L-1011-100/200	310	495
DC-10-10	289	500
A300-600	249	473
DC-10-30	265	520
B767-300ER	214	495
B767-200ER	181	488
A320-100/200	148	460
B727-200	150	437

Plane	Seats	Average Speed (km/h)
B737-400	144	414
MD-80	141	432
B737-300	131	417
DC-9-50	122	374
B737-100/200	113	389
DC-9-30	101	385
F-100	97	383
DC-9-10	71	381
B777	292	521
MD-11	253	524

Source: Data have been extracted from Fathom Dynamic Statistics™, Key Curriculum Press.

(d) A group of teenagers recorded the length of their forearm span in centimetres and their age in months. The results are shown below.

Forearm Span (cm)	20.5	23	27	30	27	24.7	25.5	24	28	26
Age (months)	214	221	237	216	216	210	216	219	209	214

2. Communication For each of the following graphs, state whether or not there appears to be a trend. If there is, state whether the correlation is strong or weak, and positive or negative.

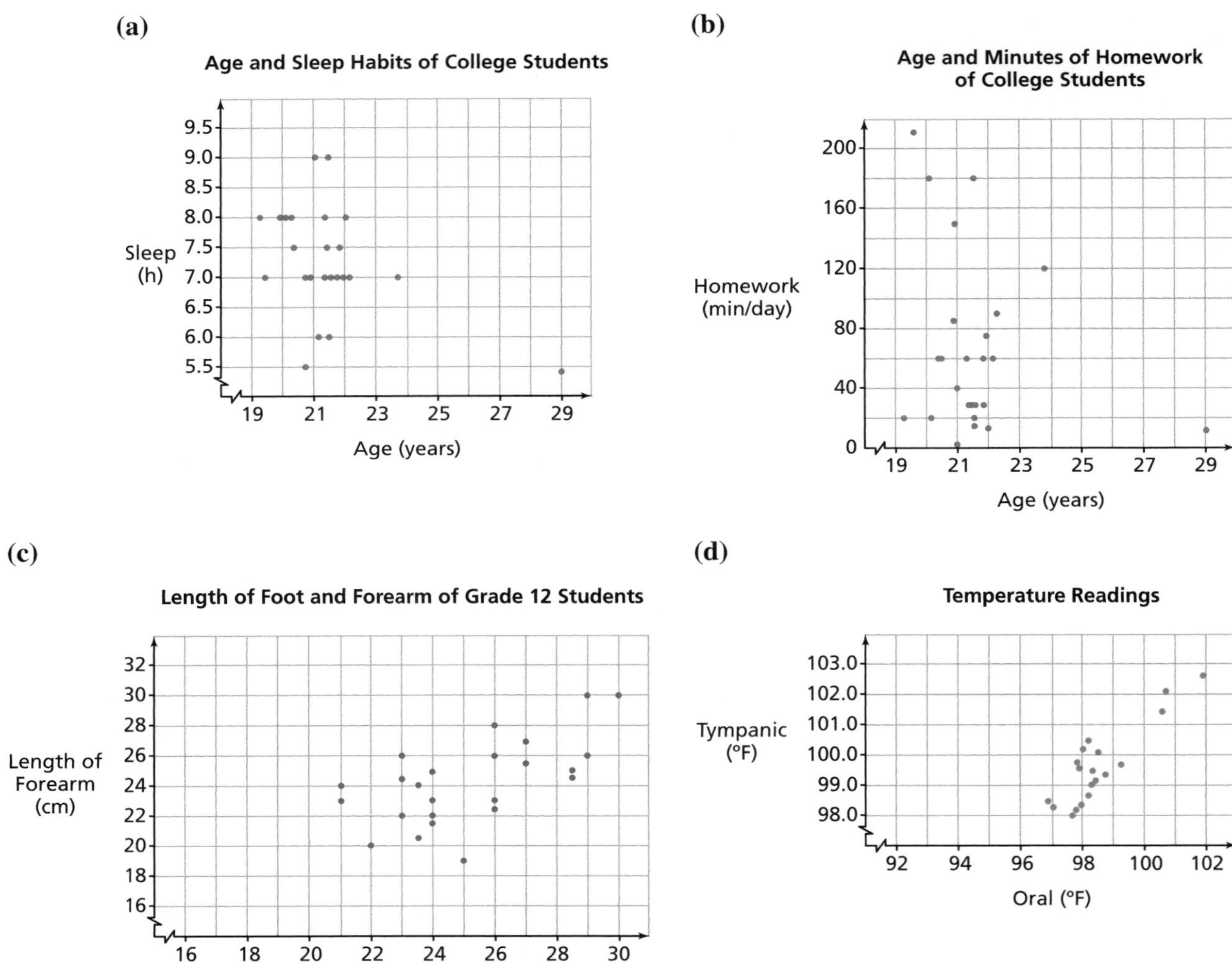

3. **Application** A car manufacturer has tested the stopping distance of a new model of car relative to the speed when the brakes are applied. All testing was done on dry pavement. The results are shown in the table below. The stopping distance is defined as the distance travelled from when the brakes are applied to the time when the vehicle comes to a complete stop.

Speed of Car (km/h)	25	35	45	55	60	70	80	90	100	110
Stopping Distance (m)	10	15	21	27	33	42	54	61	78	103

(a) Create a scatter plot.
(b) Is there a trend? Give reasons for your answer.
(c) Describe the type of correlation that might be appropriate for the data.

4. Every year, students at a local high school collect money for a local charity. They keep track of the number of students who participate, as well as the amount of money that is collected. The information for the past five years is listed in the table below.

Year	Number of Students	Amount Collected ($)
1	130	2250
2	125	2875
3	135	2500
4	147	2300
5	153	2000

(a) Create a scatter plot for the information in the table.
(b) Describe the correlation that is observed in the data.

B **5.** Attendance at school dances for last year was recorded.

Month	September	October	November	December	February	March
Attendance	250	245	200	260	285	280

(a) Create a scatter plot for the information in the table.
(b) Describe any trends that you observe.

Answer Questions 6 through 9 using a scatter plot with a median–median line.

6. The attendance at school hockey games is shown below.

Game	1	2	3	4	5	6	7	8
Attendance	125	111	122	105	100	93	85	72

Predict the attendance for Game 9. Give reasons for your answer.

7. Twenty members of your class toss a coin for five minutes and record the number of tails tossed. The totals are shown below.

Number of Tosses	Number of Tails
21	15
36	25
26	20
43	18
37	19
45	25
47	26

Number of Tosses	Number of Tails
41	17
41	14
52	25
36	24
51	25
50	14
45	30

If you were to toss the coin 30 times, how many tails would you expect? Give reasons for your answer.

8. The winning women's Olympic long-jump distance is shown in the table below.

Year	Distance (m)
1948	5.69
1952	6.24
1956	6.35
1960	6.37
1964	6.76
1968	6.82
1972	6.78

Year	Distance (m)
1976	6.72
1980	7.06
1984	6.96
1988	7.40
1992	7.14
1996	7.12
2000	6.99

Source: British Broadcasting Corporation (BBC)

If the Olympics had been held in 1944, what might the winning distance have been?

9. A local movie theatre monitors attendance during the first 10 weeks of a movie's showing. The results of one movie are listed below.

Week	1	2	3	4	5	6	7	8	9	10
Attendance	2250	2100	1950	1678	1430	1200	987	731	675	587

If less than 200 people attend a movie, the theatre loses money. How many more weeks will the movie run?

10. **Thinking, Inquiry, Problem Solving** Find a set of data that appears to have a linear correlation. You may find the data in an almanac, newspaper, magazine, or in Appendix A, or on the Internet.
   (a) Record the data in a table.
   (b) Create a scatter plot for the data.
   (c) Describe any trends in the data. Give reasons for your answer.
   (d) Construct the median–median line for the data.
   (e) Write a question that requires the median–median line to make a prediction.
   (f) Exchange your table and question with a partner. Respond to your partner's question.
   (g) Compare your answers to both questions.

ADDITIONAL ACHIEVEMENT CHART QUESTIONS

The table below shows the number of calories a person might use while in-line skating at a comfortable pace.

Time (min)	3	7	12	18	25	35
Energy Used (in calories)	28	70	119	170	241	320

11. **Knowledge and Understanding** Make a scatter plot of the data and construct the median–median line.

12. **Communication** Describe a trend in the data in terms of correlation.

13. **Application** Determine the equation of the median–median line that you constructed.

14. **Thinking, Inquiry, Problem Solving** If a person burned 1000 calories while in-line skating, determine the length of time that she or he skated. How confident are you that your prediction is valid? Give reasons for your answer.

Chapter Problem

Trends in Canada's Population

Use the data given in the chapter problem on page 2 to answer the following questions.

CP7. Create a single scatter plot that illustrates the trends in each age class since 1951.

CP8. For each age class, describe the trends that you see. Where are these trends most visible: in the table or in the graph? Explain.

CP9. For each age class, draw the median–median line on your graph.

CP10. Describe the type of correlation that exists within each age class.

CP11. Provide some possible reasons for the trends that you see.

1.4 Trends Using Technology

Visual displays of data taken from a table help not only the identification of trends, but also the drawing of valid conclusions from the information. By examining a scatter plot, for example, you can see whether the relationship between two variables is strong or weak, positive or negative.

In the past, health researchers used treadmills and bicycle ergometers to measure the exercise capacity of patients with cardiac and respiratory illnesses. As this equipment was not always available to everyone, investigators began to use a simpler test more related to day-to-day activity. The simpler test had patients cover as much ground as possible in a specified amount of time by walking in an enclosed corridor. The strength of the relationship between the two tests is important because if the results are strongly related, then one test can be substituted for the other. The strength of the relationship could show how well laboratory tests can predict a patient's ability to undertake physically demanding activities associated with daily living.

You are familiar with scatter plots and finding a line of best fit. Often, a set of data is best represented by a curve of best fit. In this section, you will investigate mathematical tools that will allow you to evaluate the strength of any conclusions drawn from a data set. These tools will give you more confidence in analyzing data and describing trends, which are important mathematical skills.

regression—the process of fitting a line or curve to a set of data

Think about Sanjev's Observations

Sanjev noticed that the turning point for tuition increases was around 1990. What other observations could be added to the list?

Project Connection

When displaying your data in a graph, consider the type of graph that best displays the data.

Example 1 Finding the Best Model to Fit the Data

Sanjev is planning to enter college or university in 2005. He creates a scatter plot to help him predict the relative costs of tuition fees and must decide which model of **regression** (linear or quadratic) best fits the data.

Solution

The scatter plot with the line of best fit is shown to the right. Extend the line to the year 2005 to predict the relative cost of tuition fees by reading from the graph or by using the equation of the line.

Canadian Tuition CPI

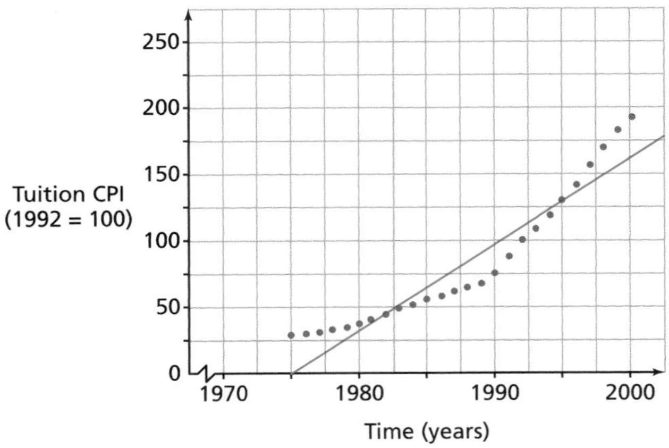

Tuition CPI (1992 = 100)

250
200
150
100
50
0

1970 1980 1990 2000

Time (years)

Source: Statistics Canada

The scatter plot shown represents the CPI for tuition fees relative to 1992 levels. For example, the point (1995,130) means the average tuition in the year 1995 was 130% of the 1992 average, or 1.3 times 1992 levels.

? **Think about**
The Type of Graph and a Line of Best Fit
Why is a scatter plot an appropriate way to display the data? How would you decide where to draw a line of best fit?

Rounded to two decimal places, the linear model gives the equation $y = 6.35x - 12\,534.45$. Substituting $x = 2005$ into the equation gives the following:

$$\begin{aligned} y &= 6.35x - 12\,534.45 \\ &= 6.35(2005) - 12\,534.45 \\ &= 197.3 \end{aligned}$$

Sanjev observes that the relative cost of 197.3 in 2005 from his line is about the same as the actual relative cost in the year 2000. Since the cost of tuition is always rising, this value does not seem reasonable to him. Another model is needed.

He notices that there is a curved pattern in the data, so he tries a quadratic regression model.

The quadratic model gives the equation

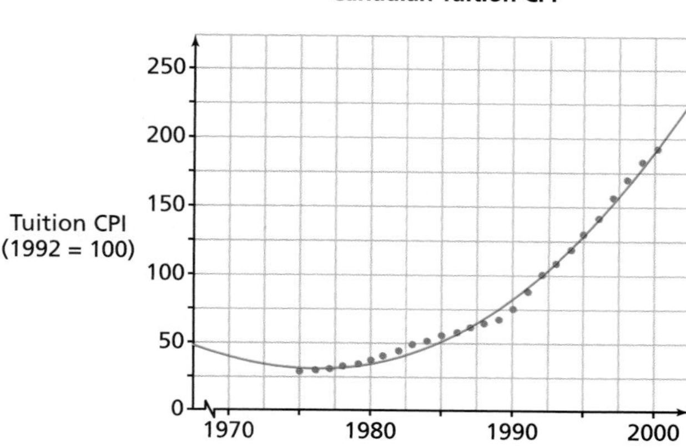

$$y = 0.306\,916\,971\,9x^2 - 1213.646\,792x + 1\,199\,818.279$$

Substituting $x = 2005$ into the equation gives the following:

$$\begin{aligned} y &= 0.306\,916\,971\,9x^2 - 1213.646\,792x + 1\,199\,818.279 \\ &= 0.306\,916\,971\,9(2005)^2 - 1213.646\,792(2005) + 1\,199\,818.279 \\ &= 270.36 \end{aligned}$$

Sanjev concludes that the quadratic model is a better fit than is the linear model since the curve passes through or near the majority of data points. The model suggests that, in 2005, tuition fees will be 2.7 times the 1992 levels. Based on the data, this seems reasonable.

SCATTER PLOTS AND CORRELATION

The following three scatter plots show different types and strengths of correlation.

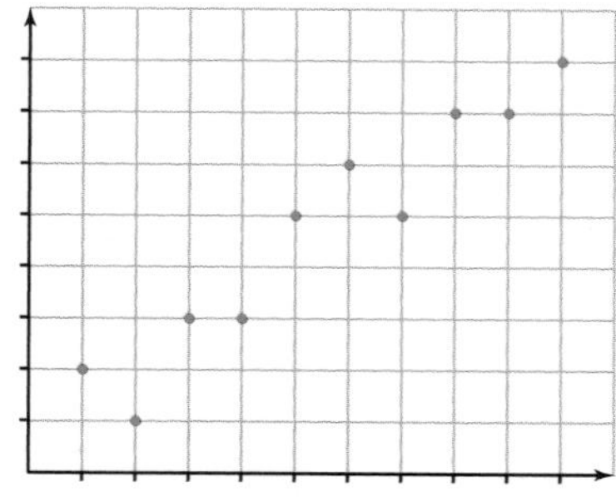
Strong Positive Correlation

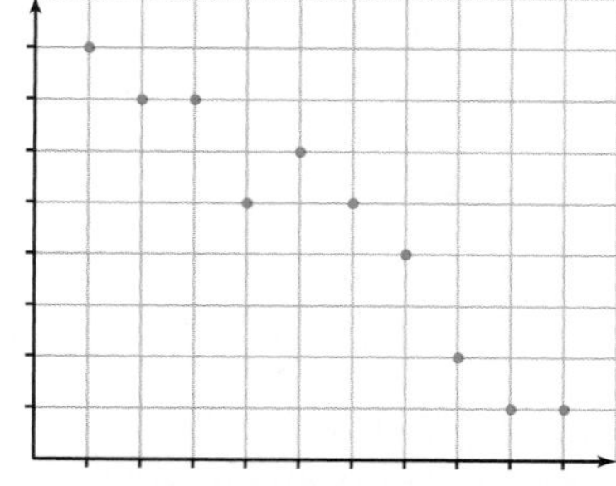
Strong Negative Correlation

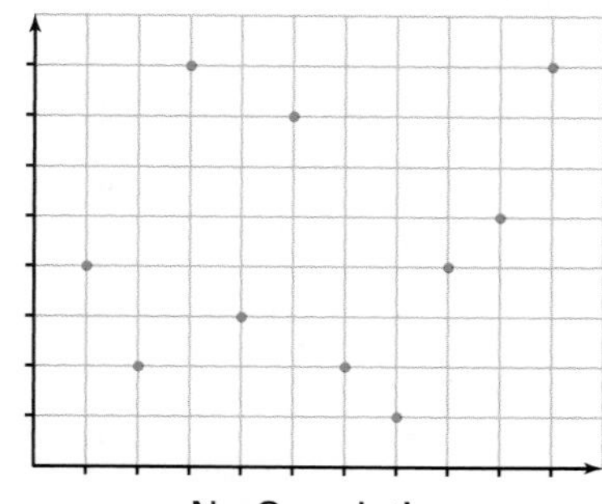
No Correlation

When two variables increase in the same proportion and simultaneously, they have a positive correlation. If one variable increases in the same proportion as the other decreases, they have a negative correlation.

INVESTIGATION: THE CORRELATION COEFFICIENT

Purpose

To investigate the correlation coefficient between two variables using technology.

Procedure—Using Fathom™

Technolink
For more information about creating scatter plots in Fathom™, see Appendix D.6 on page 421.

A. Enter the data shown below into a new case table, labelling the attributes x and y.

x	1	3	5	7	9
y	2	4	4	8	3

B. Drop a new graph into the workspace, and drag x to the horizontal axis and y to the vertical axis to create a scatter plot.

Scatter ...

	x	y
1	1	2
2	3	4
3	5	4
4	7	8
5	9	3

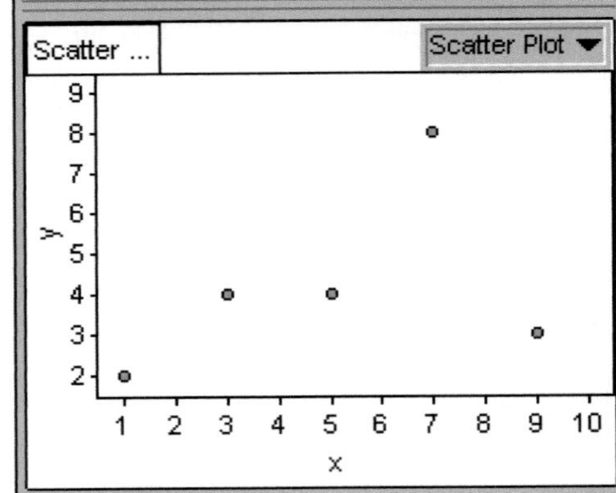

C. Drag the points so that the value of r^2 is as large as possible. Record the greatest value of r.
D. Adjust the points so that the value of r^2 is as small as possible. Record the smallest value of r.
E. Adjust the points so that r^2 is 0. Do this in as many ways as possible.
F. Drag the points so that they are on top of each other.

Discussion Questions

1. What is the largest value of r^2?
2. Describe the relationship between the points when r^2 is a maximum.
3. What is the smallest value of r^2?
4. Describe the relationship between the points when r^2 is a minimum.
5. What happens when you try to drag the points on top of each other? Zoom in on the points to help explain the results.

THE LINE OF BEST FIT: LINEAR REGRESSION

If a data set shows a linear correlation, a line of best fit is drawn to model the data.

Example 2 Using a TI-83 Plus Calculator to Draw a Line of Best Fit

One of the science classes is growing a bean plant. The height of the plant is measured every few days. The results are randomly collected in the table below.

Day	0	10	8	13	9	11	14
Height (cm)	1	12	7	14	10	11	13

(a) Find the line of best fit.

(b) How confident are you in your answer to part (a)?

(c) Use the equation to predict the height of the bean plant at 20 days.

Technolink
See Appendix C starting on page 401 for instructions on entering data into lists, creating a scatter plot, and graphing a line of best fit.

If your calculator does not display r and r^2, refer to page 402 of Appendix C and activate **Diagnostic On**.

coefficient of correlation—a number from +1 to −1 that gives the strength and direction of the relationship between two variables

coefficient of determination—a number from 0 to +1 that gives the relative strength of the relationship between two variables. (If r^2=0.44, this means that 44% of the variation of the dependent variable is due to variation in the independent variable.)

Solution

(a) Enter the data into L_1 and L_2 using Stat Editor.

To construct a line of best fit, you must choose the type of line/curve you think will best fit the data, where the data are located, and where you would like the equation of the line to be written.

The slope and y-intercept of the line are given, as well as two measures of correlation: r, the **coefficient of correlation**, and r^2, the **coefficient of determination**. Plot the points and the line of best fit.

(b) You can be confident in the conclusion that the relationship is linear because the r and r^2 values are very close to 1. Also, the line of best fit appears to fit the data closely.

(c) Using the **CALC** feature on a TI-83 Plus calculator, select **1:value**, hit ENTER, and enter 20 for the x-value. The y-value returned is 19.9. The plant would be approximately 19.9 cm in height, provided that it continued to grow at the rate demonstrated by the data.

CORRELATION COEFFICIENT

The correlation coefficient, r, is an indicator of both the strength and direction of a linear relationship. A value of $r = 0$ indicates no correlation, while $r = \pm 1$ indicates perfect positive or negative correlation.

The coefficient of determination, r^2, does not give the direction of correlation, but does make the scale constant. A value of $r^2 = 0.4$ indicates that 40% of the variation in y is due to the variation in x.

Example 3 Using Fathom™ to Draw the Line of Best Fit

The manager of a service station changes the price of unleaded gasoline and records the amount of gas sold per hour at each price. The results are shown in the table below.

Technolink
For instructions on creating a collection, a case table, a scatter plot, and the least-squares line using Fathom™, refer to pages 416, 417, and 421 of Appendix D.

Price (¢/L)	54.5	55.0	55.9	56.3	58.4	59.2	60.2	62.3
Amount Sold (L/h)	186	178	172	150	127	112	102	83

(a) Is the relationship linear? Give reasons for your answer.

(b) How many litres of gasoline would be sold if the price were $0.57/litre?

Solution

(a) Using Fathom™, start a new worksheet and create a collection with two attributes: **price** and **litres**. Enter the data from the table. Drag a new graph onto the worksheet and drag the attribute names onto the appropriate axes.

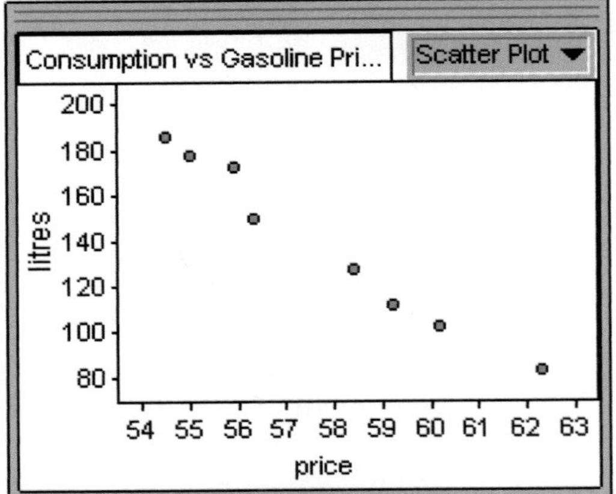

Select the graph and choose **Least-Squares Line** under the **Graph** menu.

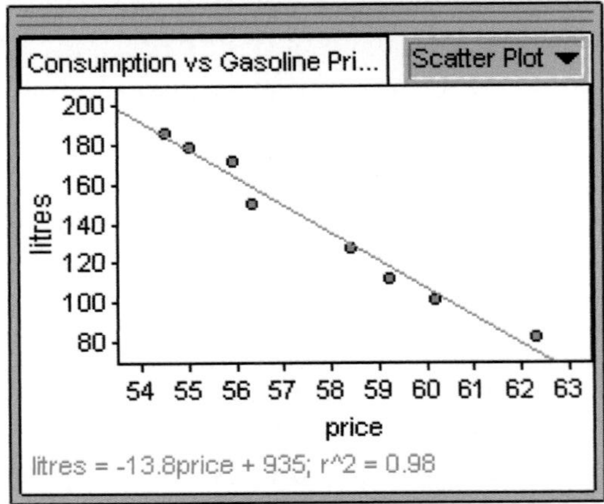

Based on the r^2 value, the data are linear. The line shown on the graph appears accurate.

(b) Substitute 57 for the *price* in the equation

$$
\begin{aligned}
litres &= -13.8price + 935 \\
&= -13.8(57) + 935 \\
&= 148.4 \text{ L}
\end{aligned}
$$

Example 4 Using a Spreadsheet to Draw a Line of Best Fit

For each player, the basketball coach keeps track of the amount of time played (in minutes) and the number of points scored. The results are shown below.

Name	Minutes Played	Points Scored
Fred	151	50
Tony	19	11
Samir	164	38
Jared	87	28
Anuj	135	39
Matt	111	39
Steve	54	8
Ali	163	61
Darcy	192	52
Ryan	98	33
Travis	71	26

Technolink
See Appendix E.I on page 425 for instructions on finding lines of best fit.

(a) Create a scatter plot and find a line of best fit.

(b) If Jude scored 45 points, how many minutes did he play?

Solution

(a) Open a new spreadsheet. Enter the titles and data in columns A, B, and C.

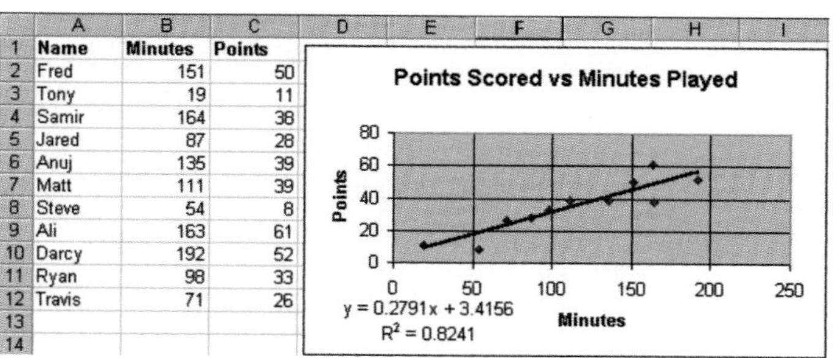

	A	B	C
1	Name	Minutes	Points
2	Fred	151	50
3	Tony	19	11
4	Samir	164	38
5	Jared	87	28
6	Anuj	135	39
7	Matt	111	39
8	Steve	54	8
9	Ali	163	61
10	Darcy	192	52
11	Ryan	98	33
12	Travis	71	26
13			
14			

Select the entries in columns B and C, select **insert chart**, select **XY(Scatter)**. Column B contains the independent data and column C contains the dependent data.

To add the line of best fit, the equation of the line of best fit, and the value of r^2, select **add trendline** from the **chart** menu. Be sure that a checkmark appears in the box before **Display equation on chart** and **Display R squared value on chart**.

(b) Substitute $y = 45$ and solve for x. This gives a value of 149, so Jude played 45 min.

RESIDUALS

Although the r-value indicates the strength and direction of a linear relationship, a lower r-value does not necessarily mean that the linear model should be rejected. Another method of analyzing data is also useful. This involves analyzing the distance the data points are from the line of best fit.

residual value (residual)—the vertical distance between a data point and the line of best fit

The vertical distance between a data point and the line of best fit is called the **residual value** (or **residual**). It may be calculated for a single point (x_1, y_1) by subtracting the calculated value from the actual value

$$R_1 = y_1 - [a(x_1) + b]$$

where a and b are the slope and intercept of the line of best fit, respectively.

The residuals should be graphed. If the model is a good fit, the residuals should be fairly small, and there should be no noticeable pattern. Large residuals or a noticeable pattern are indicators that another model may be more appropriate. If only a few pieces of data cause large residuals, you may wish to disregard them.

Example 5 Using a TI-83 Plus Calculator to Determine the Residuals

Using the data in Example 2 and the line of best fit you created, graph the residuals.

Solution

Technolink For instructions on creating a residual plot using a TI-83 Plus calculator, refer to Appendix C.10 on page 407.

When the calculator computes a line of best fit, it also computes the residuals and stores these in a list called **RESID**. Copy these values into $\mathbf{L_3}$ for easy comparison. Press [STAT] **Edit** and move the cursor onto list $\mathbf{L_3}$. When you press [ENTER], the blinking cursor moves to the command line at the bottom of the screen. You can then insert the list name **RESID** by pressing [2nd] [LIST] and selecting the list name **RESID**.

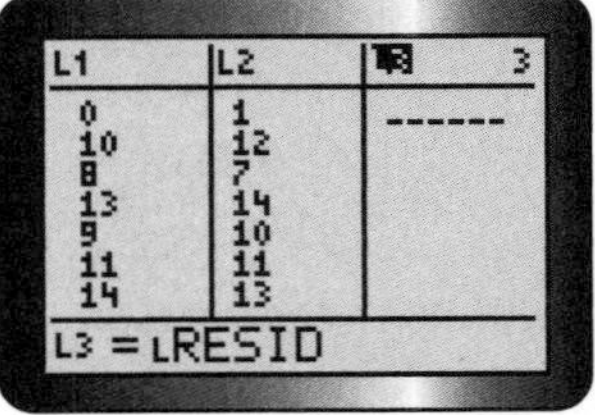

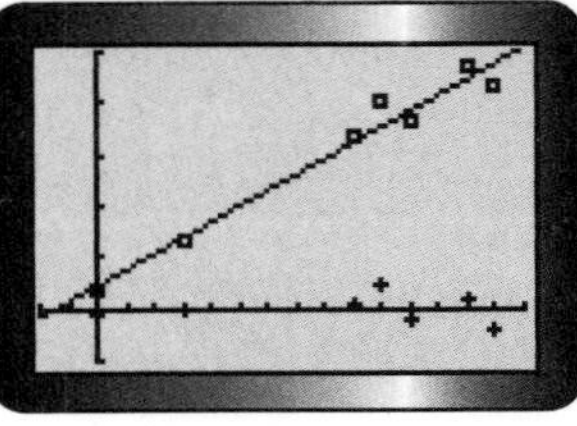

When you press [ENTER], the residual values are copied into $\mathbf{L_3}$. Set up **STAT PLOT 2** to plot the values of the residuals for each point.

The residuals are small and show both positive and negative values. This means that the line of best fit chosen is a good fit.

Example 6 Using Fathom™ to Determine the Residuals

Use the gasoline data given in Example 3 and create a residual plot.

Solution

Select the graph and choose **Make Residual Plot** under the **Graph** menu. The residuals are small and show both positive and negative values. This means that the line of best fit chosen is a good fit.

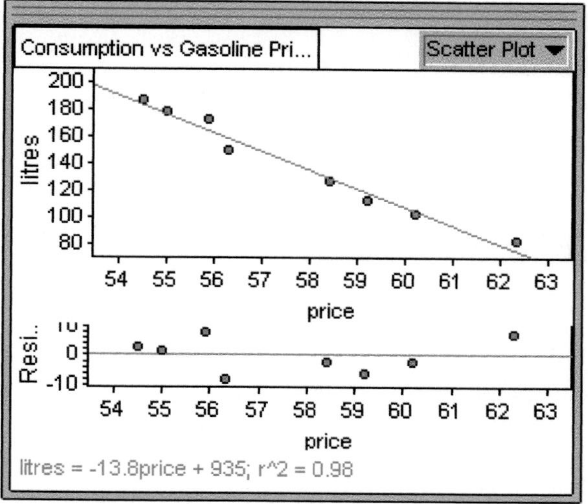

Technolink
For detailed instructions on creating a residual plot using Fathom™, refer to Appendix D.7 on page 422.

Example 7 Ontario Youth Crime on the Rise?

When you read the newspaper or watch the news on television, you sometimes hear something like:

...the Young Offenders Act is not tough enough. Crimes committed by today's youth are out of control and something needs to be done.

What is the current rate and general trend of youth crime in Ontario? What model might be appropriate to display trends and allow you to make reasonable predictions for the future?

Solution

The data table to the right displays the number of young males and females from Ontario who have committed crimes between the years 1983 and 1998.

L1	L2	L3	L4
1983	13146	2690	15836
1984	12156	2671	14827
1985	24233	5227	29460
1986	30406	6816	37222
1987	32026	7352	39378
1988	31762	7471	39233
1989	34376	8331	42707
1990	36662	9214	45876
1991	41567	10980	52547
1992	39812	11698	51510
1993	37796	11018	48814
1994	36762	10138	46900
1995	37608	10849	48457
1996	36221	11045	47266
1997	33482	10801	44283
1998	33026	10276	43302

Source: Statistics Canada

Note
The headings L1, L2, L3, and L4 represent Year, Number of Males, Number of Females, and Total Number of Males and Females who committed crimes between 1983 and 1998, respectively.

Technolink
The electronic version of the data is on the textbook CD and can be loaded into a TI-83 Plus calculator.

Technolink
For additional help creating scatter plots and using regression to determine an algebraic model, refer to page 404 of Appendix C.

Totals

The following scatter plots were created on a TI-83 Plus calculator.

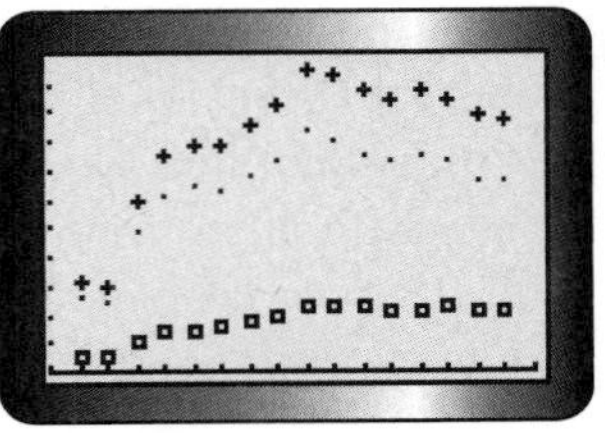

+ STAT PLOT 1 is L1 and L4.
• STAT PLOT 2 is L1 and L2.
□ STAT PLOT 3 is L1 and L3.

Linear regression formulas are shown in the margin for the three series of data. The table and the scatter plots show that

Males

- except for 1988, there was a steady increase in the number of youth crimes from 1983 until around 1991–92
- except for 1995, the number of crimes has been slowly decreasing since 1991

A linear model for the data is shown to the right. The graphing calculator gives the linear regression information for each plot. Notice that the correlation coefficient, r, is closer to 1 for Males than for the other two groups. The graphs show that the linear model is reasonable for the relationship pertaining to Males. The linear models for Females and Totals do not capture the decreasing trend since 1992 and are, therefore, not appropriate.

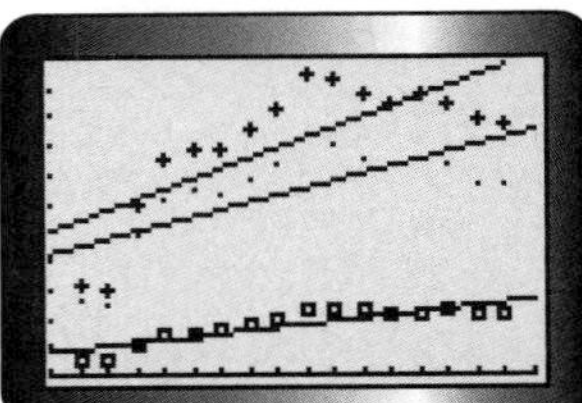

Females

A quadratic model for the same data is shown here. This models the data better than does the linear model. It captures the decreasing trend in the number of youth crimes in Ontario since 1992, and allows you to predict the number of crimes for each gender, provided that the trend continues.

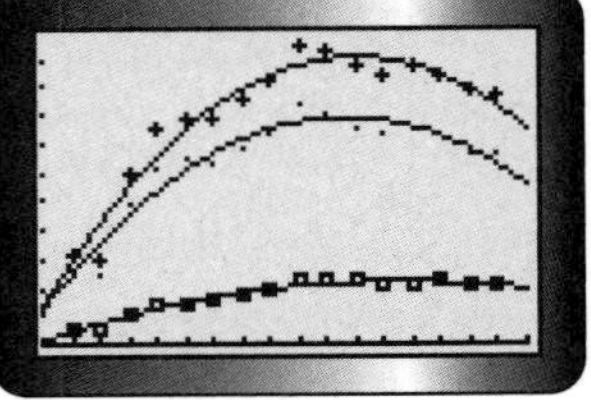

Technolink

To perform a quadratic regression on a TI-83 Plus calculator, refer to Appendix C.3 on page 403.

KEY IDEAS

predictive models—linear and quadratic—a linear model is based on the relationship $y = mx + b$, and a quadratic model is based on the relationship $y = ax^2 + bx + c$, where x is the independent variable and y is the dependent variable

coefficient of correlation, *r*—a number from $+1$ to -1 that gives the strength and direction of the relationship between two variables

coefficient of determination, r^2—a number from 0 to $+1$ that gives the relative strength of the relationship between two variables. (If $r^2=0.44$, this means that 44% of the variation of the dependent variable is due to variation in the independent variable.)

residual value (residual)—the vertical distance between a data point and the line of best fit

1.4 Exercises

A

1. **Knowledge and Understanding** Classify these scatter plots as having a correlation that is positive or negative, and describe the strength.

(a)

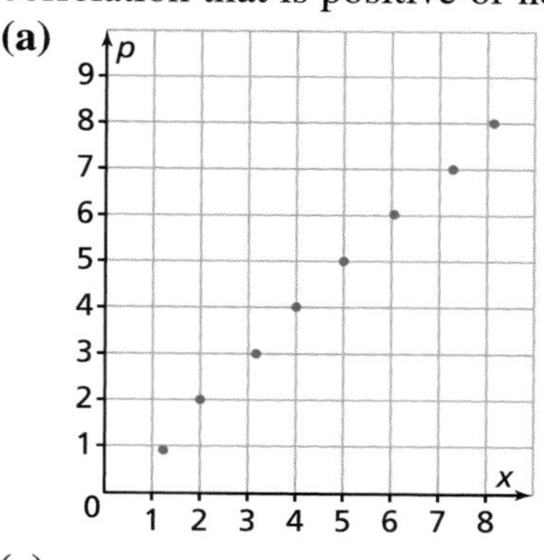

(b)

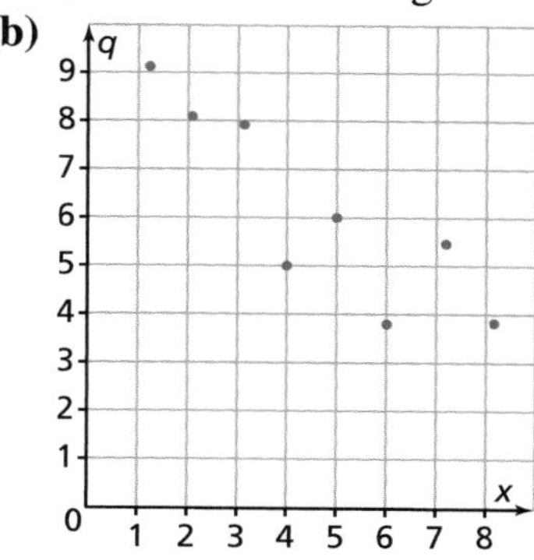

(c)

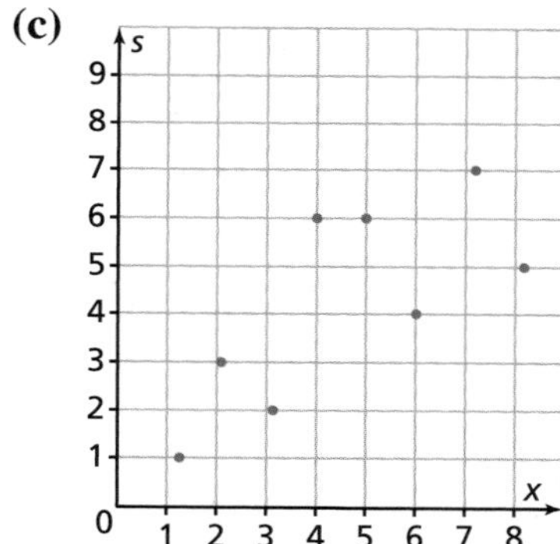

(d)

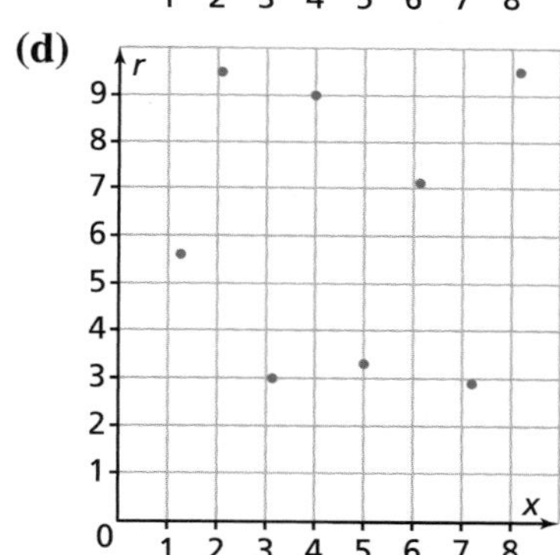

2. **Application** Do the following situations describe relationships with positive or negative correlations? Give reasons for your answers.
   (a) As you get older, the number of years until retirement changes.
   (b) The taller you are, the longer your arms.
   (c) The farther you drive, the less gas you have.
   (d) The more you study, the higher your marks.

B

3. Use technology to create scatter plots and lines of best fit.

(a)

Age (years)	Height (cm)
0	20
1	40
2	65
3	80
4	92
5	108

(b)

Speed (km/h)	Time (min)
10	60
20	30
30	20
40	15
60	10

(c)

Study Time (h)	Mark
0	50
1	62
2	68
3	72
4	74
5	75

4. Use technology to calculate the correlation coefficient for each of the data sets in Question 3. Tell how each describes the strength of the relationship.

5. Create a residual plot for each of the data sets in Question 3. How do the residual plots enable you to determine the strength of each relationship?

6. Sketch the residual plot for each of the following.

(a)

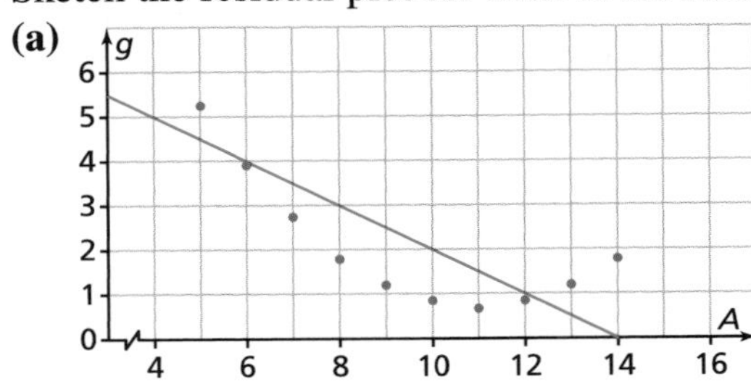

(b)

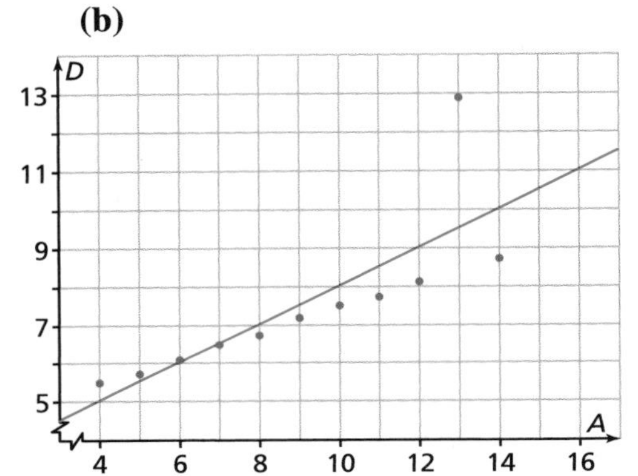

(c)

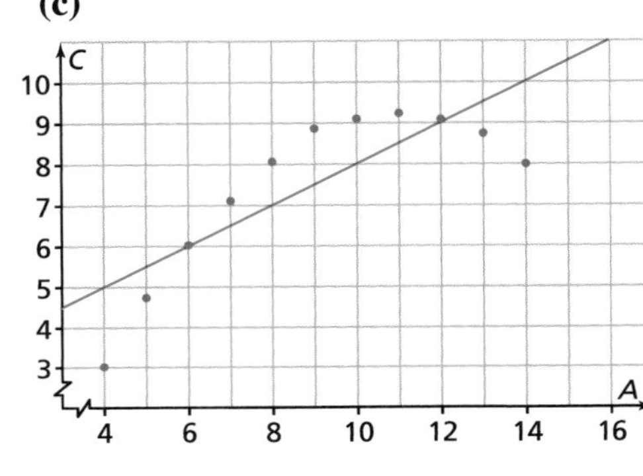

7. Consider the following residual plots.

(i)

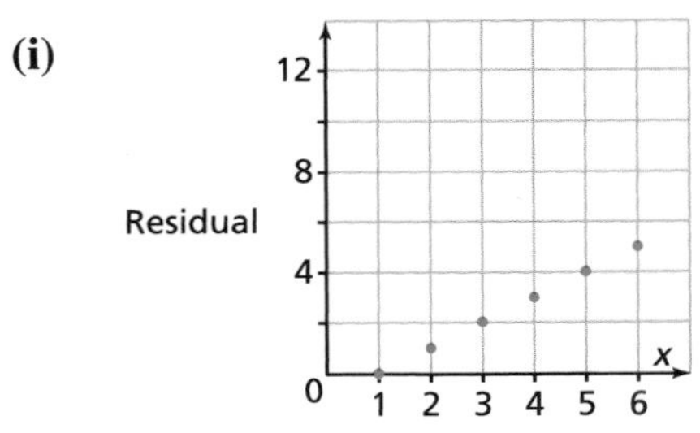

(ii)

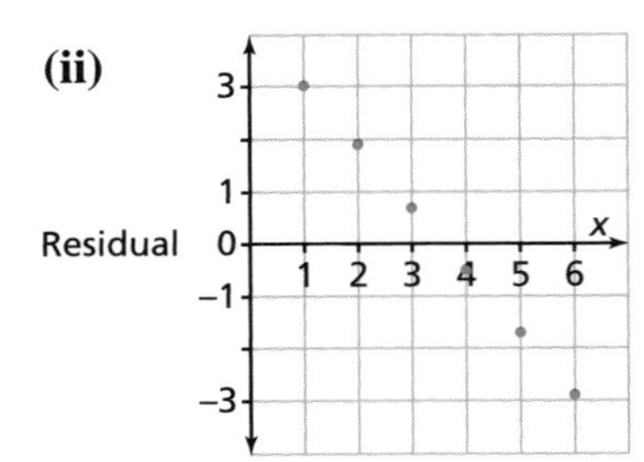

(a) Sketch a graph for each of the residual plots.
(b) What do the residual plots tell you about the line of best fit?
(c) Describe the residual plot for a perfect line of best fit.
(d) Based on your responses in parts (a) and (b), describe the general characteristics of a residual plot for a line of best fit that accurately models the data.

8. Given the following coefficients of correlation, state what percent of variation in y is due to the variation in x.

(a) $r = 0.5$ **(b)** $r = 0.85$ **(c)** $r = 0.66$
(d) $r = 0.9$ **(e)** $r = -0.1$ **(f)** $r = 0.32$

9. Roll a pair of dice 10 times and record the values shown on the first die, x, and on the second die, y. It is easier to keep track of the values if the dice are different colours.

(a) Make a scatter plot of the data. The data consists of random pairs of values (x, y). What would you expect the correlation coefficient to be? Give reasons for your answer.

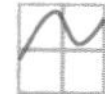

(b) Use technology to calculate the correlation coefficient. Compare your value to those generated by other students in your class. What percent of the students had a correlation coefficient greater than 0.5?

10. **Communication** Correlation does not necessarily prove causation. For example, amount of study time and marks may have a positive correlation, but other factors besides study time may cause higher marks. Before doing an experiment and evaluating the correlation coefficient, you must examine the possibility of cause and effect. Examine the scenarios below and decide whether a cause-and-effect relationship exists. Give reasons for your answers.

(a) A medical study tracks the use of aspirin and the incidence of heart attacks. A weak negative correlation is found between the amount taken and the likelihood of having an attack. Does it appear that aspirin is preventing heart attacks?

(b) Consider the hypothesis that severe illness is caused by depression and anger. It has been observed that people who are ill are very often depressed and angry. Thus, it follows that the cause of severe illness is depression and anger. So, a good and cheerful attitude is the key to staying healthy.

(c) Over the course of several weeks, the needles from the pine trees along the Wombat River fell into the water. Shortly thereafter, many dead fish washed up on the riverbank. When environmental officials investigated, the owners of Wombat River Chemical Company claimed that the pine needles had killed the fish.

11. Complete the activities that follow using the data on the textbook CD that show the changes in Canada's population.

(a) Describe the trends in the data.

(b) Find the model that best represents the data.

(c) Use your model to predict what the population of Canada would have been in 1998, provided that the population growth is consistent. Check your answers with data from the Statistics Canada Web site.

(d) Use your model to predict what the population would have been for the most recent year for which data is available, provided that the population growth had continued in the same manner. Check your answers with data from the Statistics Canada Web site.

12. The winning distance for the Olympic men's discus event is provided below.

Year	Distance (m)	Year	Distance (m)	Year	Distance (m)
1896	29.15	1932	49.50	1972	64.39
1900	36.04	1936	50.48	1976	67.50
1904	39.28	1948	52.78	1980	66.65
1908	40.89	1952	55.04	1984	66.60
1912	45.21	1956	56.35	1988	68.82
1920	44.68	1960	59.18	1992	65.12
1924	46.15	1964	61.00	1996	69.40
1928	47.32	1968	64.78	2000	69.30

Source: British Broadcasting Corporation (BBC)

(a) Describe any trends in the data. Give reasons for your answer.
(b) Create a graph to display the data.

13. The population, births, deaths, and infant deaths for Canada for the years 1948 to 1972 are listed in the table below.

Year	Population	Births	Deaths	Infant Deaths
1948	13 167 000	359 860	122 974	15 965
1949	13 475 000	367 092	124 567	15 935
1950	13 737 000	372 009	124 220	15 441
1951	14 050 000	381 092	125 823	14 673
1952	14 496 000	403 559	126 385	15 408
1953	14 886 000	417 884	127 791	14 859
1954	15 330 000	436 198	124 855	13 934
1955	15 736 000	442 937	128 476	13 884
1956	16 123 000	450 739	131 961	14 399
1957	16 677 000	469 093	136 579	14 517
1958	17 120 000	470 118	135 201	14 178
1959	17 522 000	479 275	139 913	13 595
1960	17 909 000	478 551	139 693	13 077

Year	Population	Births	Deaths	Infant Deaths
1961	18 238 000	475 700	140 985	12 940
1962	18 614 000	469 693	143 699	12 941
1963	18 964 000	465 767	147 367	12 270
1964	19 325 000	452 915	145 850	11 169
1965	19 678 000	418 595	148 939	9 862
1966	20 048 000	387 710	149 863	8 960
1967	20 412 000	370 894	150 283	8 151
1968	20 729 000	364 310	153 196	7 583
1969	21 028 000	369 647	154 477	7 149
1970	21 297 100	371 988	155 961	7 001
1971	22 962 082	362 187	157 272	6 356
1972	22 219 560	347 319	162 413	5 938

Source: Data have been extracted from Fathom Dynamic Statistics™, Key Curriculum Press.

(a) Find a model that best fits the data given. Use it to predict the population, live births, deaths, and infant deaths for 1973.

(b) Consider the following data from 1974 to 1997. If these data were included in the table, how would your model change?

Year	Population	Births	Deaths	Infant Deaths
1974	22 808 446	345 645	166 794	5192
1975	23 142 275	348 110	167 404	5130
1976	23 449 793	348 857	167 009	4847
1977	23 726 345	361 400	167 498	4475
1978	23 963 967	358 852	168 179	4289
1979	24 202 205	366 064	168 183	3994
1980	24 516 278	370 709	171 473	3868
1981	24 820 382	371 346	171 029	3562
1982	25 117 424	373 082	174 413	3385
1983	25 366 965	373 689	174 484	3182
1984	25 607 555	377 031	175 727	3058
1985	25 842 590	375 727	181 323	2982

Year	Population	Births	Deaths	Infant Deaths
1986	26 100 587	372 431	184 224	2938
1987	26 449 888	369 441	184 953	2706
1988	26 798 303	375 743	190 011	2705
1989	27 286 239	391 925	190 965	2795
1990	27 700 856	404 669	191 973	2766
1991	28 030 864	411 910	196 050	2677
1992	28 376 550	398 642	196 535	2432
1993	28 703 142	388 394	204 912	2448
1994	29 035 981	385 112	207 077	2418
1995	29 353 854	378 011	210 733	2321
1996	29 671 892	364 732	213 649	2042
1997	30 003 955	361 785	216 970	1925

Source: Data have been extracted from Fathom Dynamic Statistics™, Key Curriculum Press.

(c) Using the data from 1974 to 1997, find the equation(s) you would use to predict the live births in the future, provided the trend continues.

C **14. Thinking, Inquiry, Problem Solving**

(a) Find some data containing two or three sets that show trends relating to the general direction of growth or decline.

(b) Describe the rate of the trend and state whether or not the trend shows a change that is steady or erratic. Give reasons for your answer.

(c) Provide a model that could be used for predictions.

(d) Explain why your model is accurate.

ADDITIONAL ACHIEVEMENT CHART QUESTIONS

15. Knowledge and Understanding Use the graphing technology of your choice to create a scatter plot, the line of best fit, and the residual plots for men's and women's data shown below.

Retail Merchandising in Canada

Year	1993	1994	1995	1996	1997	1998
Men's clothing stores ($ millions)	1730	1687	1623	1516	1570	1582
Women's clothing stores ($ millions)	4303	4812	5377	5522	5830	6259

Source: Statistics Canada

16. **Application** The table below shows the value of RRSP holdings of Canadians (in millions of dollars) from 1983 to 1997. Determine whether a linear or a quadratic model more accurately fits the data, and then use your model to predict the RRSP holdings in 2010.

Year	1983	1984	1985	1986	1987
RRSP ($ millions)	70 736	76 292	85 084	92 916	102 660

Year	1988	1989	1990	1991	1992
RRSP ($ millions)	115 884	116 356	132 316	143 704	158 212

Year	1993	1994	1995	1996	1997
RRSP ($ millions)	163 548	171 468	179 032	177 220	183 832

17. **Thinking, Inquiry, Problem Solving**

(a) Search the Statistics Canada Web site to find a set of data that shows a strong negative correlation.

(b) Verify this using appropriate models and technology.

(c) Describe the behaviour shown between the variables and investigate the reasons for the behaviour.

18. **Communication**

(a) What is a trend in data?

(b) What type of graph should be used when looking for trends in data? Give reasons for your answer.

(c) Describe how you can use the correlation coefficient produced by regression analysis to determine the accuracy of fit of a particular algebraic model.

Chapter Problem

Trends in Canada's Population

Use the technology of your choice to answer the following questions.

CP12. For each age class since 1951, determine whether a linear or a quadratic model best represents the data. Justify your decision with the appropriate equations and correlation coefficients.

CP13. Use your models to predict the percent of the population within each age class in the year 2000.

CP14. Use the 2000 Census data from the Statistics Canada Web site (**www.statcan.ca**) to check the accuracy of your models. Comment on any differences that you see.

1.5 The Power of Data—The Media

The media are major users of data. In addressing issues and presenting points of view, the media rely on information based on data. One of the main purposes of the media, as producers of mass communication, is to inform the general public about world events in as an objective manner as possible. Ideally, the information is accepted as being accurate; however, the media may sometimes provide misleading or false impressions to sway the public or to increase ratings or circulation.

An important reason to study statistics is to understand how information is represented or misrepresented. The ability to correctly interpret tables/charts, diagrams, and graphs presented in the media is an invaluable skill.

Example 1 Changing the Scale on the Axes

When you purchase a new vehicle, its value drops dramatically the moment it is driven off the car dealer's lot, and then continues to drop each year thereafter. A graph is used to show this change in value over time. It is possible to communicate different messages using the same data by changing the vertical scale.

These graphs show the change in the value of the same car from $9000 in Year 2 to $1000 in Year 10.

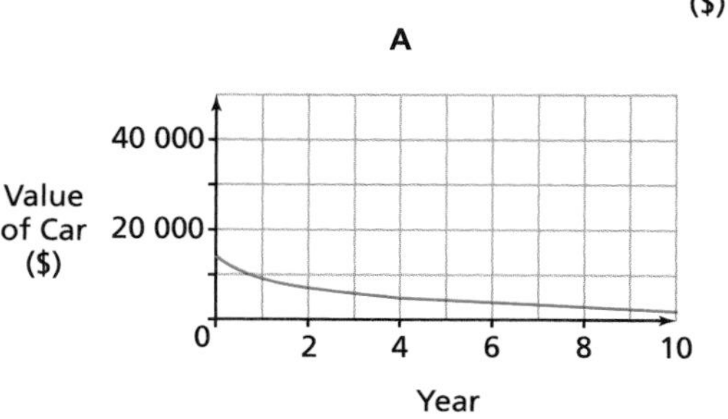

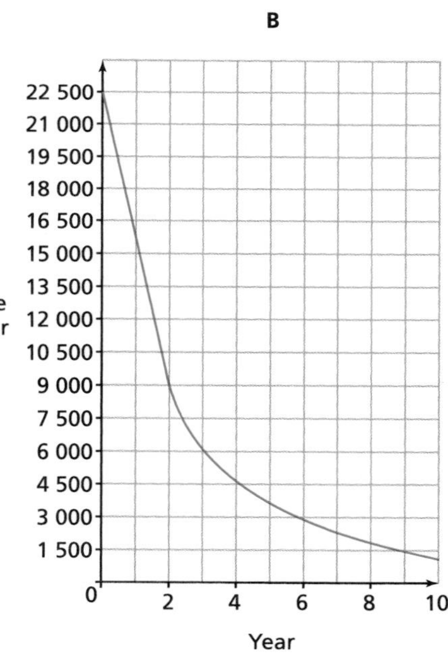

Project Connection
Changing the scales is one way to misrepresent data; however, it may be an effective way to support your point of view.

(a) Look quickly at each graph. What impression does graph A give you about the change in value of the car compared to graph B?

(b) Once you look more carefully at both graphs, how does your impression change? What information changed your first impression of the graphs?

(c) Who might prefer the look of graph A? Who might prefer the look of graph B? Give reasons for your answers.

Solution

(a) The value of the car in graph A seems to be decreasing but at a much slower rate than the value of the car in graph B.

(b) The change in the value of the car is actually the same. However, your impression likely changed when you looked at the scale provided for the two graphs.

(c) Car dealers and bankers might use graph A to convince people to buy a car. The gradual decrease makes it seem as if the car holds its value longer. Environmentalists might prefer graph B because they would want to encourage people to use public transportation. Showing consumers the rapid decrease in the value of a car might discourage them from buying a new car. Insurance companies might also prefer graph B because it would help to justify paying lower replacement costs if a claim were made against the vehicle.

Example 2 Surveying a Small Sample of the Population

The following article appeared in a local newspaper.

> **York Region a great place to do business: Survey**
>
> York Region is ranked the second best place in the Greater Toronto Area (GTA) to start or expand a business, a study revealed this week.
>
> The study was conducted by the Canadian Federation of Independent Business, a national lobby group, in the city of Toronto and across the GTA in March and April of 2001. About 650 people in Toronto and the GTA took part.
>
> Respondents were asked to give opinions on a number of issues, including taxation and local administration, which affect their operations.
>
> While Mississauga ranked first in terms of satisfaction with local government, York Region was second, with 10% of respondents saying they were very satisfied and another 65% saying they were somewhat satisfied with the local government's management and handling of the economy.
>
> Source: *The Liberal,* Sunday, September 16, 2001.

(a) What is the purpose of the article? Who might be interested in the information and why?

(b) The article mentions that 650 people in Toronto and the GTA took part in the survey. What proportion of people in the population is represented by the sample?

(c) Estimate the number of respondents who might have come from Toronto. From Mississauga. From York Region. Justify your answer.

? Think about The Sample Size

How large must the sample be to be representative of the population?

(d) Use your York Region numbers from part (c) to determine the number of respondents who were

(i) very satisfied **(ii)** somewhat satisfied

(e) Do your answers in part (d) suggest that the sample is not large enough to form a valid conclusion?

(f) Suggest a more appropriate sample size.

(g) What other characteristics of a sample result in sampling errors?

Solution

(a) The purpose is to get the message out that York Region is a great place to do business. It is meant to encourage businesses to establish their operations in the area. Current or prospective business owners might be interested in this information. If current businesses in the area are happy, then new establishments might also be happy. Members of the York Region business community would also be interested—it gives them "bragging rights" at national meetings.

(b) If the population of Toronto and the GTA is approximately 4 500 000 people and 650 people were surveyed, the percent of the population that answered the survey is $650 \div 4\,500\,000 \times 100 = 0.014\ \%$. This means that relatively few people were surveyed.

(c) Assuming the populations of Toronto, Mississauga, and York Region are approximately 2 500 000, 550 000, and 450 000, respectively, and that the respondents for the survey were chosen based on regional proportional representation of the total population, the number of respondents from each region is calculated as follows:

$$\text{Toronto} = 2\,500\,000 \div 4\,500\,000 \times 650 = 361$$
$$\text{Mississauga} = 550\,000 \div 4\,500\,000 \times 650 = 79$$
$$\text{York Region} = 450\,000 \div 4\,500\,000 \times 650 = 65$$

(d) The number of respondents who were

(i) very satisfied $= 65 \times 10 \div 100 = 6.5$. This means that approximately seven people were satisfied.

(ii) somewhat satisfied $= 65 \times 65 \div 100 = 42.25$. This means that approximately 42 people were somewhat satisfied.

(e) The results of the survey are very suspect because so few people have actually responded to the survey. If even a few of the respondents were to change their mind and decide that they are dissatisified, the title of the article could be "York Region: An awful place to do business!"

Technolink
For more on appropriate sample size, go to **www.publicagenda.org/aboutpubopinion/aboutpubop4.htm.**

(f) A sample size of between 800 and 1000 is appropriate to ensure strong representation in York Region.

(g) If all of the people surveyed came from one geographical area, their responses may be representative of what is happening in their area but may not reflect what is happening in other areas. If the respondents are all from a particular age group, they may have a different view of what is happening. If the geographical region is overrepresented in the sample, bias will result.

KEY IDEAS

ways to display data properly—use the most appropriate type of graph; use proper scales on the axes

ways to misrepresent data—sample size is too small; sample is not representative of the population; there is insufficient information

making sense of misrepresented data—interpret charts/tables, diagrams, and graphs carefully

1.5 Exercises

1. **Knowledge and Understanding** The two graphs below show the profits of the Crazy Car Company.
   (a) How are the graphs similar? How are they different?
   (b) How much has the profit increased on each graph?
   (c) What false impressions are conveyed by the two graphs?

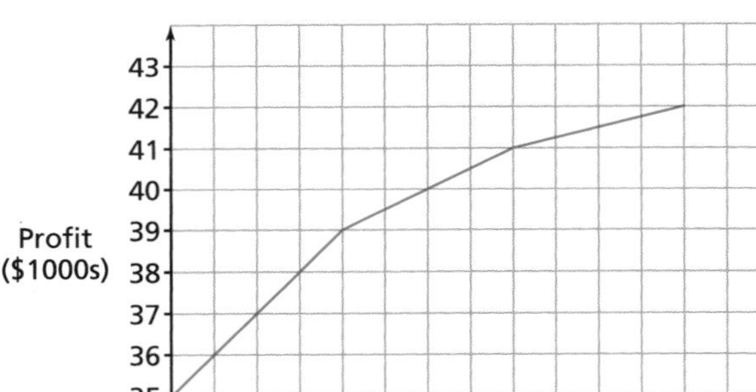

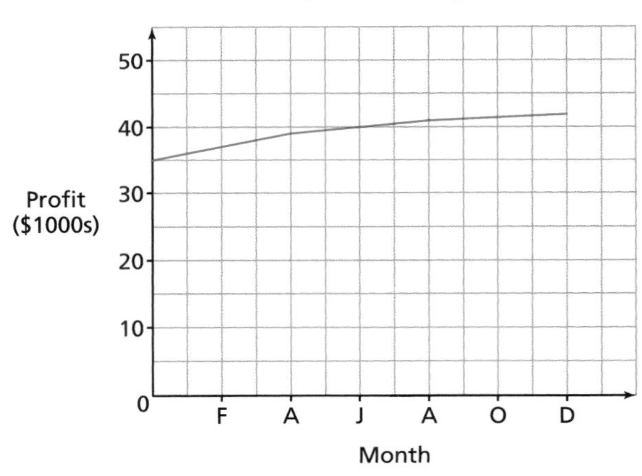

2. The increase in the size of homes purchased is shown in the graph.

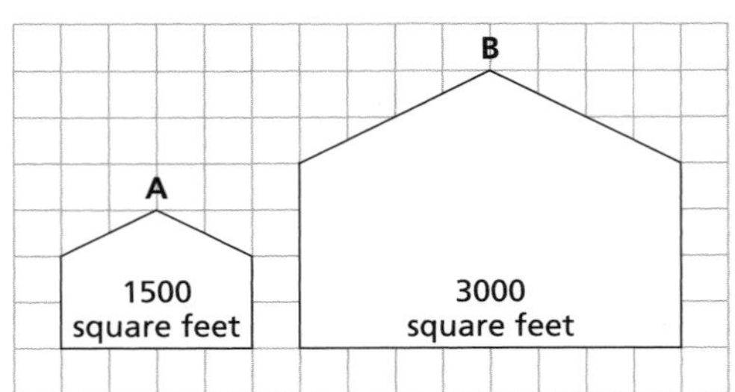

(a) What is similar about the homes?
(b) How many times bigger is the area of house B than the area of house A?
(c) By how much has home size increased?
(d) List any false impressions conveyed by the graph.

3. List the false impressions conveyed by this graph. How would you change the graph to correct the false impressions?

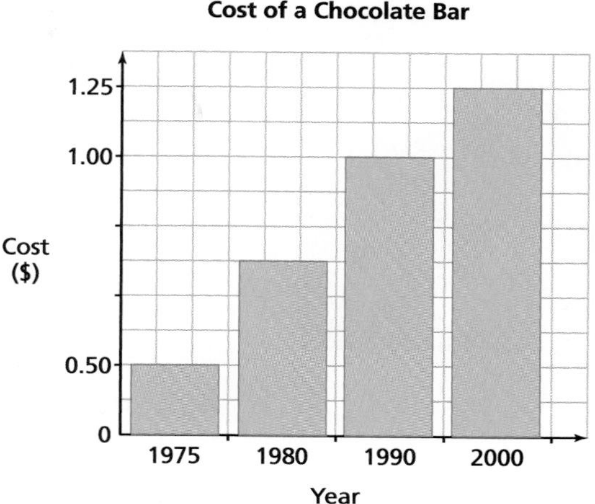

4. Use the data in the graph to construct a graph that distorts the information and gives a false impression.

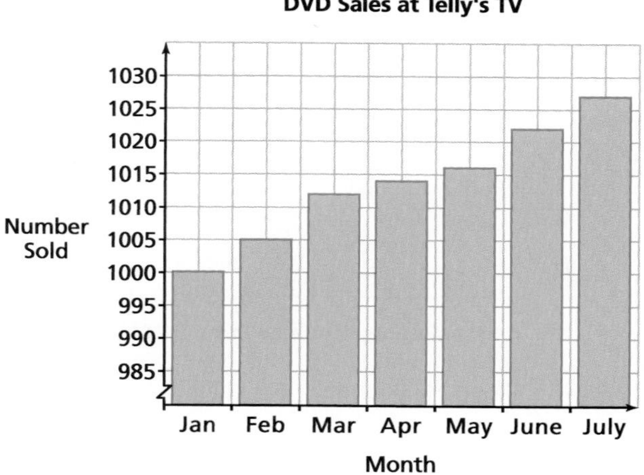

5. On December 4, 1999, the following headlines appeared in three different Canadian newspapers: "Boom pushes jobless rate to 18-year low" (*The Globe and Mail*), "Golden era: Jobless rate at 19-year low" (*National Post*), "Jobless rate sinks to near 20-year low" (*The Kingston Whig-Standard*). The writers of the articles had interviewed the same economist and had access to the same data. Give reasons for the differences in the data in the headlines.

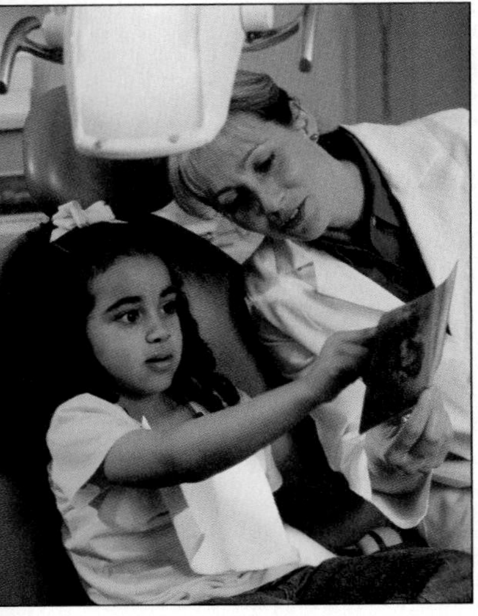

6. Read the following statements and decide if each is misleading or not. Explain your answers.
   (a) A toothpaste company boasts four out of five dentists recommend product X.
   (b) A drug company claims that 80% of the residents of Bruce Mines use their product.
   (c) A local high school claims that 75% of its graduates go on to obtain a university degree.
   (d) Fifty-three percent of Canadians want closer ties to the United States.
   (e) Canadian students ranked 21st in the latest international math test. The previous ranking was 20th. This means our students are doing poorly in math.

7. **Communication** Find data that have been misrepresented. There is no need to limit your search exclusively to graphs. Explain what caused the misinformation.

8. A report appearing in the December 7, 2000, issue of *Nature* outlined the results of an experiment conducted to examine reasons for the confusion associated with the 2000 presidential election ballots in Florida. The experiment sample consisted of 324 Edmonton college students who used either a regular ballot or a butterfly ballot to vote in a mock federal election. The experiment was repeated in a local mall and involved 116 shoppers. A number of international newspapers picked up on the *Nature* story and subsequently used the results of the experiment to suggest how the outcome of the election might have been altered. Were the media duped?

B

9. Examine the graphs below. Then, complete the activities in parts (a) through (c) for each graph.

(i)

DaimlerChrysler Share Price, $ (U.S), NYSE

100
80
60
40
20
1998 1999 2000 2001 (1st half)

Source: ROB magazine, October 2001

(ii)

Central Bank Interest Rate Targets

per cent
6.5
6.0
5.5
5.0
4.5
4.0
3.5
3.0
2.5
2.0
Canada
U.S.
Jan-00 Apr-00 Jul-00 Oct-00 Jan-01 Apr-01 Jul-01 Oct-01

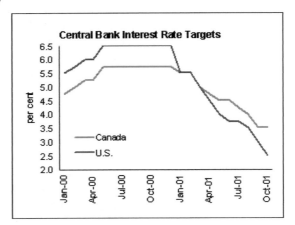

Source: Phillips, Hager & North Investment Management Ltd.

(iii)

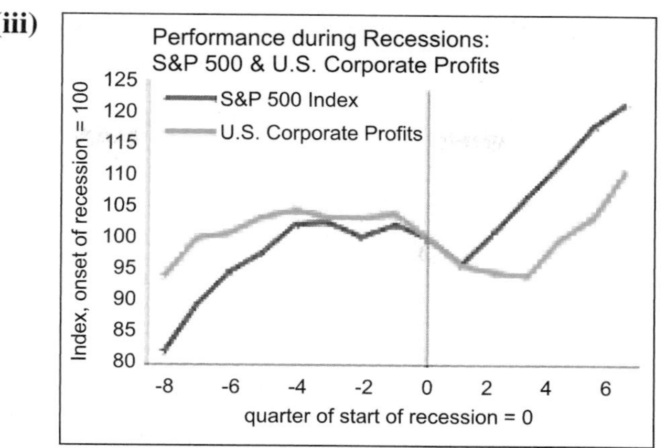

Source: Phillips, Hager & North Investment Management Ltd.

(iv)

FINANCIAL POST / CHAMBER OF COMMERCE / CIBC POLL

CANADIAN BUSINESS LEADERS ON THE ECONOMY AND THE MILITARY

CANADA'S BUSINESS LEADERS FAVOUR A COMMON NORTH AMERICAN ECONOMIC PERIMETER . . .

■ **QUESTION:** Regarding a common perimeter with the United States including common rules for visitors, immigrants, and refugees, how essential is this to protecting access to the U.S. market for Canadian exporters?

Response	%
Extremely essential	38
Very essential	36
Somewhat essential	17
Not really essential	8
Not at all essential	2

. . . AND WANT CANADA TO STRENGTHEN ITS MILITARY . . .

■ **QUESTION:** Regarding strengthening Canada's military and our ability to contribute to the Western military alliance, how essential is this for protecting Canada's economic and business interests in Canada-U.S. relations?

Response	%
Extremely essential	14
Very essential	35
Somewhat essential	32
Not really essential	16
Not at all essential	3

. . . AND BELIEVE EMPLOYERS SHOULD GIVE RESERVISTS TIME OFF FOR MILITARY TRAINING.

■ **QUESTION:** About 3400 employers have decided to give employees who belong to the Reserve two weeks off for military training, sometimes with pay and sometimes without. Should Canadian business make this kind of commitment to Canada's security preparedness?

Response	%
Definitely	43
Probably	26
Possibly	15
Probably not	11
Definitely not	4

CANADA'S BUSINESS LEADERS ARE UNCERTAIN ABOUT THE COUNTRY'S ECONOMIC PROSPECTS . . .

■ **QUESTION:** Looking forward six months, do you predict that economic conditions in Canada will be much better than right now, somewhat better, about the same, somewhat worse, or much worse?

Response	%
Much better	4
Somewhat better	32
About the same	29
Somewhat worse	30
Much worse	5

. . . BELIEVE MILITARY SPENDING WILL ESCALATE . . .

■ **QUESTION:** Given the new military and security situation, do you predict federal and provincial governments will be spending a lot more than people predicted before Sept. 11, somewhat more, about the same, somewhat less, or a lot less?

Response	%
A lot more	44
Somewhat more	45
About the same	7
Somewhat less	4
A lot less	0

. . . AND TEND TO BELIEVE THIS SPENDING WILL BE POSITIVE FOR THE ECONOMY.

■ **QUESTION:** Will upcoming spending levels by federal and provincial governments be very positive for the economy, somewhat positive, neutral, somewhat negative, or very negative?

Response	%
Very positive	6
Somewhat positive	42
Neutral	31
Somewhat negative	18
Very negative	4

NOTE: Totals may not add up to 100 because of rounding.

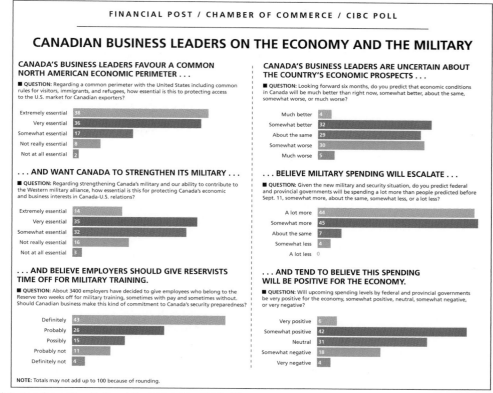

Adapted from *The National Post*, Oct. 29, 2001, A2.

Source: COMPAS Inc.

(a) **Application** Have the data been misrepresented to bias the reader? Give reasons for your answer.

(b) **Application** If you answered *yes* to part (a), then modify the graph to display the data accurately.

(c) **Communication** Explain why your graph is more appropriate.

10. Find two examples of an appropriate representation of data.

(a) **Thinking, Inquiry, Problem Solving** For each example, state a conclusion from the data.

(b) **Application** Modify the representation of data in a way such that it will give a biased impression.

(c) **Communication** How could the new representation still be used to support the initial conclusion?

11. Find a recent biased article. Identify the bias and outline specific changes that would make the article bias-free.

12. Consider the information that follows.

Newspapers: On any given day, 65% of Canadians read a daily newspaper, and 72% read a newspaper on weekends. Canadians spend an average of 45 min a day reading the daily newspaper and almost 90 min on weekend editions.

Books and Magazines: Almost 40% of adult Canadians spend about 40 min a day reading books and 10 min a day reading magazines.

Radio: The average adult listener tunes in for about 21 h a week. The youth population segment (12 to 17 years old) listens for only half that amount of time.

Television: On average, adult Canadians watch more than 22 h of television a week, or slightly more than 3 h a day. Canadian children between the ages of 2 and 11 watch approximately 18 h a week, or 2.57 h daily. Adolescents between the ages of 12 and 17 watch an average of 17.3 h a week, or 2.47 h daily.

For each type of media, the information gives comparative data within that category.

(a) Create graphs to represent the data properly for each media type.

(b) Write a statement in the form of a conclusion for each media type.

(c) Use a technique for misrepresenting the data to support each conclusion in part (b).

ADDITIONAL ACHIEVEMENT CHART QUESTIONS

13. **Knowledge and Understanding** Find an example of an appropriate representation of data and explain what was done correctly. Find another example that shows a misrepresentation of data and identify the errors in it.

14. **Application** The graph below shows the population of Hong Kong from 1993 to 1999. Explain why this graph would cause incorrect interpretations of the data.

Population of Hong Kong

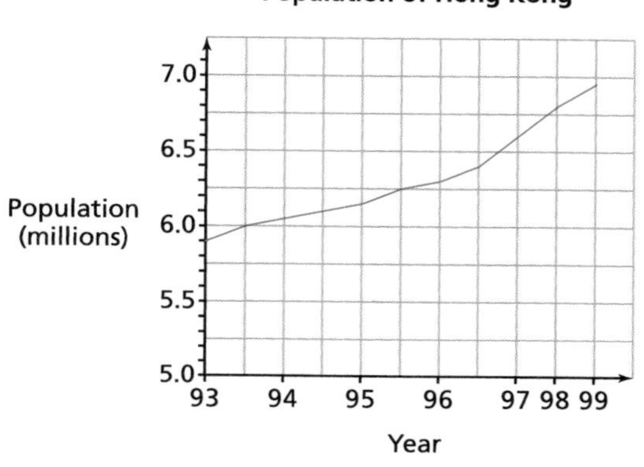

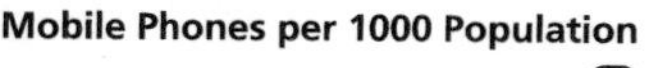

15. **Thinking, Inquiry, Problem Solving** Why would a media source willingly distort information and misrepresent data in articles and reports? Research to find out when, where, and why this happens.

16. **Communication** Suppose that in a recent magazine article, the graphic in the margin was used to show how the use of cell phones changed between 1994 and 1998. Explain why this picture is misleading.

Chapter Problem

Trends in Canada's Population

It was recently reported that the life expectancy of Canadians is on the rise.

CP15. Does this information agree or disagree with the trends you have observed? Explain.

CP16. Research the life expectancy of Canadians and find data that supports the claim above. Describe any changes you see. Comment on the impact that these data have had on the Age Structure of the Population data you have been analyzing.

CP17. Provide some contributing factors that account for the changes in the life expectancy of Canadians.

Project Connection

Selecting Your Topic

It is important to take some time before selecting a topic for your final project. Consider your options. Remember that research findings are only one of several components integral to your project. You must also take into consideration your thoughts, personal insights, and ideas about the findings, which are of equal importance.

Criteria for Selecting Your Topic

1. Characteristics of Unsuitable Topics

Apply good judgement, decision-making skills, and research techniques when selecting your topic. The success of your final project depends on it!

What follows is a list of criteria that will help you to determine if a subject you are considering is unsuitable.

A. The necessary research cannot be completed in the time allocated.
Although a subject may strike you as particularly compelling, you may find that the research cannot be completed in the time allocated. For example, consider the following topic: *Does a particular new brand of golf ball travel farther than other golf balls?* Now, imagine it's February and all the local golf courses are closed for the season. How will you be able to determine the distance each golf ball can achieve if there are no golfers from which to obtain data?

B. The topic does not lend itself to research.
Consider this topic: *How many kilometres can an airplane fly before it crashes?* No commercial airline would allow a particular airplane to fly if there were even the slightest chance the plane might crash. As a result, it would be impossible to research this topic.

C. The topic is only information-based.
Suppose you wanted to find out what university or college had the highest entry requirements. Although the information you seek may be readily available, there is nothing to prove. This topic is only information-based; it would not enable you to predict future trends.

D. The topic is inappropriate.
Topics that may offend members of the audience to whom you will be presenting your research findings must be avoided. There are many inappropriate topics, so consider your choice carefully and consult with your teacher before deciding to pursue a specific topic.

2. Criteria for Suitable Topics

You should carefully select a topic that you want to learn more about. Shown below are some criteria that can be used to help you select your topic.

A. Think about your purpose.
Your purpose is to convince others of your perspective on a given topic. Make sure that, for any topic you choose, there are at least two sides to the issue for which you can find data, allowing you to argue one side or the other.

B. Always select a topic that interests you.
You will find completing this project a lot more fun and interesting if you are dealing with a topic that interests you. A topic that you find boring or tedious will make working on your project less enjoyable than it otherwise might be.

C. Be practical.
Make sure there is sufficient information and research completed for your topic. The earlier example of how far airplanes can fly before they crash is not practical. However, researching whether airplanes fly with too much fuel on board might be more practical.

D. Beware of "popular" topics.
A new, "popular" topic may be exciting, but it may also be so new that there is no current research available, or the research that people have done is so preliminary that nothing can be trusted.

E. Consider your audience.
You will be presenting your research to people in your class. Make sure that your topic will be interesting to others in your class so that they will be more attentive to your presentation. For example, students in your class may not be interested in the history of calculus. However, they might be interested in how fashion affects school spirit.

F. Do not think that every question needs to be answered.
Your topic may raise more questions than you can possibly answer. However, do not eliminate a topic simply because you may not be able to find all the answers. You are presenting a position only.

3. Create Your List of Topics

Make a list of topics that may interest you. In the next chapter, you will be asked to select a topic from the list and create a question that you would like to answer. At this point, however, simply select topics that you would like to research further; subjects are general ideas only!

Chapter 1 Wrap-Up

EXTRA PRACTICE

1. The results of a federal political poll show the following results: NDP, 12%; Liberal, 28%; PC, 21%; Alliance, 24%; BQ, 11%; the rest are undecided.

(a) Illustrate the data using a bar graph and a circle graph.

(b) Which graph do you think best illustrates the data? Give reasons for your answer.

2. The following data represent the number of personnel years spent on technical research, by region throughout Canada. Should a bar graph or a histogram be used to display the data? Construct the most appropriate graph.

Region	Atlantic Canada	Quebec	Ontario	National Capital	Prairies	British Columbia
Personnel Years	900	600	1550	3700	1350	630

3. Construct a suitable graph to display each of the following sets of data.

(a)

Age (years)	Pulse Rate (beats/min)
Newborn	135
1–9	87
10–19	71
20–59	72
60–69	73
70 and over	75

(b)

Year	Wins	Losses	Ties	Points
1990–91	37	33	8	82
1991–92	33	31	14	80
1992–93	27	41	10	64
1994–95	35	27	16	86
1996–97	31	33	14	76
1997–98	28	35	15	71

(c)

Total Monthly Precipitation in Thunder Bay (in millimetres)

J	F	M	A	M	J	J	A	S	O	N	D
59	42	32	30	42	58	58	73	56	61	55	54

4. "North Americans use more water than the rest of the world combined!" This headline jumped out from the top of Raul's morning paper and was supported by the following chart.

Country	USA	Canada	Switzerland	UK	Nigeria	West Germany	Belgium	India
Average Consumption per Day (L)*	690	385	294	195	142	130	97	65

*Data does not include water used by agriculture and industry.

Source: World Resources Institute

(a) Do you think the data support the conclusion?
(b) How confident are you about this conclusion? What other information might you want in order to feel more comfortable with the conclusion?
(c) Why might the writer of the article have reached this conclusion?
(d) What conclusions might you draw from these data?
(e) What might you want to research further based on these data?

5. As a project, Rhonda and her partner tried to determine the average masses of boys in various age groups at a local elementary school. They recorded the following data.

Age (years)	5	6	7	8	9	10	11	12	13	14
Mass (kg)	24	25	27	28	31	34	38	41	47	55

(a) Construct a scatter plot of the data.
(b) Estimate the line of best fit for the data.
(c) Based on your line of best fit, estimate the average mass of a boy 16 years of age.
(d) Now find an equation for the line of best fit and repeat part (c). What do you notice about your estimates? In which estimate will you have the most confidence?

6. Fatima, production manager at All Arabia Newspapers and Printing, kept a record for one week of the number of times that each employee needed help with a task. The results are shown below.

Employee	A	B	C	D	E	F	G	H	I	J
Length of Employment (weeks)	24	11	47	58	3	70	76	44	33	87
Requests for Help	14	20	10	13	25	10	6	15	19	6

(a) Construct a scatter plot of the data.
(b) Has employee C needed help more or less often than Fatima might have predicted?

7. The amount of fuel consumed by a car travelling a distance of 100 km was measured at various speeds. The data recorded appears below.

Speed (km/h)	10	20	30	40	50	60	70	80
Gas Consumed (L)	8.2	7.9	7.5	6.9	6.7	6.4	6.2	5.9

(a) Use graphing technology to construct a scatter plot of the data and determine the line of best fit.
(b) Describe the correlation for these data. Is this what you would expect? Why?

8. (a) Toss a coin five times and record the number of times heads turns up.
(b) Repeat part (a) 10 times, 15 times, 20 times, ..., 40 times.
(c) Use graphing technology to construct a scatter plot for the data using number of tosses and number of heads, and then find the line of best fit.
(d) If you were to toss a coin 50 times, how many heads would you expect? Use your line of best fit to find the number of heads you would expect with 50 tosses of a coin. What do you notice? How can you explain this?

9. Shown below is a creative-looking piece of art that compares data.
(a) Describe the impression that is given.
(b) Determine whether this impression is accurate.
(c) Describe how you might fix the graph so that it is more accurate.

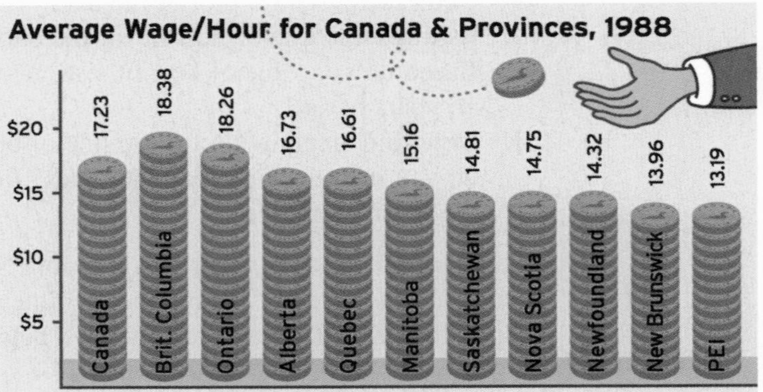

Source: XPLANE Corp. (Adapted from Sources of Differences in Provincial Earnings in Canada; Statistics Canada)

Chapter 1 Test

1. **Communication** A headline in a national newspaper on January 9, 2001, claimed "Kids around the world agree: Math teachers are nerds!" Researchers at Plymouth University asked 300 12- and 13-year-old students to draw pictures of mathematicians and they arrived at the conclusion in the headline.

(a) Do you agree with this headline? Why?

(b) Why do you think 12- and 13-year-old students may have felt this way?

2. **Knowledge and Understanding** During a nutrition survey, teenagers were asked to record the number of cans of pop they drank during a one-week period: 3, 5, 0, 7, 2, 3, 1, 2, 6, 3, 2, 4, 8, 4, 3, 5, 0, 2, 1, 3, 1, 6, 2, 5.

(a) Display the data using a bar graph.

(b) Is there a better way to display the data? Explain

3. Data were collected on the mass of a kitten, in kilograms, and its age in weeks.

Age (weeks)	1	2	3	4	5	6	7
Mass (kg)	0.8	1.1	1.2	1.4	1.5	1.5	1.7

(a) Construct a scatter plot of the data.

(b) Find the line of best fit.

(c) Predict the mass of the kitten when it is 10 weeks old.

(d) How would you describe the correlation?

4. Would you expect strong, weak, or no correlation if each of the following were investigated? Why?

(a) a person's age and blood pressure

(b) the amount of rainfall and the growth of vegetation

(c) automobile mass and fuel consumption in litres per 100 km

5. The numbers of points scored by a basketball team this season are recorded below.

45	71	55	62	57	68	62	48	52	60	59
75	51	49	57	56	54	63	55	67	61	58

(a) Construct a stem-and-leaf plot to display the data.

(b) Use the plot to determine the number of games where fewer than 55 points were scored.

(c) On what percent of games were more than 65 points scored?

(d) The basketball team must score more that 68 points to win the championship game. Considering the data above, how likely do you think this will happen? Explain.

6. Application From laboratory research, data were collected on "typical" cats.

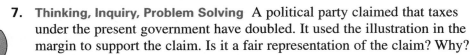

Mass of Cat (kg)	1.22	1.54	1.26	1.19	1.23
Mass of Heart (mg)	772	837	761	910	691

(a) Use graphing technology to construct a scatter plot for the data and show the line of best fit.
(b) Find the equation of the line of best fit. How did you do this?
(c) Interpret the equation in part (b). What does it show?
(d) Can you use the equation in part (b) to make predictions?

7. Thinking, Inquiry, Problem Solving A political party claimed that taxes under the present government have doubled. It used the illustration in the margin to support the claim. Is it a fair representation of the claim? Why?

8. Consider the following sales data for Precore Flooring Inc.

	Jan	Feb	Mar	Apr	May	June
Carrie	$475	$515	$390	$550	$605	$590
Musinta	$530	$525	$580	$560	$540	$510

(a) Describe how you could create a display of the sales data to make it appear as if both salespeople have similar success.
(b) Describe how you could create a display that makes Carrie's sales look like they are increasing more than they really are.

9. Given the following coefficients of correlation, state what percent of variation in y is due to the variation in x.

(a) $r = 0.41$ (b) $r = 0.82$ (c) $r = -0.93$
(d) $r = 0.44$ (e) $r = -0.5$ (f) $r = -1.0$

10. Shown below is a creative-looking piece of art that compares data.
(a) Describe the impression that is given.
(b) Determine whether this impression is accurate.
(c) Describe how you might fix the graph so that it is more accurate.

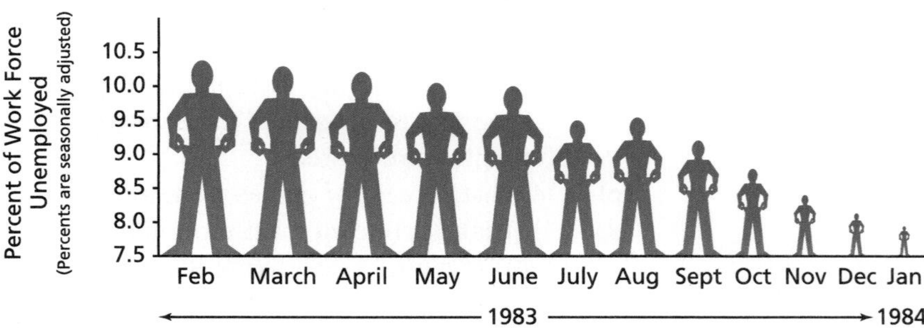

Source: Forth Worth Star-Telegram, Feb 4, 1984

2 In Search of Good Data

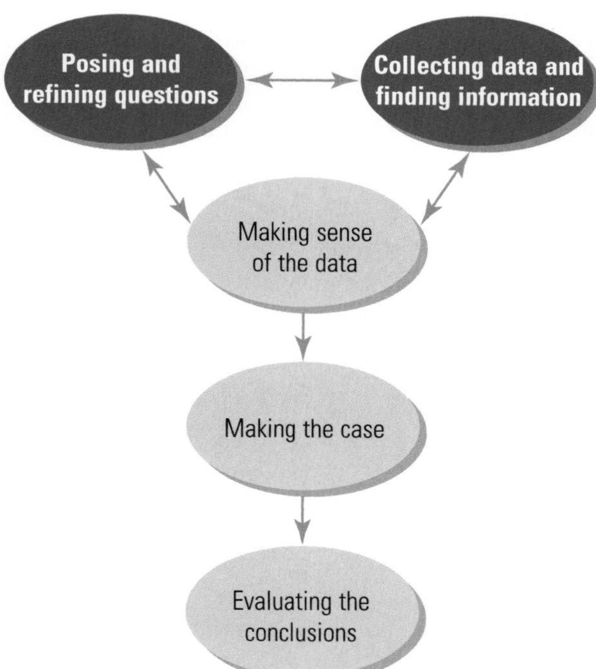

Humans are naturally curious beings. Asking questions such as *why* and *what if*… have not only helped us to make sense of our world, but they have also led to many important discoveries.

In this chapter, you will explore your personal interests. You will then focus on one or two areas of interest and begin to brainstorm a variety of unanswered questions. One of these questions should become the purpose for your major research project. To answer any question, however, you will need a large amount of data. Subsequent sections will address both the gathering of primary and secondary data, and the issues of bias, sample size, experimental design, and data organization.

In this chapter, you will

- search databases to locate data to answer significant questions
- use the Internet effectively as a source of information
- create database or spreadsheet templates to manipulate and retrieve data effectively
- understand the need for a variety of sampling techniques
- identify different types of bias
- organize and summarize data from secondary sources
- pose a significant problem whose solution would require the organization and analysis of a large amount of data

Chapter Problem

Mystery Most Mathematical

It was a dark and stormy night … Well, don't all mysteries start this way?

It was a little over three weeks ago that I began to receive some pretty strange e-mail. At first, I was curious to see where they would lead, but eventually I was totally preoccupied with figuring out who the "perp" was. By the way, "perp" is short for perpetrator. Simply put, I just wanted to know the identity of the person who was driving me crazy.

There were only so many out there who would dare to drive me to such distraction:

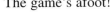

Penelope—My younger sister has a twisted sense of humour. She knows I am addicted to my computer and I will inevitably try to find out who is sending me e-mail even when it's Spam.

Percival—My dad always boasts that he was the world's greatest prankster at university. Although I haven't seen evidence of this, there is always a first time.

Perigesh—Isn't it the truth that the people you trust the most (your best friend, for instance) are the very ones who have the biggest surprises up their sleeves.

Ms. P. (a.k.a. **Peerwany**, my math teacher—she is commonly, but respectfully, addressed using her surname)—There seemed to be some connection to the mathematics we were doing in class, so she became an automatic suspect.

I am reaching out to you. Every time you encounter an e-mail, help me solve the problem. Gather the information to see what you can deduce and prepare a full report outlining your findings and conclusions.

The game's afoot!

Project Connection

Early on in this chapter, you will establish the area of interest for your inquiry and clearly state your research question. By the end of this chapter, you will have determined whether to use primary or secondary sources of data to answer your question and will have begun to collect relevant data.

2.1 Developing a Thesis

In this section, you will compile a personal interest inventory and will compare your results with those of your classmates. You will also work at developing a thesis question, which will become the focus of your project. To complete the course project, you may wish to work as a team with other students who share your interests.

Personal Interest Inventory

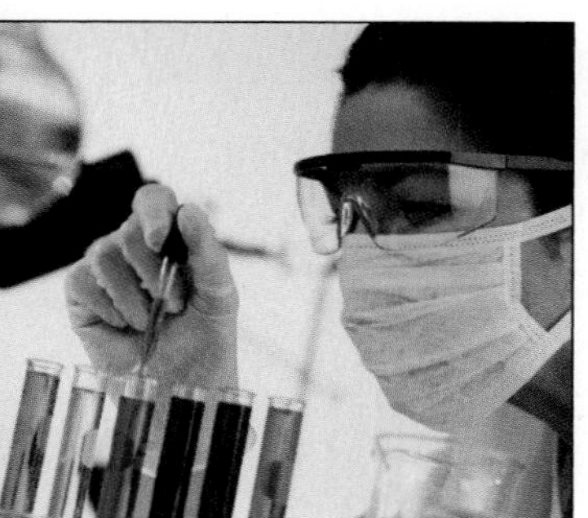

Academic Subjects

A1	Anthropology	A10	Geology	A19	Politics
A2	Astronomy	A11	German	A20	Psychology
A3	Biology	A12	History	A21	Religion
A4	Chemistry	A13	Law	A22	Sociology
A5	Computers	A14	Literature	A23	Spanish
A6	Economics	A15	Mathematics	A24	Visual Arts
A7	English	A16	Phys. Ed.	A25	World Issues
A8	French	A17	Physics		
A9	Geography	A18	Poetry		

Select your three favourite academic subjects from the 25 listed above and rank them in order. Do the same with the 25 non-academic interests listed below and record them in a chart. You can add or delete certain topics from these lists.

Non-Academic Interests

N1	Baseball	N9	Football	N18	Reading
N2	Basketball	N10	Gymnastics	N19	Rugby
N3	Camping	N11	Hiking	N20	Singing
N4	Carpentry	N12	Hockey	N21	Skiing
N5	Cars	N13	Painting	N22	Travelling
N6	Computer Programming	N14	Part-Time Job	N23	Volleyball
		N15	Physical Fitness	N24	Volunteering
N7	Cycling	N16	Playing Music	N25	Writing
N8	Figure Skating	N17	Politics		

INVESTIGATION 1: CLASSROOM INTEREST COMPARISON

index—an arbitrarily defined number that provides a measure of scale

Are there other students in your class who have interests similar to yours? Using an **index**, you can measure the similarity between you and your classmates.

Purpose

Calculate an interest index for each student in your class to determine which students have interests that are most closely related to yours.

Procedure

A. (*Without technology*) Record your ranked set of favourite subjects and interests on paper in a chart similar to the spreadsheet below. To make the comparison easier, use the labels from the list instead of the actual subject and interest names.

	A	B	C	D	E	F	G	H
1		Academic Subject			Non-Academic Interest			
2		Favourite	Second	Third	Favourite	Second	Third	
3	*My interests*	A15	A2	A16	N12	N6	N25	
4	**Student**							**Score**
5								

B. In finding a score for each of your classmates, try to match each of their selections to one of yours using the following guide to assign points:

	Their Favourite	Second	Third
Your Favourite	10	6	3
Second	6	3	2
Third	3	2	1

For example, if you and a classmate share the same favourite, give that student 10 points; if your second choice is that student's third choice, give her or him 2 points. If you don't share any favourites with that classmate, assign 0 points. The classmate with the highest score is the one with interests most similar to yours.

A. (*With spreadsheet technology*) Create a spreadsheet similar to the one above and record your favourites as shown.

B. Since you have used consistent entries, you can write a formula using logical operators to add up the score each person should receive. Use the CD that accompanies this textbook to access these formulas.

	A	B	C	D	E	F	G	H
1		Academic Subject			Non-Academic Interest			
2		Favourite	Second	Third	Favourite	Second	Third	
3	*My interests*	A15	A2	A16	N12	N6	N25	
4	**Student**							**Score**
5	Carlos	A10	A5	A3	N3	N1	N2	13
6	Phoebe	A2	A3	A16	N1	N2	N3	7
7	Ralph	A4	A5	A6	N7	N8	N9	0
8	Wanda	A23	A14	A15	N12	N8	N1	13
9	Dorothy	A2	A16	A10	N12	N23	N25	19
10	Keisha	A14	A1	A3	N8	N10	N13	0

Based on the example above, you share the most interests with Dorothy.

? **Think about Spreadsheet Formulas**
If you are using a spreadsheet formula, why is it important to use a standardized entry like the labels here (e.g., A15) instead of words?

Technolink
For more information on using logical operators and formulas with spreadsheet software, see Appendix E, pages 425 and 426.

Technolink
This spreadsheet and its formulas are included on the textbook CD.

Discussion Questions

1. What is the significance of the score that the formula produces?
2. What are some weaknesses of this system of finding similarities between people?
3. How could you determine if there is a relationship between a student's gender and interests?

FINDING A TOPIC

thesis—a formal statement or question that your project will answer or discuss

mind map—a visual display used in brainstorming to illustrate relationships

You may be struggling with simplifying a large project idea and turning it into a more manageable project **thesis**. A **mind map** can help you organize the information you have.

A mind map is a brainstorming tool that can illustrate how a topic relates to other concepts. You can use it to expand on the interests you discovered in your investigation.

To see how to construct a mind map, consider how Riyaz uses them as he expands on the results of his investigation.

Example 1 Constructing a Mind Map

Riyaz identified astronomy, geography, and world issues as his three favourite academic subjects, and politics, travelling, and hockey (sports in general) as his three favourite non-academic interests. Use a mind map to illustrate how these topics relate and expand each subject or area of interest one level further.

Solution

Starting from the centre, connect all six interests in the most meaningful way possible. One obvious connection would be to link the three non-academic interests and the three academic subjects. In addition, divide his purely scientific interests from his interests in social science. His political and non-political interests should also be separated.

Project Connection

A mind map is a great way to get started. Take your six favourites and create one of your own.

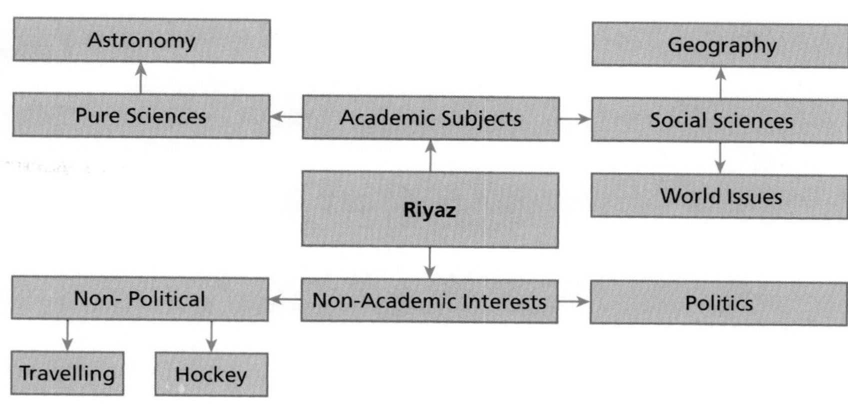

To expand this map one level further, brainstorm about each endpoint on his map and work at connecting these new points back together in meaningful ways.

Geography could be divided into human and physical geography. Physical geography is strongly related to environmental science, a pure science. Similarly, politics at the national level is related to world issues.

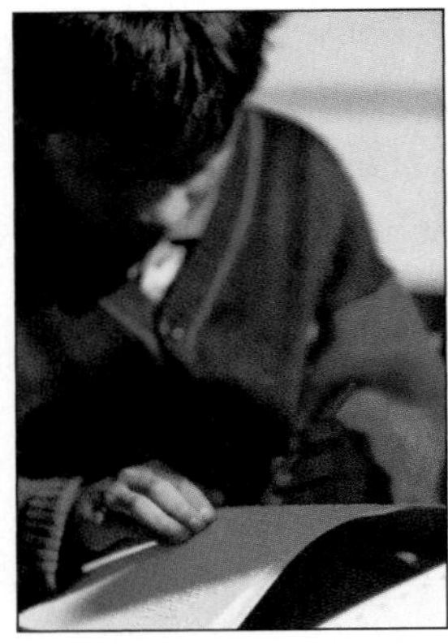

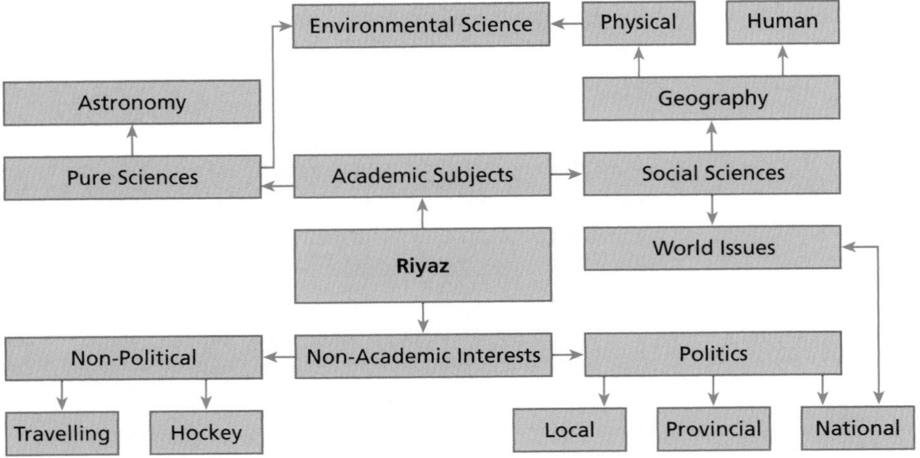

When working with mind maps, remember the following:

- Start off as simply as possible and draw lines between related words.
- Work from the inside out.
- Do not be afraid to start over; a dead end is simply a reason to try again.

Example 2 Expanding a Thesis Topic

Riyaz is interested in doing a project related to his studies in world issues. Expand this part of the mind map by brainstorming related concepts and construct a number of thesis questions.

Solution

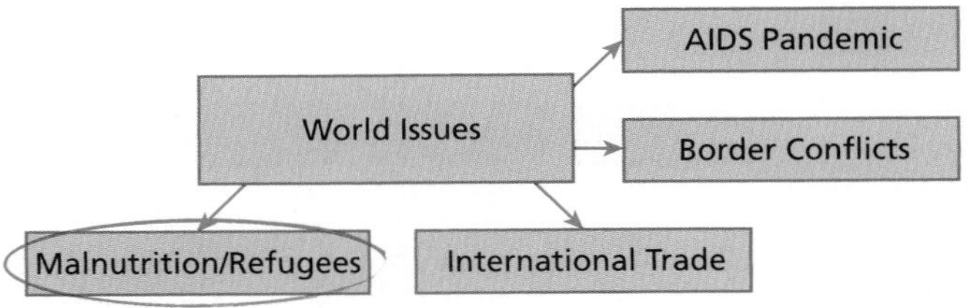

Riyaz can think of four related topics; however, malnutrition/refugees strikes him as a topic worthy of study. With this in mind, he brainstorms and creates a number of questions that can be explored with the use of statistical information.

Project Connection

From your mind map, take an endpoint of interest or a junction between two parts and work at developing a thesis question.

(a) Is there a relationship between the number of refugee camps located in a nation and the rate of malnutrition for that country?

(b) How has the issue of malnutrition changed from 1950 to the present?

(c) Where are malnourished people in Canada most likely to live? Do they live mostly in rural or urban areas?

(d) Using statistical analysis, determine the characteristics of a typical resident of a refugee camp in Southeast Asia. Make a comparison with a typical resident of a refugee camp in Africa.

(e) Given a country with a high rate of malnutrition, examine changes over time in that country's agricultural production, education and medical practices, industrial production, international borrowing, political stability, and so on. Are there any relationships?

variable—a measurable characteristic that can change

To analyze a thesis question properly, consider the following:

1. What are the main **variables** in my question?
2. Can these variables be measured statistically?
3. Is there enough data to make an interesting analysis?

Example 3 Thesis Question Analysis

Consider the questions Riyaz has developed for Example 2.

Analyze each of the questions using the steps above and determine which one(s) would provide the most insightful answer. In addition, make sure that your question has a result that is interesting and worthy of study.

Solution

Riyaz uses a chart to analyze his questions.

	Main Variables	Can These Be Measured?
Question (a)	Number of camps Rate of malnutrition	Yes Not easily
Question (b)	Change in malnutrition	No
Question (c)	Location of malnourished people	Not easily
Question (d)	Characteristics of refugee camp residents	Yes (dependent on characteristics chosen)
Question (e)	Agricultural production Education and medical practices Industrial production International borrowing Political stability	Yes Yes Yes Yes Not easily

Project Connection

Remember, the analysis of your thesis must make use of the tools you discover in this course. You must also be able to present your findings to your class.

While both Questions (d) and (e) can be statistically measured, it is clear that Question (e) has more data available and would, therefore, make a more interesting analysis. Question (e) requires the knowledge of some basic economic statistics for various countries in the developing world and can be summarized in a way that will be interesting. Question (e) makes the best thesis question.

Example 4 Thesis Question Analysis

Stephanie has a strong interest in sports. Review Stephanie's mind map by brainstorming related concepts and develop a number of thesis questions.

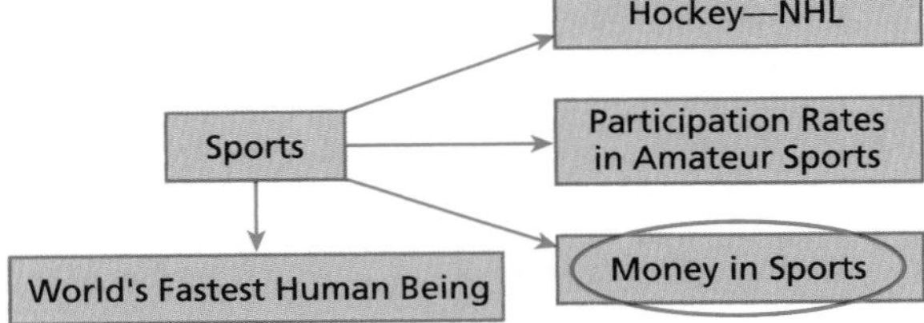

Solution

After coming up with four topics of interest, Stephanie chose the topic Money in Sports. With that in mind, she thought of four questions:

(a) How do people at my school feel about high salaries in professional sports?

(b) How have salaries paid to professional hockey players and professional football players in Canada changed from 1960 to the present?

(c) Is there a relationship between a very large salary increase to an athlete and his or her subsequent performance?

(d) Does the amount (either overall or calculated per capita) that a country spends to prepare its athletes for the Olympics correspond to the country's success at the Games?

KEY IDEAS

personal interest inventory—use the personal interest inventory to brainstorm possible topics for your project

mind map—related themes and issues can be studied in a mind map; topics for your major project can usually be found in the endpoints of a mind map

thesis question—the focus of your project is answering your thesis question. When considering a thesis question, determine

- the main variables in your question
- whether the variables can be measured statistically
- whether there is enough data to make an interesting analysis

2.1 Exercises

A

1. Sort each list of words into two or three categories.
   (a) packing, shopping list, drive, sleeping bag, unpack, canoe, relax, sunscreen, swim, sleep, eat, bug bite, picnic
   (b) pedal, steer, wheel, brake, tire, shift, push, dial, radio, pull, seat, turn, switch, window
   (c) hard drive, type, click, mouse, download, plug-in, CD-ROM, read, keyboard, play, record, cable, save, load, monitor
   (d) dig, seeds, hose, plant, prune, water, clip, harvest, garden, hoe, shovel, fertilizer
   (e) wake up, copier, shower, breakfast, lunch, drive, break, meeting, phone, fax
   (f) ref, blue line, slashing, puck, fans, net, goalie, forward, defence, face off, skate, shoot, save

2. Using the sorted lists from Question 1, draw lines between related words to create a mind map.

3. **Application** Take the first few pages of a recent newspaper and draw a mind map that connects a major issue or current event with related articles.

4. Determine the main variables in the following thesis questions.
   (a) How is the accuracy of a person's ability to estimate height and distance related to his or her height? To his or her age?
   (b) Are females better than males at estimating the size of a large crowd?
   (c) Is there a relationship between the quality of a person's clothing and her or his mid-term average?
   (d) What is the relationship between mid-term average and favourite subject?

5. Consider the variables identified in Question 4. Rate them on a scale of 1 to 10, with 1 meaning *easily defined and measurable* and 10 meaning *not measurable or well-defined.*

B

6. Dawn has wanted to become an entrepreneur ever since her brother started a carpet-cleaning service last year. For her course project, she wants to study small business in Canada. Create five questions related to this topic that can be statistically studied and that provide enough data to make Dawn's project interesting.

7. Gord loves to watch TV and would like to study the TV-watching habits of his classmates. Create five questions related to this topic that can be statistically studied. Ensure they will provide enough data to make Gord's project interesting.

8. **Knowledge and Understanding** Hafiz started getting more sleep this semester and has noticed that his grades are improving. He would like to study whether this is true of people in general. Create five questions related to this topic that can be statistically studied and that will provide enough data to make an interesting project. Identify a challenge associated with each question.

? Think about Thesis Questions

When evaluating a thesis question, ask yourself:

- What are the main variables in my question?
- Can these variables be statistically measured?
- Is there enough data to make an interesting analysis?

9. Flavia wants to study the shopping habits of people in her community. Her thesis question is *What is important to people when they go shopping?* What challenges will Flavia face in using this question? How could her thesis question be improved to make the project easier to study and more insightful?

10. Joylene wants to do her project on music, but needs help with a thesis question. Create five questions related to this topic and write them in order from most effective to least effective.

11. Deborah wants to study her classmates' reactions to a recent theatrical release, but her teacher has asked her to expand the scope of her project. What changes would you suggest Deborah make to her study? Create a suitable thesis question for this new project.

12. Saima wants to study the attributes of Canadians who donate to international charities that provide food to developing countries. Her teacher has asked that she adjust the scope of her project to make it easier to collect data. What changes would you suggest that Saima make to her study? Create a suitable thesis question for this new project.

13. **Communication** Choose three of the following thesis questions and explain with details why you think each one would be the basis for a feasible and worthwhile project.
    - **(a)** How is the accuracy of a person's ability to estimate height and distance related to her or his height?
    - **(b)** Are females better than males at estimating the size of a large crowd?
    - **(c)** What is the relationship between a student's mid-term average and his or her favourite subject?
    - **(d)** Which local fast-food outlet is the best?
    - **(e)** What do students at your school think about local school uniforms?

C 14. Create a mind map consisting of at least three levels that relates Canada, politics, and poverty. Develop three thesis questions about an endpoint in the mind map and then evaluate each question.

15. **Thinking, Inquiry, Problem Solving** Create two rating systems (one for women and one for men) based on the table on the following page to determine which dish is most nutritionally balanced. State all of your assumptions. Is the most balanced meal the same for both women and men? How would you explain the difference, if any?

Guideline for Daily Nutritional Requirement[1]

	Men	Women
Calories	2500–3000	2000
Protein	63 g	50 g
Total fat	60–75 g	50–60 g
Saturated fat	20–25 g	15–20 g
Cholesterol	300 mg	300 mg
Fibre	20–30 g	20–30 g
Carbohydrate	340 g	275 g
Sodium	2400 mg	2400 mg

[1] Reader's Digest, *The How-To Book of Healthy Cooking: Good Food That's Good For You* (Pleasantville, New York: The Reader's Digest Association, Inc., 1995) 9.

Dishes[2]

	Greek Poached Chicken and Lemon Stew	Pork Chops Stuffed with Apples and Pears	Poached Salmon Steaks	Hearty Beef, Turkey, and Mashed-Potato Pie
Calories	291	384	262	393
Protein	50 g	40 g	29 g	31 g
Total fat	7 g	15 g	11 g	7 g
Saturated fat	2 g	5 g	3 g	2 g
Cholesterol	135 mg	113 mg	75 mg	68 mg
Fibre	2 g	3 g	1 g	8 g
Carbohydrate	25 g	21 g	11 g	52 g
Sodium	313 mg	133 mg	200 mg	360 mg

[2] Reader's Digest 61, 106, 133, 159.

ADDITIONAL ACHIEVEMENT CHART QUESTIONS

16. Knowledge and Understanding

(a) What is a thesis?

(b) List the characteristics of a good thesis question or statement.

17. Application

(a) Misa has identified the following three areas of interest: Canada, hockey, and politics. Create a mind map that shows how these three topics connect with one another.

(b) Use your mind map to formulate a possible thesis question.

18. **Thinking, Inquiry, Problem Solving** The general mind map that follows could be used as a framework for your project. Use this template to create a project mind map for your thesis question or statement.

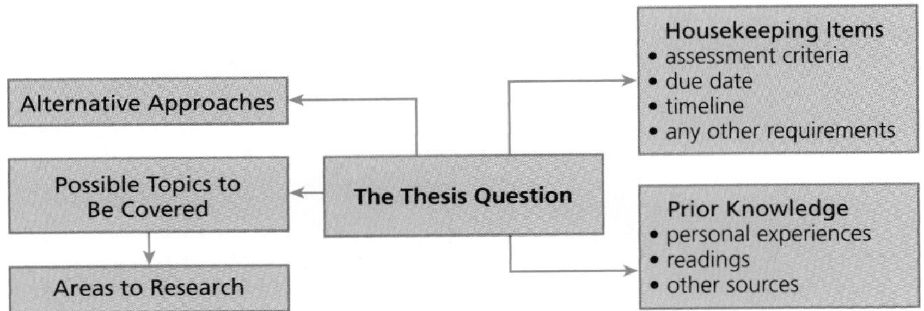

19. **Communication** Consider the following thesis question: *Are most of the problems faced by countries in the world—such as poverty, hunger, and environmental destruction—the consequences of excessive population growth?* Determine whether or not this is an example of a good thesis question and justify your reasoning.

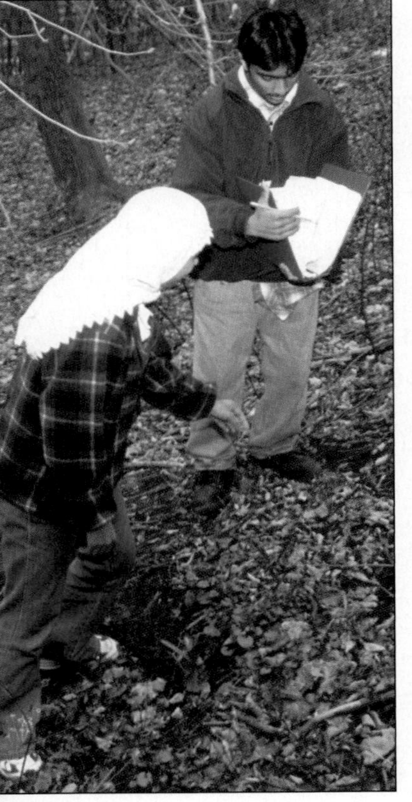

Chapter Problem

Mystery Most Mathematical—Part I

Here is a copy of the first e-mail that I received:

```
Subject:   Re: Puzzle - Part 1
Date:      Monday 08:47:35 -0700 (EDT)
From:      314159@homework.com
To:        jto@coldmail.com

Five groups of five. See where your interests lie.

parallax, Ramapithecus, robot, Glomar Challenger,
white dwarf, Pocketronic, Paul Langerhans, mammog-
raphy, P waves, sonar, Abell clusters, Buckminster
Fuller, Nereid, Palenque, pre-Cambrian shield,
dialysis, nebula, angioplasty, Gottlieb Daimler,
papyrus, Daniel Barringer, pancreas, Meave Leakey,
mineral, Minoan

Determine the common denominator for each group of
five. Pick the topic that interests you the most and
design a research question.

Good luck!
```

Project Connection

Your Topic

The word **subject** denotes a broad category, a general area of interest that you may wish to explore further. The word **topic** denotes a specific aspect of the subject that requires detailed research. Some examples of subjects and topics are shown in the chart below. Copy the chart in your notebook, and then use the spaces provided to

- add one more topic for each subject given
- list the subject and related topics that you would like to research

Complete the chart before you formulate your thesis question.

Subject	Topic
Television	Ratings wars Digital cable versus regular cable Cable versus satellite dishes
Medicine	Hospital closures and staff cutbacks Doctor and/or nurse shortages Health-care funding levels
Post-Secondary Education	Tuition fees Entry requirements Degree requirements
Travel	Air safety Vacation destinations Cost
Music	Musical styles Music and sports Comparing musicians

2.2 Characteristics of Data

"Data! Data! Data!" he cried impatiently.
"I can't make bricks without clay."

— Sherlock Holmes

data—a body or series of facts or information

It is evident from the definition that virtually anything can qualify as **data**. Although some data requires an immediate response and relatively little analysis (for example, the data your nervous system transmits to your brain after touching a hot stove), other data, specifically research data, takes years to collect and requires detailed analysis to understand it.

In this section, you will learn to refine your thesis question in order to collect specific kinds of information. You will then adapt your thesis question to gather data from a specific group.

POPULATION DATA VERSUS SAMPLE DATA

population—a group of individuals that is the focus of a study

sample—a selection of individuals taken from a population

A project that considers the attitudes and characteristics of students at your school is using the student body as the **population**. The collection of student records your school has is an example of population data. If you were to forecast the results of a federal election, the population would be the list of eligible voters. For most studies, it is impractical to collect data from the entire population because there are too many people. Instead, you would select a representative **sample** and study it instead.

When carrying out a study in a high school, the permission of the teachers involved and the principal is generally required.

Example 1 Identifying the Population

Suppose you had observed that the heights of Grade 9 students were quite varied. By the time these students reach Grade 12, of course, most are taller. State a thesis question that gives your study a focus and identifies the population.

Solution

Your first attempt at a thesis question might be *What is the pattern of growth (height) of students from the time they enter high school until they graduate?*

This is a good start, but it is not clear precisely who is the target of the study. Are any students to be considered, or only the students in their first and last year of high school? Are females and males treated alike for the purpose of this study? Can an **inference** be made about growth patterns of high school students beyond the borders of your school community?

inference—a conclusion about the population that is made from the sample

Project Connection

Be careful not to define a project that is too broad in scope.

The population needs to be defined more clearly in this question, and it would be wise to focus on only the students who are attending your high school. Also, you should define two populations of subjects: females and males. Now, restate your research question: *What is the pattern of growth (height) of females and males at my school from the time they enter high school until they graduate?*

CROSS-SECTIONAL AND LONGITUDINAL STUDIES

census—information gathered about an entire population

cross-sectional study—a study that considers individuals from different groups at the same time

longitudinal study—a study that considers individuals over a long period of time

Before you can decide whether you will conduct a **census** or select a sample, you must determine what kind of study you wish to perform.

A **cross-sectional study** is carried out during a specific timeframe and focuses on a wide range of individuals. A **longitudinal study** typically focuses on a small group of individuals over an extended period. Often, research to determine the effects of a treatment for cancer is a longitudinal study that may extend over 20 years or more!

Example 2 Identifying the Type of Study

The need for a better student centre has always been an issue in your school. Identify a thesis question for this topic that clearly defines the population, and then suggest a method of study.

Solution

The first draft of your thesis question is *How do the opinions about the student centre change among students from Grade 9 to Grade 12?*

You have clearly identified the population for your study as only the students who attend your school; however, it is unclear what type of study you wish to undertake. Do you want to ask students from each grade (a cross-sectional study), or do you intend to interview a selection of Grade 9 students and then return to ask them again next year when they are in Grade 10, and so on (a longitudinal study)?

time series data—data that have accumulated over a long period of time

A longitudinal study allows you to analyze the way a variable like a person's opinion changes over time. This form of data is called **time series data**. Longitudinal studies are usually expensive and can be very difficult to undertake. Despite these challenges, it is the method of choice for psychological and medical studies.

Since you are in Grade 12, it is impractical for you to return to your school for the next three years to collect data for a longitudinal study (also, your teacher is unlikely to approve such a study). A cross-sectional study is quicker, easier, and more suitable in this situation.

When outlining the type of study, you should also mention whether you plan to collect sample data or population data by taking a census. Since it is unlikely that you can interview all the students in your school, you must focus on a random sample of the students instead. You will learn more about sampling in Section 2.3.

A second draft of your thesis question is *How do the opinions about the student centre among a random sample of students in Grades 9 and 12 differ?*

QUALITATIVE AND QUANTITATIVE VARIABLES

quantitative variables—variables that can be measured numerically

qualitative variables—variables that cannot be measured numerically

discrete data—data that can be described using whole numbers. A count will always give discrete data.

continuous data—data that are only measurable with real numbers. A measure of quantity will always be continuous.

Variables that can be measured numerically are called **quantitative** (e.g., height, distance); variables that cannot be measured numerically are called **qualitative** (e.g., eye colour, opinion). Quantitative data are said to be **discrete** if they can be described with whole numbers (e.g., number of students). Examples of quantitative data that are said to be **continuous** include the heights of students and the length of time a plant takes to germinate.

Example 3 Identifying Variables and Data Types

Imagine that, for years, you have been fascinated by the great performances of track-and-field athletes, and the high jump is your favourite event. Create a thesis question about this topic using your school's track team as the population. Identify the variables and data used.

Solution

Your first question might be *What attributes of an athlete's physique, training regimen, and competition history are predictors of success?*

In your question, you still need to state clearly what variables you will study. Perhaps part of your study will require you to compare quantitative data. A question might be *Is there a relationship between a high jumper's height and best jump this season?*

Another part of your project could study qualitative data, such as using a questionnaire to determine a description of the mental and physical preparation prior to jumping in a competition. A question might be *Are there common training exercises among the top five high jumpers on our track team?*

Statisticians believe that although it is helpful to collect qualitative data, quantitative data are much easier to study.

KEY IDEAS

population versus sample—the group being studied is called the *population;* a selection of individuals taken from the population is a *sample*. Data collected from the sample are called *sample data*. A *census* is a collection of population data.

inference—a conclusion about the population based on sample data

cross-sectional study—a study that considers individuals from different groups at the same time

longitudinal study—a study of a single group (or sample) over a long period of time

time series data—data that have accumulated over a long period of time

qualitative variables versus quantitative variables—all data can be characterized as either qualitative or quantitative. Quantitative data are numerical and qualitative data are non-numerical.

discrete data—data that result from a count (e.g., number of people, number of vehicles, etc.)

continuous data—data resulting from the measure of a quantity (e.g., mass, age, etc.)

2.2 Exercises

A

1. Identify each of the following variables as qualitative or quantitative.
   (a) age
   (b) favourite meal
   (c) television viewing preferences
   (d) volume of a radio
   (e) colour of hair
   (f) fabric texture
   (g) pH of water samples
   (h) seating capacity
   (i) grades
   (j) paint colours

2. For each quantitative variable mentioned in Question 1, identify whether it is continuous or discrete.

3. **Knowledge and Understanding** Identify the variables and their types, as well as the population for the following thesis questions.
   (a) Is there a relationship between weather conditions and absenteeism in Grade 9 at your school?
   (b) Is there a profile that describes people who generally buy used cars in Canada?
   (c) Is there a relationship between the amount of television watched and the level of physical fitness among adult females?
   (d) Do Grade 9 students who regularly eat breakfast perform better academically?
   (e) Are teenage drivers who have been issued speeding tickets more likely to be males?
   (f) What home conditions influence school-aged children in selecting a future career?
   (g) When is the best time of day to find a parking space within 100 m of the mall?
   (h) How much of their own money do students at your school spend on their clothes?

B

4. For each of the thesis questions in Question 3, would you collect a sample or conduct a census? Would each question require a cross-sectional study or a longitudinal study?

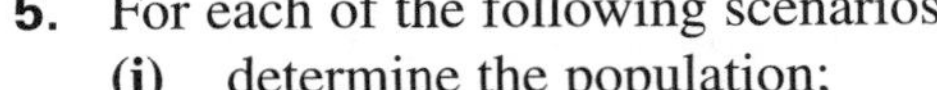

5. For each of the following scenarios,
   - **(i)** determine the population;
   - **(ii)** identify the key variables for the study;
   - **(iii)** state whether the data will be quantitative or qualitative; and
   - **(iv)** for the variables that are quantitative, state whether the data will be discrete or continuous.

   - **(a)** You must get T-shirt sizes for the 42 members of your school's environment club (26 are female).
   - **(b)** You are to canvass 200 households to determine the level of support that each of the candidates in a local by-election has.
   - **(c)** You are studying biological succession in what was 45 hectares of a farmer's cornfield. You are trying to measure plant diversity by identifying the number of each species per hectare.
   - **(d)** This summer, you have been hired to work with anthropologists from the Royal Ontario Museum. You are to gather data from the Aboriginal population on Manitoulin Island, Ojibways of Lake Huron, on how their family structures have changed in the last century.
   - **(e)** You are collecting and analyzing suggestions for a new name for your school. Data must be gathered from present and former students, students in the feeder schools, past and present teachers and administrators, support staff, parents and guardians, as well as interested members of the community.
   - **(f)** Your teacher has arranged your class in groups of three, and asked you to gather data, analyze them, and communicate whether teenagers today are economically worse off than teenagers were 20 years ago.

6. For each of the scenarios in Question 5, complete the following.
   - **(i)** Should a census or a sample be used? Explain.
   - **(ii)** Would a cross-sectional or longitudinal study be most appropriate to draw conclusions? Explain.

7. Create a suitable thesis question for the following studies. Be sure to clearly identify the population in your question.
   - **(a)** Customers leaving a local grocery store are asked how much they spent and how often they buy groceries.
   - **(b)** A furniture store wishes to use existing data to determine trends in consumer buying habits over the last five years.
   - **(c)** A company that sells books over the Internet will collect data for the next 12 months about those people who make online purchases.
   - **(d)** A researcher from the Ontario Institute for Studies in Education at the University of Toronto wants to determine if calculator use in elementary school improves student confidence in doing math.
   - **(e)** A medical officer of health needs to collect data about the frequency of senior citizen visits to doctors' offices over the last five years.
   - **(f)** Domestic and foreign cars of various ages are tested to determine their minimum stopping distance when travelling at 90 km/h.

8. **Communication** Write a thesis question that a product manager might use to focus an analysis of consumer buying habits. Be sure to clearly identify the population in your question.

9. For each of the studies described in Question 7, complete the following.
   (i) Is this study longitudinal or cross-sectional? Why?
   (ii) Why would a sample be preferable to gathering census data for each?

10. A quality control officer at a manufacturing plant selects a number of integrated circuits to ensure that they meet company standards before they are shipped to customers.
   (a) What is the population? **(b)** Describe the sample.

11. **Application** Using the Internet, find a recent study done about high school students.
   (a) Identify the thesis question of the study.
   (b) Was this study longitudinal or cross-sectional?
   (c) Do you think the results of this study are reflective of the habits and attitudes of the students at your school? Explain.

12. Using the Internet or other media, find a recent longitudinal study.
   (a) Identify the thesis question of the study.
   (b) Why did the researcher choose to use a longitudinal study and not a cross-sectional study?

C 13. **Thinking, Inquiry, Problem Solving** Describe a topic for a statistical study for each scenario. Create a suitable thesis question for each.
   (a) a longitudinal study that collects quantitative data from a sample of a population
   (b) a cross-sectional study using a census that collects quantitative data
   (c) a longitudinal census that collects qualitative data
   (d) a cross-sectional study of a population sample that collects qualitative data

ADDITIONAL ACHIEVEMENT CHART QUESTIONS

14. **Knowledge and Understanding** Consider this thesis question: *In North America, do foreign cars depreciate in value faster than domestic cars?* Now answer the questions that follow.
   (a) What is the population?
   (b) What are the key variables that must be considered? Are these quantitative or qualitative?
   (c) Should a census or a sample be used to collect the data?
   (d) Are the data continuous or discrete?
   (e) Is a cross-sectional or a longitudinal study more appropriate for drawing conclusions?

15. **Application** Find a recent study of consumer spending through online purchases on the Internet.

(a) Identify the thesis question or statement of the study.

(b) Identify whether the researcher used a cross-sectional or a longitudinal study.

(c) Are the results of this study reflective of the spending habits of your family and friends? Explain.

16. **Thinking, Inquiry, Problem Solving** Cross-sectional and longitudinal studies are often used in the field of medicine. Find an example of each from the field of medicine. Explain why both types of studies are necessary in medical research and identify the different types of information that each type of study can provide.

17. **Communication** Explain the differences between each pair of terms.

(a) population/sample

(b) cross-sectional study/longitudinal study

(c) quantitative variable/qualitative variable

(d) discrete data/continuous data

Chapter Problem

Mystery Most Mathematical—Part II

```
Subject:  Re: Puzzle - Part 2
Date:     Wednesday 17:27:11 -0700 (EDT)
From:     27182818@homework.com
To:       jto@coldmail.com

Use the research question that you designed after
receiving the first e-mail to
(a) identify the variables and indicate whether the
    variables are discrete or continuous
(b) identify the population
(c) suggest whether a cross-sectional or a
    longitudinal study would be more appropriate
    and why
```

Project Connection

Your Question

A well-written thesis question or statement clarifies exactly what your project is designed to do, and should have the following characteristics:

- The reseach *topic* is easily identifiable.
- The *purpose* of the research (probably to persuade others) is clear.
- The *order* of the presentation is implied. In other words, the order in which your research is completed and presented will be obvious after reading or listening to your question (or statement).
- It is *focused*. The people listening or reading your question (or statement) will know what you are going to prove.

A good question does not just happen. It requires some thought and some planning. Compared below are some examples of thesis questions (statements). Read each statement and then write your own question (or statement).

Unacceptable Statement	Why?	Acceptable Statement
The Great Lakes are irreplaceable.	Too general	The Great Lakes must be preserved because they offer people throughout North America resources that cannot be replaced.
Driver's Education programs for teenagers are excellent.	Too specific	Some programs designed to increase the driving ability of teenage drivers have been effective, but more efforts are needed, especially concerning teenage driving safety.

Evaluating Your Thesis

Use the following series of questions to determine if your thesis question (or statement) is effective.

1. Does my thesis question (or statement) clearly identify the main objective of my presentation?
2. After reading my thesis question (or statement) to a few classmates, is the order in which I will present my data clear?
3. Does my thesis question (or statement) use specific language that tells my audience what I am going to do, rather than vague language that does not give a clear indication of what I will do?
4. Is my thesis question (or statement) interesting? Does it make me want to research further, thus ensuring that my audience will want to listen to my research and presentation?
5. Is my thesis question too specific or too general? How should I fix it?
6. Does my thesis question show evidence of original thought? Is the topic I am proposing worth writing about?

2.3 Collecting Samples

This photograph of former U.S. President Harry Truman holding up a copy of the *Chicago Daily Tribune* shortly after the presidential election of 1948 is a classic example of survey results gone wrong. Three different polling agencies had predicted that Thomas E. Dewey would win this election. The fact that Truman has a broad grin on his face tells the real story; he actually won the election by five percentage points. To understand why this happened, you need to learn more about collecting data and creating representative samples.

In this section, you will explore different ways of collecting random samples of data. You will explore sampling techniques and the effect of sample size to learn how to use surveys more effectively.

THE STORY BEHIND THE HEADLINE

Think about The Headline "Dewey defeats Truman"
How did the pollsters come to their conclusion?

In the United States, the president is indirectly[1] elected by a popular vote. One of two major parties—the Republican Party or the Democratic Party—generally receives in excess of 95% of the votes cast.

The three agencies that conducted polls prior to the 1948 election used a sampling method that required interviewers to choose respondents "carefully." Even though the sample sizes were large (in one case, over 50 000 people) and the sampling technique was designed to elicit responses from a representative cross-section of American voters, the fact that the interviewers chose the respondents was the problem.

TYPES OF SAMPLES

random—occurring by chance

Simple Random Sampling

A simple random sample requires that

- all selections must be *equally likely*
- all combinations of selections must be *equally likely*

A random sample may not end up being representative of the population, but any deviations are due only to chance.

Systematic Random Sampling

sampling interval—found by evaluating $\frac{\text{population size}}{\text{sample size}}$

A systematic random sample is used when you are sampling a fixed percent of the population. A random starting point (i.e., individual, household, or object) is chosen and then you select every *n*th individual for your study, where *n* is the **sampling interval**.

[1] The president is technically elected by the Electoral College. This body of individuals is chosen by each state and the number of representatives is roughly proportional to each state's population. Representatives vote according to the popular vote in their state. This means that most presidential elections reflect the country's overall popular vote.

Stratified Random Sampling

When using a stratified random sample, the population is divided into groups called *strata* (e.g., geographic areas, age groups, places of work, and so on). A simple random sample of the members of each stratum is then taken. The size of the sample for each stratum is proportionate to the stratum's size.

Cluster Random Sampling

Cluster samples require that the population be organized into groups (e.g., schools, communities, companies, and so on). A random sample of groups would then be chosen. All the members of the chosen groups would then be surveyed.

Multi-Stage Random Sampling

Multi-stage samples require that the population be organized into groups. A random sample of groups is chosen and then a random sample of members of the chosen groups is taken.

Destructive Sampling

Samples from which the selected elements cannot be reintroduced into the population are called *destructive sampling* (e.g., light bulbs tested for quality control).

Partial Table of Random Numbers

00	59391	58031
01	99567	76364
02	10363	97518
03	86859	19558
04	11258	24591
05	95068	98628
06	54463	47237
07	16874	62677
08	92494	63157
09	15669	56689
10	99116	75486
11	15696	10703
12	97720	15369
13	11666	13841
14	71628	73130

Randomly selected starting digits.

Technolink For a complete random number table, refer to Appendix B.2 on page 400.

Example 1 Simple Random Sampling

An apartment building superintendent is interested in determining if tenants are satisfied with the maintenance of the building. It is impractical for Mimi to survey every apartment, so she chooses to do a simple random sample.

Solution

For simplicity, this example illustrates how a random sample of 5 units could be selected if there were only 15 apartments in total. In this case, the population consists of the odd-numbered apartments from 1 to 29.

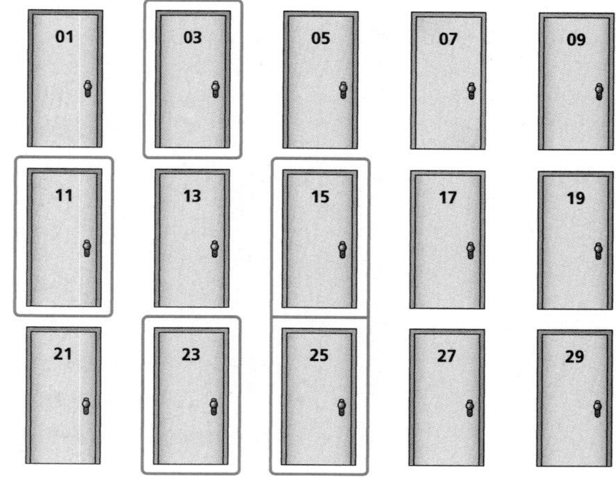

Random numbers can be generated with a calculator or a random number table. A partial table of five-digit random numbers is shown in the margin. To randomly select which columns to use, you could roll a die until you have two distinct values (not including 6). In this table, columns 3 and 4 were randomly selected so that two-digit apartment numbers could be represented. The digits in the square were then randomly

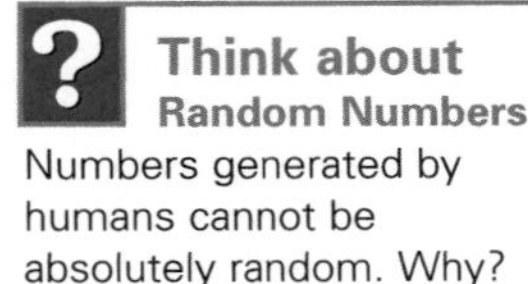

Think about Random Numbers

Numbers generated by humans cannot be absolutely random. Why?

selected as the starting point. Working down the list, each number that formed an apartment number from the population was noted. In this case, 25, 11, 03, 23, and 15 (ignoring repetition) were the apartments randomly selected.

Remember: A simple random sample requires that

- all selections must be *equally likely*
- all combinations of selections must be *equally likely*

Example 2 Systematic Random Sampling

There are 20 apartments (numbered 1 to 20) on Mimi's floor, and she wants to survey 25% of them. Develop a systematic random sample of the apartments on her floor.

Solution

Mimi must survey 25% of 20 units, or 5 units. To calculate the sampling interval, you divide the population size by the sample size.

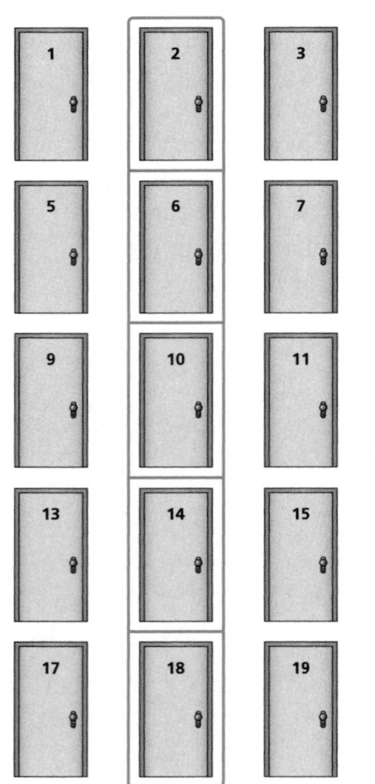

$$\frac{\text{population size}}{\text{sample size}} = \frac{20}{5}$$
$$= 4$$

This means that you must sample every fourth apartment. Mimi uses a four-sided die to decide which of the first four apartments she should start at. If Unit 2 is the random starting point, she would then select units 2, 6, 10, 14, and 18.

Systematic random sampling, like simple random sampling, has a random starting point, but it follows a rigid pattern, defined by the sampling interval.

Example 3 Stratified Random Sampling

The Canadian Multicultural Society was interested in urban Canadians' understanding of immigration's impact on the growth of their communities. How can they carry out a stratified random sample?

Solution

They could approach this by sampling and questioning residents in each of four large cities representing different regions of the country. In this case, the strata would be based on four geographic regions of Canada: the Atlantic provinces, Quebec, Ontario, and the Western provinces. Within each stratum, they would select the largest city and then randomly choose adult residents to answer their questionnaire. The number to be sampled in each city would be randomly chosen.

City	Number Sampled
Halifax	200
Montreal	300
Toronto	300
Vancouver	200

One problem with this method is that Toronto has 10 times the population of Halifax and is underrepresented in this sample. Section 2.5 will further explore avoiding bias in samples.

Example 4 Cluster Random Sampling

The Board of Education for the schools in Lincoln, Ontario, needs to determine parent/guardian opinion about offering summer mathematics courses for elementary school students. Design a cluster random sample the Board can use to select respondents for the survey.

Solution

From the list of five elementary schools in the region, the Board would randomly select two schools. (To do this, they would roll a six-sided die until two of the first five digits appear.). Once the schools are selected, the parents or guardians of each student are surveyed.

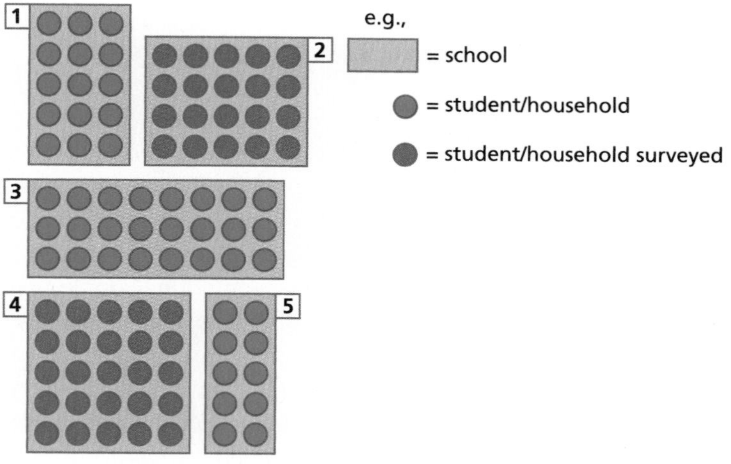

Example 5 Multi-Stage Random Sampling

A controversial issue in a school was the banning of all electronic devices from school property. The students' council responded to a few complaints by deciding to collect facts to present to the school administration. Students from the Data Management course suggested that, since this was a very large school, multi-stage sampling would make the most sense. What main steps should they suggest?

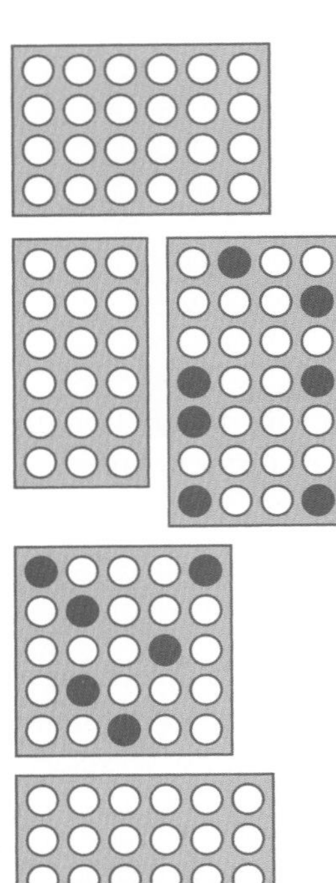

Solution

First, they analyzed how much could be accomplished by an agreed deadline given the number of students who could collect data. Their analysis showed that it was feasible to interview 240 students, or 10% of the student body. Because classroom populations vary (age, interest, and so on), they wanted to maximize the number of homerooms represented. However, the administration insisted that a minimum number of homerooms be disrupted. Thus, the students randomly selected 40% of the classes. They then chose 25% of the students to be interviewed (25% of 40% of the classes is 10% of the students).

SAMPLE SIZE: HOW MUCH IS ENOUGH?

It depends! First, the absolute size of the population will have an impact on the appropriate sample size. Furthermore, sample size is related to the reliability of the results. These are some of the factors that will affect reliability:

- the variability of the population (i.e., the more varied the people in the population are, the larger the sample needs to be)
- the degree of precision required for the study
- the sampling method chosen

In practical terms, the larger the sample, the better.

KEY IDEAS

random—occurring by chance; random sampling is used to minimize bias

random sampling techniques—

- *simple random sampling* requires that all selections and combinations of selections are equally likely
- *systematic random sampling* has a random starting point, but follows a pattern defined by the sampling interval; sampling interval is found by dividing the population size by the sample size
- *stratified random sampling* divides the population into groups called *strata*; a simple random sample is taken in each stratum
- *cluster random sampling* organizes the population into groups and then entire groups are randomly selected
- *multi-stage random sampling* organizes the population into groups and then a simple random sample is taken from randomly selected groups
- *destructive sampling* requires that the samples that are taken are destroyed in the process of testing (e.g., cars used in crash tests)

sample size—the larger the sample, the better. Some factors that will affect reliability are the variability of the population, the degree of precision required, and the sampling method chosen.

2.3 Exercises

1. **Knowledge and Understanding** Identify the type of random sampling in each of the following scenarios.
   (a) The principal randomly selects four classes and surveys each student in those classes.
   (b) William picks names out of a hat.
   (c) A hockey card collector opens a drawer of sorted cards and, after selecting a random starting point, takes out every fifth card.
   (d) The Ministry of Education randomly selects your school for testing, and 40 student names are randomly selected from a student list.
   (e) Your class submits solutions to a problem and your teacher divides the work into four piles by achievement levels (Levels 1, 2, 3, and 4). She or he then randomly picks three examples from each.

2. There are 27 students in your class and you wish to interview a random sample of six of them. Describe three practical ways you can select a random sample of this population.

3. State the advantages and disadvantages of each sampling technique listed.
   (a) simple random sampling
   (b) systematic random sampling
   (c) stratified random sampling
   (d) cluster random sampling
   (e) multi-stage random sampling

4. (a) Select 6 pages from this textbook using simple random sampling.
   (b) Select 10 pages using systematic random sampling.
   (c) Select 12 pages using stratified random sampling.
   (d) Select 10 pages using multi-stage random sampling.

5. Based on the following groups of names, identify a sampling method that may have been used to collect the samples listed in parts (a) through (e).

Shaggy	Paul	Joey	Susan
Fred	John	Monica	Elmo
Scooby	George	Rachel	Ernie
Thelma	Ringo	Ross	Oscar
Daphne		Chandler	Zoe
		Phoebe	Maria

   (a) Joey, Monica, Fred, Paul, Daphne
   (b) Susan, Elmo, Ernie, Oscar, Zoe, Maria
   (c) Shaggy, Scooby, Daphne
   (d) John, George, Ringo
   (e) Shaggy, Fred, George, John, Joey, Chandler, Susan, Ernie

B

6. **(a)** State a technique for selecting a sample of five students from your class using simple random sampling.
   (b) Use the table of random numbers or a calculator to select your sample. Repeat this process at least once.
   (c) How would you modify your approach if you needed a random sample of eight students consisting of an equal number of males and females?

7. **Communication** Describe the key difference(s) between a systematic random sample and a stratified random sample. For each technique, provide an appropriate example of its use.

8. Describe the steps you would follow to carry out a multi-stage random sample of your school to learn people's opinions about this year's graduation party. What issues would you have to resolve to ensure an accurate result?

9. Design a shuffling method for a standard deck of playing cards that selects a 13-card hand using
   (a) simple random sampling
   (b) systematic random sampling
   (c) stratified random sampling
   (d) cluster random sampling
   (e) multi-stage random sampling

10. **Application** The following is a list of serial numbers for four types of cell phones.

Model BL	Model BX	Model GB	Model GP
L501	X315	B771	P032
L502	X316	B772	P033
L503	X317	B773	P034
L504	X318	B774	P035
L505	X319	B775	P036
L506	X320	B776	P037
L507	X321	B777	P038
L508	X322	B778	P039

   (a) Select 12 phones using simple random sampling.
   (b) Select 10 phones using systematic random sampling.
   (c) Select 12 phones using stratified random sampling.

11. For Question 10, would it make any sense to select a sample of these cell phones using a multi-stage random sampling technique? Why or why not?

12. **Thinking, Inquiry, Problem Solving** For each situation listed below, identify which of the five sampling methods would be most appropriate and explain why.

(a) You require a sample of 30 students from your grade (which consists of approximately 200 students).

(b) There are 12 mixed (female and male) softball teams in a league and opinions are being gathered about changing the league's name and logo. To save time, only a sample of ballplayers may be interviewed.

(c) In a community of about 18 000 people, school uniforms have been proposed and an ad hoc committee of students wants to find out what the whole community thinks about this proposal. The committee can survey 150 people at most.

(d) There are about 3200 houses and apartment units in town and the community leaders have decided that a questionnaire about the recycling program should be conducted in 160 households.

(e) The city wishes to gather opinions on the plans to paint the community centre from this seven groups that use the building.

C 13. Do some research to determine what sampling method was used by the three polling agencies (Crossley, Gallup, and Roper) in the story at the beginning of this section. Why did this method produce misleading results?

Technolink
For help on performing simulations with Fathom™, see Appendix D.9 on page 423.

14. 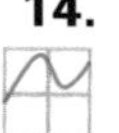 Use Fathom™ software to simulate the effect of increasing sample size on the accuracy of results for a given population. From a known population of 1000, take the different sized samples listed below and compare them. As the sample size increases, what do you observe?

first sample	25	second sample	50
third sample	100	fourth sample	250
fifth sample	500	sixth sample	950

ADDITIONAL ACHIEVEMENT CHART QUESTIONS

15. **Knowledge and Understanding** Daily production of brakes at an auto-parts manufacturer is 20 000 units. Suggest a sampling method that would enable the company to check the quality of daily production. How many items should be considered in the sample?

16. **Application** From a list of 100 Grade 12 students numbered 00 to 99, a sample of five is taken. For each example below, identify what sampling method was used. Justify your choices.

(a) 17, 37, 57, 77, and 97 **(b)** 05, 17, 52, 61, and 88
(c) 12, 34, 43, 75, and 90 **(d)** 21, 22, 83, 84, and 85

17. **Thinking, Inquiry, Problem Solving** All of the sampling techniques discussed in this section are examples of probability sampling where *all* members of the population have an equal chance of being selected. What is a non-probability sample?

18. Communication

(a) Explain the difference between cluster random sampling and stratified random sampling.

(b) Why do research organizations such as the Gallup organization use stratified random sampling when conducting polls for political elections?

Chapter Problem

Mystery Most Mathematical—Part III

```
Subject:  Re: Puzzle - Part 3
Date:     Saturday 04:55:41 -0700 (EDT)
From:     C=2*314159*?@homework.com
To:       jto@coldmail.com
```

`Suppose that you wished to determine if high school students' opinions about the quality of a movie are related to their gender or age. You only have enough time to carry out 60 interviews. Define the population for the study. Propose a sampling method and explain why you chose it. Make sure that you provide complete details about the procedures that you would use to choose the sample.`

jto@coldmail.com aside:
This is the third communication that I have received and I still haven't got a clue who is writing to me. Each time I have received a message, I reply immediately, but all my replies bounce back. The sender is clearly covering her or his tracks. There must be a pattern! It's so frustrating that I can't see it yet.

2.4 Creating Questions

Surveys are a very common data-collection device and can be conducted in a variety of ways: face-to-face interviews, focus groups, mail-in or telephone questionnaires, and even via the Internet. In all cases, however, surveys comprise a series of carefully selected questions.

In this section, you will be introduced to some of the key skills in questionnaire and survey design. Each question that is developed for a research-quality survey is tested, requiring the skills of a highly trained researcher. Although obtaining the services of a skilled researcher is beyond the scope of this course, you should test your draft questionnaire with students who will not form part of your survey sample.

primary data—data collected by the researcher

secondary data—data collected from other sources

Information you collect firsthand is called **primary data**. This type of data is easy to work with because you control how it is collected. Information obtained from similar studies conducted by other researchers is called **secondary data**. The results obtained from other surveys can be used in your study, or you can adapt the research questions to create your own survey.

One other consideration is whether to allow your respondents to remain anonymous. Often, respondents will be more forthright and honest if they are assured their identity will not be disclosed. Nevertheless, obtaining respondents' names allows you to confirm questionable responses at a later date, if necessary.

Finally, care must be taken when formatting your survey. If you want respondents to take it seriously, your questionnaire must look professional.

Project Connection
If you are using a questionnaire, have five or six classmates read it and make suggestions for improvement.

Every questionnaire must be handcrafted. It is not only the questionnaire writing that must be "artful"; each questionnaire is also unique, an original. A designer must cut and try, see how it looks and sounds, see how people react to it, and then cut again, and try again.[1]

SURVEY QUESTION STYLES

Open Questions

Questions that will be answered in the respondent's own words are open questions. This type of question allows for a wide variety of possibilities that sometimes are difficult to interpret. For example:

- How do you think most Canadians feel about the salaries paid to professional athletes?
- What is the most important issue for teenagers in your community?

[1] J. Converse and S. Presser, *Survey Questions: Handcrafting the Standardized Questionnaire* (Beverley Hills: Sage Publications, 1986) 48.

> **? Think about Closed Questions**
> How can you account for a wide variety of responses and still use a closed question?

Closed Questions

Questions that require the respondent to select from a given list of responses, or has an exact response, are closed. These answers are then easily analyzed; however, the options presented may bias the results. For example:

- Which of these statements describes how salaries for pro athletes compare to average Canadian wages?
  - ❑ much lower
  - ❑ somewhat lower
  - ❑ about the same
  - ❑ somewhat higher
  - ❑ much higher
- Which of these issues is most important for teenagers in your community?
  - ❑ homelessness
  - ❑ youth gangs
  - ❑ poverty
  - ❑ drug use
  - ❑ crime

SURVEY QUESTION TYPES

Information Questions

Circle the appropriate response.

(a)	Gender:	M	F
(b)	Age:	under 14	15 or 16
		17 or 18	19 and over

Checklist Questions

Which of the following sports do you enjoy watching? (Check as many as apply.)

- ❑ basketball
- ❑ baseball
- ❑ cricket
- ❑ hockey
- ❑ lacrosse
- ❑ soccer

Ranking Questions

Here is a list of concerns for teenagers. Please rank them in order of importance from 1 (most important) to 4 (least important).

- __ graduating high school
- __ finding a friend
- __ getting a summer job
- __ learning to drive
- __ choosing a career

Rating Questions

How satisfied were you with the DJ for the Valentine's Day dance?

- ❑ very satisfied
- ❑ satisfied
- ❑ dissatisfied
- ❑ very dissatisfied

Remember:

Good questions are

- simple
- relevant
- specific
- readable

Good questions avoid

- jargon (e.g., Are *ribbies* the most important statistic for determining batting success? Comment: *ribbies = baseball jargon for "runs batted in"*)
- abbreviations (e.g., On a scale of 1 to 5, how effective is the *CSA* in promoting space exploration to school children? *CSA = Canadian Space Agency*)
- negatives (e.g., From the list below, indicate which books you *wouldn't* recommend parents/guardians read to their toddlers.)
- leading respondents (e.g., Using the three-point scale, indicate your satisfaction with White-O, the most popular toothpaste in Canada.)
- insensitivity (insensitive questions belittle or insult individuals or groups)

KEY IDEAS

primary data—data collected by the researcher

secondary data—data collected from other sources

question styles—open questions (respondents reply in their own words); closed questions (respondents are given a limited number of responses from which to choose)

question types—information questions; checklist questions; ranking questions; rating questions

2.4 Exercises

1. **Knowledge and Understanding** Write an open question to collect the following data.
   - **(a)** the respondent's opinion on the quantity of homework assigned so far in the course
   - **(b)** the respondent's degree of preference for different musical styles
   - **(c)** the respondent's plans for post-secondary education
   - **(d)** the respondent's favourite type (genre) of television program
   - **(e)** the respondent's confidence in his or her swimming ability

2. Write a closed question to collect the same data as listed in Question 1.

3. **(a)** Create a checklist question that collects student opinions about their timetabled courses this year.
   (b) Create a ranking question that collects information about this year's student council.
   (c) Create a rating question that collects information about one TV program that your classmates watch.

4. Match each of the question types with an example.
   (a) information question **(b)** checklist question
   (c) ranking question **(d)** rating question
   (i) Please provide the following information:
   Gender _____ Grade _____
   (ii) Please provide the following information:
   Gender ❑ M ❑ F Grade ❑ 9 ❑ 10 ❑ 11 ❑ 12
   (iii) With 1 meaning *most helpful* and 10 meaning *not at all helpful*, rate each of the chapters of the textbook.
   __ Chapter 1 __ Chapter 2 __ Chapter 3
   __ Chapter 4 __ Chapter 5 __ Chapter 6
   (iv) Rank the chapters of this textbook by giving a 1 to the most useful, 2 to the second, and so on.
   __ Chapter 1 __ Chapter 2 __ __ Chapter 3
   __ Chapter 4 __ Chapter 5 __ __ Chapter 6

Criterion	Criterion Met Y/N
Simple	
Specific	
Readable	
Avoids jargon	
Avoids abbreviations	
Avoids negatives	
Avoids being leading	
Avoids insensitivity	

5. **Application** Assess each of following questions based on the criteria listed in the chart in the margin. Rewrite the questions where one or more criteria are not met.
   (a) List adjectives that describe (in an accurate and compelling way) the state of the environment and the extent of pollution in our province.
   (b) Should municipalities be responsible for water quality?
   ❑ Yes ❑ No
   (c) Should the OMB be funded to initiate waste audits across the province?
   ❑ Yes ❑ No
   (d) Given the large amount of sulfur dioxide that is spewed out of smelters, should mining companies be forced to clean up their act? Please comment.
   (e) On a 5-point scale, do you agree with the bleeding-heart Liberals that all corporations should pay higher taxes?
   (f) Why shouldn't forestry companies clear cut? Please explain.

B

6. Describe in detail the advantages and disadvantages of open and closed questions.

7. **(a)** What kind of data can be collected using each of the following types of question formats?
   (i) information questions **(ii)** ranking questions
   (iii) checklist questions **(iv)** rating questions
   (b) Provide examples of information that cannot be collected using each type of question listed in part (a).

8. Identify the question type that is best suited to collect the following information about the respondent.
   (a) name
   (b) birth date
   (c) favourite teacher
   (d) most difficult course
   (e) last major restaurant visited
   (f) type of computer at home
   (g) top three favourite books

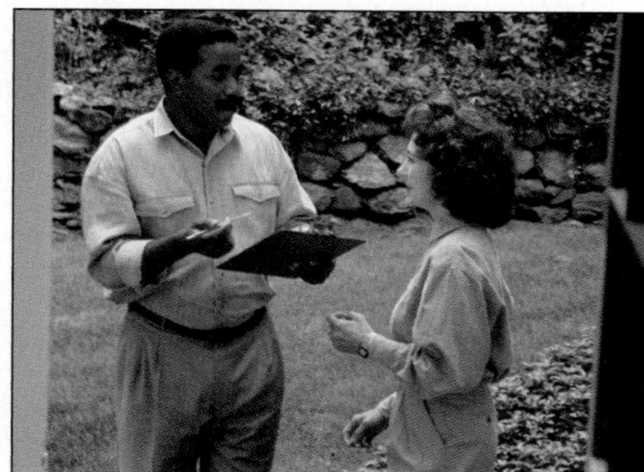

? Think about Question Writing
Remember that good questions are simple, specific, relevant, and readable. How good do you think these questons are?

9. **Communication** Create a questionnaire to determine the relationship, if any, between academic achievement and extracurricular participation. In your design, make the best use of open and closed questions in collecting
   (i) student data (e.g., age, grade, gender, and so on)
   (ii) student academic achievement
   (iii) student participation in extracurricular activities

10. **(a)** Create an effective rating question that gathers opinions from students about the quality of cafeteria food at your school.
    (b) Create an effective ranking question that gathers opinions about different musical styles.
    (c) Create an effective checklist question that gathers opinions from students about what activities to offer at a school fundraiser.
    (d) Create a questionnaire that combines rating, ranking, checklist, and information questions to collect opinions from teachers at your school about their favourite cars.

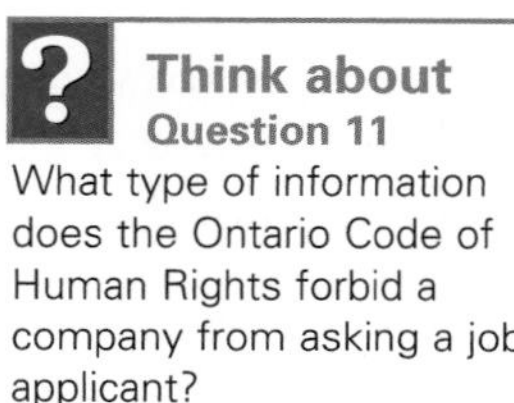

? Think about Question 11
What type of information does the Ontario Code of Human Rights forbid a company from asking a job applicant?

11. Olivia is employed by an insurance company and must design a questionnaire to obtain information about prospective customers' driving histories. What data will she need to collect to better inform her company's decision-makers about prospective customers? Design a clear, concise, single-page form to collect this data.

12. Answer the following questions for each of parts (a) through (f).

(i) Is the survey question open or closed?

(ii) If it is closed, is it an information, checklist, ranking, or rating question?

(iii) Is the survey question well-designed? If so, in what ways? If not, state why and then rewrite the question.

(a) You are presently in Grade (circle the appropriate answer):
9 10 11 12

(b) I find mathematics stimulating because:
____

(c) Rank the following foods from favourite (1) to least favourite (5):

_____ pizza　　_____ watermelon
_____ hamburgers　　_____ veggie dogs
_____ tacos

(d) Do you wear a wristwatch?

___ always　　___ sometimes
___ seldom　　___ never

(e) Name: ____________________

(f) Estimate your net income:

___ $15 000–$19 999　　___ $20 000–$39 999
___ $40 000–$59 999　　___ $60 000+

C **13.** **Thinking, Inquiry, Problem Solving** What follows is the referendum question that was posed to the voting public in the province of Québec on October 30, 1995. If the majority of Quebeckers had voted *Yes*, the Québec government would have had the mandate to take Québec out of Canada (i.e., Québec would have become a sovereign state). If they voted *No*, Québec would remain a province of Canada.

Do you agree that Quebec should become sovereign, after having made a formal offer to Canada for a new Economic and Political Partnership, within the scope of the Bill respecting the future of Québec and of the agreement signed on June 12, 1995?

Yes　　*No*

(a) Is this a clear question? Explain.

(b) Would this be a clear question if the voter had read the Bill, and in particular, the following sentence from that Bill? Explain.

We, the people of Québec, declare it is our will to be in full possession of all the powers of a State: to vote all our laws, to levy all our taxes, to sign all our treaties and to exercise the highest power of all, conceiving, and controlling, by ourselves, our fundamental law.

ADDITIONAL ACHIEVEMENT CHART QUESTIONS

14. **Knowledge and Understanding** Survey questions can be posed using different questioning techniques. Identify the four most commonly used techniques and provide an example for each.

15. **Application** The following questionnaire was developed by a beverage company that manufactures bottled water and soft drinks. The purpose of the questionnaire was to determine brand recognition and use of one of its products—Mountain Spring Water.

- How much did you earn last year?
- How many soft drinks did you consume last year?
- Do you drink bottled water?
- Do you drink Mountain Spring Water or an inferior brand?
- What is your weight?
- What product does the brand name Mountain Spring refer to?

(a) Comment on the clarity and the appropriateness of each question.
(b) Create a short questionnaire that is more suitable than the one given.

16. **Thinking, Inquiry, Problem Solving** Create a 5-to-10 question survey that measures the level of interest of your class in the physical sciences. The questions should reveal interest or lack of interest. Your inquiry could start by dividing potential reasons for student interest into different categories. For example:

- motivation (necessary for post-secondary program, a subject in which good marks are attained, career aspirations, etc.)
- inspiration (personal experiences, teachers, nuances of the subject, etc.)

17. **Communication** Explain the difference between primary data and secondary data. Describe a situation that involves the collection of primary data and another that involves the collection of secondary data.

Chapter Problem

Mystery Most Mathematical—Part IV

```
Subject:  Re: Puzzle - Part 4
Date:     Tuesday 12:05:28 -0700 (EDT)
From:     sqrt-1@homework.com
To:       jto@coldmail.com
```

Develop five questions that can be used to survey your classmates about their academic interests using at least three different question styles. Then, complete the questionnaire yourself.

Project Connection

Experimental Data

Researcher Jonas Salk

treatment group—the group that receives the drug to be tested

control group—the group that receives a placebo or the currently accepted treatment for the purposes of comparison

placebo—a treatment given to the control group that has no therapeutic value

double-blind test—testing method that guards against bias in data collection

Disease, in some form or another, has always plagued the human race. Owing to the development of vaccines, however, many fatal diseases have been virtually eliminated—among them smallpox, tetanus, and polio.

It was the early 1950s when Jonas Salk began testing his polio vaccine on humans. Because children in Grades 1, 2, and 3 were most vulnerable to the disease, Salk asked the parents of about 750 000 students if they would allow their children to participate in the study. Approximately 350 000 declined. Of the remaining 400 000 children, half were randomly selected (by a coin toss) as the **treatment group**; the other half became the **control group**.

The treatment group received an injection of the vaccine while individuals in the control group were injected with a **placebo**. This is a classic example of a **double-blind test**: neither the subjects nor the researchers were aware of which individuals received the treatment and which received the placebo until the results were compiled and the study was complete.

The table that follows shows the results of the 1954 Salk vaccine trial.

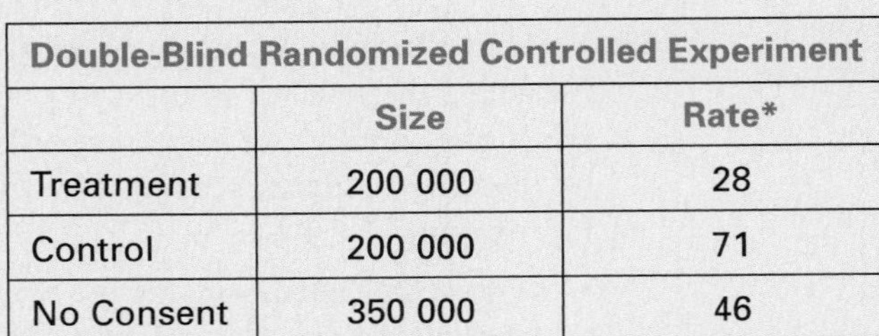

Double-Blind Randomized Controlled Experiment		
	Size	Rate*
Treatment	200 000	28
Control	200 000	71
No Consent	350 000	46

* Rate = number of polio cases occurring per 100 000 people

Clearly, the rate of developing polio was significantly lower for the treatment group than it was for the control group. Based on this evidence, the Salk vaccine was introduced to the general North American population. Polio has since no longer posed a threat.

Natural Sciences and Data Analysis

If your interests are in the areas of chemistry, biology, or physics, it is likely you have already been involved in gathering data from experiments. The data that are collected in these courses are generally physical measurements. Although the data are collected through experimentation, the analysis is fundamentally the same as techniques used in the social sciences.

Source: *Statistics* by David Freedman, Robert Pisoni and Roger Purves, W.W. Norton & Company Inc. (1978)

2.5 Avoiding Bias

In collecting data for your course project, the truth is your goal. To avoid distorting the truth, your data-collection methods must be carefully executed. In this section, you will explore how a researcher may unintentionally influence results, and you will develop ways to avoid **bias** in your research.

bias—an unintended influence on a data-gathering method

Example 1 Identifying Bias

You are the campaign manager for your best friend, Rebecca, who is running for student council president. You have been asked to determine the overall level of support for Rebecca among the 1500 students at your school. Design a sampling method that will provide the least **sampling bias**.

sampling bias—when the chosen sample does not accurately represent the population

Solution

To save time, you have decided that a sample of about 50 students will provide a good picture of the school's political landscape.

Plan A

Students have lunch in periods 2, 3, or 4. By random draw from a hat, you have decided to conduct the survey in the cafeteria during period 4. The first 50 students who enter the cafeteria are given the questionnaire, and you instruct them to fill it out and return it to you before the end of lunch.

What is wrong with this scenario?
A number of possible biases are built into this scenario. Quite often in high schools, lunch hours are populated by one or two grades due to timetabling constraints. This would result in a sampling bias.

The method by which the surveys were to be collected could also lead to a **non-response bias**. It is highly likely that only a few of the people who actually received the questionnaire would return it.

non-response bias—when surveys are not returned, thus influencing the result

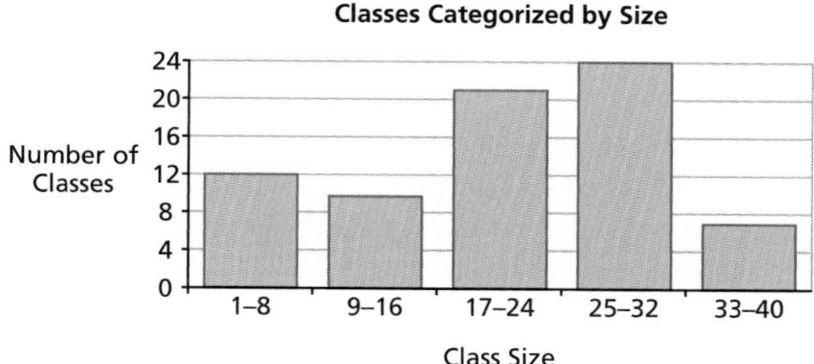

Plan B

To fix the problems with Plan A, you have decided to provide a questionnaire to one person from each homeroom (your sample size is now 73). You can wait until the respondent finishes with the questionnaire to collect it. This will eliminate the non-response bias.

What is wrong with this scenario?
Examine the graph to the left. Whereas 12 students would represent the opinions of, at most,

96 students (1 student chosen from each of 12 classes consisting of 8 students or less), only 7 students would represent between 231 and 280 students (1 student chosen from each of classes consisting of between 33 and 40 students). Overrepresentation of a particular group of students leads to a **household bias**.

household bias—when one type of respondent is overrepresented because groupings of different sizes are polled equally

Plan C

A stratified random sampling technique should be used to ensure a suitable survey of the student body. Students in each grade could be assigned a number. The appropriate number of females and males from each grade could then be selected by using a random number generator. The table to the right shows how a sample of 50 students could be selected to ensure that each grade is represented proportionately to its population.

	Females	Males
Grade 9	7	7
Grade 10	7	7
Grade 11	6	6
Grade 12	5	5
Totals	25	25

Interviews with each student selected would eliminate non-response bias.

Example 2 The Questionnaire

Consider the questionnaire developed by Rebecca's friends.

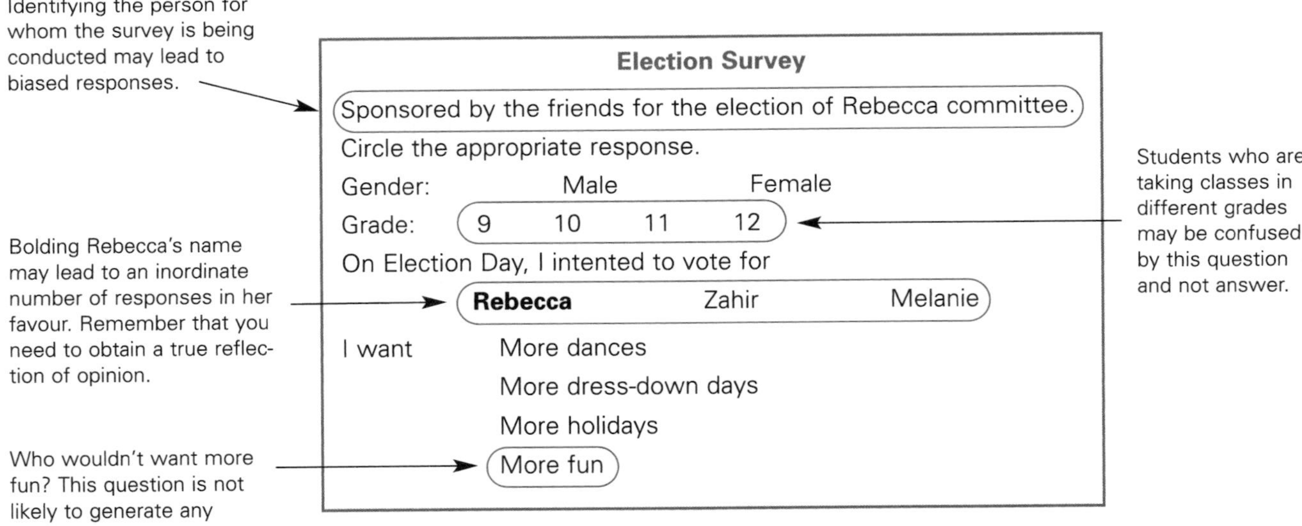

Identifying the person for whom the survey is being conducted may lead to biased responses.
Election Survey
Sponsored by the friends for the election of Rebecca committee.
Circle the appropriate response.
Gender: Male Female
Grade: 9 10 11 12
On Election Day, I intented to vote for
Rebecca Zahir Melanie
I want More dances
More dress-down days
More holidays
More fun
Students who are taking classes in different grades may be confused by this question and not answer.
Bolding Rebecca's name may lead to an inordinate number of responses in her favour. Remember that you need to obtain a true reflection of opinion.
Who wouldn't want more fun? This question is not likely to generate any useful information.

The questionnaire developed by Rebecca's friends shows examples of **response bias**. Poor question design (leading or unclear questions), interviewer tone and attitude, and extraneous information can all lead to response bias. Design a new questionnaire that would eliminate response bias.

response bias—factors in the sampling method that influence the result

Solution

The committee's identity is removed.

Every student has a homeroom designation (even those with spares in the first period).

Candidates are listed alphabetically and without bolding.

An open question is used to elicit unbiased responses.

Election Survey

Circle the appropriate response.

Gender: Male Female

Homeroom #: ________

On Election Day, I intend to vote for

Melanie Rebecca Zahir

It is my opinion that student council's priorities should be as follows (list up to three priorities):

1. ________________
2. ________________
3. ________________

KEY IDEAS

bias—an unintended influence on a data-gathering method

sampling bias—when the chosen sample does not accurately represent the population

non-response bias—when the results are influenced because surveys are not returned

household bias—when one type of respondent is overrepresented because groupings of different sizes are polled equally

response bias—factors in the sampling method that influence the result

2.5 Exercises

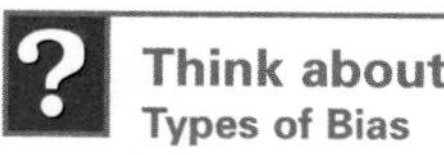

Think about
Types of Bias

- sampling bias
- non-response bias
- household bias
- response bias

1. **Knowledge and Understanding** Identify the type(s) of bias that might result from each of the following data collection methods.
   (a) You hand out surveys to your classmates to be returned to you next week.
   (b) You are interested in the study habits of Grade 12 students, so you interview students from your class.
   (c) You ask students about their recycling habits on behalf of the Greenteam, the school environment club.
   (d) You take a random sample of students during the second lunch hour to determine their attitudes toward the new school attendance policy.

2. Which of the following scenarios are examples of household bias? Explain. What type of bias might be shown?
   (a) polling random shoppers in a grocery store aisle
   (b) polling classmates about their holiday plans
   (c) polling random factory workers during shift change about banks
   (d) mailing surveys to people selected at random from the voters' list

3. Which of the following scenarios are examples of sampling bias? Explain.
   (a) A researcher selects people off the street for an interview.
   (b) A researcher randomly selects products off the assembly line for quality-control testing.
   (c) Traffic volume will be estimated by counting the number of cars travelling through an intersection during the researcher's lunch hour.
   (d) Books in the library will be tested for mildew by randomly selecting a shelf and taking every book off that shelf.

4. When a phone questionnaire is conducted, many people with call display will not answer their phone. What kind of bias does this represent? What can be done to minimize this kind of bias?

5. Identify examples of response bias in the following questionnaire.

Mega Mall Shopping Survey

Gender: ________ Age: ________ Date: ___/___/___

Which store did you visit today?

Sears   Becker's   Radio Shack   Pet Store

How much money did you spend?

$10 $20 $30 $60

Circle which other types of stores you would like to have in this mall.

Scuba-diving store   Sports shop

6. Modify the questionnaire in Question 5 to eliminate response bias.

Technolink
Visit the Stratford Festival Web site at **www.stratfordfestival.ca** for more information.

7. A Grade 12 class wants to develop a questionnaire to get feedback from the students on what to offer as part of a trip to the Stratford Festival. Create a questionnaire that collects the following data from respondents: their name, grade, and homeroom; whether they can drive and how many people they would be willing to take; the maximum price they would be willing to pay; what plays they would like to see (e.g., *Romeo and Juliet, King Lear, Pygmalion*); and so on. Remember to make the questions as closed as possible to make analysis easier.

8. A product research firm wishes to gauge public opinion on a new digital TV that it is demonstrating. Create a questionnaire to collect information from randomly selected people at a local shopping mall. Be sure to collect information about the respondent, including TV-watching habits, opinion of the digital TV display, and any other feedback.

9. **Application** A marketing company wanted to find the purchasing habits of Canadian university graduates. It contacted alumni associations to purchase their mailing lists. About 60% of the associations provided lists. The company sent a questionnaire to every person on the lists (approximately 600 000 names). Identify the types of bias that may occur in this survey. In each case, explain your thinking.

10. **Communication** The Canadian census is conducted every five years. The questionnaire provides instructions about when to fill it out and how to mail it back to Statistics Canada. The census representatives visit about 2% of households. Provisions are made to visit those people who are not at home or who may not have a permanent residence such as Aboriginal people living in Baffin Island before they migrate to their summer hunting and fishing camps. There are people who believe that a census is a great waste of money because the results will never be absolutely accurate and biases in the data collection will occur.
   (a) Identify all possible sources of bias in the Canadian census.
   (b) Provide both sides of the argument for a debate based on the following resolution:

   Be it resolved that the Canadian census is inherently inaccurate and costly; therefore, the Canadian government would be better served by gathering data using a carefully designed statistical survey of an appropriately sized sample of the Canadian population.

11. For each of the following questions,
   (i) state how it is biased
   (ii) write an unbiased version of it

   (a) Given that youth crime in urban areas is on the rise, what should be the top enforcement priority for local police forces?
   youth crime ❑ illegal drug use ❑
   car theft ❑ murder ❑
   other (please specify) ______________________

   (b) Rank the following sports by printing 1 beside the most enjoyable, 2 beside the second most enjoyable, and so on, to 10.
   ___ baseball ___ softball
   ___ fastball ___ cricket
   ___ two-pitch ___ basketball
   ___ ice hockey ___ lacrosse
   ___ shinny ___ ball hockey

   (c) You have ordered a brand new SuperDuper Triple Lutz Burger from a local restaurant and they want to know how good it tastes. Please check your rating.
   Scrumptious ❑ **Really Good** ❑
   Decent ❑ Bland ❑

   (d) Are you perfectly satisfied with your current vehicle? (Y/N)

12. Rewrite this questionnaire eliminating any sources of bias.

Student Survey of Environmental Support

Sponsored by the Greenteam

1. What is your homeroom? _____
2. On a scale of 1 to 5, to what degree is your homeroom teacher environmentally conscious?

1	2	3	4	5
Sort of		Medium		Wow

3. When you finish a can of pop in the cafeteria you
   (a) put the can in the recycling bin
   (b) toss it in the regular garbage
   (c) deposit it under the table
4. Your family saves water by
   (a) taking showers instead of baths
   (b) putting a brick in the toilet tank
   (c) washing the dishes once a week
5. You want to join the school environment club
   (a) a whole lot
   (b) if you had more free time
   (c) only for the Earth Walk event
6. Environmental topics should be addressed
   (a) across all curricula
   (b) especially in Science and Geography
   (c) in every mathematics course
   (d) all of the above
7. Your attitude toward improving the environment is
   (a) highly supportive
   (b) mostly supportive
   (c) supportive
8. Canada needs more toxic waste dumps.
   ❑ Agree ❑ Disagree
9. Based on the graph shown, do you agree that more adults are doing their part for the environment?
   ❑ Yes ❑ No

Environment Survey

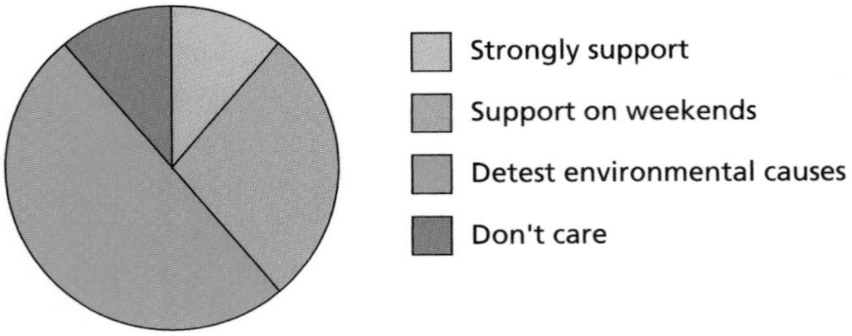

Strongly support
Support on weekends
Detest environmental causes
Don't care

Why do you think this is so?

____

____

____

C **13.** **Thinking, Inquiry, Problem Solving** Do you agree with the following proposition?

A law is proposed to alter the Constitution to establish the Commonwealth of Australia as a Republic with the Queen and Governor General being replaced by a President appointed by a two-thirds majority of members of the Commonwealth Parliament.

This is the question that all citizens of Australia considered on Saturday, November 6, 1999 (voting on a constitutional question is mandatory). If the people of Australia voted *Yes*, they would change their form of government from a constitutional monarchy to a presidential republic. A *No* nvote would mean the status quo. Is this question biased? Explain.

ADDITIONAL ACHIEVEMENT CHART QUESTIONS

14. **Knowledge and Understanding** Describe a situation that represents each of the following.

(a) sampling bias
(b) household bias
(c) non-response bias
(d) response bias

15. **Application** A publishing company wants to conduct a survey of college instructors to determine how many technology references should be included in a new mathematics textbook. Discuss the pros and cons of a voluntary online survey. Suggest another data-collection method.

16. **Thinking, Inquiry, Problem Solving** Bias in the media: fact or fiction? Do some research to find out whether bias affects the manner in which news events are reported both in print and on air (radio and TV). Write a brief report of your findings.

17. **Communication** Discuss the possible sources of bias in answers to each of the following survey questions.

(a) What is your age?
(b) What is your annual income?
(c) Which party did you vote for in the last election?
(d) What is your favourite type of program to watch on television?

Chapter Problem

Mystery Most Mathematical—Parts V and VI

Subject: Re: Puzzle - Part 5
Date: Thursday 15:37:33 -0700 (EDT)
From: 77777@homework.com
To: jto@coldmail.com

Choose the science area for which you have the greatest interest. Describe in detail the differences between how and what data can be collected from an experiment in this area and the data collected through the Canadian census.

Subject: Re: Puzzle - Part 6
Date: Sunday 19:01:58 -0700 (EDT)
From: 27182818@homework.com
To: jto@coldmail.com

The following questions appeared on a survey:

1. Given the great devastation created by global warming, including soil erosion, coastal flooding, and pestilence, would you support more tax dollars being directed to the ministry of the environment?
2. Good public schooling is critical for our children to become creative, tolerant, and productive adults. Would you support the government making this issue its top priority? Why?

Critique these questions and then rewrite them, if necessary.

jto@coldmail.com aside:
It strikes me as odd that these messages are sent at the strangest times of day. Maybe a pattern will emerge.

2.6 Secondary Sources

While all data are, at some point, primary, the vast majority of information used by researchers is secondary data. The only real distinction between the two is that with secondary sources, you do not have control over the data-collection techniques.

In this section, you will learn basic research skills to ensure that you end up with quality data. You will also look at some issues related to using the Internet as a source of data.

The time and money required to conduct primary research makes it an impractical data-collection method, particularly in the context of a high school mathematics course. Fortunately, there are reputable secondary sources that can provide the type of reliable data you may require for your course project. One of these sources is Statistics Canada (Statscan). The federal government mandates and funds Statscan to conduct a census every five years, and the vast quantities of raw data that Statscan collects can be accessed by the public. However, as a researcher, it is up to you to make sense of the data you acquire.

Technolink
Statistics Canada Web site: **www.statcan.ca**

RELIABILITY OF SOURCES

When collecting primary data, you must ensure that

- the sample size is reasonably large
- the random sampling technique is well-designed (simple, systematic, stratified, cluster, multi-stage)
- the questionnaires are designed to avoid bias
- the data is compiled accurately and experimental data is free of measurement bias

Technolink
A search of the phrase **link: www.nelson.com** on **www.altavista.ca** will give you a list of sites that have a link to the Nelson Web site.

When you obtain secondary data, you must check to ensure they are reliable. Find out the author's credentials, how up-to-date the information is, and what other researchers have cited the same data. Determine what bias might be inherent in the data-collection methods. Be especially wary of privately funded studies, which may put the interests of the organization funding the study ahead of public interest. Once you have established the credibility of the source, document key information: source name, applicable copyright information, when and where you accessed it (if it is a Web site), how the data were originally collected, and so on.

SURFING THE WEB

If you are unable to find suitable data in terms of quality or quantity using traditional sources, try searching the World Wide Web. Governments, charitable organizations, universities and colleges, corporations, sports teams, and individuals generate sites, which can be accessed via a computer and a Web-browsing program such as Netscape or Internet Explorer.

Web directory—a commercial service that provides key word searches that link to sites

search engine—a Web site that performs searches of the entire Internet

Data can be sought using either a **Web directory** or a **search engine**. In many cases, Web directories are preferable because the sites are pre-screened for quality. However, not all good sites are necessarily listed, and searching through those that are listed may take more time.

Whether you choose a Web directory or a search engine, be sure to structure your key words efficiently.

Example 1 Finding Information on Fractals

Use a Web directory to find information on fractals.

Solution

One of the most popular Web directories is Yahoo at **www.yahoo.com**. The following is a small portion of the initial categories and subcategories. (This information changes over time.)

Reference
Libraries, Dictionaries, Quotations...

Regional
Countries, Regions, US States...

Science Animals, Astronomy, Engineering...

Social Science
Archaeology, Economics, Languages...

Home->Science

First subcategory:

Libraries (33)
Life Sciences (18)
[Mathematics (1993)]
Measurements and Units (242)

Home->Science->Mathematics

Second subcategory:

[Chaos (27)]
Combinatorics (17)

Home->Science->Mathematics-> Chaos

Third subcategory (choose Fractals@ for a selection of sites with brief descriptions):

Computational Beauty of Nature, The—companion site for the book by Gary William Flake. Contains applets and source code for simulations of fractals, chaos, complex systems, and adaptation.

Contours of the Mind–Exhibition Page—celebration of fractal geometry, feedback, and chaos.

Fractal Explorer—simple tutorial on Mandelbrot and Julia sets with a nice image gallery.

Search Engines

Technolink
At the time of publication, these were the four largest "free" search engines:

Google
www.google.com

FAST
www.alltheweb.com

AltaVista
www.altavista.com

Northern Light
www.northernlight.com

Most people are familiar with using key word or phrase searches on the Internet. It is useful, however, to better understand what search engines do and then find out about how to use more powerful search techniques.

Search engine providers use Web "spiders" to reach out into the Web to find and collect data from

- titles
- content found in the initial paragraph
- meta tags (lines of text hidden within a Web page's HTML code)
- content from the entire document.

When a search is conducted, the "hits" are listed in order from the most relevant to the least relevant. Some search providers (e.g., **www.google.com**) use site-rating systems that are based on popularity (i.e., the ranking is determined by the number of Web sites that include it as a link), positioning the most popular site first. There are also metasearch programs (e.g., **www.metacrawler.com**) that will allow the user to search several providers simultaneously.

Some Advice Regarding Searches

- Words that are broad in scope may not be helpful (e.g., the word *Canada* will generate tens of thousands of hits).
- As you narrow your search, be on the lookout for words that may provide better results.
- Most search engines will allow you to limit your search to English sites only.
- Check through your search results thoroughly before trying again.
- Consider using some advanced search techniques to improve the quality of your results.

Advanced Search Techniques

query—a word or phrase sought over the Internet

Boolean operators—logical commands that instruct the computer in how to consider the search request (when used, they are entered in uppercase, or as symbols)

It is important to understand how a search engine interprets the **query** you provide. Two words separated by a space will be treated inclusively. That means that the computer will return sites that use one word, the other word, or both. Sometimes, this is not what you want. You may need to use restrictions or **Boolean operators** to find what you are looking for. Both are useful in refining a search to include only pages that relate to your topic.

Restrictions

\+ If you want a specific word to be part of your search result, a plus sign in front of the word (with no space after the sign) will restrict the search results to Web sites that include this word.

– A minus sign immediately before a word is equivalent to using the word *not*. It instructs the computer to disqualify sites that include this word.

" " Using quotation marks to surround a phrase will return sites that include the complete phrase as opposed to sites that contain each individual word.

Boolean Operators

AND (&) finds sites containing both words.
OR (|) finds sites containing at least one of the words.
( ) are used for grouping complex Boolean phrases.

domain—a subset of the whole Internet

Domain Restrictions

If you know the Web site, or family of Web sites to which you want to limit your search, use a domain restriction. For example, to search for the phrase *national parks* among all the Web sites that end in *.ca*, key in **"national parks" +domain:ca**. You can also restrict a search to a group of Web sites using the **site:** command. Searching **bruins +site:yahoo.com** will search for the word *bruins* among all the Web sites that end in *yahoo.com.*

Wildcards

By typing an asterisk at the end of a word, you can search for multiple forms of the word. For example, a query that includes **big*** will return sites that contain words such as *big, bigger, biggest, bigwig*, and so on.

Example 2 Advanced Internet Searches

Write the query for the following search requests.

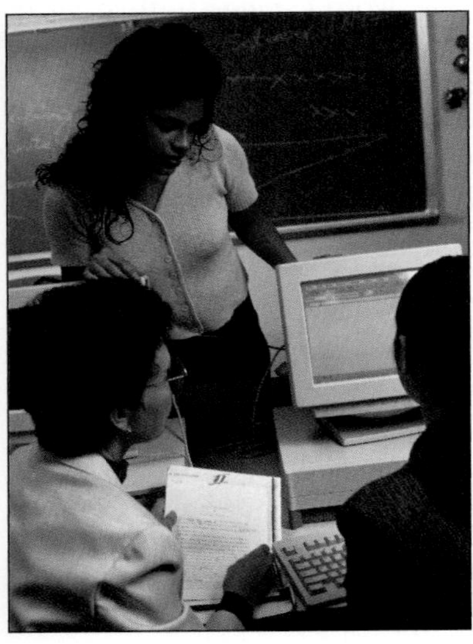

(a) Find recipes for chocolate cookies without chocolate chips.
(b) Find sites that include the phrase *The History of Algebra* in the *.org* domain.
(c) Find information on Lions, but not about the CFL's B.C. Lions.
(d) Find more information about peanut butter and jelly sandwiches, but also include *jam* as a possible synonym for *jelly*.
(e) Search for more information on bass (the fish, not the musical instrument, tone, or vocal register).
(f) Find biographical information on Gauss from somewhere on the Nelson Web site.

Solution

(a) recipe cookie +chocolate –chips
(b) "The History of Algebra" +domain:org
(c) Lions –(B.C. OR CFL)
(d) (Peanut AND Butter) AND (Jelly OR Jam)
(Peanut & Butter) & (Jelly | Jam)
(e) bass –music* +fish
(f) "Carl Friedrich Gauss" +site:nelson.com

KEY IDEAS

Web directory—a commercial service that provides key word searches that link to sites (e.g., **www.yahoo.ca**)

search engine—a Web site that performs searches of the entire Internet

advanced search techniques—
- restrictions: punctuation used to make a query more specific (+, –, " ")
- Boolean operators: words or punctuation used to specify how a query is to be treated (AND, OR, &, |, ( ))
- domain restrictions: restricting a query to only certain parts of the Internet (domain:, site:)
- wildcards: an asterisk (*) at the end of a word that is used to stand for all possible endings of that word

query—a word or phrase sought over the Internet

domain—a subset of the whole Internet

2.6 Exercises

1. Describe the kind of results each of the following search strings will generate.
   (a) Thomas Engine +trains
   (b) Gandalf +site:members.tripod.com
   (c) Sharks –hockey
   (d) Canad* +domain:ca
   (e) (Hot & Dog) | (Ketchup | Mustard)
   (f) "Slim Whitman" OR "Slim Witman"

2. **Knowledge and Understanding**
   (a) Explain the difference between a Web directory and a search engine.
   (b) For each of the following scenarios, indicate which service would provide better results: a Web directory or a search engine.
      (i) researching the history of Trinidad
      (ii) finding discussion forums on novels written by J.R.R. Tolkien
      (iii) conducting research on a brand of cell phone
      (iv) researching cell phones in general

3. Write a query for each of the following search requests.

(a) sites that sell CD burners
(b) sites with information about statistical software
(c) Canadian sites featuring literature
(d) sites with information about your high school
(e) the Ontario Ministry of Education Web site
(f) sites where you can download work from independent Canadian recording artists

4. Improve the following queries so that they will return more useful results.

(a) sites that contain quotes from Ralph Waldo Emerson: {Ralph Waldo Emerson +quotes}
(b) sites with information about the altitude of Mount Logan: {what is the height of Mt. Logan?}
(c) sites with historical information about the RCMP: {RCMP HISTORY}
(d) sites within the Canoe Web site (**www.canoe.ca**) with biographical information about Emily Carr: {Emily Carr site:canoe.ca}

B

5. **Application** For each of the following topics, provide what you would type into a search engine (e.g., using the symbols +, –, &, |, and " "). Try each one and record what the top two hits are.

(a) theatre in New York City
(b) refugees in Kosovo
(c) music, but not classical music
(d) player statistics for the Toronto Blue Jays and the Montreal Expos
(e) only Canadian mathematicians
(f) illicit drugs, not including heroin or cocaine

6. You are seeking information about municipal libraries in Ontario. In detail, describe your strategies to find these data on the Web using both a search engine and a Web directory. Write down each step in the process and a short description of the top Web site that is found.

7. Using secondary data, find three sources of background information and numerical data about each of the following.

(a) first-year university enrolment information (i.e., age of entrant, province of origin, country of origin, and so on)
(b) Canadian youth purchasing habits in the late 1990s
(c) temperature data dating back to 1900 from a variety of large Canadian cities
(d) television-viewing habits of Canadian children from 1990 to the present
(e) results from a local field hockey team

Be sure to record the Web address (URL), the date you accessed the data, and your evaluation of the usefulness of each source.

8. **Communication** Given the type of data and sources listed in each of the examples that follow, do you think the information you would obtain would be reliable or unreliable. Explain. Retrieve an example of the document (Web or library) to establish your case, if necessary.

(a) socio-economic data found on the Statscan Web site
(b) medical research found in the *British Medical Journal*
(c) crime data found in the *National Enquirer*
(d) archaeological information from the Royal Ontario Museum
(e) export data from the University of Western Ontario business school
(f) forest fire data from Lakehead University's department of forestry
(g) environment information from NASA
(h) used car sales data from **http://www.autobuyersadvice.com/**
(i) earthquake data from Encyclopedia Britannica
(j) water quality data for the Great Lakes from Pollution Probe

C **9.** **Thinking, Inquiry, Problem Solving** Use at least two sources to find information for the topics that follow. Explain what you would do to determine whether the information that you have found is reliable.

(a) the cause of the depleting cod stocks in the Grand Banks
(b) immigration patterns into Canada between 1945 and 1990
(c) the effects of famine in northern Africa since World War II
(d) teenage tobacco use in Ontario over the last 20 years
(e) gambling in Canada over the last 20 years
(f) the economic impact of war on the population of Bosnia

ADDITIONAL ACHIEVEMENT CHART QUESTIONS

10. **Knowledge and Understanding** Describe Boolean operators and what they are used for.

11. **Application** For each of the following situations, suggest two sources that could be searched to provide reliable data. Check to see if your sources produce the desired data. When you find two sources, decide which source has the most reliable data.

(a) the average income of Canadian females since 1960
(b) individual player statistics for the current Montreal Canadiens
(c) launch dates of the last five space shuttle flights
(d) the best-selling domestic car in North America over the last decade

12. **Thinking, Inquiry, Problem Solving** Find three examples of an article, report, or study, and decide whether each bases its conclusion on unreliable data. Find a reliable data source that could have been used in this situation.

13. **Communication** When searching for data from secondary sources, the reliability of the source must be taken into consideration. List several Canadian sources that could be considered reliable. What factors should you consider when judging the reliability of a source?

Chapter Problem

Mystery Most Mathematical—Part VII

Subject: Re: Puzzle - Part 7
Date: Wednesday 06:09:04 -0700 (EDT)
From: v=d?/dt@homework.com
To: jto@coldmail.com

Normally, a scavenger hunt requires the player(s) to find as many items as possible. For this one, choose only those five items that you find most interesting.

Use sources such as school and libraries, the Internet, local archives, post-secondary institutions, and city hall.

- the number of athletes participating in the first modern Olympics in Athens in 1896
- the average daily high temperature reading for July in Sault Ste. Marie, ON
- the dimensions of the Saturn V rocket that propelled Apollo 14 to the moon
- the female and male winners at the Wimbledon Tennis Championship in 1934
- the loss of life when the airship Hindenburg exploded over New Jersey on May 6, 1937
- the number of Rembrandts held in the collection in the Louvre in Paris
- the estimated population of China in 1960
- the number of goals, assists, and penalties in minutes for Maurice "The Rocket" Richard in the 1955/1956 season
- the amount of salmon (in kilograms) caught by British Columbian fishers in 1999
- the magnitude (on the Richter scale) and location of the largest earthquake in North America in 1992
- the number of road fatalities attributed to impaired driving in Ontario for 1995

2.7 Preparing Data

Data can be found in many forms. Once you find data, you must take them in the form in which you originally found them and then transform them into data that you can work with. Consider the following ways to store data.

SPREADSHEETS

Much of the data you will find will be organized in a spreadsheet. Both text and numerical information can be organized in rows and columns. Spreadsheet programs provide the user with an almost limitless number of formulas to manipulate data. Here are a few features of a spreadsheet program:

Technolink Help menus provided by spreadsheet software are very useful. For suggestions on using spreadsheets, see Appendix E starting on page 425.

Cells: Names for the positions where the data are stored. (e.g., A1 is the cell containing "Item")

Formulas: Calculations can be made within a spreadsheet using data in other cells (e.g., in cell D9, the formula **=sum(D2...D7)** is being used to sum the entries in that column)

August 31—Revenue for Sam's Hamburger Wagon

	A	B	C	D
1	Item	Price	Quantity	Revenue
2	Hamburger	$2.39	83	$198.37
3	Hot Dog	$1.59	29	$46.11
4	Fries	$1.19	117	$139.23
5	Small Drink	$0.99	32	$31.68
6	Medium Drink	$1.29	56	$72.24
7	Large Drink	$1.59	71	$112.89
8				
9			Total Revenue	$600.52
10				

TABLES (TALLY CHARTS)

Information found in tables or tally charts can either be raw individual data points or cumulative figures (see below).

Rolling a Four-Sided Die

Face Value of a Four-Sided Die	Tally	Frequency
1	~~||||~~ |||	8
2	||||	4
3	~~||||~~	5
4	~~||||~~ ||||	9

DATABASES

Databases facilitate the storage and retrieval of a wide range of data. Textual, numerical, temporal, and even pictorial information can be entered into a database. Databases can also be structured in many forms (e.g., standard, columns, or labels). Finding and sorting information are also key functions of a database.

GATHERING DATA

In some cases, you will simply copy or transcribe the data exactly as you find them. For example, a graph or a table presents data that have already been manipulated to a point where the researcher can draw conclusions. There are, however, situations in which you may need to use the data in a different manner. For example, if the graph is in the form of a scatter plot, you may wish to manually input the coordinates of each point into a spreadsheet.

Most data are available in one of several forms:

- raw data printed in tabular form
- spreadsheet data
- information in computer databases

For raw data in tabular form, you would transcribe them into a database or a spreadsheet. It is difficult to move spreadsheet data into a database efficiently, but information in columnar form can usually be copied and pasted into spreadsheets.

Spreadsheets offer a variety of useful ways to manipulate data. Formulas can be introduced into free cells to carry out simple or complex mathematical operations. For example, means, standard deviations, and correlation coefficients can be calculated automatically. Also, spreadsheets provide a method to create a number of different types of graphs, including bar graphs, histograms, broken-line graphs, circle graphs, and scatter plots.

Technolink For more information about importing data into Fathom™, see Appendix D.4 on page 418.

Fathom™, a dynamic statistics software package, provides you with opportunities to view and analyze data in unique and powerful ways. This chapter only addresses how to move data from an outside source into the program.

Example 1 Moving a Spreadsheet Into Fathom™

Take a spreadsheet and transfer it into Fathom™ for further analysis.

Solution

You can always type the spreadsheet into Fathom™; however, a larger file would become tedious. Since there are more sophisticated solutions that have less chance of introducing error, they are best even when the spreadsheet is small. Highlight and copy the cells you want to transfer from the spreadsheet program.

In Fathom™, drag a collection from the tool shelf into the workspace and then select **Edit ... Paste Cases**. You can drag a new case table from the tool shelf and drop it into the workspace. It will be automatically filled with the copied data from the spreadsheet. The data are now in Fathom™ for you to manipulate. Information in databases in column form can be copied and pasted into Fathom™ in a similar way.

Technolink
For a more detailed explanation of importing data from the Internet into Fathom™, see Appendix D.4, on page 418.

Example 2 Importing Internet Data Into Fathom™

Take university volleyball statistics from the Internet and transfer them into Fathom™ for analysis.

Total Number of Games Played					
Player Name	**#**	**Exhibition**	**Tournament**	**League**	**Total Number of Games Played**
Lana	1	6	56	47	109
Chiara	5	8	56	49	113
Sherri	4	4	24	31	59
Alison	11	8	50	45	103
Sarah	7	7	40	40	87
Lesley	2	7	39	31	77
Sam	8	4	30	25	59
Heidi	9	5	21	33	59
Carrie B.	6	4	13	11	28
Nicole	12	2	10	4	16
Carrie S.	10	4	12	18	34
Team Totals	—	59	351	334	744

Solution

Text data on a Web site are formatted for appearance and are sometimes quite difficult to make use of. Fathom™ is capable of making sophisticated adjustments to text data, making it possible to take a Web site and simply drag and drop it into your Fathom™ workspace.

Once you have Fathom™ running on your desktop, you can click on the Web page icon in the address box and drag it onto your Fathom™ workspace. Once you drop it there, a table will appear. You may need to rename attributes for each column in the table by double-clicking on the attribute at the top.

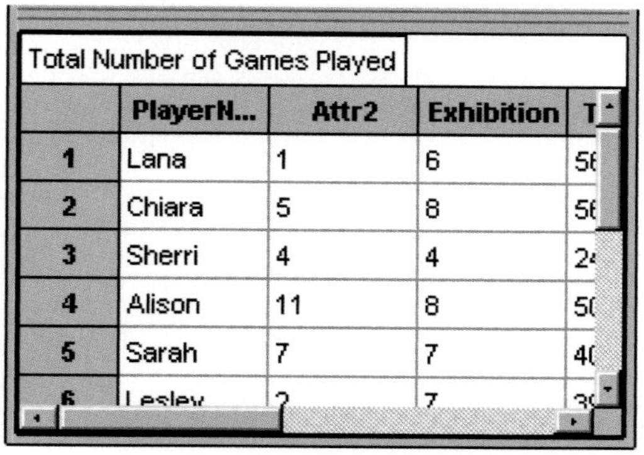

Total Number of Games Played

	PlayerN...	Attr2	Exhibition
1	Lana	1	6
2	Chiara	5	8
3	Sherri	4	4
4	Alison	11	8
5	Sarah	7	7
6	Lesley	2	7

When downloading data directly from Web sites into Fathom™, you must take care to compare the original data to the imported data. On occasion, you will have to clean up the data by relabelling attributes or making appropriate corrections.

KEY IDEAS

data sources—spreadsheets, tables (tally charts), and databases

importing a spreadsheet into Fathom™—(1) select the cells you want to move; (2) copy; (3) click on **Edit… Paste Cases**; (4) clean up data

importing data from the Internet into Fathom™—(1) drag icon from browser and drop into a Fathom™ document; (2) clean up data

2.7 Exercises

1. **Knowledge and Understanding** Brainstorm the most effective way to store and display the following data.
   (a) midterm grades for the entire class
   (b) favourite foods for your family
   (c) final scores for 12 hockey games
   (d) the new colour scheme for a renovated bathroom
   (e) RRSP contributions for 75 different clients of an investment broker
   (f) birth weights of six babies

2. Create a tally chart (using intervals 35–39.9, 40–44.9, 45–49.9, and so on) that records the following bolt measurements, in millimetres.

   55.1, 51.2, 48.2, 53.1, 61, 41.3, 45.8, 58, 63.9, 55.5, 51.9, 48.2, 39.4, 64.9, 52.4, 59.5, 45.3, 57.3, 50.7, 52.5, 64.1, 43.9, 57.9, 47.6, 41, 62.4, 36.4, 44.4, 61.1, 53.8, 57.8, 49.1

3. Use examples to show the differences between spreadsheets and databases.

4. Transcribe data from the following graph into a table. Record a population value for every five years starting in 1950.

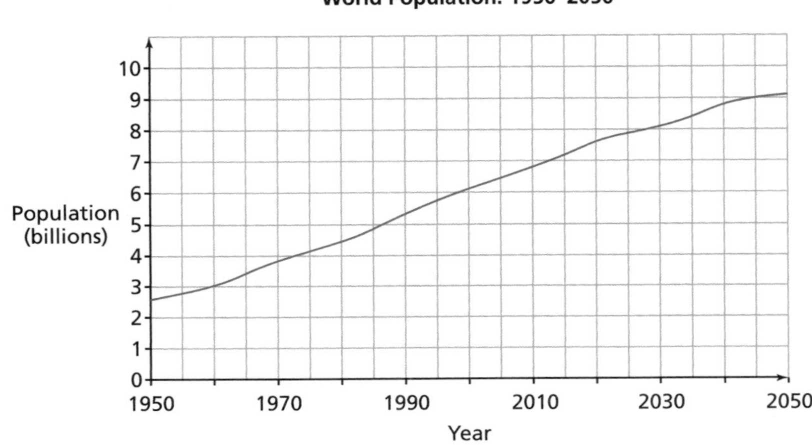

Source: U.S. Bureau of the Census, International Programs Center

5. Match each of the following sets of data to the graph that they form.

(a) 2, 3, 4, 5, 5, 5, 6, 6 , 7, 7, 7, 7, 7, 8, 8, 9, 10

(b) 1, 1, 1, 1, 2, 2, 2, 3, 3, 4, 6, 6, 6, 7, 9, 9, 9, 10, 10, 10

(c) 5, 7, 6, 8, 11, 7, 5, 6, 5, 9, 7, 5, 4, 7, 5, 7, 11, 4, 6, 8

(d) (1, 5), (3, 6), (2, 7), (5, 9), (3, 5), (0, 3), (7, 9), (4, 5), (6, 9), (1, 4), (2, 4), (6, 8), (1, 6), (4, 7)

(e) (5, 1), (9, 4), (8, 3), (7, 1), (8, 5), (5, 3), (9, 7), (4, 0), (3, 1), (5, 2), (8, 5), (6, 1), (2, 0), (6, 4)

(f) (2, 5), (5, 3), (8, 3), (3, 9), (7, 9), (1, 9), (6, 9), (9, 4), (0, 8), (5, 5), (2, 2), (5, 1), (7, 6), (6, 7)

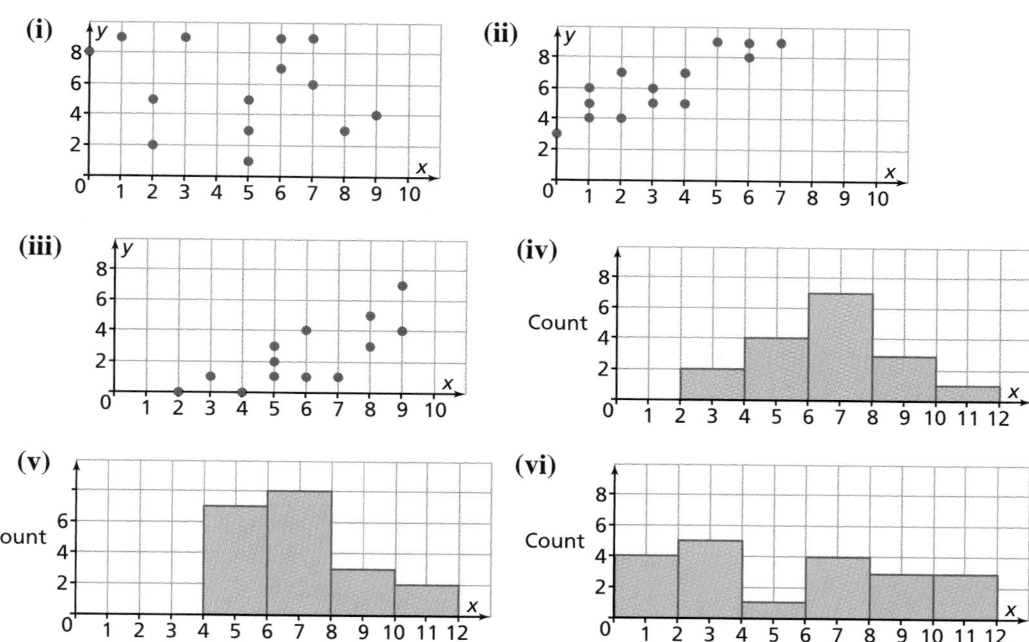

6. Estimate the coordinates of ordered pairs that are displayed in the scatter plot below.

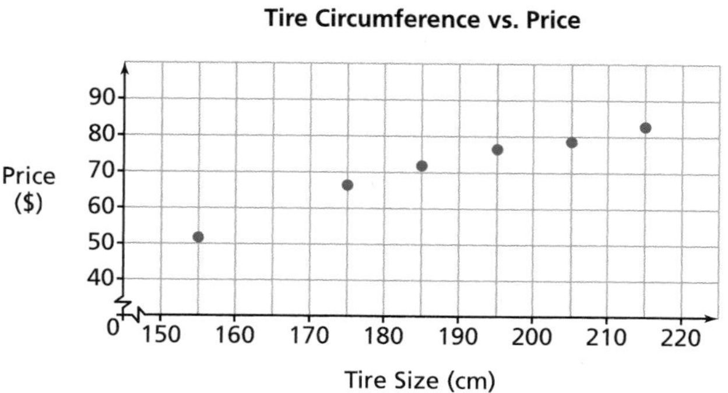

B

7. **Application** The following data are in tabular form.

x	12.3	13.8	11.9	10.2	15.1	13.2	14.6	11.5
y	7.1	6.6	6.4	7.0	6.9	7.4	8.4	6.9

x	13.7	11.6	14.0	15.1	13.9	13.5	12.9	14.2
y	7.2	7.5	6.3	6.2	7.4	7.6	6.8	7.7

Perform these operations.

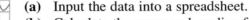

(a) Input the data into a spreadsheet.
(b) Calculate the mean and median for x-and y-values.
(c) Create a scatter plot.
(d) Input the data into Fathom™.
(e) Make a case table.
(f) Create a scatter plot in Fathom™.

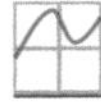

8. Search the Internet for data from a professional hockey team and import player statistics into Fathom™. Create a case table from the data, and then use a scatter plot to explore the relationship between points and games played. Make sure that you clean up the data where necessary.

9. Find Canadian census data about household incomes from the Statscan Web site. Import the data into Fathom™ and create a case table. Make three scatter plots representing relationships between three distinct pairs of attributes.

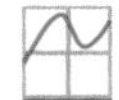

10. **Thinking, Inquiry, Problem Solving** Construct a database to record information about the thirteen South American countries. Create the following fields.

(a) country name **(b)** population
(c) land area **(d)** primary language
(e) major export **(f)** map

Use an appropriate *layout* so that you can import these data into Fathom™. Which fields do not import at all or must be cleaned up?

11. Using the classified section of a major newspaper, find eight or more ads selling a particular model of car. Record the asking price and the model year of the vehicle in a chart. Create a scatter plot of the data points that are formed and calculate the equation of the regression line.

Think about Question 12

How could you adapt this spreadsheet to calculate the profit from each day's sales?

12. Create a spreadsheet like this one used by Vern's Flooring.

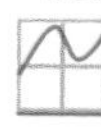

	A	B	C	D	E	F	G	H	I	J
1		Sales								
2	Item	M	T	W	Th	F	Margin	Price	Cost	Revenue
3	Textured Saxony	46					$3.80	$4.43		
4	Straight Set Saxony						$3.50	$4.10		
5	Plush Saxony						$3.75	$4.39		
6	Court Berber						$2.60	$3.07		
7	Destiny Berber						$1.90	$2.49		
8	Status Berber						$2.55	$2.84		
9	Solid Oak Strip						$4.70	$5.15		
10	Laminate Flooring						$3.25	$3.99		
11	Granite Floor Tile						$9.54	$10.45		
12	Marble Floor Tile						$7.25	$7.95		
13	Ceramic Floor Tile						$1.75	$1.95		

(a) Use the formula **=INT(RAND()*50)** in all the cells in columns B, C, D, E, and F to create a random number between 0 and 50 in each. This will simulate a week's worth of sales.

(b) Enter a formula to calculate the product of the margin and the total sales for the week, and enter it in column I.

(c) Enter a formula to calculate the product of the price and the total sales for the week, and enter it in column J.

(d) Create a graph that shows which day was the most successful.

(e) Create a graph that shows which product was the bestseller.

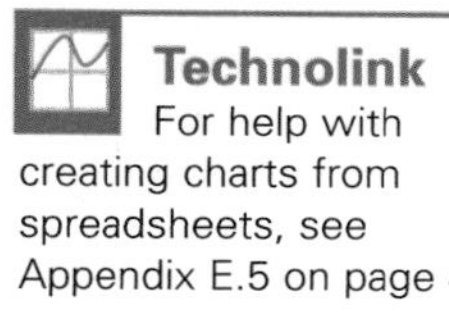

Technolink

For help with creating charts from spreadsheets, see Appendix E.5 on page 428.

13. Consider the following data returned by the Viking Lander from the surface of Mars in July 1976.

Sol	Temp (°C)	Sol	Temp (°C)	Sol	Temp (°C)
1.02	–78.28	2.06	–80.78	3.10	–82.51
1.10	–82.96	2.14	–83.03	3.18	–85.38
1.18	–85.40	2.22	–85.84	3.26	–83.73
1.26	–83.99	2.30	–74.29	3.34	–59.73
1.34	–58.94	2.38	–56.44	3.42	–44.93
1.42	–48.94	2.46	–39.73	3.50	–37.89
1.50	–34.26	2.54	–35.09	3.58	–33.39
1.58	–30.24	2.62	–26.86	3.66	–28.02
1.66	–29.10	2.70	–36.60	3.74	–51.92
1.74	–49.54	2.78	–52.38	3.82	–64.00
1.82	–62.88	2.86	–68.57	3.90	–71.83
1.90	–69.19	2.94	–72.48	3.98	–77.38
1.98	–74.56	3.02	–79.38		

Source: Project "Live From Earth and Mars," Dept. of Atmospheric Sciences, University of Washington – J.E. Tillman

Think about Mars

To account for the longer day on Mars (24 h, 38 min), scientists measure time on Mars in decimal form. Each day is called one Sol.

(a) Record the daily high and low temperature.

(b) Calculate the daily average temperature.

C **14.** The following graph displays temperature changes recorded by Viking Lander 1 on five consecutive days on the surface of Mars.

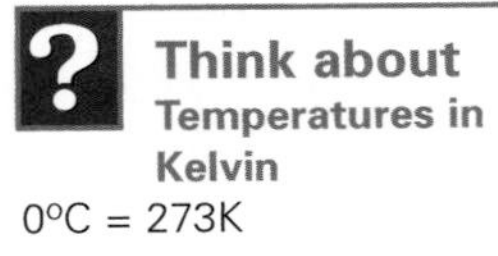

$0°C = 273K$

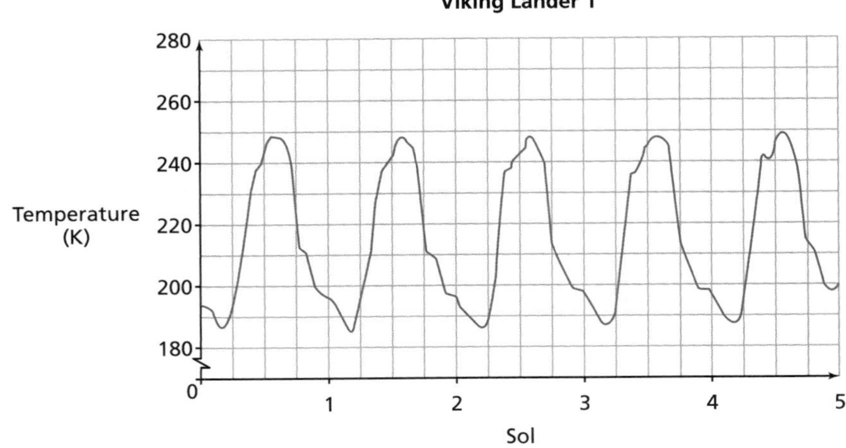

Source: Project "Live From Earth and Mars," Dept. of Atmospheric Sciences, University of Washington – J.E. Tillman

(a) Using the graph only, record the daily high and low temperature.

(b) How would you calculate the average daily temperature? Use your method and compare your results with Question 13(b).

? **Think about Mars**

Atmospheric pressure on Mars is about 1% of what we are accustomed to.

15. The following graph shows changes in the atmospheric pressure recorded by Viking Lander 1 on five consecutive days on the surface of Mars.

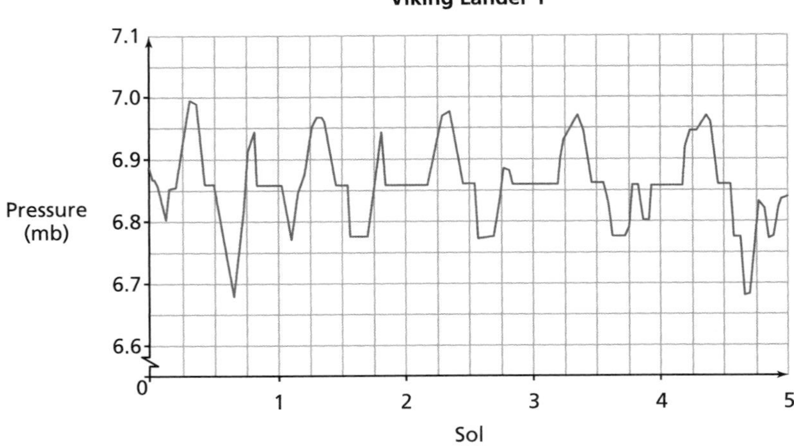

Source: Project "Live From Earth and Mars," Dept. of Atmospheric Sciences, University of Washington – J.E. Tillman

(a) Record the daily high and low atmospheric pressure.

(b) How would you calculate the average daily atmospheric pressure? Use your method to calculate a daily average.

Chapter Problem

Mystery Most Mathematical—Part VIII

Subject: Re: Puzzle - Part 8
Date: Wednesday 06:09:04 -0700 (EDT)
From: 3*cone=314159*r^2*?@homework.com
To: jto@coldmail.com

You have had much choice in selecting tasks in the first seven puzzles. Carefully review your choices to see if a theme emerges. In other words, do you tend to focus on broad social or environmental issues, science questions, or issues of importance to you and your peers? If you are having some difficulty in deciding upon a topic for your course project, this analysis might provide some clues.

By the way, have you figured out who I am?

Chapter 2 Wrap-Up

EXTRA PRACTICE

1. Antonia has completed her interest inventory and has five thesis questions that she could use for her project.
   (a) Study the relationship between television viewing and the academic standing of Grade 12 students in Ontario.
   (b) Study the growth of the use of lotteries by Ontario citizens in the past 10 years.
   (c) Investigate the relationship between socio-economic status of families and the highest level of education achieved by their children.
   (d) Study the relationship between the total payroll of a major league hockey team and its success.
   (e) Investigate the relationship between literacy rates and poverty.

   Evaluate one of these questions by identifying the variables and stating whether the data would come from primary or secondary sources. Can the data be easily measured? Identify any difficulties that you might have in gathering the data.

2. You are studying the impact of taxation levels on the smoking habits of teenagers in your community.
   (a) What is the population?
   (b) Identify the key variables for the study.
   (c) State whether each variable is quantitative or qualitative.
   (d) For the variables that are quantitative, state whether the data will be discrete or continuous.

3. Identify and explain five methods for choosing a sample from a population. For each method, state one advantage and one disadvantage.

4. For each of the following, decide which random sampling method should be used in order for the result to be unbiased.
   (a) choosing a member of the Olympic team to carry the flag
   (b) selecting someone from your school for the hockey skills competition
   (c) selecting a bank teller to take a customer service course

5. Would you use a sample or the entire population to collect data to answer the following questions? Why?
   (a) Are the apples in your orchard ripe?
   (b) How many of 800 new TVs are defective?
   (c) You purchased 2000 cases of grapes to make juice. Are the grapes sweet enough?

6. Lorraine has been asked by a local car dealership to conduct a survey that will find the typical amount of time that a prospective buyer spends purchasing a new vehicle.
   (a) What is the population for Lorraine's survey?
   (b) Describe a sampling method that will obtain a representative sample of 200 people.

7. About 3.6% of Canada's population lives in Saskatchewan. Suppose you want to find the popularity of the federal government across Canada.
   (a) How many people from across the country do you think you should sample? Why?
   (b) How many people should you select from Saskatchewan?

8. Discuss the possible sources of bias in answers to the following survey questions.
   (a) What is the value of RRSPs that you own?
   (b) At the last federal election, which party did you vote for?

9. Write the query for the following Internet search requests.
   (a) Find information on blue jays, but not about the Toronto Blue Jays.
   (b) Find more information about music, but not jazz or rock and roll.

10. Search the Internet for data from a professional baseball team and import player statistics into Fathom™. Create a case table from the data, and then use a scatter plot to explore the relationship between hits and the number of at-bats. Make sure that you clean up the data where necessary.

Chapter 2 Test

1. An experiment is done to study how long it takes water to evaporate. Thin layers of water are spread on a surface, and the surface area and time it takes for each pool to evaporate at different temperatures are recorded.

Surface area (cm^2)	10	10	10	15	15	15	20	20	20
Temperature (°C)	10	20	30	10	20	30	10	20	30
Time (min)	20	10	5	5	2.5	1.25	1.25	0.625	0.3125

   (a) What factors influence the time it takes a sample of water to evaporate? Use a mind map to help you.
   (b) Arrange the table to show how the time it takes for water to evaporate depends on the temperature of the water.

2. Which of the five random sampling methods would you choose to collect data about the following?
   (a) time needed to scan and pay for one bag of groceries
   (b) popularity of a new musical artist
   (c) length of time Canadians keep their cars
   (d) quality of sausages processed in a meat plant
   (e) quality of parachutes manufactured

3. Explain the differences between doing an Internet search using a Web directory and doing a search with a search engine.

4. You are designing a questionnaire on a topic of your choice. Create one example for each of the following types of questions.
   (a) open question **(b)** closed question **(c)** rating question
   (d) ranking question **(e)** checklist question

5. You wish to conduct a survey among Grade 9 and 10 students to determine their attitudes toward junk foods with respect to their overall diets. Create four questions that are biased and explain why each question is biased. Then, rewrite each of your questions to eliminate any source of bias.

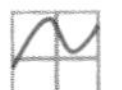

6. Transcribe the following data just as you see it into a Fathom™ document. Create a scatter plot where *Magnitude* is on the vertical axis and *Average Annually* is on the horizontal axis. What is wrong with the scatter plot you created? What do you need to do to clean up the data?

	A	B	C	D
1	Descriptor	Magnitude	Average Annually	
2				
3	Great	8 and higher	1	
4	Major	7 – 7.9	18	
5	Strong	6 – 6.9	120	
6	Moderate	5 – 5.9	800	
7	Light	4 – 4.9	6200	estimated
8	Minor	3 – 3.9	49000	estimated
9	Very Minor	2 – 2.9	1000 per day	estimated
10		1 – 1.9	8000 per day	estimated

3 Tools for Analyzing Data

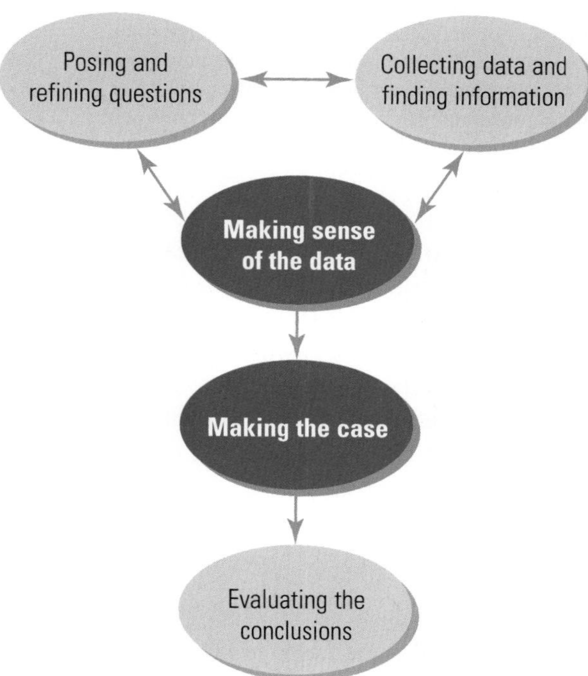

Descriptive statistics is the branch of mathematics that describes a data set using visual displays such as graphs and numbers. It is often useful to summarize large data sets in order to make comparisons upon which decisions will be based. For naturally occurring data, you may want to determine how one piece of data compares to the rest.

While many of the measures you will investigate will be familiar to you, this chapter will deepen your understanding of these measures and make them applicable to your course project.

In this chapter, you will

- create histograms and bar graphs for quantitative information
- determine and interpret the measures of central tendency, deviation, and indices based on a data set
- use normal distribution to describe a population and to make comparisons between one value and the rest of the normal distribution

Chapter Problem

Comparing Marks

The *Maclean's Guide* to Canadian Universities and Colleges 2001

The University Crunch

By Ann Dowsett Johnston

Two years ago, the wave began to roll. Canadian universities witnessed their largest one-year jump in enrolment since 1991; last year, enrolment rose again. How high will the demand run over the next decade? A conservative estimate would be a 20% increase across Canada. In British Columbia and Ontario, it will run as high as 40%. "We're on the verge of the greatest growth in more than 30 years," says Ken Snowdon, vice-president of policy and analysis at the Council of Ontario Universities.

Justin is a Grade 12 student planning to go to university next year. He has studied hard and is proud of his overall average of 82%. However, Justin is uncertain of where he stands in relation to other classmates applying to university. By using his understanding of statistics, Justin hopes to determine his chances of being accepted into the university of his choice.

Here is a list of the average marks of all the Grade 12 students in Justin's school who are applying to university.

75	72	76	63	64	66	70	82	76	72
53	48	81	77	64	79	71	75	78	72
78	67	63	90	87	77	75	70	59	75
76	78	55	74	71	73	69	85	63	54

You may already know of some statistical methods you can use to begin analyzing Justin's situation. What initial observations can you make, given this table of 40 values?

Project Connection

Your course project requires you to work with large sets of data. In order for you to answer your project-specific questions, you will have to summarize the data in a variety of ways.

If your project features normally distributed data, you will learn how to compare one piece of data to the population.

3.1 Graphical Displays of Information

With all the data available today, it is important to be able to filter out the unnecessary data and to present the useful data in an accessible format. One of the best formats for presenting data is a graph or other visual display.

In this section, you will discover some important considerations when choosing, designing, and interpreting a graphic image representing quantitative data, such as Charles Minard's classic depiction of Napoleon's march to Moscow in 1812 and subsequent return (shown below). The thickness of the band represents the size of his army.

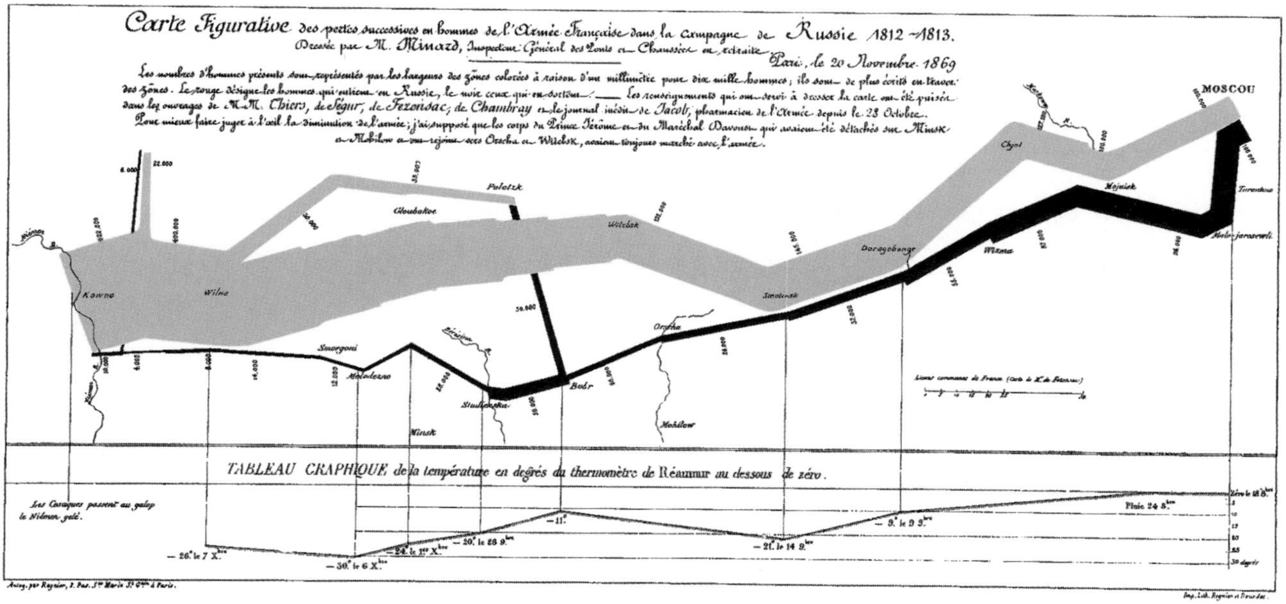

DATA TABLES

Richter Scale—a logarithmic scale used to measure the magnitude of earthquakes

Earthquakes are measured on a scale known as the **Richter Scale**. There data are a sample of earthquake magnitudes in Canada between 1960 and 1965.

5.0	5.0	6.4	5.0	6.0	5.6	6.5	6.5	5.0	5.5
6.4	7.2	5.0	5.7	5.6	5.0	5.0	5.0	5.0	5.7
5.0	7.0	5.5	5.2	4.6	6.3	7.2	6.0	5.4	5.8
6.0	5.7	6.5	5.0	5.7	5.0	5.6	6.0	5.6	6.2

Source: United States Geological Survey, National Earthquake Information Center

The table form makes it difficult to do any analysis beyond determining the mildest and most severe earthquake. To make more sense of the data, you need to sort the magnitudes into groups or classes and count the number of earthquakes that fall into each class. A histogram, unlike a bar graph, often contains continuous data like this, grouped in class (frequency) intervals, displaying how they are spread over a specified range.

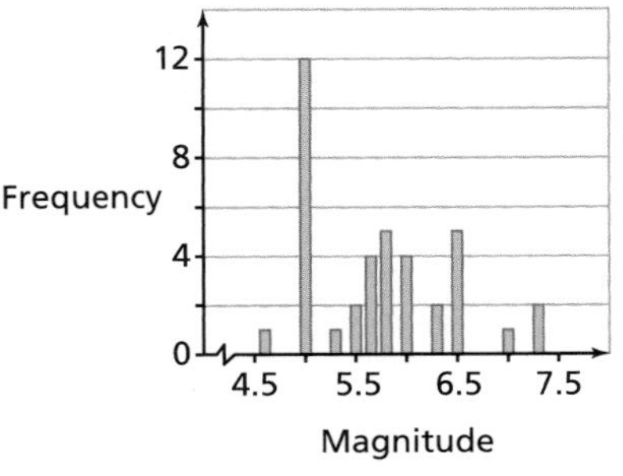

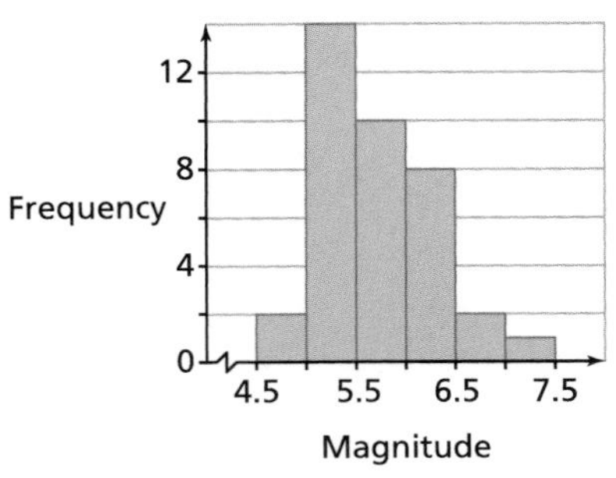

bin width—the width of each interval in a histogram

The width of each bar is known as the **bin width**. Different bin widths will produce different results. A small bin width may result in a histogram that does not effectively summarize the distribution (too many small bars). Bin widths should be set so that they are equal, and there should be at least five intervals in the data set so that a representative display is achieved. If a bin width has a frequency of zero, no bar will appear and it no longer looks like a histogram.

Example 1 Creating Effective Histograms

Create an effective histogram of the earthquake data.

Solution 1 *No technology required*

When creating a histogram by hand, determine a bin width that will provide a display that accurately summarizes the distribution of the data.

The range that must be covered is $7.2 - 4.6 = 2.6$, which could be rounded up to 3. Since 6 divides the range nicely, use a bin width of 0.5, as follows:

$$\begin{aligned} \textit{Bin width} &= \frac{\textit{range}}{\textit{number of intervals}} \\ &= \frac{3.0}{6} \text{ or } 0.5 \end{aligned}$$

? Think about Bin Widths
Make sure that you do not use intervals that will allow one piece of data to be in two intervals. Why is this?

To ensure no piece of data lies on the borderline between two intervals, make the intervals 4.35–4.85, 4.85–5.35, 5.35–5.85, 5.85–6.35, 6.35–6.85, and 6.85–7.35. Then, create a frequency distribution in which you record the number of pieces of data that falls into each class interval. Draw the resulting histogram.

Frequency Distribution

Class	Tally	Frequency
4.35–4.85	|	1
4.85–5.35	~~||||~~ ~~||||~~ |||	13
5.35–5.85	~~||||~~ ~~||||~~ ||	12
5.85–6.35	~~||||~~ |	6
6.35–6.85	~~||||~~	5
6.85–7.35	|||	3

Magnitude of Canadian Earthquakes, 1960–1965

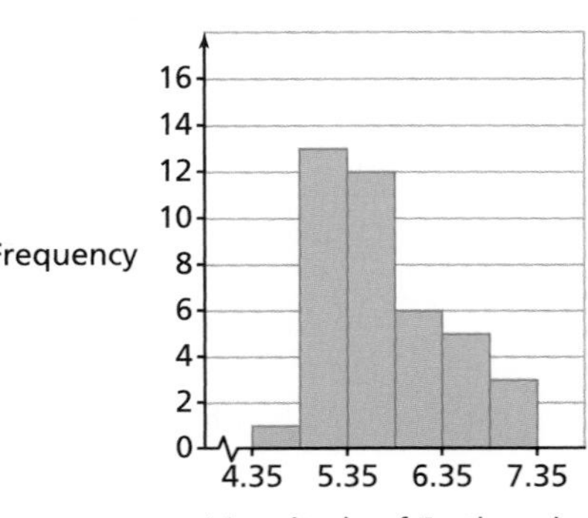

Solution 2 *Using a TI-83 Plus calculator*

Enter the data into L_1 and press [2nd] [Y=] [ENTER] to set up **Plot 1** as shown. Be sure to select the histogram icon.

Technolink
See Appendix C.6 on page 405 for more information on creating histograms with a TI-83 Plus calculator.

Press [ZOOM] and choose **9:ZoomStat**. The calculator determines an appropriate bin width and organizes the data into these class intervals. The [TRACE] button will allow you to check the intervals and frequencies from the data using the arrow keys.

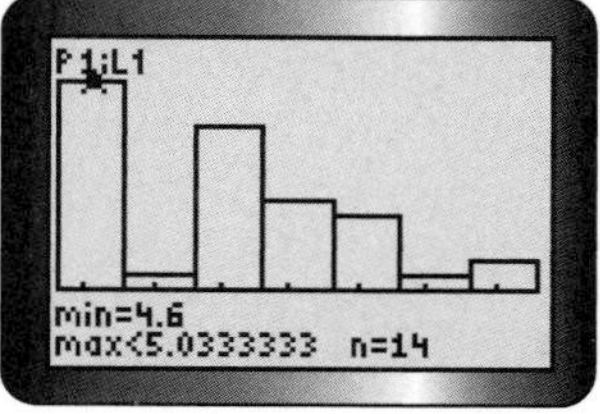

Solution 3 *Using Fathom™*

To create a histogram using Fathom™, enter the earthquake data into a new **Case Table**. Drag a new graph into the Fathom™ document and drag the attribute "magnitude" over to the horizontal axis of the graph. Change the graph type in the upper-right corner to **Histogram**. You can change the bin width by dragging the edges of a bin or by double-clicking on the graph and manually entering the values in the graph information dialogue.

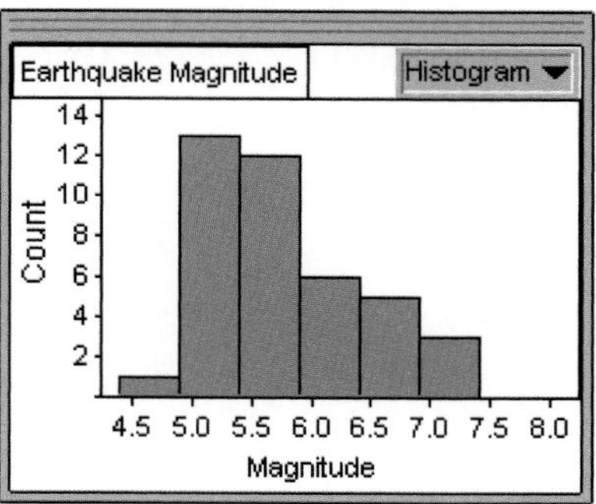

Technolink
See Appendix D.8 on page 422 for more information on creating histograms with Fathom™.

DISTRIBUTION OF DATA

A frequency distribution is categorized by the general shape of its corresponding histogram. Typically, it is described in one of four ways.

Gillian plays a number of different games in her spare time. The following frequency distributions list samples of her scores. Each one of these samples represents a different type of distribution.

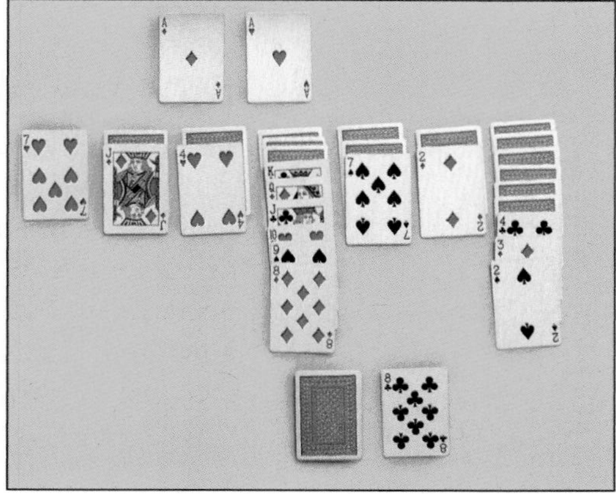

bimodal—a distribution that has two peaks

U-SHAPED DISTRIBUTION

A U-shaped distribution occurs when there are peaks at either end of the range. It may also be described as a **bimodal** distribution. The scores from the game of spider solitaire form this type of distribution.

Spider Solitaire Scores

Frequency

Score

Spider Solitaire

Score	400–449	450–499	500–549	550–599	600–649	650–699	700–749	750–799	800–849
Frequency	15	10	6	4	0	4	6	10	15

UNIFORM DISTRIBUTION

When each outcome has a similar frequency, it is called a uniform distribution. The height of each bar is roughly equal. This is the distribution you would expect from an experiment such as rolling a die.

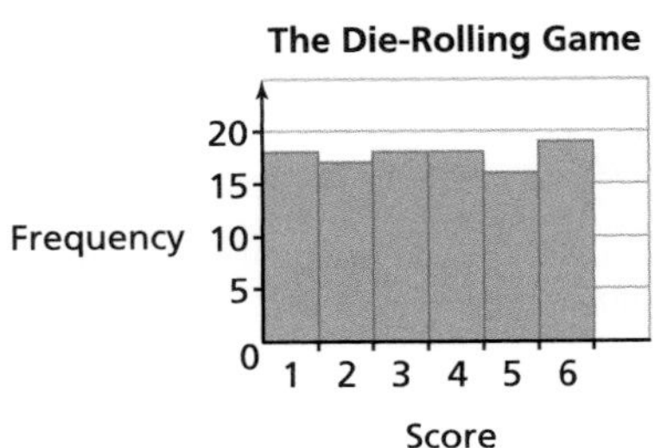

The Die-Rolling Game

Score	1	2	3	4	5	6
Frequency	18	17	18	18	16	19

MOUND-SHAPED DISTRIBUTIONS

In this distribution, there is an interval with the greatest frequency, and the frequencies of all other intervals decrease on either side of that. The frequency distribution then takes on a mound shape. Rolling a pair of dice and recording the sum results in this type of distribution.

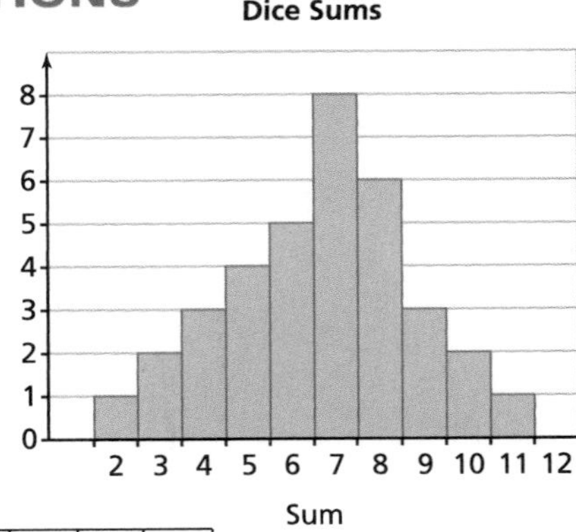

Dice Sums

Sum	2	3	4	5	6	7	8	9	10	11	12
Frequency	1	2	3	4	5	8	6	3	2	1	0

symmetric distribution—when the data show a mirror symmetry about the centre

Each of these three distributions is **symmetric**.

? Think about Skewed Distributions

What does the shape of the distribution say about your likelihood of achieving a high score?

SKEWED DISTRIBUTIONS

In a skewed distribution, the interval or group of intervals that contains the greatest frequencies is near one end of the histogram. As a result, these distributions seem to tail off to the left or right. The direction of the skew is determined by the direction the mean has shifted. This will be discussed in detail in Section 3.2.) Scores from a game of solitaire produce a distribution that is skewed to the right (right-skewed).

Solitaire

Score	0–19	20–39	40–59	60–79	80–99	100–119	120–139	140–159
Frequency	20	15	12	7	5	2	1	1

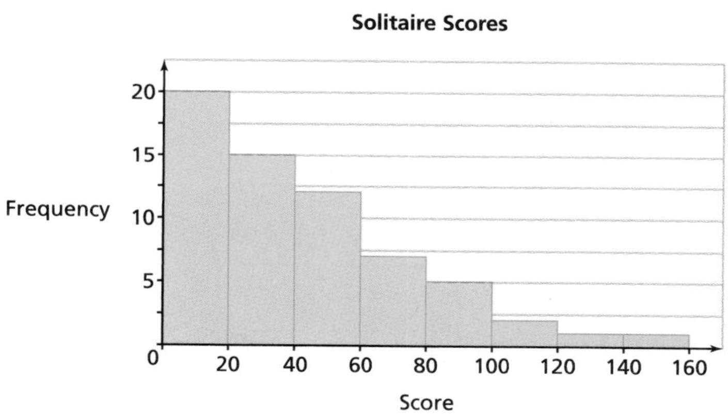

? Think about Symmetric Distributions

Explain why uniform, mound-shaped, and U-shaped distributions are also referred to as symmetric distributions.

KEY IDEAS

bin width—calculated as $\frac{range}{number\ of\ intervals}$; changing bin width may have a dramatic effect on the interpretation of data

U-shaped distribution—peaks at either end of the range; can be described as bimodal

uniform distribution—each outcome has a similar frequency

mound-shaped distribution—symmetrical about a line passing through the interval with the greatest frequency

symmetric distribution—shows mirror symmetry about the centre (e.g., uniform, U-shaped, and mound-shaped distributions)

skewed distribution—an assymetrical distribution where the direction denotes skew type (right-skewed, left-skewed)

3.1 Exercises

A

1. **Knowledge and Understanding** Describe each of the distributions that follows using the vocabulary of this section.

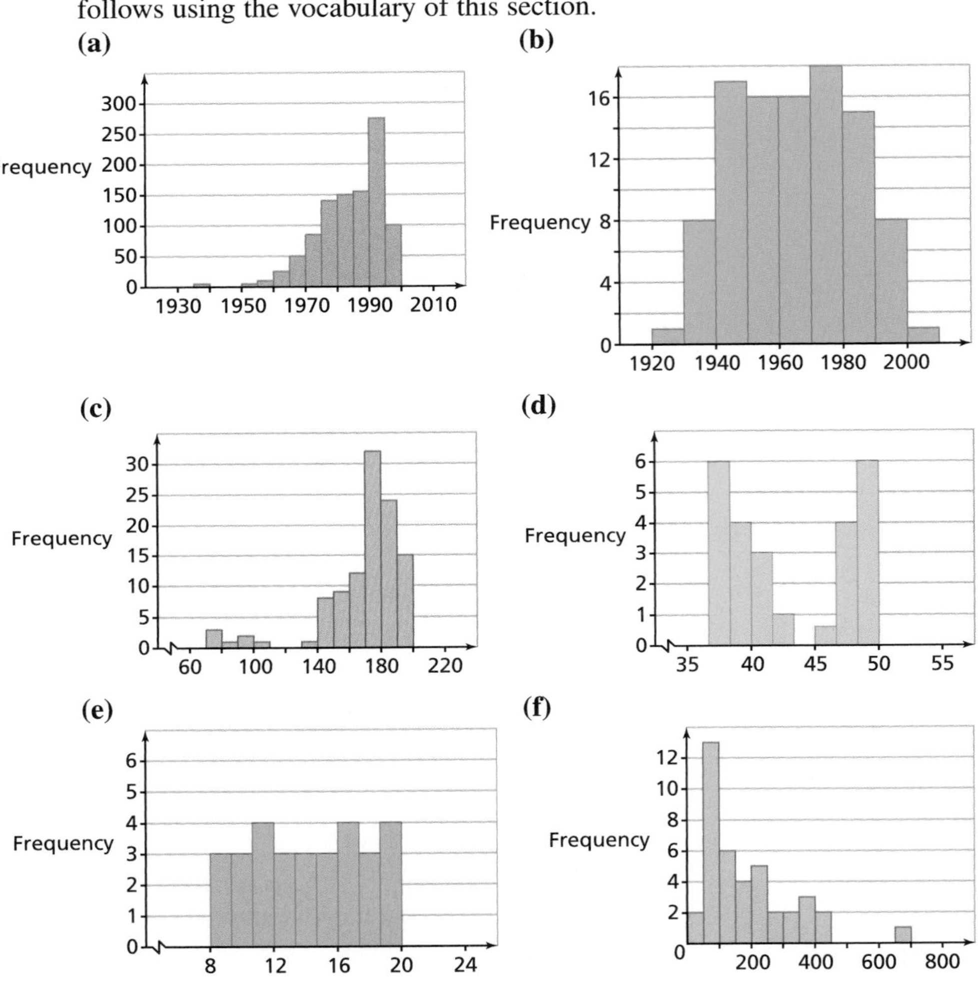

2. Match each of the preceding distributions with one of the scenarios described below.
   - **(a)** cost of the "cheap seats" at 30 baseball stadiums
   - **(b)** bowling scores
   - **(c)** the gestation period in days of various animals
   - **(d)** the year shown on a penny
   - **(e)** the production year of the American Film Institute's top 100 films
   - **(f)** amounts shown on an electric bill

3. **Communication** How can the bin width used in a histogram be used to misrepresent the data? Give examples.

4. **Knowledge and Understanding** Calculate a bin width that would form five uniform intervals for the following data.
   (a) 13, 7, 5, 7, 9, 10, 5, 11, 8, 7, 9, 10, 10, 11, 14, 10, 6, 12, 6, 9, 7, 12, 9, 10, 6
   (b) 0.59, 0.46, 0.48, 0.52, 0.15, 0.60, 0.86, 0.55, 0.97, 0.86, 0.37, 0.70, 0.60, 0.34, 0.65, 0.94, 0.60, 0.35
   (c) 186, 124, 196, 206, 148, 162, 144, 167, 184, 152, 182, 184, 127, 183, 179, 185, 170, 135, 141, 126, 157, 126, 206, 196, 185, 186, 117, 129, 155, 146
   (d) 0.8, −0.8, 0.0, 0.8, 0.1, 0.5, 0.9, 0.4, 0.3, 1.1, −0.8, −0.2, −2.2, 0.8, 1.9, −1.9, 0.1, 1.3, 0.9, −0.1, 0.8, 1.6, 1.4, 0.4, −0.8, 0.5, −0.3, −1.0, 1.2, −0.4, −1.1, 0.0, 0.2, −1.7, −0.3, 0.1, −1.6, −1.8, −0.6, −0.9

5. Calculate the starting and ending point for each of the five intervals in Question 4.

B

6. Use the intervals in Question 5 to create an appropriate histogram.

7. **Application**
   (a) Construct an appropriate graphical display of the following information from the Men's Professional Golf Association.

Rank	Name	Events	Earnings ($)
1	Tiger Woods	19	5 687 777
2	Phil Mickelson	23	4 403 883
3	David Toms	28	3 791 595
4	Vijay Singh	26	3 440 829
5	Davis Love III	20	3 169 463
6	Sergio Garcia	18	2 898 635

Rank	Name	Events	Earnings ($)
7	Scott Hoch	24	2 875 319
8	David Duval	20	2 801 760
9	Bob Estes	26	2 795 477
10	Scott Verplank	26	2 783 401
11	Mike Weir	23	2 777 936
12	Chris DiMarco	29	2 595 201

Source: CNN/Sports Illustrated

   (b) The same information is given below for the Ladies' Professional Golf Association. Construct a graphic representation of the two tables that allows you to compare the winnings of the top 12 male and top 12 female golfers on tour.

Rank	Name	Events	Earnings ($)
1	Annika Sorenstam	26	2 105 868
2	Se Ri Pak	21	1 623 009
3	Karrie Webb	22	1 535 404
4	Lorie Kane	22	947 489
5	Maria Hjorth	29	848 195
6	Rosie Jones	23	785 010

Rank	Name	Events	Earnings ($)
7	Dottie Pepper	23	776 482
8	Mi Hyun Kim	29	762 363
9	Laura Diaz	27	751 466
10	Catriona Matthew	29	747 970
11	Rachel Teske	27	713 129
12	Wendy Ward	26	686 906

Source: CNN/Sports Illustrated

relative frequency—the percent that an interval represents of the whole population

cumulative frequency—the total of all frequencies up to a certain value of the variable

8. The table to the right gives the number of people by age group in a town of 100 000.

Age	Frequency
$A \le 5$	12 100
$5 < A \le 15$	22 300
$15 < A \le 25$	19 600
$25 < A \le 35$	16 000
$35 < A \le 45$	12 200
$45 < A \le 55$	8 400
$55 < A \le 65$	5 300
$A > 65$	4 100

(a) Add two columns to the table. In the first, calculate the **relative frequency** by dividing the number of people by the total.

(b) In the second, calculate the **cumulative frequency** by finding the sum of all groups less than or equal to that group (the total so far).

(c) Construct a histogram of the relative frequency in which the bar height is the percent each interval represents of the population.

(d) Construct a histogram of the cumulative frequency.

(e) Use the histogram to describe the distribution.

(f) What effect does the bin size of the first and last groups have on your interpretation of these data?

9. The amounts withdrawn from an ATM are recorded over a single day.

\$20	\$60	\$100	\$ 20	\$80	\$ 40	\$50
\$20	\$30	\$ 60	\$ 40	\$20	\$ 40	\$60
\$40	\$60	\$110	\$ 30	\$40	\$ 40	\$80
\$80	\$40	\$ 20	\$100	\$40	\$ 60	\$40
\$50	\$80	\$ 20	\$ 60	\$80	\$200	\$40

(a) What bin width gives a good representation of the data?

(b) What do you notice about the larger amounts? How does this affect the graph?

10. Record the age (in years and months) of each of your classmates, and then create a histogram for the data. What observations can you make?

11. Create a bar graph for each city.

	Temperature (°C)											
	Jan	Feb	Mar	Apr	May	June	July	Aug	Sept	Oct	Nov	Dec
Belleville, ON	−7.4	−6.5	−0.7	6.7	13.2	18.3	21.4	20.3	15.9	9.4	3.4	−4.1
Hamilton, ON	−5.5	−4.6	0.2	6.9	13.2	18.7	21.7	20.7	16.5	10.1	4.3	−2.2
Kapuskasing, ON	−19.0	−16.0	−9.0	0.5	8.6	13.8	17.0	15.3	10.0	4.2	−4.6	−15.0
Thunder Bay, ON	−15.0	−13.0	−5.6	2.7	9.0	13.9	17.7	16.4	11.2	5.4	−2.6	−11.0
Alert, NT	−31.9	−34.0	−33.0	−25.0	−12.0	−1.0	3.4	1.0	−9.7	−20.0	−27.0	−30.0

Source: Environment Canada

C **12.** **Thinking, Inquiry, Problem Solving**

(a) Use scale creatively to make Alert look like Kapuskasing.

(b) Make Hamilton look different from Thunder Bay using scale.

13. Considering the climate data in Question 11, which city has the most moderate climate (i.e., least difference between high and low)? Justify your position with the data.

ADDITIONAL ACHIEVEMENT CHART QUESTIONS

14. **Knowledge and Understanding** Create a bin width that will divide the following data into seven equally sized intervals: 2, 7, 20, 4, 11, 25, 6, 28, 3, 6, 18, 5, 13, 4, 10, 16, 23, 22, 5, 8, 3, 12, 6, 13, 12, 7, 8, 26.

15. **Application** Create a histogram using the data in Question 14.

16. **Thinking, Inquiry, Problem Solving** The following histograms show the number of production errors on vehicles coming off the assembly line during the first, second, third, and fourth hour of the day shift.

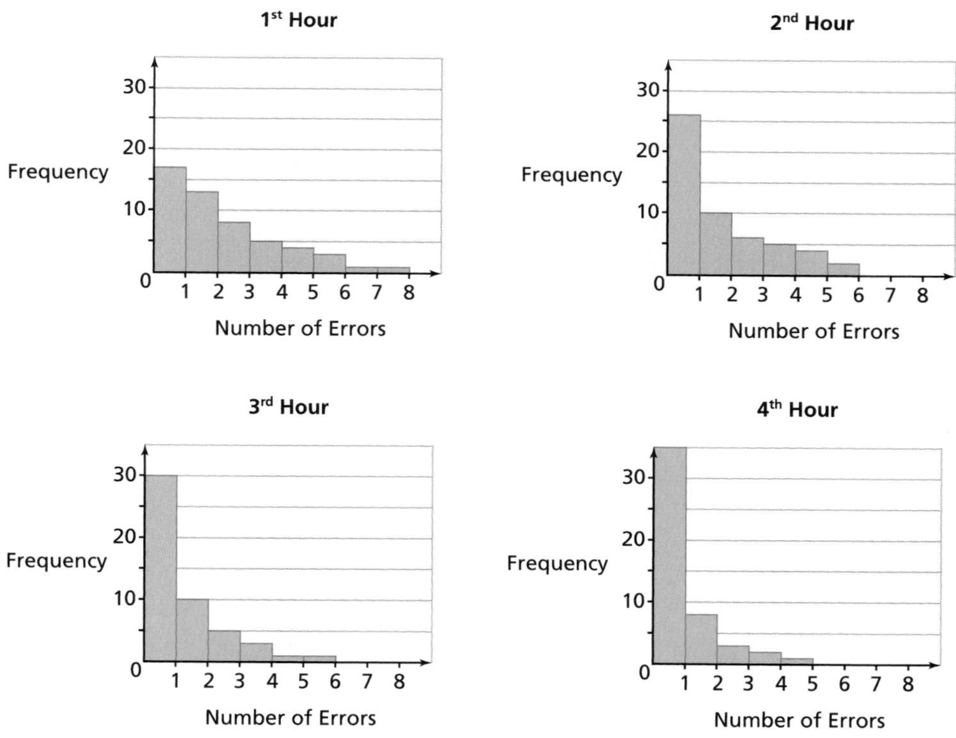

Describe the relationship between time and the number of errors. Create one histogram that summarizes this relationship.

17. Communication For a histogram to be an accurate display of the distribution of data, it must use intervals of equal width. Explain why this is necessary.

Chapter Problem

Comparing Marks

Justin would like to display the information graphically in order to determine whether the average marks of his fellow students are typical of the general population of students applying to university.

Use technology to create a histogram of the data on page 140 that visually displays the distribution of marks.

CP1. What bin width gives a good impression of the performance of Justin's schoolmates?

CP2. Comment on the appropriateness of the histograms that follow.

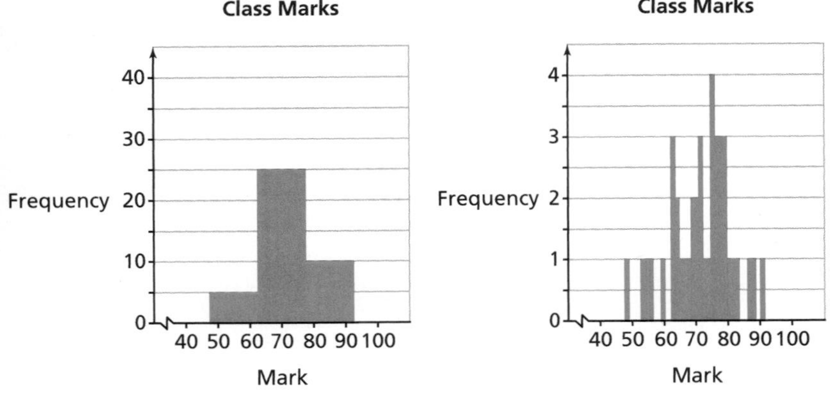

CP3. Where does Justin's overall average of 82% fall in relation to the rest of his fellow applicants?

CP4. What does this tell Justin about his prospects?

Project Connection

Research

As you continue with your course project, you will need to conduct some outside research. The strategies that follow will help you begin collecting your data.

Identify Key Words

Start by listing words and phrases that are central to your topic. You might also list synonyms for your topic. This step will help you to identify possible resources and keep you focused only on information that is relevant. Be sure to include in your list the expanded form of any abbreviations specific to your subject area. For example, if your topic were related to the publishing field, you might need to know that ISBN stands for International Standard Book Number, a 10-digit number assigned to every book prior to publication; ed. stands for editor or edition; CIP stands for Cataloguing in Publication, which is data that helps librarians catalogue the book; and so on.

Consult Others

List the names of people who might be able to assist you with obtaining the information you need, and then identify how you might go about contacting each person on your list. Your school or community librarian can be of invaluable assistance in helping you locate relevant information in encyclopedias, almanacs, periodicals, government documents, and other resources. Community college or university libraries are another excellent source of reference material. As well, ask your teachers, parents/guardians, community leaders, professionals, and so on, for their input. If they are unable to provide you with the information you are seeking, they may be able to direct you to others who can help.

3.2 Measures of Central Tendency

The purpose of this section is to enable you to describe a set of numeric data using a single value. The value you calculate will describe the *centre* of the set of data.

There are various ways to describe this notion of centre. For example, a car dealer might claim that the average selling price of a two-year-old used car is $14 500. What does this average tell you? Does this average take into account the number of each type of car sold? What if the dealer doesn't sell very many used cars, but occasionally sells a very expensive car? The influence an **outlier** such as this can have must be taken into consideration.

outlier—an element of a data set that is very different from the others

It is important to know what kind of average is being used. You are already familiar with the mean, the median, and the mode. The examples that follow outline situations in which each measure of central tendency is most useful.

mean—a measure of central tendency found by dividing the sum of all the data by the number of pieces of data

THE MEAN

The formula for the mean of a set of values, x_i, is given as

$$\bar{x} = \frac{\sum_{i=1}^{n} x_i}{n} \text{ or } \bar{x} = \frac{\sum x}{n}$$

The Greek letter $\sum$ (sigma) indicates that all the individual values of x_i from $i = 1$ to n are added together. The sum is divided by the number of values in the set, n.

The mean of the set of values {5, 7, 9, 10, 50} is calculated as

$$\frac{5 + 7 + 9 + 10 + 50}{5} = 16.2$$

In what way does this value describe the centre of the set of values? The value reported by this calculation may be better understood by examining the following situation involving weights and balances.

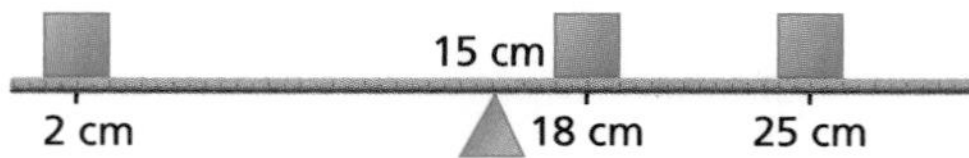

If three identical blocks were placed on a ruler as shown—one at the 2-cm mark, one at the 18-cm mark, and one at the 25-cm mark—where should the triangular fulcrum be placed so that the ruler and blocks balance?

The location of the fulcrum is called the *centre of gravity* and is the same as the arithmetic mean; in this case, 15 cm. At this location, the block on the left is 13 cm from the fulcrum and the two blocks on the right are 3 cm and 10 cm from the fulcrum, respectively. The sum of the distances from the fulcrum is the

deviation—the difference between a data value and the mean

same on the left and right side. In statistics, this distance is called the **deviation** from the mean. If you consider distances to the left of the fulcrum as negative, then the mean is the value that makes the sum of the deviations from the mean equal to zero.

WEIGHTED MEAN

Suppose that the individual blocks from the previous situation have different masses: the block at 2 cm is 10 g, the block at 18 cm is 15 g, and the block at 25 cm is 12 g. Where would you place the fulcrum now?

The simplest way to approach this is to imagine that you have a total of 37 identical 1-g blocks: 10 stacked at 2 cm, 15 stacked at 18 cm, and 12 stacked at 25 cm. To find the average, multiply the number of blocks by the distance to determine the sum, and then divide by the total number of blocks.

Distance	Number	Distance × Number
2	10	20
18	15	270
25	12	300
Total	37	590

The weighted mean is calculated as $\bar{x} = \frac{590}{37} \doteq 15.9$.

Therefore, you would place the fulcrum at 15.9 cm.

In general, the weighted mean can be calculated as

$$\bar{x} = \frac{\sum_{i=1}^{n} x_i w_i}{\sum_{i=1}^{n} w_i} \text{ or } \frac{\sum xw}{w}$$

where x_i represents each data value and w_i represents its weight, or frequency.

Example 1 Calculating Weighted Means

A teacher weights student marks in her final calculation as follows: Knowledge and Understanding, 25%; Application, 15%; Problem Solving, 20%; Communication, 10%; and the Final Exam, 30%. A student's marks in these categories are 78, 75, 80, and 85, respectively. The final exam, has not, as yet, been written.

(a) Calculate the student's term mark before the final exam.

(b) What mark must the student achieve on the final exam to earn a final grade of 82?

Solution 1 *Without technology*

(a) Using the formula

$$\bar{x} = \frac{\sum_{i=1}^{n} x_i w_i}{\sum_{i=1}^{n} w_i}$$

the term mark is calculated as

$$t = \frac{78 \times (0.25) + 75 \times (0.15) + 80 \times (0.20) + 85 \times (0.10)}{(0.25 + 0.15 + 0.20 + 0.10)}$$

$$t \doteq 78.9$$

Solution 2 *Using a TI-83 Plus calculator*

(a) First, enter the four term values in $\mathbf{L_1}$ and the weights in $\mathbf{L_2}$. Next, return to the home screen and press [2nd] [STAT] [>] [>] [3] to retrieve the mean function. Enter the list names by pressing [2nd] [1] and [2nd] [2] separated by a comma, and then press [ENTER].

(b) The term mark of 78.9 is worth a total of 70% and the final exam is worth 30%. The final exam mark, *E*, may be calculated algebraically as

$$0.70(78.9) + 0.30E = 82$$

$$E = \frac{82 - 0.70(78.9)}{0.3}$$

$$E \doteq 89.2$$

USING GROUPED DATA

Suppose your data have already been organized into a frequency table with a class interval not equal to 1. You no longer have actual data values, so you must then use the midpoint of each class to estimate a mean weighted by the frequency.

Example 2 Finding the Mean for Grouped Data

A sample of car owners was asked how old they were when they got their first car. The results were then reported in a frequency distribution. Calculate the mean.

Age	16–20	21–25	26–30	31–35	36–40
Frequency	10	18	12	8	2

Solution

Finding the average of grouped data is the same as finding a weighted average; that is, using the interval midpoint as the data value.

Age	Frequency, f	Midpoint (Age), m	$f \times m$
16–20	10	18	$10 \times 18 = 180$
21–25	18	23	$18 \times 23 = 414$
26–30	12	28	$12 \times 28 = 336$
31–35	8	33	$8 \times 33 = 264$
36–40	2	38	$2 \times 38 = 76$

The mean can now be calculated as

$$\bar{x} = \frac{\sum(f \times m)}{\sum f}$$

$$\bar{x} = \frac{180 + 414 + 336 + 264 + 76}{10 + 18 + 12 + 8 + 2}$$

$$\bar{x} = 25.4$$

median—the middle value of an ordered data set

THE MEDIAN

The median value is the middle data point in an ordered set dividing the set into two sets of equal size. If the set has an even number of data points, then the median is halfway between the two middle-most values.

? **Think about Finding the Median**
Does it matter whether the data are arranged in descending or ascending order?

Example 3 Finding the Median

Monthly rents downtown and in the suburbs are collected from the classified section of a newspaper. Calculate the median rent in each district.

Downtown: \$850, \$750, \$1225, \$1000, \$800, \$1100, \$3200
Suburbs: \$750, \$550, \$900, \$585, \$220, \$625, \$500, \$800

Solution

Downtown: The set 750, 800, 850, 1000, 1100, 1225, 3200 has seven elements, so the median is the 4th element. The median rent downtown is \$1000/month.

Suburbs: The ordered set {220, 500, 550, 585, 625, 750, 800, 900} has eight elements, so the median is halfway between the 4th and 5th elements; in this case, halfway between 585 and 625. The median rent in the suburbs is \$605/month.

mode—the most frequent value or interval

THE MODE

The mode is simply the most frequent value or range of values in a data set. It is easy to determine the mode from a histogram as it is the highest column. In the histogram shown here, the modal interval is \$4 to \$5.

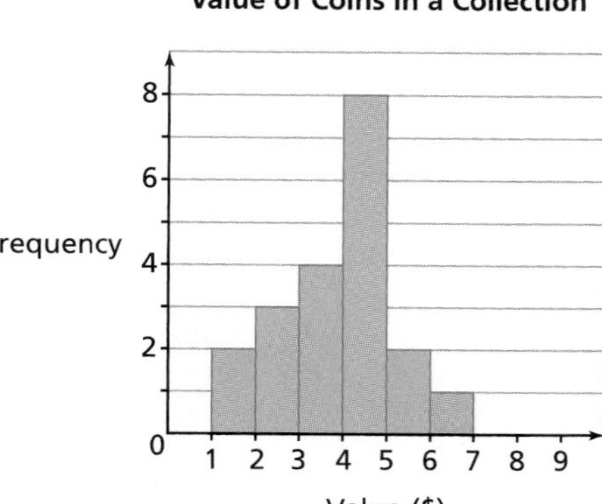

If there are two or more measurements that occur most often, the data set is called bimodal (or trimodal or multimodal). If no measurement is repeated, the data set has no mode.

Example 4 Analyzing Qualitative Data

The graph to the right represents the results when Ontario youths were asked if they have a lot of friends. Which measure of central tendency can be used to represent these data?

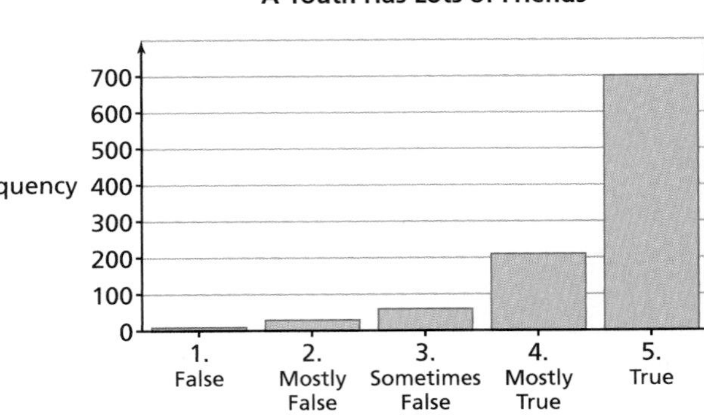

Solution

The mode is the only appropriate measure of central tendency for qualitative data such as this. The modal interval is the one where the youths answered "true." Since the mean and median depend on quantitative data that can be measured numerically, it is not meaningful to calculate a mean or median for these data.

Example 5 Exploring Distributions and Central Tendency

Compare the following data sets. What is the relationship between the shape of the distribution and the mean, median, and mode?

right skew—a distribution where the mean is skewed to the right (median < mean)

left skew—a distribution where the mean is skewed to the left (mean < median)

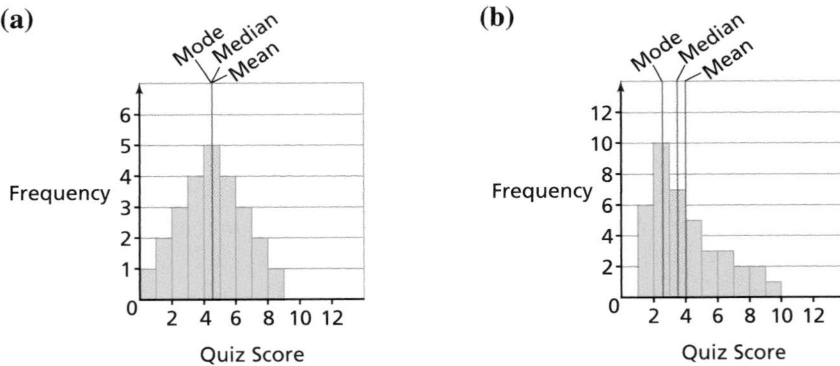

Solution

In part (a), the distribution is mound-shaped and symmetric. The mean, median, and mode are all equal. In part (b), the distribution is skewed right. Notice that mode < median < mean. When the distribution is skewed left, you would typically find that mean < median < mode. The outliers affect the mean more than they do the median and mode. In addition, notice that the median is typically between the mean and mode for non-symmetric distributions.

WHAT MEASURE SHOULD YOU USE?

While there can be no single rule governing which measure of central tendency you should use to describe a set of data, take the following into consideration:

- Outliers will affect the mean the most. If data contain outliers, use the median to avoid misrepresenting the data.
- If the data are strongly skewed, the median may best represent the central tendency of the data.
- If the data are roughly symmetric, the mean and the median will be close, so either is appropriate.
- If the data are not numeric (e.g., colour) or if the frequency of the data is more important than the value (e.g., shoe size), then the mode should be used.

Example 6 Measuring Central Tendency

Describe the central tendency of each of the following monthly incomes for six salespeople working on commission using the most appropriate measure.

(a) January: \$1241, \$1499, \$2020, \$1371, \$1622, \$1853

(b) February: \$1529, \$0, \$2127, \$1933, \$1686, \$1893

(c) March: \$1712, \$2540, \$1392. The remaining three salespeople received \$1000 in holiday pay.

Solution

(a) Mean $\frac{\$1241 + \$1499 + \$2020 + \$1371 + \$1622 + \$1853}{6} = \$1601$

Median $\frac{\$1499 + \$1622}{2} = \$1560.50$

Mode None as no repeated data

The values in this set are evenly distributed. Both the mean and median provide a good measure of the central tendency.

(b) Mean $\frac{\$1529 + \$0 + \$2127 + \$1933 + \$1686 + \$1893}{6} = \$1528$

Median $\frac{\$1686 + \$1893}{2} = \$1789.50$

Mode None as no repeated data

The one salesperson who earned nothing represents an outlier, which makes it appear as if most commissions are down in February. On the contrary, every other salesperson improved on the previous month's results. The median income figure represents a more accurate measure of central tendency.

(c) Mean $\frac{\$1712 + \$2540 + \$1392 + \$1000 + \$1000 + \$1000}{6} \doteq \$1440.67$

Median $\frac{\$1000 + \$1392}{2} = \$1196$

Mode \$1000

Because three of the six salespeople received the same amount—\$1000 in holiday pay—the mode most effectively captures this month's results.

KEY IDEAS

measures of central tendency—values that describe the centre of a body of data

outlier—an element of a data set that is very different; affects the mean more than the median or the mode

mean—measure of central tendency found by dividing the sum of all the data by the number of elements; calculated as $\bar{x} = \frac{\sum_{i=1}^{n} x_i}{n}$

deviation—difference between a data value and the mean; sum of the mean deviations is 0

weighted mean—calculated by multiplying all the data values by their weights and dividing by the sum of the weights: $\bar{x} = \frac{\sum_{i=1}^{n} x_i w_i}{\sum_{i=1}^{n} w_i}$

median—middle value in an ordered data set; the most appropriate measure of central tendency when outliers are present

mode—most frequently occurring value; highest rectangle on a histogram; only measure of central tendency for qualitative data

distributions—when skewed right, median < mean; when skewed left, mean < median

3.2 Exercises

1. **Knowledge and Understanding** Use technology to calculate the mean, median, and mode of the following data sets.

   (a) marks on a set of tests {66, 65, 72, 78, 93, 70, 68, 64}
   (b) monthly rent ($){625, 750, 800, 650, 725, 850, 625, 650, 625, 1250}
   (c) survey responses (1 = never, 2 = sometimes, 3 = often, 4 = always) {1, 2, 3, 4, 3, 3, 4, 3, 2, 3, 3, 2, 3, 2, 1, 2, 3, 4, 3, 3, 2, 3, 2, 3, 2, 3, 3}
   (d) waiting time, in minutes, at a fast-food restaurant {5, 5.5, 6.5, 7, 7.5, 7, 7, 5, 6.5, 5, 5, 8.5, 0.5, 4.5, 7}
   (e) points scored by a basketball player {12, 15, 8, 12, 15, 10, 3, 14, 15}
   (f) daily sales totals ($) {0, 0, 0, 17 000, 0, 0, 28 455, 0, 0, 41 590}

2. **Communication** Of the three measures calculated in Question 1, which is the most appropriate for each situation? Why?

3. Use the relative location of the mean, median, and mode calculated in Question 1 to describe the sets as symmetric, skewed left, or skewed right.

4. Hakim's Shoes reported the following sales results:

Size	4	5	6	7	8	9	10
Frequency	5	11	15	18	19	13	7

(a) Calculate the mean, median, and mode shoe size.
(b) Which measure of central tendency is most appropriate? Why?

5. Match each distribution with its mean, median, and mode.

(a) mean: 6.2 median: 6 mode: 3.8
(b) mean: 6 median: 6 mode: 10, 2
(c) mean: 6 median: 6 mode: 6
(d) mean: 8.1 median: 8.5 mode: 10

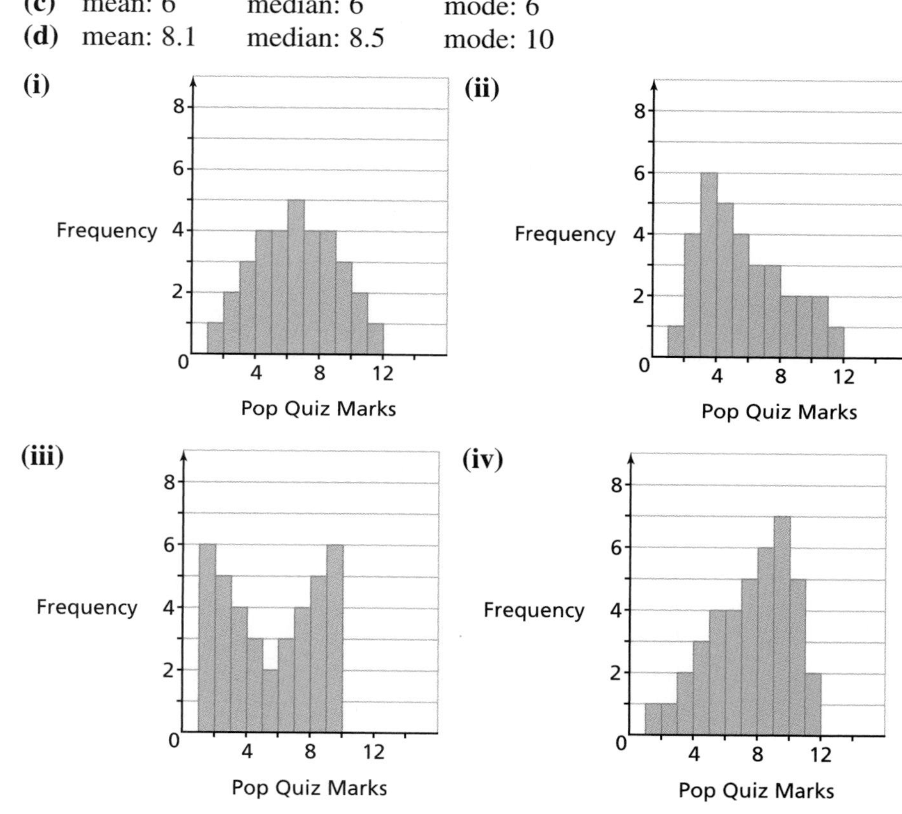

B **6.** For each of the following, determine if the argument is valid. Explain.

(a) A sales team has a mean monthly sales record of \$12 500. Therefore, half the team members sold more than that.

(b) The mean mark of one class is 65, while the mean mark of another class is 75. Therefore, the mean of the two classes is 70.

(c) The mean of four whole numbers is 5. Therefore, the maximum value must have been 20.

(d) My median monthly expense total is \$500, so my total for the year must have been \$6000.

(e) The mean salary before a 10% raise was \$30 000. Therefore, the mean salary after is \$33 000.

(f) The median salary before a 10% raise was \$30 000. Therefore, the median salary after is \$33 000.

(g) A survey shows that 80% of all salaries were below the mean. Therefore, there must be a mistake.

(h) The most popular type of music sold in a store is classical. Therefore, more than half the sales are of classical music.

7. Highway fuel efficiency for cars in 1977 is shown below.

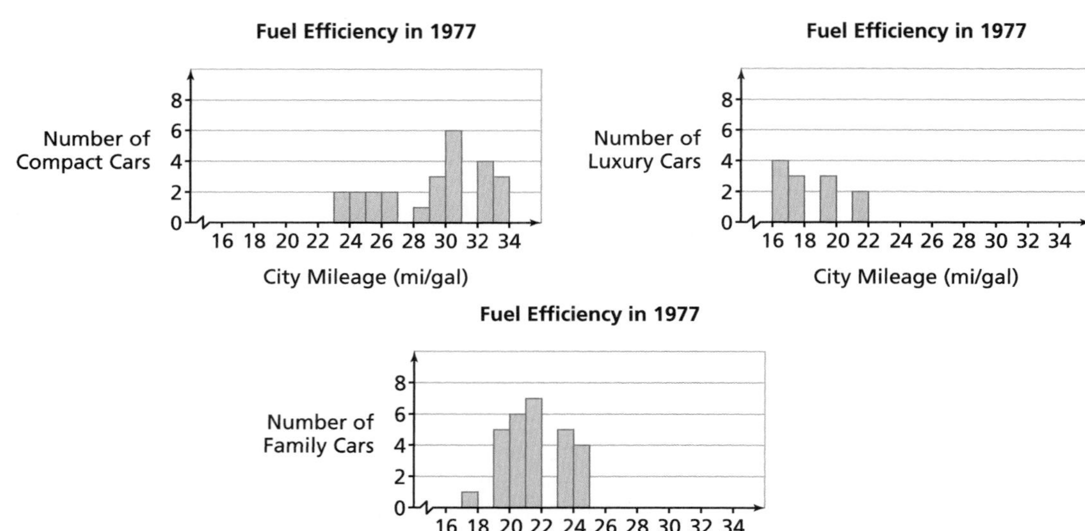

Source: Data have been extracted from Fathom Dynamic Statistics™, Key Curriculum Press.

(a) Estimate the mean and median values for each type of car.

(b) Explain the relative location of the mean and median in each case.

(c) Open the file **cars1** on the textbook CD and calculate the actual values for each type.

8. Create a data set of at least five values that has the following properties.

(a) The mean, median, and mode are all equal to 10.

(b) The median is 5 and the mean is greater than 10.

(c) The mean is 5 and the median is greater than 10.

9. **Knowledge and Understanding** Calculate the mean temperature for the two Canadian cities given below.

Calgary												
	Jan	Feb	Mar	Apr	May	June	July	Aug	Sept	Oct	Nov	Dec
Temp (°C)	−10.2	−8.0	−3.4	4.1	9.6	13.5	16.4	15.3	10.5	5.5	−2.5	−7.2

Source: Environment Canada

Ottawa												
	Jan	Feb	Mar	Apr	May	June	July	Aug	Sept	Oct	Nov	Dec
Temp (°C)	−11.0	−10.1	−3.6	5.1	12.8	18.2	20.6	19.3	14.7	8.1	0.7	−7.9

Source: Environment Canada

10. The mean of one class is 65 and the mean of another class is 75. Explain the steps you would need to take to calculate a combined class average.

11. A pair of dice is rolled numerous times. The sum of the dice, as well as the frequency, is recorded. Calculate the mean, median, and mode for the results.

Sum	2	3	4	5	6	7	8	9	10	11	12
Frequency	2	3	5	7	9	11	8	7	4	2	1

12. Jasmine records the dates on 125 pennies. Estimate the mean and find the median and modal interval of the pennies.

Date	1990–1999	1980–1989	1970–1979	1960–1969
Frequency	56	42	21	6

13. A student's term mark is 75. The term mark counts for 70% of the final mark. What mark must the student achieve on the exam to earn a final mark of
    (a) at least 70? **(b)** 75? **(c)** 85?

C 14. **Thinking, Inquiry, Problem Solving**
    (a) Create a data set of at least six values that has the following.
        (i) a mean and a median of 10
        (ii) a mean of 10 and a median of 12
    (b) Write a short paragraph to explain why the median is more resistant to outliers than the mean is.

15. A data set is made up of four values $\{a, b, c, d\}$. Write an expression for (i) the mean of the four values and (ii) the median of the four values.
    (a) $a < b < c < d$.
    (b) The four values are multiplied by k.
    (c) The four values are increased by adding the constant p.

ADDITIONAL ACHIEVEMENT CHART QUESTIONS

Contract negotiations between a union and the management of a local company have recently begun. The chart to the right represents the distribution of salaries.

Salary ($)	Number of Employees
18 000–20 999	4
21 000–23 999	16
24 000–26 999	14
27 000–29 999	7
30 000–32 999	3
33 000–35 999	0
36 000–38 999	0
39 000–41 999	0
42 000–44 999	2
45 000–47 999	0
48 000–50 999	1

16. **Knowledge and Understanding** Calculate the median and modal salary interval.

17. **Application** Calculate the weighted mean salary.

18. **Thinking, Inquiry, Problem Solving** Create an employee proposal using one measure of central tendency to justify a salary increase.

19. **Communication** Which measure is fair? Which measure of central tendency would management use to describe current salary levels? Why?

Chapter Problem

Comparing Marks

Justin would like to analyze the overall performance of his school's university applicants by looking at the central tendency. Refer to the data on page 140.

CP5. What measures of central tendency would be most appropriate to describe the performance of the students applying to university?

CP6. Use technology to calculate the median and mean for the set of marks in the table.

CP7. What can you conclude about the distribution of average marks by comparing the two calculated values?

3.3 Measures of Spread

In a group of test results, how different are the values 80 and 90? To answer the question, one must learn about the distribution of the data. If all the data are clustered around 85, with 80 and 90 at either extreme, the values would be considered very different. On the other hand, if the data values were dispersed from 40 to 100, 80 and 90 would not be so different.

In this section, you will learn how to calculate numerical measures of spread and will use measures of spread to describe data sets.

How would you describe the difference between these two data sets?

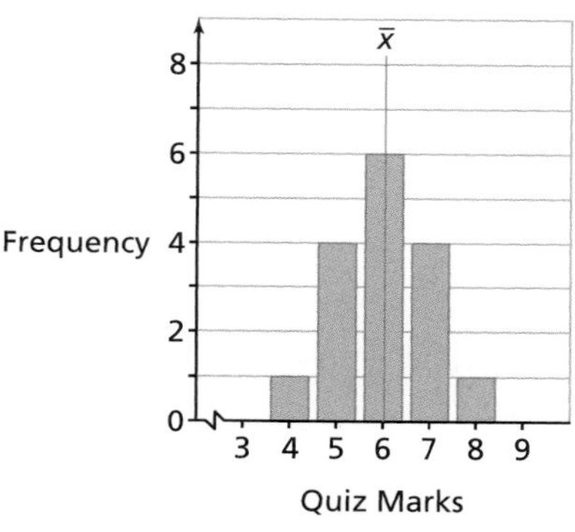

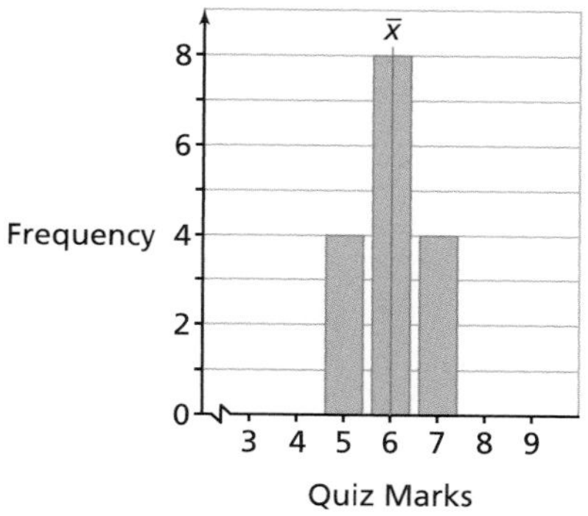

While both have 16 elements and a mean of 6, the data appear more spread out on the left and more tightly clustered about the mean on the right.

The terms *spread*, *dispersion*, and *variation* all refer to a measure of the way a data set is distributed about some central value. These measures will give us another numerical value that will allow us to describe a data set.

INTERQUARTILE RANGES

range—the difference between the maximum value and the minimum value

quartile—one of three values (**Q1**, **Q2**, and **Q3**) that divide a body of data into four equal parts

Here is a set of files from a computer, organized by size. The sizes vary from 2kB to 142kB. This could be a first indication of the spread of data (the **range**). In this case, the files have a range of 140kB, the difference between the maximum and minimum values.

The red box indicates the median of the file sizes, 25kB or **Q2**. The two blue boxes indicate the files in the middle of the lower and upper halves. These are the first and third **quartiles**, **Q1** and **Q3**. Q1 contains the lower 25% of the data and Q3 contains the upper 25% of the data.

Name	Size
Start	2kB
Ding	12kB
It_begin	16kB
Chimes	16kB
Canyon	21kB
Beethoven's Fur Elise	21kB
Passport	23kB
Chord	25kB
Debussy's Claire de Lune	28kB
In the Hall of the Mountain King	38kB
It_end	42kB
It_new	73kB
It_inter	74kB
Beethoven's 5th Symphony	91kB
Bach's Brandenburg Concerto No...	142kB

Files sorted by size

interquartile range (IQR)—the difference between the first and the third quartiles

The difference between these two values is 57kB. This is known as the **interquartile range**, or **IQR**. The IQR contains the middle 50% of the data.

A list of values must be written in order from least to greatest before the quartile values can be determined. If the quartile division comes between two values, the quartile value is the average of the two.

Example 1 Finding the IQR

Sondrine keeps track of the waiting time, in minutes, at two different fast-food restaurants. Find the quartile values—Q1, Q2, and Q3—and calculate the interquartile range (IQR) of both restaurants in order to compare the waiting times.

Burgers: 9.5, 0.9, 8.3, 9.1, 7.7, 5.2, 5.3, 7.3, 10.5, 3.6, 0.4, 3.7, 7.7, 6.5, 2.9, 8.9, 9.6, 8.9, 7.4, 7.1

'n Fries: 4.1, 3.3, 4.7, 5.8, 6.6, 4.4, 2.6, 7.3, 5.3, 5.2, 6.1, 3.2, 0.8, 5.0, 5.5, 6.5, 4.3, 4.4, 3.3, 3.5

Solution

The first step is to create a table with the data written in order from least to greatest. This will enable you to find the quartile values.

	Burgers Time (min)		'n Fries Time (min)
	0.4		0.8
	0.9		2.6
	2.9		3.2
	3.6		3.3
	3.7		3.3
Q1	**4.45**	Q1	**3.4**
	5.2		3.5
	5.3		4.1
	6.5		4.3
	7.1		4.4
	7.3		4.4

	Burgers Time (min)		'n Fries Time (min)
Q2	**7.35**	Q2	**4.55**
	7.4		4.7
	7.7		5.0
	7.7		5.2
	8.3		5.3
	8.9		5.5
Q3	**8.9**	Q3	**5.65**
	8.9		5.8
	9.1		6.1
	9.5		6.5
	9.6		6.6
	10.5		7.3

? Think about Quartile Values

When a quartile division falls between two values (for example, 3.7 and 5.2 in the table to the right), average the two to find the quartile value. What are the quartile values in these tables?

The interquartile range (IQR) for each of the restaurants is

Burgers: $Q3 - Q1 = 8.9 - 4.45$
$= 4.45$

'n Fries: $Q3 - Q1 = 5.65 - 3.4$
$= 2.25$

Since the median waiting time for 'n Fries is lower, it appears to be the faster restaurant of the two. In addition, the IQR for 'n Fries is also lower, thus indicating that waiting times are more consistent at 'n Fries.

While interquartile range is an effective measure of spread, it is awkward to calculate and has limited usefulness. A more useful measure of spread from a mathematical point of view is the standard deviation. It is a complex measure of spread with some interesting properties.

STANDARD DEVIATION

variance—a measure of dispersion that is found by averaging the squares of the deviation of each piece of data

standard deviation—a measure of dispersion found by taking the square root of the variance

Recall from Section 3.2 that deviation is the distance a particular piece of data is from the mean. If you were to take all the deviations for an entire set of data, square each one of them, and then find the average, you would have what is called the **variance**. The square root of the variance is called the **standard deviation**. The Greek letter sigma is used to represent variance (σ^2) and standard deviation (σ).

Standard Deviation (Ungrouped Data)

$$\sigma = \sqrt{\frac{\sum(x_i - \bar{x})^2}{n}}$$

Fortunately, you do not have to perform this complex calculation every time you calculate the standard deviation. Your calculator can be used for this purpose. It is important, however, for you to understand what this measure means.

In a sense, the standard deviation averages the square of the distance that each piece of data is from the mean. If most of the data is clustered about the mean, then there is little dispersion and the standard deviation will be small. If the data are widely scattered, the standard deviation will be large. In short, the smaller the standard deviation, the more compact the data set.

Example 2 Calculating and Interpreting Standard Deviation

Felix and Melanie are laying down patio stones. They record how many stones they put in place each hour.

	1st	2nd	3rd	4th	5th	6th
Felix	34	41	40	38	38	45
Melanie	51	28	36	44	41	46

(a) Which worker gets more done during the day?

(b) Which worker is more consistent?

Solution

(a) Felix manages to place 236 stones during the six hours, while Melanie places 246 stones. Melanie gets more work done.

(b) Consistency can be evaluated by comparing the standard deviation of the two sets of numbers. The set of numbers having the smallest standard deviation would indicate the more consistent worker.

Felix—Calculating σ by hand

$$\bar{x} = \frac{34 + 41 + 40 + 38 + 38 + 45}{6} \doteq 39.3$$

Stones Placed	$(x - \bar{x})$	$(x - \bar{x})^2$
34	34 − 39.3 = −5.3	28.09
41	1.7	2.89
40	0.7	0.49
38	−1.3	1.69
38	−1.3	1.69
45	5.7	32.49
		$\sum(x - \bar{x})^2 = 67.34$

$$\therefore \sigma = \sqrt{\frac{\sum_{i=1}^{6}(x - \bar{x})^2}{6}}$$

$$= \sqrt{\frac{67.34}{6}}$$

$$= \sqrt{11.22\dot{3}}$$

$$\doteq 3.35$$

Melanie—Calculating σ using a TI-83 Plus calculator

Enter the number of stones placed into **L1**. Press [STAT] and scroll over to the CALC menu. Press [1] for **1-Var Stats**, then [2nd] [L1] [ENTER]

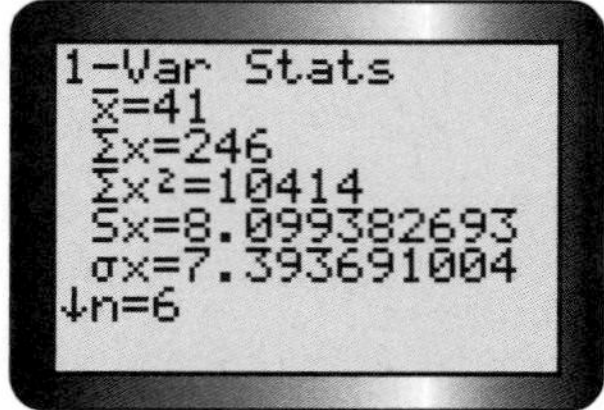

The calculator displays $\bar{x} = 41$ and $\sigma \doteq 7.39$.

The standard deviation of Felix's set of numbers is smaller. This means his data are more closely clustered about the mean; in other words, he is a more consistent worker. The standard deviation of Melanie's numbers is considerably larger, indicating that the data are more widely dispersed away from the mean. As a result, Melanie is less consistent.

The calculation for standard deviation for grouped data is similar.

Standard Deviation (Grouped Data)

$$\sigma = \sqrt{\frac{\sum f_i(x_i - \bar{x})^2}{n}}$$

Example 3 Calculating Standard Deviation for Grouped Data

A railway line gives out small bags of peanuts to its travellers, and each bag does not always contain the same number of peanuts. The following table represents a sample of 31 bags showing the number of peanuts per bag.

Number of Peanuts	28	29	30	31	32	33
Frequency	2	5	10	9	4	1

(a) Calculate the mean number of peanuts per bag.

(b) Calculate the standard deviation for this sample.

Solution 1 *Without technology*

(a) $\bar{x} = \frac{(2 \times 28) + (5 \times 29) + (10 \times 30) + (9 \times 31) + (4 \times 32) + (1 \times 33)}{31}$

$\doteq 30.4$

(b) It is tedious to calculate the standard deviation by hand; however, it can be found if you use the formula below.

$$\sigma = \sqrt{\frac{\sum f_i(x_i - \bar{x})^2}{n}}$$

$$= \sqrt{\frac{2(28 - 30.4)^2 + 5(29 - 30.4)^2 + 10(30 - 30.4)^2 + 9(31 - 30.4)^2 + 4(32 - 30.4)^2 + (33 - 30.4)^2}{31}}$$

$$= \sqrt{\frac{43.16}{31}}$$

$$\doteq 1.2$$

Solution 2 *Using a TI-83 Plus calculator*

Technolink For more help on using a TI-83 Plus calculator to calculate statistical measures, see Appendix C starting on page 401.

Enter the number of peanuts into L_1 and the frequency into L_2. Press STAT and use the arrow keys to scroll over to the CALC menu. Press 1 for **1-Var Stats** and then press 2nd L1 , , 2nd L2. Press ENTER. The calculator will show statistical information that includes the mean and the standard deviation. Here, the mean is 30.4 and the standard deviation is 1.2

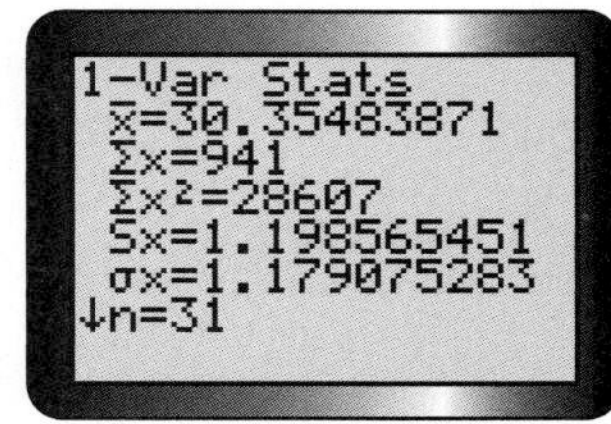

Most statistical calculators have two methods for calculating standard deviation:

s_x or σ_{n-1} for sample data

σ_x or σ_n for population data

To explain the difference between the two would go beyond the scope of this course. For exercises in this course, calculate standard deviation for population data.

KEY IDEAS

range—difference between the maximum value and the minimum value

quartiles—three values that divide a body of data into four equal parts

interquartile range—difference between Q1 and Q3; 50% of the data lies in this range

standard deviation (σ)—mathematician's choice for measuring the spread of data; the measure of dispersion found by taking the square root of the variance

For ungrouped data, $\sigma = \sqrt{\dfrac{\sum(x_i - \bar{x})^2}{n}}$ and for grouped data,

$$\sigma = \sqrt{\frac{\sum f_i(x_i - \bar{x})^2}{n}}$$

For the purposes of this course, you will use population standard deviation (σ_x or σ_n). A graphing calculator is an efficient tool for determining σ.

variance (σ^2)—measure of dispersion that is found by averaging the squares of deviation of each piece of data

3.3 Exercises

A

1. **Knowledge and Understanding** Listed below are the life expectancies (in years) of men in 28 countries.

46.8	67.8	70.9	74.1	44.2	58.2	37.3	55.0	62.9	63.6
68.6	64.3	75.1	**75.9**	59.4	70.1	51.7	53.2	51.6	63.5
73.6	69.4	73.8	69.8	55.0	68.0	71.7	51.5		

Think about
Life Expectancies
How does Canada's result (in **bold**) compare to those of the other 27 countries?

(a) What are the maximum and minimum values?
(b) What is the range of life expectancies?
(c) What is the median value?
(d) What percent of the population is represented by the upper quartile?
(e) What is the interquartile range?

2. Calculate the range, quartile values, and interquartile range of the data sets that follow.
(a) {1, 3, 3, 5, 6, 6, 7, 7, 7, 8, 9}
(b) {10, 14, 16, 20, 30, 50, 60, 68, 70, 90}
(c) {1, 5, 5, 5, 7, 8, 9, 11, 12, 15, 15, 15, 16, 16, 18, 25, 29, 31}
(d) {0, 2, 2, 3, 4, 5, 5, 5, 6, 6, 6, 6, 6, 6, 6, 6, 7, 8, 10, 12, 12, 18, 24, 28}

3. **Knowledge and Understanding** Calculate the standard deviation for each of the following sets of data.

(a) {0.2, 0.2, 0.3, 0.5, 0.5, 0.8, 0.8, 0.8, 0.9, 1.0, 1.0, 1.1, 1.2, 1.5}

(b) {17, 18, 19, 20, 21, 22, 23, 24, 25, 26}

(c) {5, 5, 5, 5, 5, 5, 6, 7}

(d) {12 943, 12 942, 12 947, 12 941, 12 939}

4. Match each of the following standard deviations to the corresponding data distribution.

(a) $\sigma = 2.9$ **(b)** $\sigma = 1.0$ **(c)** $\sigma = 0.66$ **(d)** $\sigma = 154.8$

(i)

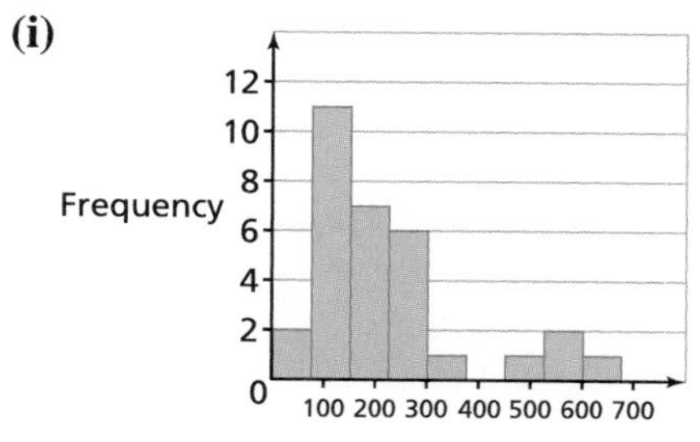

(ii)

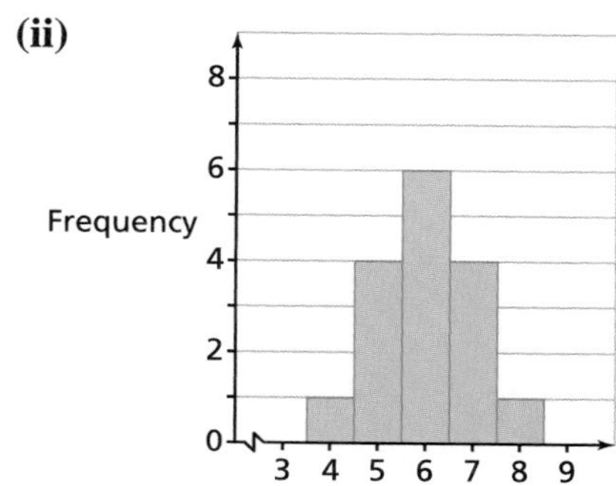

(iii)

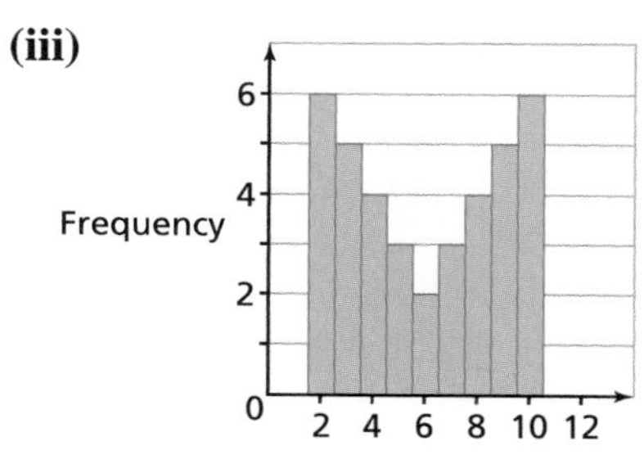

(iv)

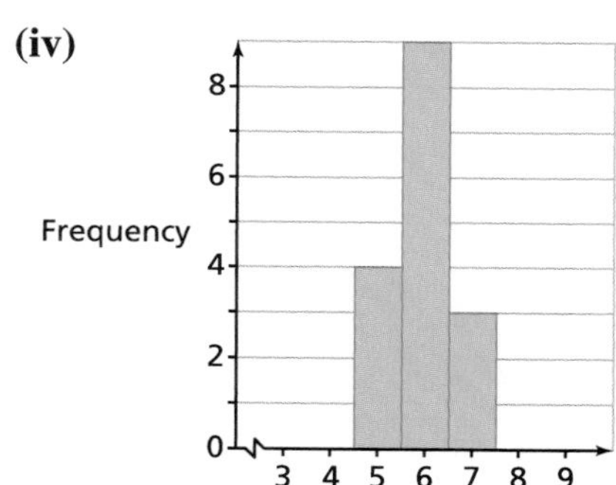

5. Find the quartile values, the interquartile range, and the standard deviation of the salaries listed below.

Salary ($)	Frequency
28 000	4
30 000	6
32 000	7
34 000	4
36 000	2
38 000	1

6. **Communication** Can the standard deviation of a set of data ever be equal to zero? Explain.

B 7. **Application** Four classes recorded their pulse rates.

Class A	63	78	79	75	73	72	62	75	63	77	77	65	70	69	80
Class B	72	66	73	80	74	75	64	68	67	70	70	69	69	74	74
Class C	68	75	78	73	75	68	71	78	65	67	63	69	59	68	79
Class D	78	75	76	76	79	78	78	76	74	81	78	76	79	74	76

(a) Use the mean and standard deviation to determine which class has the lowest pulse rate and which class has the most consistent pulse rate.

(b) Does the median and interquartile range contradict your results in part (a)? Why or why not?

8. The table to the right lists average temperature, average monthly high, and average monthly low in degrees Celsius for Ottawa from 1951 to 1984.

(a) Which month shows the most variability? Justify using the table.

(b) Calculate the mean temperature, mean high, and mean low.

(c) Calculate the range, interquartile range, and standard deviation for each column.

(d) How many monthly temperatures are within one standard deviation of the mean for each column?

	Average Temp (°C)	Average High (°C)	Average Low (°C)
Jan	−11.7	−6.6	−14.9
Feb	−11.0	−4.3	−13.1
Mar	−4.4	1.4	−6.9
April	4.6	10.7	0.8
May	12.1	18.3	7.2
June	17.4	23.5	12.7
July	19.8	26.1	15.3
Aug	18.4	24.6	14.1
Sept	13.9	19.5	9.7
Oct	7.4	12.7	4.0
Nov	0.1	4.8	−1.5
Dec	−8.7	−3.5	−10.6

Source: Environment Canada

9. **Thinking, Inquiry, Problem Solving** Jaime has 20 min to get to her after-school job. Despite her best efforts, she is frequently late and has recorded her travel time (in minutes) as {18, 20, 22, 27, 16, 23, 25, 26, 19, 28}. Her boss has told her that unless she shows more consistency, she will lose her job. Over the next two weeks, Jaime records her travel time: {22, 20, 22, 24, 24, 23, 25, 21, 19, 21}. Should Jaime lose her job? Use statistics to justify your answer.

10. (a) Calculate the range, standard deviation, and interquartile range of the following data set: {5, 7, 8, 9, 10, 12}.

(b) If you were to multiply each of the values by 2, what would happen to each of the measures of spread? Check your answer.

(c) If you were to add 10 to each of the values, what would happen to each of the measures of spread? Check your answer.

11. Which province has been most consistent in providing financial assistance to those on welfare in their province? Use data to justify your answer.

Canada Assistance Plan Payments ($ millions)				
	1970	1980	1990	1996
Newfoundland	85.7	53.0	47.9	72.0
Prince Edward Island	9.4	10.1	8.6	11.7
Nova Scotia	51.8	56.1	78.4	103.1
New Brunswick	54.3	72.0	67.2	67.1
Quebec	477.4	563.0	556.0	813.2
Ontario	354.9	405.0	676.0	1214.6
Manitoba	58.7	53.4	66.9	85.8
Saskatchewan	55.6	47.0	54.1	80.6
Alberta	84.4	94.6	148.8	105.6
British Columbia	113.7	144.5	216.0	369.9
Yukon	–	7.4	1.0	1.7
Northwest Territories	–	7.4	9.6	11.8

Source: Human Resources Development Canada

C **12.** Show that $\frac{\sum(x - \bar{x})^2}{n} = \frac{\left(\sum x^2 - n\bar{x}^2\right)}{n}$. Remember: $\bar{x} = \frac{\sum x}{n}$ and $\sum \bar{x} = n\bar{x}$.

13. A teacher gives six unit tests to his class over a semester and finds that two students have the same average on the six tests, but have a different standard deviation. Is this possible? Explain.

14. Mila and Serva have measured the height of each person in their immediate family. They find that the standard deviation of the heights is the same for both families, but the interquartile range is different. Is this possible? (**Hint**: Both families may have more than four members.)

NV		VV	
47.2	5.6	19.7	3.6
22.0	4.7	16.2	3.5
20.4	4.7	15.9	3.3
19.7	4.3	15.4	3.3
17.4	4.2	9.7	2.9
14.7	3.9	8.9	2.8
13.4	3.4	8.6	2.7
13.0	3.1	8.6	2.4
12.3	3.1	7.4	2.3
12.2	2.7	6.3	2.0
10.3	2.4	6.1	1.8
9.7	2.3	6.0	1.7
9.7	2.3	6.0	1.7
9.5	2.1	5.9	1.6
9.1	2.1	4.9	1.4
8.9	2.0	4.6	1.2
8.9	1.9	1.0	1.1
8.4	1.7	3.8	
8.1	1.7		
7.9	6.9		
7.8	6.3		
6.1			

ADDITIONAL ACHIEVEMENT CHART QUESTIONS

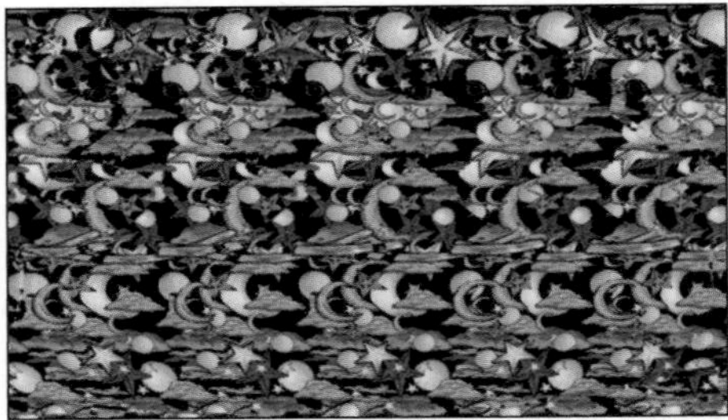

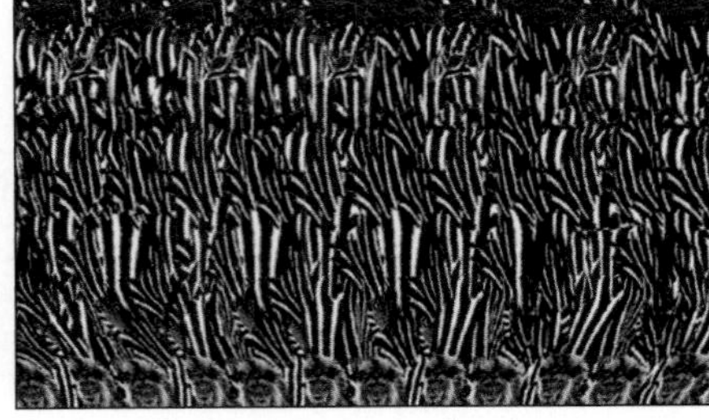

A random dot stereogram or Magic Eye image is a seemingly random collection of dots or shapes with an embedded 3-D image. A study was done to see if people could "fuse" the image faster if they knew the shape they were looking for. The results of the experiment are shown in the table to the left. Listed is the number of seconds the subjects needed to correctly observe an image. The group NV was given no information, while the group VV was given visual information about the shape.

15. **Knowledge and Understanding** Find the quartile values and the interquartile range.

16. **Application** Calculate the mean and the standard deviation for each group.

17. **Thinking, Inquiry, Problem Solving** Were the subjects who were told what the image was faster at identifying it? Which group was more consistent?

18. **Communication** In this study, what other variables should be controlled?

Chapter Problem

Comparing Marks

In order to make some valid comparisons, Justin needs to know the spread of data in his school.

75	72	76	63	64	66	70	82	76	72
53	48	81	77	64	79	71	75	78	72
78	67	63	90	87	77	75	70	59	75
76	78	55	74	71	73	69	85	63	54

CP8. Calculate the quartile values Q1 and Q3, and the IQR.

CP9. In which quarter of the group does Justin's average mark of 82% fit?

CP10. Use technology to calculate the standard deviation of the group.

3.4 Normal Distribution

In Section 3.1, you learned about histograms that were skewed left or right and histograms that were symmetrical. While no situation in the real world is perfect, many natural relationships, when displayed as a histogram, will form a bell-shaped distribution like the centre image below.

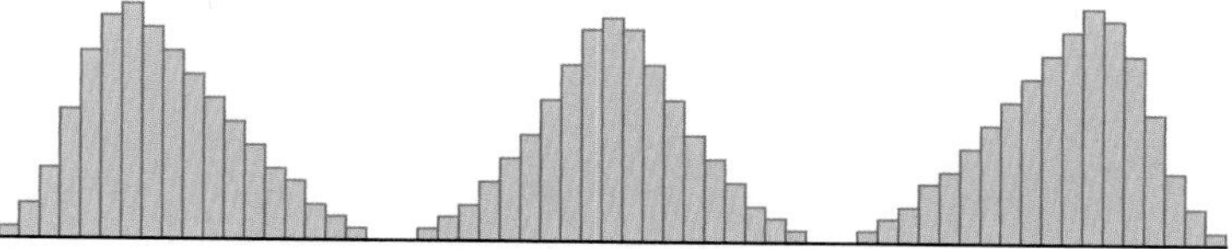

normal distribution—a symmetrical, bell-shaped histogram used in statistical analysis

In this section, you will learn about **normal distribution**, a symmetrical, bell-shaped histogram with a number of significant statistical properties.

Example 1 Exploring Height

Marlon's class has been challenged to guess their teacher's height in centimetres. Listed below are the estimates, submitted anonymously. Calculate the mean and standard deviation, and then create a histogram.

183	183	174	212	178	207	186	178
204	172	189	183	184	190	184	168
190	180	183	190	185	162	200	206
196	187	204	185	206	175		

Solution

Using a calculator, Marlon determines that the mean, $\overline{x}$, is 187, and the standard deviation, σ, is 12.1. Marlon would like seven intervals in his histogram, so he rounds up the range to 56 and gets a bin width of $\frac{56}{7} = 8$.

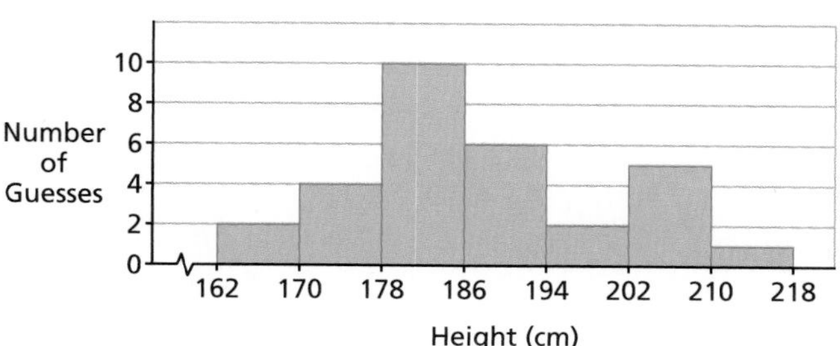

Marlon decides to collect 120 more samples and the histogram becomes the following:

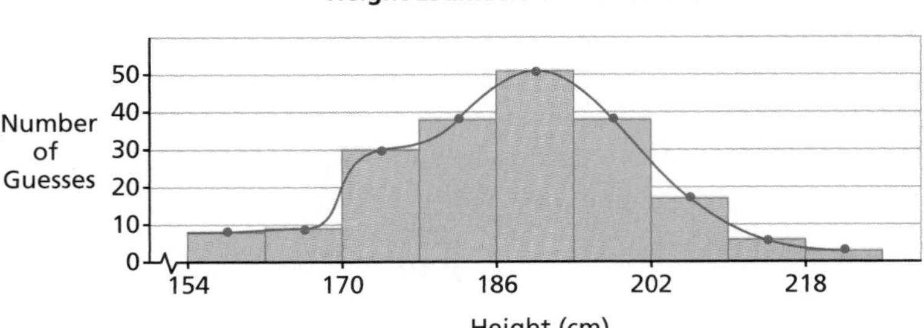

If you draw a smooth curve close to or through the tops of the rectangles in the histogram, you get a curve that looks like a normal curve, like the one shown below.

Given enough data and small enough intervals, Marlon would eventually get a perfectly symmetrical bell-shaped curve. A distribution with a histogram that follows a normal curve is called a normal distribution.

CHARACTERISTICS OF NORMAL DISTRIBUTIONS

A normal distribution has the following properties:

- It is symmetrical; the mean, median, and mode are equal and fall at the line of symmetry for the curve.
- It is shaped like a bell, peaking in the middle and sloping down toward the sides. It approaches zero at the extremes.
- Approximately 68% of the data is within one standard deviation of the mean.
- Approximately 95% of the data is within two standard deviations of the mean.
- Approximately 99.7% of the data is within three standard deviations of the mean.
- The notation used to describe a normal distribution, of the variable X, is $X \sim N(\bar{x}, \sigma^2)$, where $\bar{x}$ is the mean and σ^2 is the variance (the square of the standard deviation).

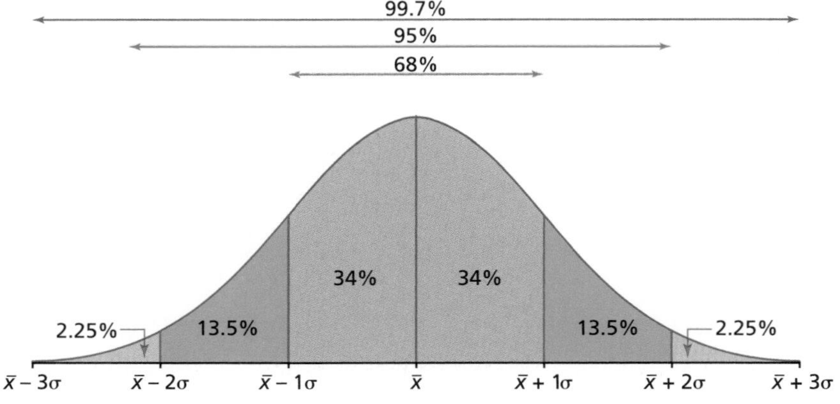

The graph of the normal distribution $X \sim N(\bar{x}, \sigma^2)$

Example 2 Using Normal Distribution

Julie is an engineer who designs roller coasters. She wants to develop a ride that 95% of the population can ride. The average adult in North America has a mass of 71.8 kg, with a standard deviation of 13.6 kg.

(a) What range of masses should she be prepared to anticipate?

(b) If she wanted to provide for 99.7% of the general population, what range of masses should she be prepared to anticipate?

(c) What assumption is Julie making in this example that could cause problems?

Solution

(a) In a normal distribution, 95% of the data is within two standard deviations of the mean. With a mean of 71.8 and a standard deviation of 13.6, that means that 95% of the data will likely be between $71.8 - 2(13.6)$, or 44.6 kg and $71.8 + 2(13.6)$, or 99 kg.

(b) To get an interval into which 99.7% of the data fits, you need to widen it to three standard deviations from the mean (the interval 31 kg to 112.6 kg).

(c) Julie has assumed that adult masses are normally distributed about the mean, which is unlikely due to the large difference between men and women. To use the properties of normal distribution, Julie needs to separate male and female data, and then calculate the new mean and standard deviation for each population. She could then determine the appropriate intervals.

The area under every normal curve equals 1. In any normal distribution, the percent of the data that lies between two specific values, *a* and *b*, is the area under the normal curve between endpoints *a* and *b*.

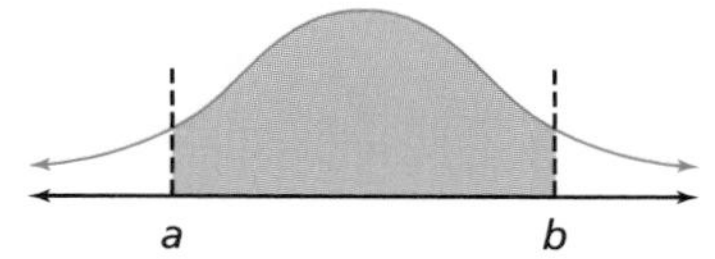

Example 3 Area Under a Normal Curve

If $X \sim (50, 5^2)$, draw a diagram that represents the percent of data that have these values for X:

(a) $x > 55$ **(b)** $40 < x < 60$ **(c)** $x < 38$

Solution

(a)

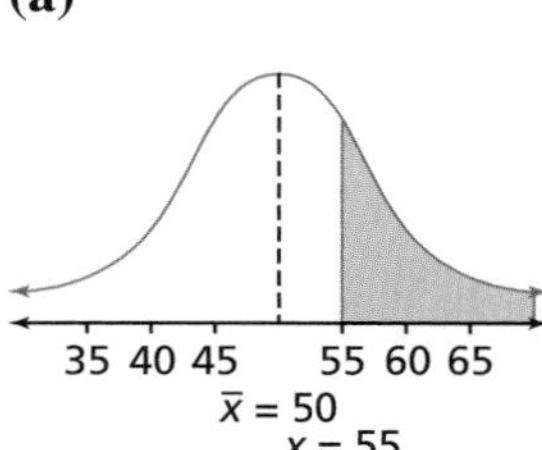

(b)

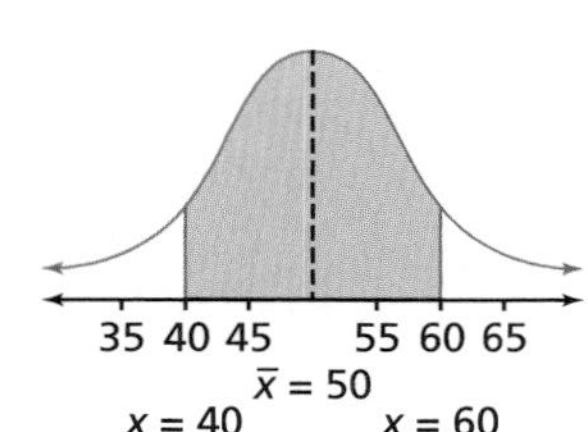

(c)

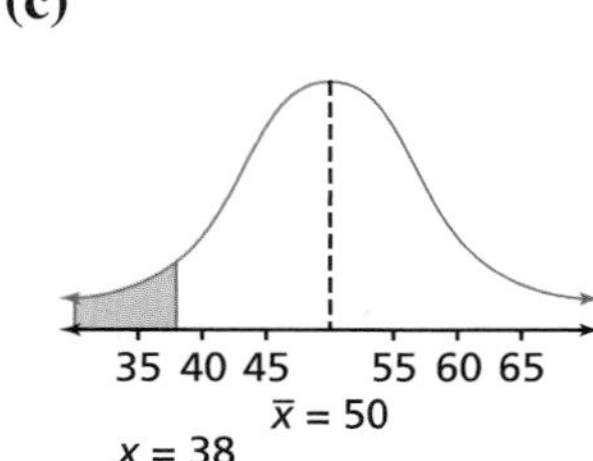

KEY IDEAS

Data that are normally distributed have the following properties:

- Normal distributions are symmetrical and approach zero at the extremes.
- Of the data, 68% is within one standard deviation of the mean; 95% is within two standard deviations of the mean; and 99.7% is within three standard deviations of the mean.
- The mean, median, and mode are equal and fall on the line of symmetry of the distribution.
- The notation used to describe a normal distribution, of the variable X, is $X \sim N(\bar{x}, \sigma^2)$, where $\bar{x}$ is the mean and σ^2 is the variance (the square of the standard deviation).
- The area under any normal curve is 1. The percent of the data that lies between two values in a normal distribution is equivalent to the area under the normal curve between these values.

3.4 Exercises

1. **Knowledge and Understanding** Which of the following statements are properties of a normal distribution? Explain.
   (a) It is symmetrical about the mean.
   (b) Exactly half of the values fall within one standard deviation of the mean.
   (c) As you get farther from the mean, the frequency approaches zero.
   (d) Almost all the data is within three standard deviations of the mean.
   (e) The most frequent value is 1.
   (f) The mean is exactly equal to the median and the mode.

2. Why do mathematicians use standard deviation to measure the spread of a body of data instead of interquartile range?

3. **Application** For each of the following data sets,
   (i) calculate the mean, median, and standard deviation;
   (ii) create a histogram or bar graph; and
   (iii) explain why you think the distribution is or is not approximately normal.

   (a) {41.5, 42.4, 42.6, 42.7, 42.9, 43.0, 43.6, 44.0, 44.5, 44.6, 44.6, 44.8, 45.0, 45.3, 45.5, 45.5, 45.6, 45.7, 45.8, 46.1, 46.3, 46.4, 46.5, 46.6, 46.8, 47.0, 47.2, 47.6, 47.6, 47.9}
   (b) {2, 4, 5, 6, 6, 6, 7, 7, 7, 7, 8, 8, 8, 8, 8, 8, 9, 9, 9, 10, 10, 11, 11, 11, 12, 12, 13, 13, 15}

4. Which of the following tables of data resembles a normal distribution? Explain.

(a)

10–19	20–29	30–39	40–49	50–59	60–69
3	5	17	20	11	4

(b)

2–5	6–9	10–13	14–17	18–21	22–25
2	8	8	3	4	5

(c)

10–24	25–39	40–54	55–69	70–84	85–99
2	7	16	10	4	1

5. Using the properties of normal distribution, estimate the standard deviation of the normal data samples in Question 4.

B

6. Out of 100 packages of jawbreakers, 68 packages contain between 120 and 150. Use your knowledge of normal distribution to estimate the average number of jawbreakers and the standard deviation of the sample.

7. **Communication** As a general rule, statistical analysis states that the standard deviation can be estimated using the formula $\sigma = \frac{range}{6}$.
   (a) Do you think this estimate of σ is reasonable? Explain.
   (b) Using the data in Question 3, what estimations of σ do you get?

8. An upcoming renovation to your school will leave exposed beams in the hallways. It is estimated that the tallest 15% of students might hit their head on these new beams. If your school has a mean height of 173 cm with a standard deviation of 7.7 cm, estimate what range of students would be affected? (**Hint**: Consider the tall half of a normal distribution.)

9. The amount of coffee an automatic machine dispenses (in ounces) can be represented by the normal distribution $X \sim N(10.2, 0.6^2)$.
   (a) What range does 68% of the quantity of coffee dispensed lie between?
   (b) Draw a diagram that represents each of the following.
      (i) the percent of cups dispensed that contains greater than 10.8 oz
      (ii) the percent of cups dispensed that contains between 9.6 oz and 10.2 oz
      (iii) the percent of cups dispensed that contains less than 9 oz
   (c) Is there a significant risk of a 12-oz cup overflowing? Explain.

10. Burns Appliance Co. offers a replacement warranty on their toaster ovens, which have a mean lifespan of 8.5 years, with a standard deviation of 0.8 years. How long a warranty would they establish if they could only afford to repair no more than 2.5% of the toaster ovens they make? (**Hint**: Consider the lower half of a normal distribution.)

Technolink For more information on using the **randNorm** command, see Appendix C.7 on page 406.

11. Using a TI-83 Plus calculator, generate a random sample of 15 numbers with $\bar{x} = 10$, $\sigma = 2$ that is normally distributed by following these steps.

(i) Press MATH and use the arrow keys to select the **PRB** menu.
(ii) Press 6 to select the **randNorm(** command.
(iii) Key in 10, 2, 15) and press STO▸ 2nd L1 ENTER.
(iv) Press 2nd Y= to access the STAT PLOTS menu. Press 1 and turn it on using the arrows and ENTER. Make sure only one Stat Plot is on.
(v) Select the histogram using the arrow keys and press ENTER.
(vi) Press ZOOM 9 to set up a standard display.

(a) Describe the distribution. Is it symmetrical? Bell-shaped?
(b) How many data are within one standard deviation of the mean?
(c) Change the number in Step (iii) from 15 to 100. What changes do you see in the distribution? How about 500?

12. The bowling scores of two players are being compared.

Kate: 89, 99, 120, 100, 91, 110, 125, 91, 95, 133, 124, 78, 92, 128, 139, 88, 100, 125, 144, 76, 84, 92, 110, 104, 103, 128, 72, 86, 102, 73

Bernie: 71, 82, 88, 89, 90, 90, 94, 95, 97, 98, 99, 100, 100, 101, 102, 102, 102, 104, 105, 106, 109, 110, 112, 114, 115, 118, 119, 133, 137, 144

(a) Calculate the mean and standard deviation for each player.
(b) What percent of each player's scores fall within one standard deviation of the mean?
(c) What bowling score would be three standard deviations above the mean for Kate? For Bernie?

Technolink For more information on using Fathom™ to simulate normal distributions, see Appendix D.9 on page 423.

13. Using Fathom™, generate a random sample of 20 numbers with $\bar{x} = 25$, $\sigma = 5$ that is normally distributed by following these steps.

(i) Drop a **New Case Table** into the Fathom™ workspace.
(ii) Change the attribute label **<new>** to **X** and press **Enter**.
(iii) Select **New Cases…** from the **Data** menu, key in 20, and press **Enter**.
(iv) Double-click on the collection icon and double-click in the **Formula** column across from **X**.
(v) Key in **randomNormal(25,5)** in the text box and click on **OK**.
(vi) Drag a **New Graph** off the toolshelf and drop it into the Fathom™ document. Drop the **X** attribute from the Case Table on the horizontal axis and change the graph type to histogram.
(vii) Set the bin width to 5 by double-clicking within the graph and changing the value displayed in the text box that appears.

(a) Describe the distribution. Is it symmetrical? Bell-shaped?
(b) How many data are within one standard deviation of the mean ?
(c) Add 100 new cases by clicking on the **Case Table** and selecting **New Cases…** from the **Data** menu. What changes do you see in the distribution? (You will have to adjust your scale by clicking on the graph and selecting **Rescale Graph Axis** from the **Graph** menu.)
(d) Change the number in part (c) from 100 to 500. What changes do you see in the distribution?

C **14.** **Thinking, Inquiry, Problem Solving** Rajinder's Data Management class wrote a unit test and the teacher reported that the results were normally distributed with a mean of 61 (out of 85) and a standard deviation of 7.2.

(a) Angelique claims that she scored 38 on the test. Using your knowledge of normal distribution, is this result likely?

(b) What would Rajinder expect the highest mark to be, given the statistical data that he knows about the test?

ADDITIONAL ACHIEVEMENT CHART QUESTIONS

15. **Knowledge and Understanding** If automobile windshields have a thickness of 14.6 mm and a standard deviation of 0.02 mm, use your knowledge of normal distribution to predict what percent of windshields have a thickness

(a) between 14.58 mm and 14.6 mm

(b) less than 14.58 mm

(c) more than 14.64 mm

(d) between 14.56 mm and 14.62 mm

16. **Application** If the mass of 35 dogs in your neighbourhood were normally distributed, with a mean of 11.2 kg and a standard deviation of 2.8, how many dogs would you expect to have a mass

(a) between 8.4 kg and 14 kg?

(b) between 5.6 kg and 16.8 kg?

(c) between 2.8 kg and 19.6 kg?

(d) 11.2 kg or less?

17. **Thinking, Inquiry, Problem Solving** Flooring materials being produced at a lumber mill have an average thickness of 7.9 mm, with a standard deviation of 0.4 mm.

(a) What range do about 68% of the flooring materials fall within?

(b) If you wanted 95% of the materials to fall within the range 7.7 mm and 8.15 mm, what mean and standard deviation would be required?

18. **Communication** Explain why a selection of 10 students from your class can have marks that aren't normally distributed when the marks of the whole class are normally distributed?

Chapter Problem

Comparing Marks

Recall the mean you calculated on page 162 and the standard deviation you calculated on page 172. Refer to the data on page 140.

CP11. How many Grade 12 students in Justin's school have an average mark within one standard deviation of the mean? Two? Three?

CP12. Is this distribution a normal distribution?

3.5 Applying the Normal Distribution: Z-Scores

In the previous section, you learned about the normal curve and the normal distribution. You know that the area under any normal curve is 1, and that 68% of the data is within one standard deviation of the mean, 95% is within two standard deviations, and almost all (99.7%) of the data is within three standard deviations. How can you use the normal curve to accurately determine the percent of data that lies above or below a given value? How can the normal curve be used to compare two different data from two different data sets?

Two students have been nominated for a $500 Data Management Mathematics award to be presented at graduation. Caley has a mark of 84 and Lauren has a mark of 83. Upon first glance, Caley should be given the award. However, other factors should be taken into consideration to compare the marks of these students. Caley's class has a mean of 74 and a standard deviation of 8, while Lauren's class has a mean of 70 and a standard deviation of 9.8. Assuming that the set of marks in both classes is normally distributed, a fair comparison cannot be made since both distributions are clearly different.

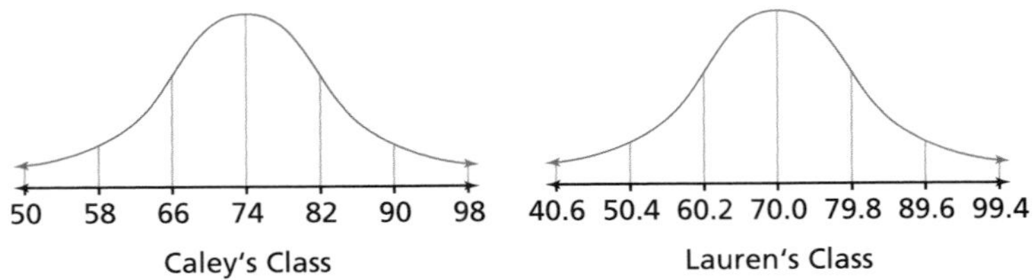

However, a comparison can be made if both students' marks are compared on a common distribution. This can be done using the standard normal distribution.

STANDARD NORMAL DISTRIBUTION

standard normal distribution—a special normal distribution with a mean of 0 and a standard deviation of 1

The normal curve is not the only bell-shaped curve, but it is the most useful one for statistics. A normal curve with a mean of 0 and a standard deviation of 1 is called **standard normal distribution**. As with all normal distributions, it has the property that the area under the whole curve is equal to 1.

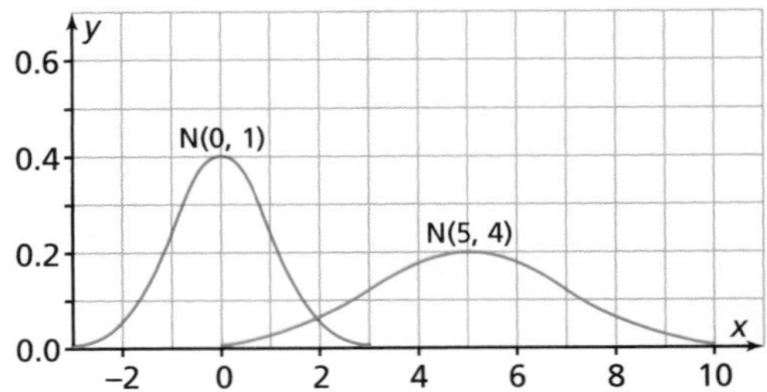

The standard normal distribution is written as $X \sim N(0, 1^2)$. N(5, 4) would refer to a population that is normally distributed about a mean of 5 and with a standard deviation of 2. Each element of a normal distribution can be *translated* to the same place on a standard normal distribution by determining the number of standard deviations a given score lies away from the mean.

For a given score, x, from a normal distribution, you know that $x = \overline{x} + z\sigma$, where $\overline{x}$ and σ are the mean and standard deviation of the distribution, respectively. The value z is the number of standard deviations the score lies above or below the mean. Solving for z,

$$\frac{x - \overline{x}}{\sigma} = \frac{z\sigma}{\sigma}$$

Therefore,

$$z = \frac{x - \overline{x}}{\sigma}$$

z-score—the number of standard deviations a given piece of data is above or below the mean

This new value, z, is called the **z-score** of a piece of data. A positive z-score indicates that the value lies above the mean and a negative z-score indicates that the value lies below the mean.

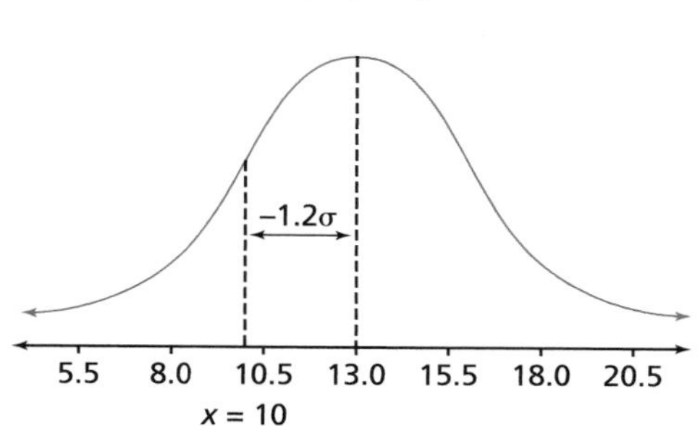

N(0, 1)

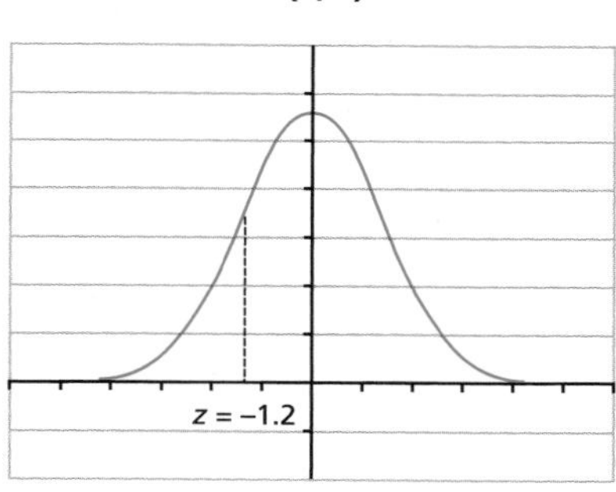

The graphs above show how the value $x = 10$ is 1.2 standard deviations below the mean. This value will also have the same position on the standard normal distribution shown to the right. Its z-score is calculated using the formula

$$\begin{aligned} z &= \frac{10 - 13}{2.5} \\ &= -1.2 \end{aligned}$$

The process of reducing a normal distribution to the standard normal distribution N(0, 1) is called *standardizing*. In this case, the value $x = 10$ has been standardized to N(0, 1). Remember, the standardized normal distribution has a mean of zero and a standared deviation of one.

Example 1 Calculating Z-Scores

For the distribution $X \sim N(14, 4^2)$, determine the number of standard deviations each piece of data lies above or below the mean.

(a) $X = 11$ **(b)** $X = 21.5$

Solution

(a) $z = \dfrac{11 - 14}{4}$
$= -0.75$

This piece of data is 0.75 standard deviations below the mean.

(b) $z = \dfrac{21.5 - 14}{4}$
$= 1.875$

This piece of data is 1.875 standard deviations above the mean.

Example 2 Comparing Data with Z-Scores

Caley scored 84 on her Data Management course, while Lauren, who attends a different Data Management class, scored 83. If Caley's class average is 74 with a standard deviation of 8, and Lauren's class average is 70 with a standard deviation of 9.8, use z-scores to determine who has the better mark.

Solution

To compare these values from two different normal distributions, you need to calculate the z-score for each student.

Caley

$$z = \frac{84 - 74}{8}$$
$$\doteq 1.25$$

Lauren

$$z = \frac{83 - 70}{9.8}$$
$$\doteq 1.326$$

Lauren's result is 1.326 standard deviations above the mean, while Caley's is 1.25 standard deviations above the mean. Lauren's result is slightly better.

Z-scores can be used to compare data values from different normal distributions, but they are more frequently used to estimate how many other pieces of data in a population are above or below a given value.

Z-SCORE TABLE

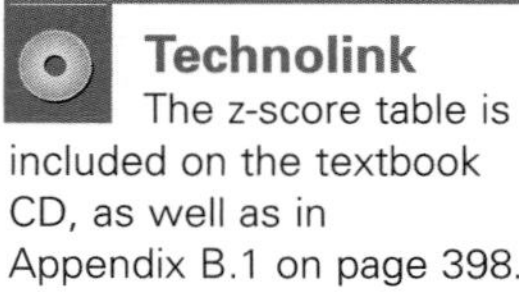

Technolink The z-score table is included on the textbook CD, as well as in Appendix B.1 on page 398.

The z-score table shown below is used to find the proportion of data that has an equal or lesser z-score than a given value.

	0.00	0.01	0.02	0.03	0.04	0.05	0.06
−2.9	0.0019	0.0018	0.0018	0.0017	0.0016	0.0016	0.0015
−2.8	0.0026	0.0025	0.0024	0.0023	0.0023	0.0022	0.002
−2.7	0.0035	0.0034	0.0033	0.0032	0.0031	0.0030	0.002
−2.6	0.0047	0.0045	0.0044	0.0043	0.0041	0.0040	0.003
−2.5	0.0062	0.0060	0.0059	0.0057	0.0055	0.0054	0.00
−2.4	0.0082	0.0080	0.0078	0.0075	0.0073	0.0071	0.006
−2.3	0.0107	0.0104	0.0102	0.0099	0.0096	0.0094	[illegible]
−2.2	0.0139	0.0136	0.0132	0.0129	0.0125	0.01	
−2.1	0.0179				0.0162		

For example, if Patrick's error total in keyboarding class is 2.43 standard deviations below the mean, then his total has a z-score of −2.43. He can compare this value to the chart above, find −2.4 in the column on the left, and then move across to the 0.03 column. The z-score table states that only 0.75% of a normal distribution has a lower z-score.

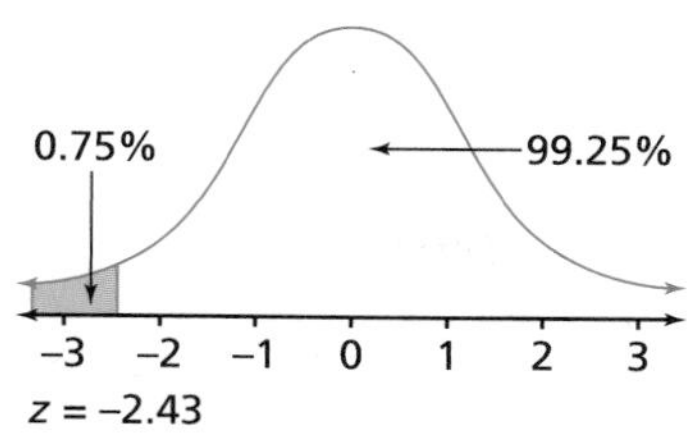

Therefore, only 0.75% of the class has fewer errors. Similarly, 99.25% (1 − 0.0075) has more errors than Patrick.

Example 3 Using the Z-Score Table

Perch in a lake have a mean length of 20 cm and a standard deviation of 5 cm. Find the percent of the population that is less than or equal to the following lengths (the **percentile**).

percentile—the *k*th percentile is the least data value that is greater than *k*% of the population

(a) 22 cm **(b)** 16 cm **(c)** 28 cm **(d)** 4 cm

Solution 1 *Without technology*

	0.00	0.01	0.0
0.0	0.5000	0.5040	0.50
0.1	0.5398	0.5438	0.54
0.2	0.5793	0.5832	0.58
0.3	0.6179	0.6217	0.62
0.4	0.6554	0.6591	0.6
0.5	0.6915	0.6	

(a) The z-score for this length is

$$z = \frac{22 - 20}{5} = 0.40.$$

Checking the z-score table, you see that 0.6554 or 65.54% of the data is equal to or less than this z-score value.

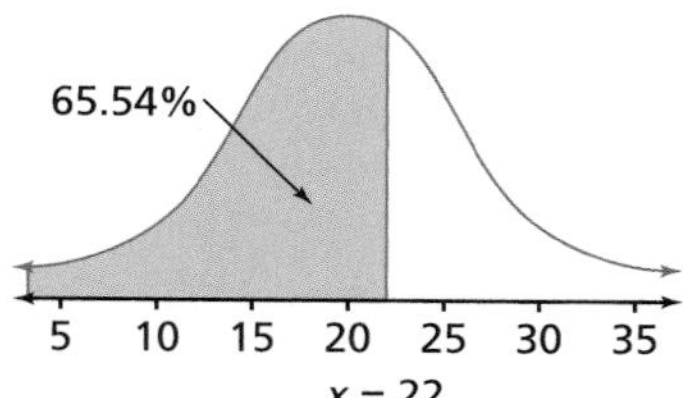

Of the fish in the lake, 65.54% are 22 cm long or less. This fish is in the 66th percentile.

−1.0	0.1587	0.1562
−0.9	0.1841	0.1814
−0.8	0.2119	0.2090
−0.7	0.2420	0.2389
−0.6	0.2743	0.2709
−0.5	0.3085	0.3050
−0.4	0.3446	0.3409
−0.3	0.3821	

(b) The z-score for this length is

$$z = \frac{16 - 20}{5} = -0.80.$$

Checking the z-score table, you see that 0.2119 or 21.19% of the data is equal to or less than this z-score value.

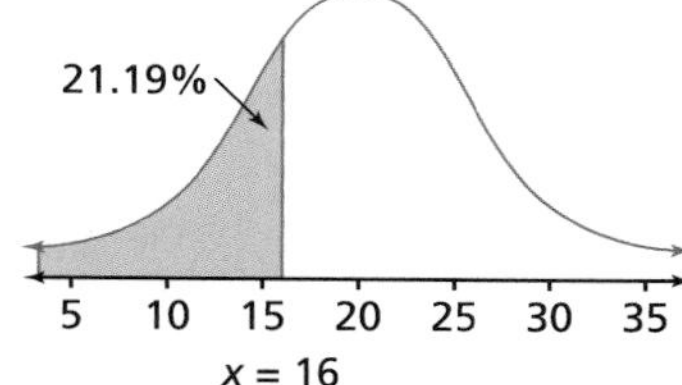

Of the fish in the lake, 21.19% are 16 cm long or less. This fish is in the 21st percentile.

1.3	0.9032	0.9049	0.
1.4	0.9192	0.9207	0.92
1.5	0.9332	0.9345	0.93
1.6	0.9452	0.9463	0.94
1.7	0.9554	0.9564	0.95
1.8	0.9641	0.9649	0.96
1.9	0.9713	0.9719	0.97

(c) The z-score for this length is

$$z = \frac{28 - 20}{5} = 1.60.$$

Checking the z-score table, you see that 0.9452 or 94.52% of the data is equal to or less than this z-score value.

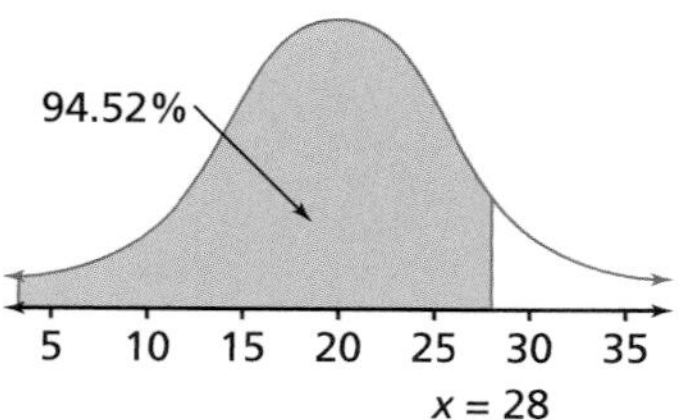

Of the fish in the lake, 94.52% are 28 cm long or less. This fish is in the 95th percentile.

(d) The z-score for this length is $z = \frac{4 - 20}{5} = -3.20.$

Checking the z-score table, you notice that the values only go down to -2.99. Any value whose z-score is less than -3 is considered an outlier. Its percentile is considered to be 0%. Likewise, any variable whose z-score is greater than 2.99 is also considered an outlier. Its percentile is considered to be 100%.

Solution 2 *Using a TI-83 Plus calculator*

> **Technolink**
> For more information on using **normalcdf(**, see Appendix C.8 on page 406.

Once you have calculated the z-scores manually, you can use the **normalcdf(** function to calculate the proportion of data between that z-score and the left most extreme (use $-1E99$, which means -1×10^{99}).

Press [2nd] [VARS] [2] and then enter the parameters as shown.

(a) normalcdf($-1E99$, 0.4) = 0.6554

(b) normalcdf($-1E99$, -0.8) = 0.2119

(c) normalcdf($-1E99$, 1.6) = 0.9452

(d) normalcdf($-1E99$, -3.2) = 0.0007

Using your problem-solving skills, you can also determine the percent of the population that lies between two values.

N(13, 2.5)

x = 10 x = 15

N(0, 1)

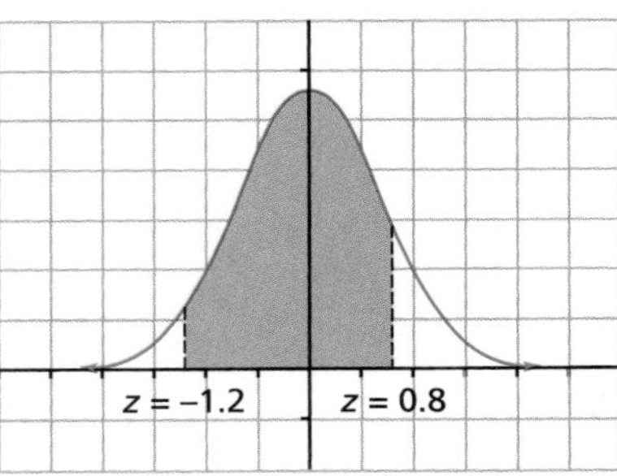

What percent of the data lies between $x = 10$ and $x = 15$? If you first find the percent of data that is less than 15 ($z = 0.8$), you can then subtract the percent of data that is less than 10 ($z = -1.2$).

The z-score table shows that 78.81% of the data is to the left of the x-value 15.

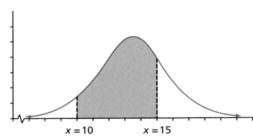

0.6	0.7257	0.7291	0.7
0.7	0.7580	0.7611	0.76
0.8	0.7881	0.7910	0.79
0.9	0.8159	0.8186	
1.0	0.8413	0.8438	
1.1	0.8643	0.8665	

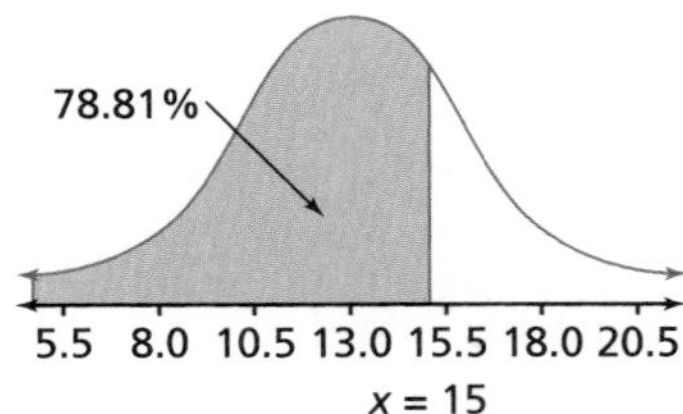

The z-score table shows that 11.51% of the data is to the left of the x-value 10.

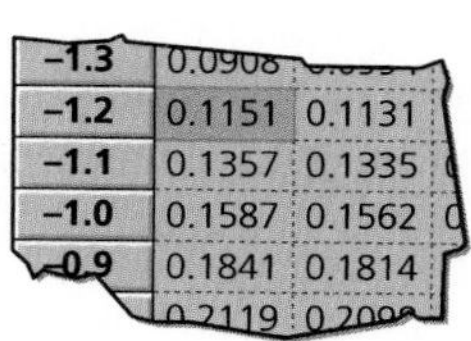

−1.3	0.0968	
−1.2	0.1151	0.1131
−1.1	0.1357	0.1335
−1.0	0.1587	0.1562
−0.9	0.1841	0.1814
	0.2119	

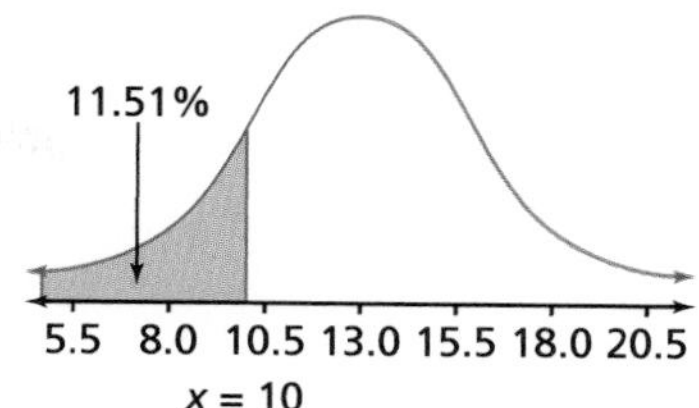

Therefore, the difference between the two percents that lie below $x = 10$ and $x = 15$ is $78.81\% - 11.51\% = 67.3\%$. Therefore, 67.3% of the data lies between $x = 10$ and $x = 15$.

Example 4 Using the Z-Score Table

Using the normal distribution $X \sim N(7, 2.2^2)$, find the percent of data that is within the given intervals.

(a) $3 < X < 6$ **(b)** $7 < X < 15$

Solution 1 *Without technology*

(a) For $x = 3$, $z = \frac{3 - 7}{2.2} \doteq -1.81$.

For $x = 6$, $z = \frac{6 - 7}{2.2} \doteq -0.45$.

By subtracting the corresponding z-score values, you obtain $0.3264 - 0.0351 = 0.2913$. Therefore, 29.13% of the data fills this interval.

(b) For $x = 7$, $z = \frac{7 - 7}{2.2} = 0.0$.

For $x = 15$, $z = \frac{15 - 7}{2.2} \doteq 3.6$.

The z-score for $z = 3.6$ is off the chart. Its percentile can be considered equal to 100%. By definition, the z-score for $z = 0$ must be 50%. Therefore, 50% of the data lies in this interval.

Solution 2 *Using a TI-83 Plus calculator*

Press [2nd] [VARS] [2] and key in the z-score values to determine the percent of data between the two given z-score values.

(a) normalcdf(-1.81, -0.45) $= 0.2912$

(b) normalcdf(0, 3.6) $= 0.4998$

Technolink
Solution 2
You can also find the answer without calculating the z-scores by evaluating the following:
(a) normalcdf(3, 6, 7, 2.2)
(b) normalcdf(7, 15, 7, 2.2)

KEY IDEAS

standard normal distribution—symmetrical, approaching zero at the extremes; has a mean of 0 and a standard deviation of 1 N(0, 1); total area under the curve is equal to 1; used to compare data from different data sets

z-score—the number of standard deviations a given piece of data is above or below the mean; calculated using the formula $z = \frac{x - \bar{x}}{\sigma}$

z-score table—lists proportion of data values, in a normal distribution, with an equal or smaller z-score; normalcdf(*lowerbound, upperbound*) performs the same function on a TI-83 Plus calculator; found in Appendix B.1 on page 398

percentile—*k*th percentile is the least data value that is greater than *k*% of the population

3.5 Exercises

A

1. **Knowledge and Understanding** Calculate a z-score for each x-value, correct to one decimal place, given the mean and standard deviation provided.
   (a) $\bar{x} = 6, \sigma = 2$
   (i) $x = 5.3$ **(ii)** $x = 7.2$ **(iii)** $x = 9.9$ **(iv)** $x = 0.8$
   (b) $\bar{x} = 75, \sigma = 4$
   (i) $x = 65.5$ **(ii)** $x = 77.9$ **(iii)** $x = 86.0$ **(iv)** $x = 70.7$
   (c) $\bar{x} = 24, \sigma = 8$
   (i) $x = 20.1$ **(ii)** $x = 5.5$ **(iii)** $x = 37.9$ **(iv)** $x = 8.0$
   (d) $\bar{x} = 6.6, \sigma = 2.5$
   (i) $x = 8.0$ **(ii)** $x = -0.4$ **(iii)** $x = 10.6$ **(iv)** $x = 6.7$

2. Which of the following statements are properties of a standard normal distribution? Explain.
   (a) The area under the curve is infinite.
   (b) The mean is 0 and the standard deviation is 1.
   (c) The mean, median, and mode are approximately equal.
   (d) Standard notation for a standard normal distribution is N(0, 1).

3. Tanya's baby brother has a length of 55 cm. This puts him in the 95th percentile. In a group of 800 babies, how many of them would have a length less than Tanya's brother if the lengths are normally distributed?

4. Using the z-score table, find the percentile that corresponds to each of the following z-scores.
   (a) $z = 0.44$ **(b)** $z = 2.33$ **(c)** $z = -0.83$ **(d)** $z = -1.85$

5. Using the z-score table, find the z-score that corresponds to each of the following percentiles.
   (a) 45th (b) 73rd (c) 7th (d) 98th

6. Given a normally distributed data set whose mean is 50 and whose standard deviation is 10, what value of x would each of the following z-scores have?
   (a) $z = 1.00$ (b) $z = -1.00$ (c) $z = 2.50$
   (d) $z = -0.50$ (e) $z = -1.81$ (f) $z = 0.20$
   (g) $z = 1.62$ (h) $z = -2.24$

B

7. Adrian's average bowling score is 174, and is normally distributed with a standard deviation of 35.
   (a) What z-score corresponds with the following scores?
      (i) 180 points (ii) 264 points
   (b) In what percent of games does Adrian score less than 200 points? More than 200 points?
   (c) The top 10% of bowlers in Adrian's league get to play in an all-star game. If the league average is 170, with a standard deviation of 11 points, and is normally distributed what average score does Adrian need to have to obtain a spot in the all-star game?

Think about IQ Scores

How many geniuses are there in Toronto? What problems would you run into answering this question?

8. IQ scores of people around the world are normally distributed, with a mean of 100 and a standard deviation of 15. A genius is someone with an IQ greater than or equal to 140. What percent of the population is considered genius?

9. The number of red blood cells (in millions per cubic microlitre) is normally distributed, with a mean of 4.8 and a standard deviation of 0.3.
   (a) What percent of people have a red blood cell count of less than 4?
   (b) What percent of people have a count between 4.7 and 5.0?
   (c) To be in the top 5%, what count would someone need to have?

10. (a) A student's score is 675 on a standardized test known to be normally distributed with a mean of 500 and a standard deviation of 110. What percentile is she in?
   (b) Another student taking the same test wants to score in the 90th percentile. What score must he get?

11. Each 450-g box of cereal is routinely returned if its mass has a z-score of −2.7 or less. Research has shown that the standard deviation of masses is 8 g and is normally distributed.
   (a) What is the minimum-sized cereal box that is not returned?
   (b) What percent of cereal boxes is returned?

12. The weights of 75 model planes at a local convention are normally distributed. The average weight is 4.4 kg, with a standard deviation of 0.41 kg.
   (a) How many planes have a mass less than 4 kg?
   (b) How many planes would be disqualified if it were against the rules to have a plane with a mass of more than 5.5 kg?
   (c) How many planes have a mass between 3.5 kg and 5 kg?

13. **Communication** The mean temperature in Collingwood is normally distributed and is 21.7 °C in July, with a standard deviation of 3.1 °C. If your friend spent the weekend in Collingwood and said that the temperature was more than 30 °C all three days, would you believe him? Explain.

C 14. Mr. Median is a very precise teacher. Each class he teaches *has* to be normally distributed with a class average of 71 and a standard deviation of 11. What would the quartiles of Mr. Median's class be?

15. A snake farm advertises that 25% of their snakes are longer than 2.5 m and 10% of them are longer than 3 m. The lengths are normally distributed. What is the mean length of snakes at this farm? What is the standard deviation?

ADDITIONAL ACHIEVEMENT CHART QUESTIONS

16. **Knowledge and Understanding** For the distribution $X \sim N(14, 3^2)$, calculate the corresponding z-scores for the following *x*-values.
   (a) $x = 11.5$ **(b)** $x = 17$ **(c)** $x = 20.4$ **(d)** $x = 13.2$

17. **Application** For the distribution N(3, 0.55), determine the percent of the data that is within the given interval.
   (a) $X > 2.44$ **(b)** $1.8 < X < 2.3$ **(c)** $X < 1.91$

18. **Thinking, Inquiry, Problem Solving** On the final exam, Jalice's class had an average of 61.1% with a standard deviation of 11.4%.
   (a) If there are 27 students in the class, how many of them scored less than 50%?
   (b) If the teacher were to adjust everyone's grade so that the class average is 65% with a standard deviation of 11.4%, how many would score less than 50%?

19. **Communication** The teacher of a Data Management class, in which the class average is 68% with a standard deviation of 8.5%, has offered to help up to 10% of the students after school with their projects. Using the normal distribution, how should the teacher decide who will get help? Explain.

Chapter Problem

Comparing Marks

Refer to the data on page 140.

CP13. Calculate a z-score for Justin's average mark using the mean and standard deviation you used in Section 3.3.

CP14. What percentile is Justin in?

CP15. Using the z-score table, what percent of the class should have a lower average mark than Justin? Is this true? Why or why not?

CP16. What would Justin have to raise his average mark to if he wanted to be in the 90th percentile?

3.6 Mathematical Indices

index—an arbitrarily defined number that provides a measure of scale

In July 2001, CTV and *The Globe and Mail* ran a series of special reports on fitness in Canada. According to their surveys, 47.9% of Canadians are overweight with a body mass **index** (BMI) of 25 or more, while 15% are obese with a BMI in excess of 30. The body mass index is an example of a type of measure used for comparison. In this section, you will look at the BMI and other indices in order to see how they are used.

BODY MASS INDEX

? Think about Body Mass Index
What is the effect of dividing by the height squared as opposed to simply dividing by the height?

Health experts have adopted a mathematical formula called body mass index (BMI) to determine whether a person's mass puts them at risk for health problems. It is a crude measure of obesity that takes into account a person's height as well as mass. This helps to compensate for those who have a higher mass because they are tall. It is calculated by dividing a person's mass in kilograms by the square of their height in metres.

$$\text{BMI} = \frac{\text{mass}}{\text{height}^2}$$

Example 1 Calculating Body Mass Index

Calculate the BMI for the following individuals.

(a) height = 180 cm, mass = 70 kg **(b)** height = 165 cm, mass = 60 kg

Solution

(a) $\text{BMI} = \frac{70}{1.8^2} = 21.6 \text{ kg/m}^2$ **(b)** $\text{BMI} = \frac{60}{1.65^2} = 22.04 \text{ kg/m}^2$

Example 2 Using BMI to Calculate Mass

For a person whose height is 1.85 m, what mass would yield a BMI of 25? Of 30?

Solution

$$\begin{aligned}\text{Mass} &= 25 \times (1.85)^2 \\ &= 85.6 \text{ kg}\end{aligned}$$

$$\begin{aligned}\text{Mass} &= 30 \times (1.85)^2 \\ &= 102.7 \text{ kg}\end{aligned}$$

SLUGGING PERCENTAGE

Baseball is the most statistically analyzed sport in the world, with a number of indices used to measure the value of a player. In addition to a batting average, a player's offensive abilities can be measured by the slugging percentage. It takes into account not only the number of hits, but also the number of bases earned (i.e., a double is worth two bases, a triple is worth three, and a home run is worth four). So, a player's slugging percentage may be calculated as

$$\text{SP} = \frac{\text{total bases}}{\text{at-bats}}$$

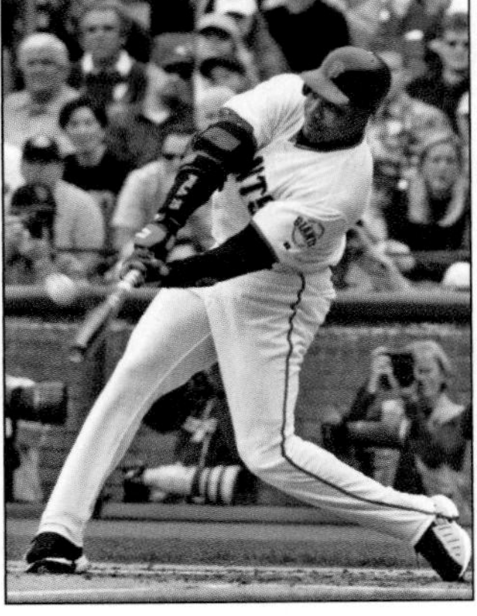

Example 3 Calculating Slugging Percentage

Here are some recent statistics for Barry Bonds. Compare his slugging percentage for these three years.

Year	AB	H	2B	3B	HR	AVG
1999	355	93	20	2	34	0.262
2000	480	147	28	4	49	0.306
2001	476	156	32	2	73	0.328

AB = at-bats; H = hits of any kind; 2B = two-base hits; 3B = three-base hits; HR = home runs (4 bases); AVG = $\frac{\text{H}}{\text{AB}}$

Solution

To determine the total number of bases (TB), use the formula TB = H + 2B + 2(3B) + 3(HR), since every double produces one extra base, every triple produces two extra bases, and every home run produces three extra bases.

In 1999,
$$\begin{aligned}\text{SP} &= \frac{93 + (20) + 2(2) + 3(34)}{355}\\ &= \frac{219}{355}\\ &= 0.617\end{aligned}$$

In 2000,
$$\begin{aligned}\text{SP} &= \frac{147 + (28) + 2(4) + 3(49)}{480}\\ &= \frac{330}{480}\\ &= 0.688\end{aligned}$$

In 2001,
$$\begin{aligned}\text{SP} &= \frac{156 + (32) + 2(2) + 3(73)}{476}\\ &= \frac{411}{476}\\ &= 0.863\end{aligned}$$

CONSUMER PRICE INDEX

The consumer price index (CPI) provides a broad picture of the cost of living in Canada by comparing the costs of a wide variety of consumer goods, such as food, clothing, fuel, heating costs, transportation, shelter, and recreation. It is an important index since it is used to calculate increases in CPP payments to seniors, as well as increases to other plans indexed to the cost of living.

The consumer price index uses a formula that weights the influence of any particular item by how frequently it is purchased by the consumer. Food, which is purchased almost daily, is given a greater weight than clothing. Costs are compared to a base year, which at present is 1992. If the "shopping basket" of goods for 1992 had a value of $100, then, in the year 2000, it had a value of $113.50. This way, it is easy to express the increase as a percent.

This table shows the CPI for the 12-month period from August 2000 to July 2001.

Aug	Sept	Oct	Nov	Dec	Jan	Feb	Mar	Apr	May	June	July
113.9	114.4	114.6	115.0	115.1	114.7	115.2	115.6	116.4	117.4	117.5	117.1

A plot of these values shows a great deal of fluctuation.

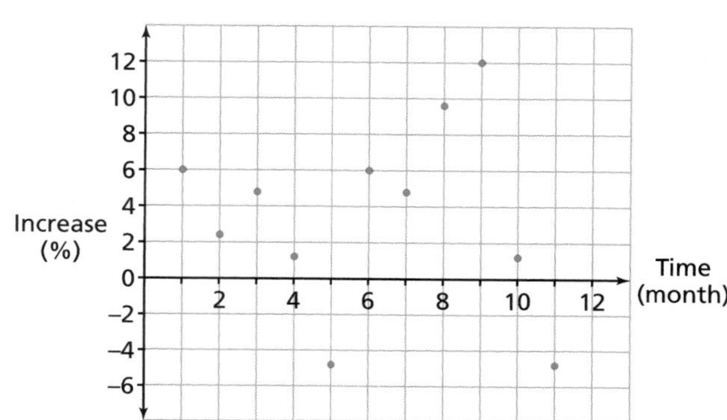

Source: Statistics Canada

Technolink
To perform a moving average analysis in Fathom™, look in the numeric tools menu and click Analyze: Moving Average.

One way to smooth out fluctuations is to calculate a moving average.

moving average—an average of a number of consecutive points from time series data

MOVING AVERAGES

A moving average is used when time-series data show a great deal of fluctuation. It is used frequently in stock analysis where the price of a stock may vary greatly from day to day but the important feature is the long-term trend.

A moving average takes the average of the previous n values. For example, a three-day moving average reports the average stock price of the previous three days. Stock analysts may also use longer averages, such as 10-day, 30-day, 100-day, or 200-day averages.

Example 4 Calculating Moving Averages

Find the three-month moving average (annual percent interest) for the 12-month CPI increase given in the table at the top of this page.

Solution

The first moving average that can be calculated is the average of the first three-month period (Aug, Sept, and Oct).

$$\frac{(114.4 - 113.9) \times 12 + (114.6 - 114.4) \times 12 + (115.0 - 114.6) \times 12}{3} = 4.4$$

The remaining results are shown in the table that follows. A plot of moving averages shows a general decrease over the first two months, followed by an increase, and then a decrease.

Months	Annual % Change
Aug, Sept, Oct	4.4%
Sept, Oct, Nov	2.8%
Oct, Nov, Dec	3.6%
Nov, Dec, Jan	4.0%
Dec, Jan, Feb	5.2%
Jan, Feb, Mar	6.8%
Feb, Mar, Apr	8.8%
Mar, Apr, May	7.6%
Apr, May, June	6.0%
May, June, July	2.0%

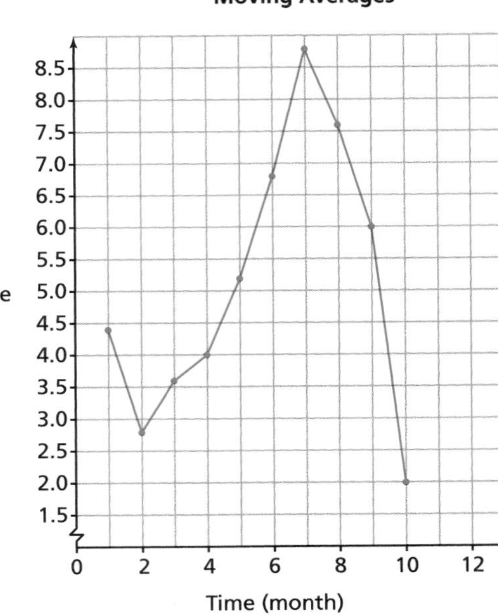

Think about Annual % Increase

To calculate an annual percent increase, calculate the relative percent change for one month, and then multiply by 12. How does this give you the required percent?

Other moving averages will smooth out fluctuations over greater time periods. Many stock investment Web sites will provide 100- or 200-day moving averages.

KEY IDEAS

mathematical indices—an arbitrarily defined number that provides a measure of scale; determined by a mathematical calculation that combines various attributes of each case in order to make comparisons

body mass index (BMI)—an index designed to measure body mass

$$\text{BMI} = \frac{\text{mass}}{\text{height}^2}$$

slugging percentage—an index that measures the number of bases per at-bats

moving average—average of a number of consecutive points from time-series data; computed using the average of the previous n time periods (so you can calculate a three-day, a five-day, or an average of any number of days)

3.6 Exercises

A

1. **Knowledge and Understanding**
   (a) Calculate the body mass index for the following individuals.
      (i) mass = 80 kg, height = 1.65 m
      (ii) mass = 70 kg, height = 1.70 m
      (iii) mass = 55 kg, height = 1.58 m
      (iv) mass = 90 kg, height = 2.10 m
      (v) mass = 100 kg, height = 2.15 m
   (b) Rank the individuals in increasing order of their body mass index.
   (c) How does the actual mass of each individual compare to the body mass index?

2. Calculate the mass that would yield a BMI of 20 or less for each of the following heights.
   (a) 150 cm **(b)** 185 cm
   (c) 170 cm **(d)** 200 cm

3. An athlete's BMI is 20. For each mass, how tall is the athlete?
   (a) 65 kg **(b)** 80 kg
   (c) 75 kg **(d)** 55 kg

4. Calculate the slugging percentage for these players on the 2001 Blue Jays.

Name	Games	2B	3B	AB	H	HR
Bush	78	11	1	271	83	3
Cruz Jr.	146	38	4	577	158	34
Delgado	162	31	1	574	160	39
Gonzalez	154	25	5	636	161	17
Stewart	155	44	7	640	202	12
Team Total		287	36	5663	1489	195

B

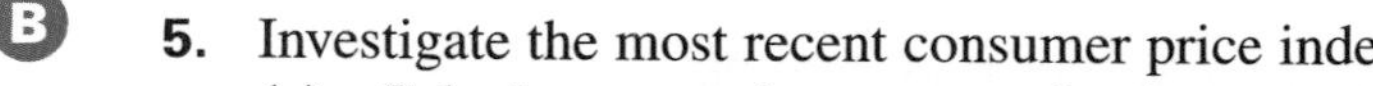

5. Investigate the most recent consumer price index.
   (a) Calculate a moving average for the past 12 months.
   (b) If there are any startling changes, can you associate them with any recent events that may have occurred?

Technolink
Up-to-date CPI data are available on the Statistics Canada Web site at **www.statcan.ca**.

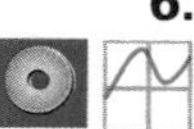

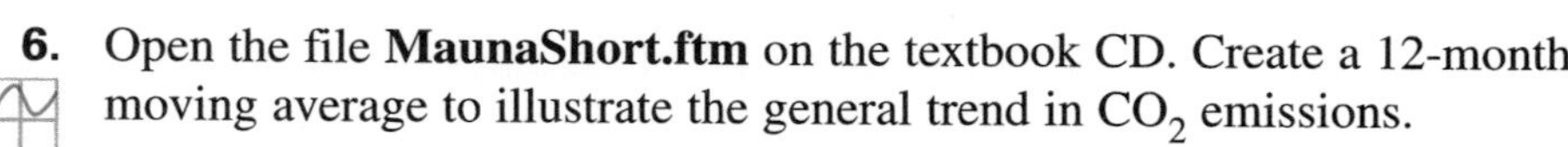

6. Open the file **MaunaShort.ftm** on the textbook CD. Create a 12-month moving average to illustrate the general trend in CO_2 emissions.

7. **Application** The following table shows operating cost, seating capacity, and speed for several types of planes.

Plane	Seats	Speed (km/h)	Cost ($/h)
B747–400	396	538	6859
B747–100	447	520	6447
L–1011–100/200	310	495	3720
DC–10–10	289	500	5281
A300–600	249	473	5237
DC–10–30	265	520	6078
B767–300ER	214	495	3558
B757–200	186	465	2675
B767–200ER	181	488	3348

Source: Data have been extracted from Fathom Dynamic Statistics™, Key Curriculum Press.

(a) Create an index that calculates the cost to send 100 passengers on a 1000-km trip.
(b) Calculate this index for each type of airliner and rank them by increasing cost.

8. The following table shows prices in dollars of tickets and other items at some baseball parks.

Team	Adult	Child	Parking	Program	Cap	Soft Drink	Hot Dog
Atlanta	20.17	20.17	8.40	5.25	12.60	1.58	2.75
Baltimore	20.81	20.81	5.25	3.15	12.60	1.84	2.75
Boston	25.25	25.25	12.60	2.10	10.50	2.63	2.75
Ottawa	19.35	19.35	10.50	2.63	10.50	2.10	2.48
Colorado	16.58	16.58	8.40	5.25	12.60	2.89	3.03
Detroit	12.84	12.84	8.40	4.20	10.50	1.84	2.48
Florida	12.78	11.38	5.25	4.20	8.40	2.63	2.75
Montreal	9.85	8.68	6.94	3.48	10.42	1.73	2.00
New York	20.88	20.88	7.35	4.20	10.50	3.68	4.13
Toronto	27.45	17.33	8.33	3.48	7.98	1.44	1.55

(a) Create an index that calculates the cost of two adult tickets, two children's tickets, parking, two caps, four drinks, and four hot dogs.
(b) Calculate the value of this index for each park and rank the parks from least to most expensive.
(c) Your trip to the ballpark may not include all of the items listed in part (a). List the items you would purchase and calculate the index for your trip to each park.

9. Calculate a three-day moving average for the following stock price.

Day	Price ($)
1	9.99
2	10.99
3	11.72
4	11.82
5	11.56
6	15.38

Day	Price ($)
7	13.23
8	14.13
9	13.59
10	14.87
11	15.94

(a) Create a time-series graph showing the price and the moving average.
(b) If you are waiting until the price hits $20, how long might you wait?
(c) When was the actual price greater than the three-day average?
(d) Describe the effect of the price spike on day 6.

10. Design an index that you could use to compare soccer players on different teams. Could you use this index to compare male with female scores? Explain.

11. The following table lists the price of a stock over an interval of 14 business days.

Day	Price ($)
1	4.11
2	4.07
3	4.22
4	4.18
5	4.05
6	4.28
7	4.16

Day	Price ($)
8	4.22
9	4.29
10	4.25
11	4.25
12	4.51
13	4.37
14	4.21

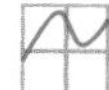

(a) Use technology to create a three-day and a five-day moving average for these stock prices.
(b) Create a time-series graph and plot both sets of values.
(c) What effect does changing the number of days have on the display of the average?

12. The reading level of a book can be estimated by selecting 10 consecutive sentences and counting the number of words with more than three syllables. Find the square root of this total and add three.
(a) Estimate the reading level of this textbook.
(b) Compare this reading level with (i) a newspaper; (ii) a novel.
(c) What weaknesses do you perceive in this index?

C **13.** **Communication** The United Nations calculates a Human Development Index (HDI) each year, largely for the purpose of measuring improving living conditions in the developing world. The HDI uses health (average life expectancy), knowledge (average education level), and economic well-being (average incomes) in measuring the quality of life in a country. Is this a fair evaluation? What other factors do you think are important?

14. Every year *Maclean's* magazine publishes its annual rankings of Canadian universities. It does this by creating an index that combines a number of factors, but the magazine does not reveal its actual formula for calculating the index. List factors that are important to you in considering a post-secondary school. Find *Maclean's* most recent ranking. Do you agree with their findings? Explain.

Chapter Problem

Comparing Marks

Many colleges in the United States use a numerical score called the Grade Point Average (GPA). It assigns a value between 0 and 4 for each final grade and computes an average weighted by the number of credits. Most of Justin's courses are full-credit courses, but he did take a half-credit course in Civics.

CP17. Use the table to the right to assign a numerical value for each of Justin's marks and calculate his weighted GPA.

Justin's Marks (all worth one credit unless noted)

English	86
Calculus	83 (2 credits)
Geometry	78
Data Management	88 (1.5 credits)
History	74
Physics	77
Civics	92 (0.5 credits)

Mark Range	Letter Grade	Numerical Value
93–100	A+	4.0
86–92	A	4.0
80–85	A–	3.7
77–79	B+	3.3
73–76	B	3.0
70–72	B–	2.7
67–69	C+	2.3
63–66	C	2.0
60–62	C–	1.7
57–59	D+	1.3
53–56	D	1.0
50–52	D–	0.7
<50	F	0

Project Connection

Statistical Tools in This Chapter

Throughout the chapter, you have been presented with many statistical tools that can be used on your data. You need to decide which is the best statistical tool to use and when, because your data will be scrutinized by others. A summary of the chapter is given below. Some questions have been provided here to assist you in determining which tools might be best for your project.

Measures of Central Tendency

mean—the most common measure of central tendency; calculated as the sum of all the data items divided by the number of data items

median—the middle value in a set of data when the values are written from least to greatest; often used when the range in the data is large

mode—the data piece that appears most often; the only measure that can be used with qualitative data

Selecting which measure of central tendency to use depends on the distribution of data. Whichever measure most accurately describes the tendencies of the population should be used.

Case Study 1

There are 21 homes in a neighbourhood and you, as a real estate agent, are trying to convince a couple that they could afford to live there. You know their combined income last year was $49 000 and they drive a 1999 Chevrolet Cavalier. The following data about the neighbourhood are available to you:

Household Income for Each Home

$35 000, $52 000, $38 000, $102 000, $47 000, $44 500, $38 000, $45 000, $35 000, $38 000, $22 000, $68 000, $54 750, $72 000, $57 890, $38 000, $56 850, $64 790, $46 250, $53 800, $38 000

Property Taxes Paid by Each Home

$2100, $2567, $2250, $2800, $1900, $2538, $2567, $1890, $1995, $2188, $2316, $2198, $2567, $2087, $2000, $2318, $2077, $1999, $2048, $2100, $2199

Cars Driven by Homeowners

4 families drive a Cavalier
2 families drive mini-vans
3 families drive a Monte Carlo
1 family drives a Jaguar
1 family drives a Jeep
2 families drive a Volkswagen
3 families drive a Plymouth Horizon
1 family drives a Lexus
3 families drive a new Saturn
1 family drives a Cadillac

(a) Describe how you would present the data to the couple so they would feel that they could afford to live in the area. Explain why you selected the measure of central tendency that you used as "average."

(b) As a real estate agent, what other information might you also like to have to help you convince the couple to move into the neighbourhood? Why?

Measures of Spread

Both the range and the standard deviation tell you information about the spread of data in a data set. But why might you want to know this information? Consider the following case study.

Case Study 2

Suppose you were Jacques Cartier exploring the St. Lawrence River in 1535. You become stranded and must cross the river without a boat. Your second-in-command says, "Don't worry, Jacques, the average depth of the St. Lawrence is only 1 m. We can walk."

(a) Would you want to know the measure of central tendency used to communicate the average?

(b) Would you now be interested in knowing the spread of the data used to arrive at an average of only 1 m? The range? The standard deviation? Why? Would you be interested to know the actual data?

(c) Is there any other data that you might want to know before you begin your trip across the St. Lawrence River? Why?

Z-Scores

You have seen that z-scores can be used to compare pieces of data from two different sets. You have also seen that the z-score table in Appendix B can be used to find the area to the left of, and underneath, the normal distribution that has a mean of 0 and a standard deviation of 1. To find the z-score for any piece of data in a set that is normally distributed, you can use the formula $z = \frac{x - \bar{x}}{\sigma}$, where x is any observed piece of data, $\bar{x}$ is the mean of the entire data set, and σ is the standard deviation of the entire data set.

Case Study 3

Miguel has been in a car accident. To determine whether he will walk again, he does a range-of-motion test. The average score for the range of motion is 21, with a standard deviation of 3.3. To determine if he will be able to walk again, he must score in the top 90%. What score will Miguel need to achieve to be able to walk again?

Chapter 3 Wrap-Up

EXTRA PRACTICE

1. Calculate a bin width that would form six uniform intervals for the following data.
   (a) 5, 7, 9, 10, 11, 11, 12, 12, 12, 13, 13, 13, 13, 13, 14, 14, 14, 14, 14, 14, 15, 15, 15, 15, 16, 16, 17, 18, 20
   (b) 5.1, 4.7, 8.1, 0.2, 1.1, 2.7, 4.2, 5.8, 10.2, 5.3, 2.7, 7.9, 9.1, 4.0, 4.5, 6.1, 8.8, 4.7, 10.8, 0.6, 8.4, 4.7, 6.3, 7.0, 1.4, 8.6, 2.4, 6.2, 0.4, 4.0
   (c) 136, 132, 151, 142, 156, 145, 139, 164, 107, 137, 118, 156, 130, 165, 144, 106, 139, 97, 152, 165, 157, 116, 115, 145, 167, 163, 197, 127, 145, 109
2. Using the bin width calculated for each part in Question 1, create a frequency distribution and an effective histogram of the data.
3. Calculate the mean, median, and mode for the data in Question 1. Which measure best describes the central tendency of the data? Why?
4. The number of repairs performed on each car owned by ABC rental cars is listed in the table below.

Number of Repairs	0–4	5–9	10–14	15–19	20–24	25–29
Frequency	25	15	6	3	2	4

   (a) Calculate the mean, median, and modal interval of the data given.
   (b) Which measure is most effective in describing the distribution?
5. Listed below are the number of tech-support questions successfully answered each day by Jamil and Antonia over a two-week period.

Antonia	11	13	12	15	10	16
	14	10	10	17	14	13
Jamil	8	15	10	11	16	10
	9	15	11	13	14	17

   (a) Who is the more effective employee?
   (b) Who is the more consistent employee?
6. A local high school wishes to purchase light bulbs with an average life that is normally distributed 9900 h with a standard deviation of 3000 h. Assuming the lifespans of the light bulbs are normally distributed,
   (a) what percent of the bulbs will last at least 13 000 h?
   (b) what percent will burn out before 8000 h?

Chapter 3 Test

1. **Knowledge and Understanding** Create a graph of the following data.

   12.0, 15.0, 13.7, 15.5, 12.7, 14.5, 14.4, 12.8, 14.3, 13.8, 15.2, 16.2, 14.0, 12.4, 15.0, 16.1, 12.9, 13.6, 12.8, 15.2, 13.9, 13.7, 14.6, 16.6, 16.9, 15.1

2. **Application** Consider the following Scrabble scores.

   Min: 140, 110, 130, 155, 182, 132, 175, 107, 168, 174, 135
   Jan: 210, 208, 190, 238, 203, 222, 159, 234, 253, 256, 243
   Gigi: 171, 181, 212, 160, 177, 167, 241, 145, 156, 215, 204

   (a) Calculate the mean, median, and mode of each player's scores.
   (b) Calculate the quartile values, interquartile range, and the standard deviation of each player's scores.
   (c) How many of each player's scores fell within one standard deviation of the mean? Two standard deviations? Three standard deviations?

3. **Communication** Marnie is canvassing for the Canadian Institute for the Blind. Using your knowledge of normal distribution, what range of values should Marnie be prepared to accept this year, if the average donation is \$75 with a standard deviation of \$15. Explain.

4. Researchers have observed that regular smokers have an average lifespan that is normally distributed and is 68 years with a standard deviation of 10 years. What percent of smokers will live beyond age 76?

5. **Thinking, Inquiry, Problem Solving** The lifespan of computers is normally distributed. If computer monitors have an average lifespan of 4.8 years with a standard deviation of 1.42 years, and your company bought 45 monitors (which includes 8 extras), how long until you need to buy more?

6. Calculate a three-day moving average for gas at the local gas station, and create a time-series graph showing the price (¢/L) and the moving average.

65.2	68.1	61.1	63.4	68.7	65.5	63.9	69.1
63.5	65.8	69.9	68.1	71.0	67.7	69.0	69.5

7. An index for comparing professional hockey players uses the formula below. Rank the following players in order by evaluating their "Q-value."

$$Q = 2G + A + \frac{PIM}{5}$$

	G	A	PIM
Jerome Iginla	31	40	62
Joe Thornton	37	34	107
Paul Kariya	33	34	20
Joe Sakic	54	64	30
Doug Weight	25	65	91

G = goals; A = assists; PIM = penalties in minutes

4 Dealing with Uncertainty— An Introduction to Probability

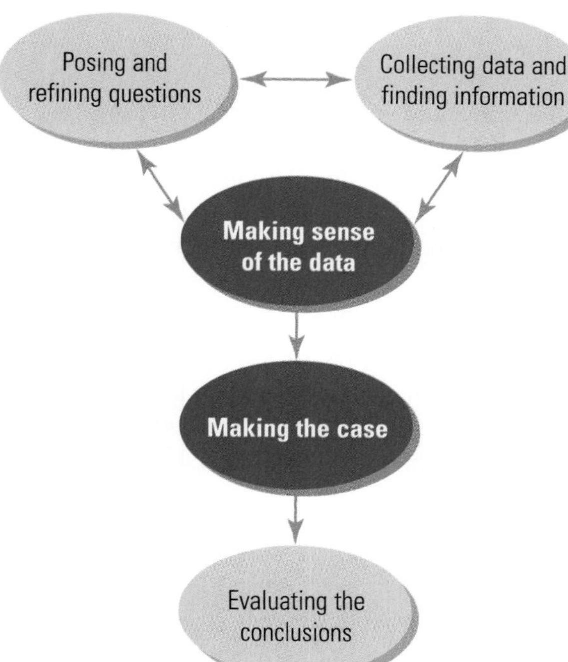

Throughout history, people have been interested in forecasting future events and making predictions. Mathematicians are no exception. One of the major branches of modern mathematics is the "mathematics of chance," commonly referred to as probability.

Our everyday lives are influenced by applications of probability. Meteorologists use probability to predict the weather for the days ahead. Governments and businesses use probability to plan budgets. Insurance companies calculate premiums using tables based on probabilities. Scientists and statisticians use probability to assess the validity of their research.

This chapter will lay the foundation for you to use probability as a means of assessing the validity of your research.

In this chapter, you will

- determine and interpret the experimental probability of an event
- design and carry out simulations
- determine and interpret the theoretical probability of a simple event
- determine and interpret the theoretical probability of a combination of events
- solve counting and probability problems when order matters
- solve counting and probability problems when order doesn't matter

Chapter Problem

Analyzing a Traditional Game

Many games played in North America have their origins in Europe, but some have originated here.

One such game is Da-un-dah-qua. This is a traditional game played at fall and winter festivals by the Cayuga, Aboriginal people from the regions of Western New York and Southern Ontario. Variations of Da-un-dah-qua have also been played by many different Aboriginal nations across North America.

Rules of the Game: Da-un-dah-qua

- If all six counters land with the same side showing, the player earns 5 points and gets another turn.
- If five of the six counters land with the same side showing, the player scores 1 point and gets another turn.
- For all other results, the player scores no points and the other player gets a turn.
- The first player to score 40 points wins the game.

Do you think that scoring 5 points, 1 point, or 0 points are equally likely? Why is the scoring system structured this way? In this chapter, as you learn new concepts involving probability, you will apply what you have learned to answer these and other questions. For help with this problem, you will be asked questions throughout this chapter.

Project Connection

Probability can be used to check whether or not the collected data are representative of what will typically happen. This can then help you assess the validity of any conclusions you draw from a sample or simulation.

This chapter will introduce you to some of the basic concepts involving probability. In the chapter that follows, you will put these concepts into practice and will see how probability concepts can be applied to your project.

4.1 An Introduction to Simulations and Experimental Probability

"This medical test will identify an illness correctly 90% of the time."

— Katherine Strain

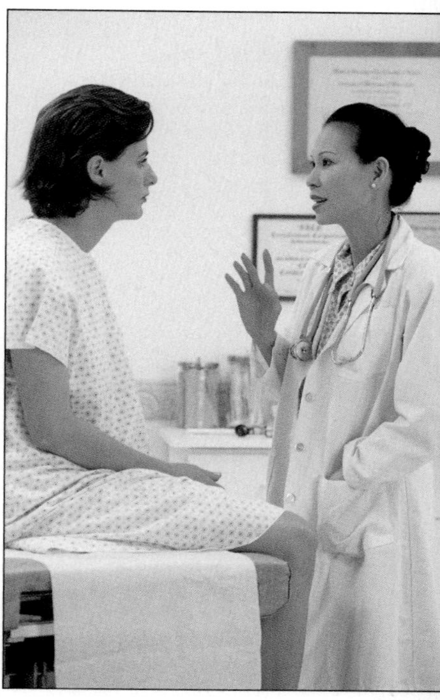

Some probability statements deal with events that are very personal. For example, you may predict your chances of getting a job. A measure of probability for an event like this can only be estimated, based on experience, and cannot be calculated exactly.

When dealing with events like the survival rates for certain medical procedures, probability measures can be determined by looking at real data, such as the frequency of death, gathered over a period of time. It may also be helpful to design a simulation that will assist you in estimating the probability of an event.

INVESTIGATION 1: THE COFFEE GAME

Suppose each morning you play a simple game with a friend to determine who pays for coffee. Your friend tosses a coin and you call it. If you are right, your friend pays $2.00 ($1.00 for each cup of coffee); otherwise, you pay.

fair game—a game is fair if
- all players have an equal chance of winning, or
- each player can expect to win or lose the same number of times in the long run

Purpose

To determine (a) if this is a **fair game**, and (b) how much you would expect to pay each five-day workweek.

Procedure

A. Have a friend flip a coin while you predict the outcome.
B. Your friend pays if you call the result correctly; otherwise, you pay. Record who pays $2.00 that day.
C. Repeat this four more times to simulate one workweek.
D. Repeat the simulation in Steps A to C nine more times.
E. Graph your average daily coffee cost over the simulated 10-week period.

? Think about Step E
How does graphing the average weekly coffee cost help you determine how much you should expect to pay each week?

Each toss of the coin represents what is called a simple event; the results, *heads* or *tails,* are called outcomes.

One week's worth of coffee payments represents a compound event, which is the result of combining five coin tosses or **trials**, one for each weekday. The daily cost of coffee is a quantity that is the result of a random event, and is called the **random variable**. It has a finite number of possible values ($0.00 or $2.00), so it is called a **discrete random variable**.

trial—one repetition of an experiment

random variable—a variable whose value corresponds to the outcome of a random event

discrete random variable—a variable that assumes a unique value for each outcome

expected value—informally, the value the average of the random variable's values tends toward after many repetitions

It is possible that, for any given week, either you or your friend could lose every coin toss. Nevertheless, if the game is fair, both of you should expect to win or lose half the time. Since the total cost of coffee is $2.00 a day, the **expected value** for your daily coffee cost is $1.00. The expected value for the week is, therefore, $5.00.

Discussion Questions

1. Based on your results, explain whether or not the coffee game represents a fair game.
2. How many trials would be needed before you could predict the expected weekly cost with confidence? Explain your answer. (**Note:** You need to make sure that the number of trials is large enough to permit a valid generalization.)
3. **(a)** Would the game be fair if, instead of tossing a coin, your partner rolled a six-sided die and you had to guess the result? Explain your answer.
   (b) In part (a), how much would you expect to have to pay each day? How much would your partner expect to pay? Explain your answer.

Defining Probability

An experiment consists of repeated trials in which a particular event and the outcomes of that event are noted.

A measure of the likelihood of an event is called the *probability* of the event and is based on how often that event occurs in comparison with the total number of trials. The probabilities examined in this section are derived from experiments and are, therefore, called **experimental probabilities**.

? Think about Probability
If an experiment has six equally likely events, what is the probability of each event?

event—a set of possible outcomes of an experiment

Experimental Probability

Experimental probability is the observed probability (sometimes called the relative frequency) of an **event**, A, in an experiment and is found using the following formula:

$$P(A) = \frac{\text{number of times the desired event occurred}}{\text{number of trials}}$$

INVESTIGATION 2: SIMULATING THE COFFEE GAME

simulation—an experiment that models an actual event

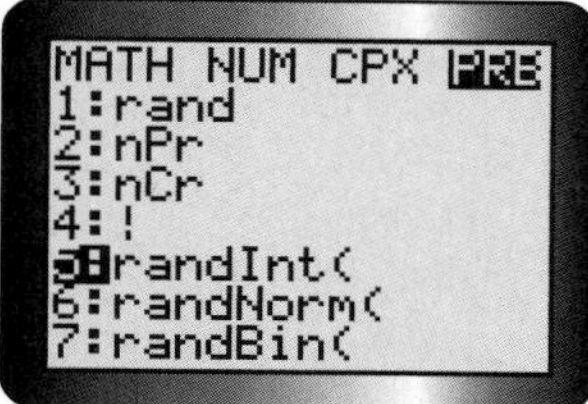

Investigation 1 simulated 10 weeks of coffee purchases; your results likely varied from one week to the next. To be more confident of your result, you need to perform a larger number of trials.

In this **simulation**, you will first combine the data collected by the entire class to increase the number of trials. You will then conduct a simulation using a TI-83 Plus calculator, which will generate the random integers 0 or 1. (**Note:** The **randInt** command is used to generate random integers between two given integer values. This command is accessed using the MATH key.)

The first random integer will represent the actual coin toss. (Outcomes will be 0 = heads and 1 = tails.) The second random integer will represent your guess. You win when the two integer outcomes are the same and you lose when they are different.

Technolink
For more information on using **randInt**, see Appendix C. 11 on page 408.

Purpose

To test the validity of your results from Investigation 1 by performing a large number of trials.

Procedure 1—Combining Data

A. Combine the data that was gathered during Investigation 1 by each pair of students in your class.

Discussion Questions

Think about Trials
Why does increasing the number of trials provide a better prediction for the expected values?

1. How many trials does this represent?
2. Use the results to estimate the fraction of trials that resulted in
   (a) your winning **(b)** your losing
3. Use the results to estimate the following.
   (a) the probability that you will have to buy coffee at some point during the week
   (b) the probability that you won't have to buy coffee at all during the week
   (c) your average or expected daily coffee cost
   (d) your average or expected weekly coffee cost
4. Compare your initial expected weekly coffee cost with the result obtained in part (d) above. Which result do you feel is the best indicator of what will happen when you play this game? Why?

Project Connection
If your project involves analyzing a process, you might want to construct a simulation to help you determine the likelihood of a result.

Procedure 2—TI-83 Plus Calculator Simulation

A. Select the MATH key. Use the **randInt** command to create a pair of random integers. Press the ENTER key five times to simulate one week.

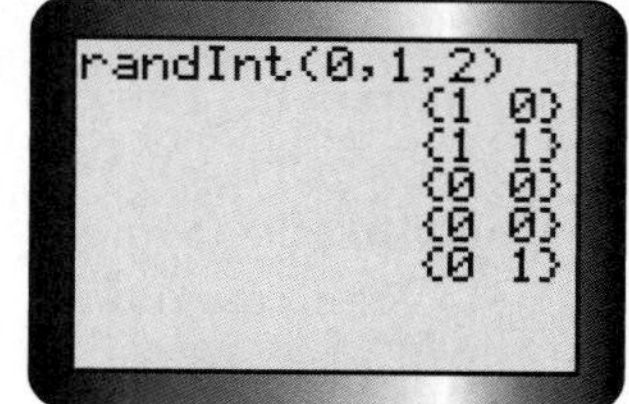

B. Record the results of the weekly simulation in a chart similar to the one below. Remember that {0 0} and {1 1} are wins for you and everything else is a win for your partner.

Week	Wins	Losses	Total Cost
1	3	2	$4.00
2			

C. Repeat Steps A and B 30 times, recording the weekly results in your chart each time.

Discussion Questions

1. After 30 weeks, use your results to estimate the fraction of the daily trials that you

(a) win **(b)** lose

2. Use your simulation results to estimate the following.

(a) the probability that you will have to buy coffee at some point during the week
(b) the probability that you won't have to buy coffee at all in a week
(c) your expected daily coffee cost
(d) your expected weekly coffee cost

3. Design and carry out a simulation of the coffee game using a six-sided die instead of a coin. You win if you guess correctly. Use your simulation results to estimate the following.

(a) the probability that you will have to buy coffee at some point during the week
(b) the probability that you won't have to buy coffee at all in a week
(c) your expected daily coffee cost
(d) your expected weekly coffee cost

Example 1 Simulating Birth Sequences

Suppose a family plans to have four children. Use a simulation to estimate the likelihood that the family will have three girls in a row and then a boy.

Solution 1 *No technology required*

Since there are only two possible outcomes for each birth, tossing a single coin four times in a row will provide a good simulation of one trial. Associate heads (H) with the birth of a girl and tails (T) with the birth of a boy.

We could speed up the process by using four different coins (to represent the four births) and tossing them simultaneously. Associate a penny with birth 1, a nickel with birth 2, a dime with birth 3, and a quarter with birth 4.

Record 30 trials on paper and then calculate the experimental probability.

Solution 2 *Using a TI-83 Plus calculator*

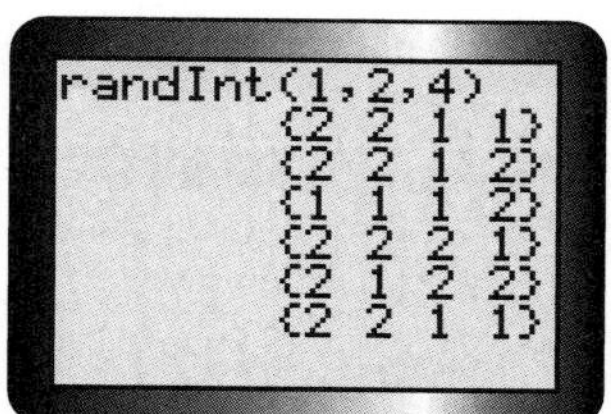

randInt(1,2,4) will generate a list of four random integer values between 1 and 2. Associate 1 with a female birth and 2 with a male birth. One of the six trials shown represents three girls followed by a boy. Using only these trials, we could estimate the likelihood of this pattern as one in every six sequences of four births. However, more trials are needed to be confident of that result. Generate 30 trials and then calculate the experimental probability.

Solution 3 *Using a spreadsheet*

Technolink

The formula used to generate a random integer between 1 and 2 is =INT(2*RAND()+1). For more information on using formulas in spreadsheets, see Appendix E.1 on page 425 and Appendix E.3 on page 426.

A full spreadsheet for this simulation showing the results of 1000 trials can be found on the textbook CD.

A spreadsheet can also be used to simulate a large number of trials. Copy the given formula to 30 rows and then use your results to calculate the experimental probability.

	A	B	C	D	E
1	Trial #	Birth 1	Birth 2	Birth 3	Birth 4
2	1	2	1	1	1
3	2	1	2	1	2
4	3	2	1	1	1
5	4	1	2	1	1
6	5	2	2	1	2
7	6	1	1	1	1
8	7	1	2	2	2
9	8	2	1	2	1
10	9	1	1	1	1
11	10	2	1	1	1

Example 2 Batting Averages

Suppose that Nicola has a batting average of 0.320. This indicates 32 hits in every 100 attempts (or 8 hits in 25 attempts). Use a simulation to estimate the likelihood that this player has no hits in a game (assuming three at-bats per game).

Solution 1 *No technology required*

Think about
Replacement

Why is it important for the chosen slip to be returned to the container?

Fill a container with 25 slips of paper, 8 of which have the word HIT written on them. Draw one slip of paper out of the container and record the result, making sure to return it before you draw again. Repeat the draw a total of three times to simulate one game.

After recording 30 game simulations, count the number of outcomes that satisfy the condition and calculate the experimental probability.

Solution 2 *Using a TI-83 Plus calculator*

randInt(1,1000,3) will generate a list of three random integer values between 1 and 1000. Associate 1 through 320 with a hit and 321 through 1000 with an out.

{778 215 35}
{568 2 325}
{664 895 655}
{60 382 452}
{260 157 894}
{887 593 523}
{739 344 651}

In the seven trials shown, there are

- three games (third, sixth, and seventh) in which the batter did not get a hit;
- two games (first and fifth) in which the batter got two hits; and
- two games (second and fourth) in which the batter got one hit.

Conduct 30 game simulations, then count the number of outcomes that satisfy the condition and calculate the experimental probability.

Solution 3 *Using Fathom™*

Fathom™ was used to generate 100 cases in which three at-bats were simulated using random integers between 1 and 1000. Each case had three at-bats. A filter is a logical test used to exclude all cases except the ones that meet that condition. When a filter was applied to display only those cases for which all three at-bats were 321 or more, 37 cases met that condition. A portion of this case table for this simulation appears below.

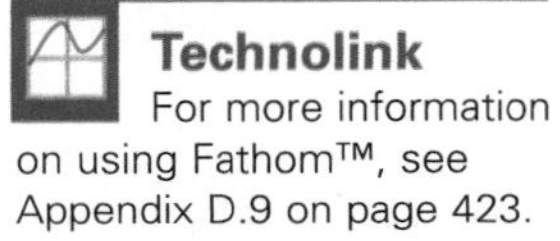
Technolink
For more information on using Fathom™, see Appendix D.9 on page 423.

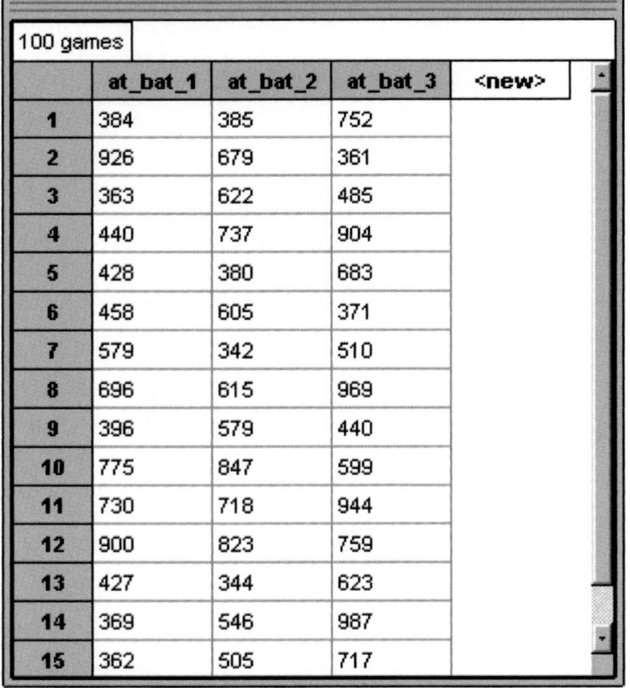
100 games

	at_bat_1	at_bat_2	at_bat_3	<new>
1	384	385	752	
2	926	679	361	
3	363	622	485	
4	440	737	904	
5	428	380	683	
6	458	605	371	
7	579	342	510	
8	696	615	969	
9	396	579	440	
10	775	847	599	
11	730	718	944	
12	900	823	759	
13	427	344	623	
14	369	546	987	
15	362	505	717	

The simulation provided an estimate that the player would get no hits in 37 of the 100 games during the season.

KEY IDEAS

fair game—all players have an equal chance of winning, or each player can expect to win or lose the same number of times in the long run

trial—one repetition of an experiment

random variable—a variable whose value corresponds to the outcome of a random event

discrete random variable—a variable that assumes a unique value for each outcome

expected value—informally, the value the average of the random variable's values tends toward after many repetitions

experimental probability—the observed probability of an event, A, in an experiment is found using the formula

$$P(A) = \frac{\text{number of times the desired event occurred}}{\text{number of trials}}$$

simulation—an experiment that models an actual event

4.1 Exercises

1. Explain how you could conduct a simulation to determine the probability of these situations.
   (a) guessing the correct answer on at least 7 of 10 true/false questions
   (b) choosing a yellow tulip bulb from a bin if one in six of the bulbs in the bin is yellow

2. **(a)** Shuffle a standard deck of 52 cards, draw a single card, and record it. Return the card to the deck, reshuffle, draw another card, and record it. Repeat the process at least 50 times. Use your experimental results to estimate the probability of drawing a queen from the deck on each draw.

   (b) For this experiment,
   (i) describe what constitutes a simple event;
   (ii) determine the required number of trials; and
   (iii) describe the event that is of interest to the experimenter.

3. **Knowledge and Understanding**
   (a) Toss a coin 100 times. Complete a chart like the one below using your results.

Number of Repetitions	Total Number of Heads	Observed Probability
10		
20		
30		
⋮		
100		

   (b) For this experiment,
      (i) graph the relative frequency versus the number of trials;
      (ii) describe what constitutes a trial;
      (iii) determine the simple event that is the focus of this experiment; and
      (iv) identify what happens to the observed probability as the number of tosses increases.

4. When tossed, a thumbtack can land one of two ways: on its head with the point sticking up, or on its side with the point resting on the ground.
   (a) Conduct an experiment to estimate the probability that a thumbtack, when tossed, will land with its point sticking up.
   (b) What is the probability that a thumbtack, when tossed, will land on its side?
   (c) What is the expected number of tacks that will land with their point sticking up when 500 are tossed simultaneously?

5. What is the probability of scoring 50% or better on a true/false quiz if you guess at every answer?
   (a) Use 10 coins to design a simulation that enables you to estimate this probability.
   (b) Carry out your simulation 20 times.
   (c) Combine your results with those of three or four classmates, and estimate the probability of passing the quiz if you guess at every answer.

Technolink
Remember that **randInt** can be used to generate a list of random numbers.

6. Use a TI-83 Plus calculator to simulate 100 trials of the experiment described in Question 3. Record your results. Use the results of your simulation to find the experimental probability of
   (a) getting a head
   (b) getting a run of three or more heads in a row

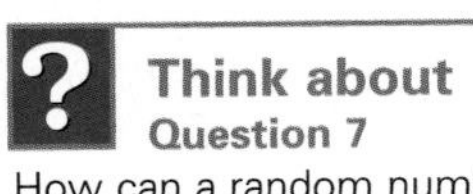

Think about Question 7
How can a random number represent a card taken from a standard deck?

7. Use a TI-83 Plus calculator to simulate 100 trials of the experiment described in Question 2. Record your results. Use the results of your simulation to find the experimental probability of
   (a) drawing a queen
   (b) drawing a queen three times in a row

8. Imagine that you are taking a multiple-choice test in which all questions have five possible answers, only one of which is correct. Suppose that the correct choices are A, E, C, D, D. Describe a simulation that would help you determine the probability of getting exactly three questions correct strictly by guessing.

B

9. **Communication** The following spreadsheet shows the results of a simulation experiment in which three coins were tossed simultaneously.

	A	B	C	D	E	F
1	Coin 1	Coin 2	Coin 3	Coin 1	Coin 2	Coin 3
2	1	0	1	1	0	0
3	0	1	1	1	1	0
4	1	0	0	1	0	1
5	0	1	1	1	1	0
6	0	0	1	1	0	0
7	0	1	0	0	1	1
8	0	1	0	0	0	0
9	1	1	1	1	1	1
10	0	0	1	0	0	1

(a) Explain how a collection of randomly generated ones and zeros can simulate the experiment described above.

(b) Suppose that 1 represents a head and 0 represents a tail. Based on the results of this simulation, what is the experimental probability of getting three heads in one toss of the three coins? Explain your answer.

(c) Describe what you would do to get a better estimate for the probability in part (b).

(d) Explain how this experiment could also be used to simulate the sequence of the gender of three children born to a given family.

(e) Describe the advantages of using a spreadsheet to simulate this experiment instead of repeatedly tossing the coins.

10. A field-goal kicker for a high school football team has an 80% success rate based on his attempts this year. Design and describe a simulation that will help you determine the experimental probability that he might miss three field goals in a row.

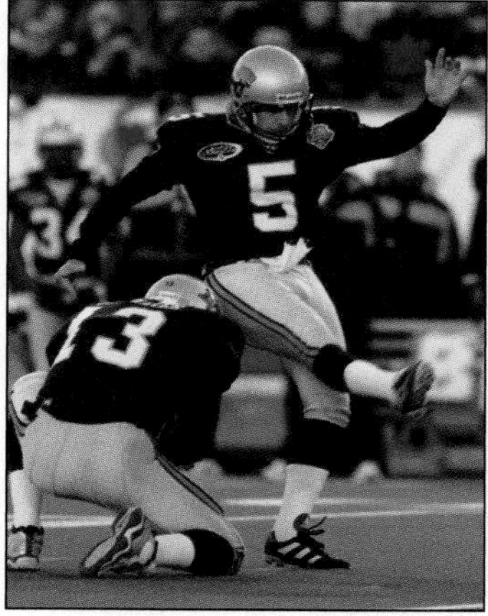

11. Ten percent of the keyboards a computer company manufactures are defective. Design and describe a simulation that will determine the experimental probability that one or more of the next three keyboards to come off the assembly line will be defective.

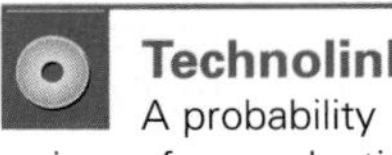

Technolink A probability spinner for conducting simulations can be found on the textbook CD.

12. Suppose that 70% of all people in Ontario wear seat belts.

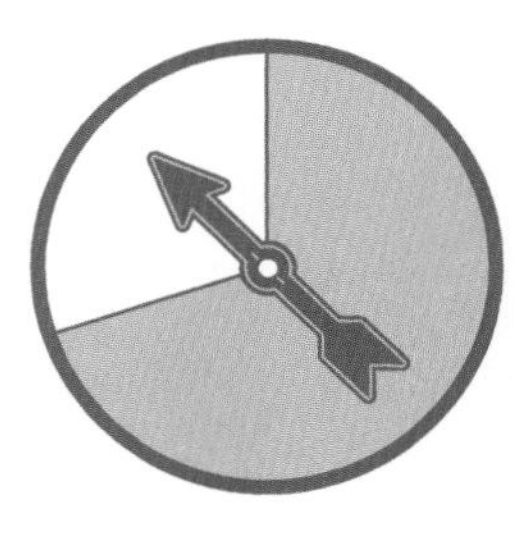

(a) Explain how the spinner shown could be used to simulate how many people in a random sample wear seat belts.
(b) If you would like to know how many people out of a randomly selected group of 30 are likely to wear seat belts, would 30 trials give you enough data? Explain.

13. Suppose there is one of six bonus stickers in each pack of hockey cards and there is an equal chance of getting each sticker. Describe a simulation to find the number of packs of hockey cards you might need to buy in order to get all six stickers.

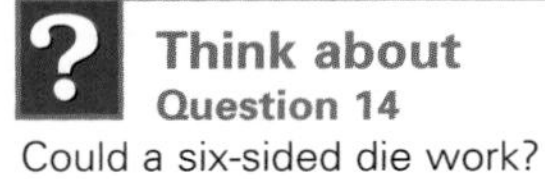

Think about Question 14
Could a six-sided die work?

14. **Application** Imagine that the first traffic light you encounter on your way to school each morning has a 60-s cycle in which it is green for 20 s. Design and carry out a simulation experiment to estimate the probability that you will get a green light on the next three morning trips to school.

Technolink For more information on programming with a TI-83 Plus calculator, see Appendix C.12 on page 408.

15. **Thinking, Inquiry, Problem Solving** Look up the commands associated with the PRGM menu key in the TI-83 Plus calculator user guide and learn how to write a program on a TI-83 Plus calculator. Write a program that simulates the situation described in Question 14 using 100 trials, and displays a bar graph that compares the number of green lights and red lights at the intersection.

ADDITIONAL ACHIEVEMENT CHART QUESTIONS

16. **Knowledge and Understanding** Design a simulation that will allow you to estimate the probability of having five boys in a family of five children. Carry out the simulation and estimate the probability of this event.

17. **Application** A matchbox, when tossed, can land one of three ways: on its front/back, on its end, or on its side. Estimate the probability that when a matchbox is tossed, it lands on its end.

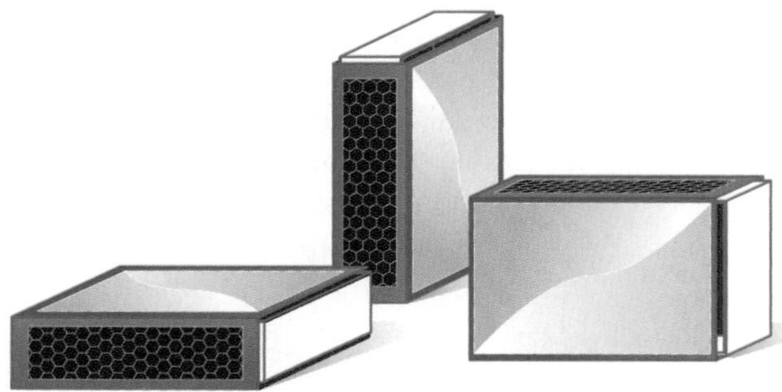

18. Thinking, Inquiry, Problem Solving

(a) Do some research to find the particulars of the needle probability problem investigated by Comte de Buffon in 1760. What was the problem and what were his findings?

(b) Conduct your own simulation to validate his findings and write a report that describes your findings.

19. Communication What are some advantages and disadvantages of using simulations to make predictions about real-world situations?

Chapter Problem

Analyzing a Traditional Game

CP1. Make a list of all possible outcomes for one toss of the counters in the game Da-un-dah-qua.

CP2. Which event do you think is most likely? Explain.

CP3. Design a simulation for this game. If you choose not to use technology, mark the counters so that both faces are different colours. Use black on one side and red on the other.

CP4. With a partner, play the game until someone wins (accumulates 40 points). You may need to refer to page 202 to review the rules of the game. On a piece of paper, record the outcome of each turn.

CP5. Use the results of your game to estimate the probability of each possible outcome in this game. Do your estimates seem reasonable?

CP6. How could you gather additional data to refine your estimates?

4.2 Theoretical Probability

North Wind Picture Archives

The study of probability began with the analysis of games of chance by the mathematicians Cardano, Galileo (pictured), Pascal, and Fermat. When you state the probability of an event, you are making a statement about the likelihood of that event occurring.

How do you find the probability of an event without performing an experiment?

GENERAL DEFINITION OF PROBABILITY

The previous section introduced you to the concept of experimental probability. Actual data were used to determine the relative frequency of a particular event.

Probability is often used to predict the likelihood that a particular event will occur. Experimental probabilities or relative frequencies determined from surveys only give an estimate of the likelihood that a particular event will occur.

It is possible to determine a more accurate probability for some events, such as rolling a 4 on a die. For example, in rolling a die six times, 4 may show up twice, so the experimental probability is $\frac{2}{6}$.

simple event—an event that consists of exactly one outcome

However, we know that there are six possible outcomes when a die is rolled. Only one of these outcomes is the event of rolling a 4. This is an example of a **simple event**. Since the possible outcomes are all equally likely to happen, it is reasonable to expect that the fraction of the time you roll a 4 is the ratio of the number of ways a 4 can occur to the number of possible outcomes.

$$P(\text{rolling a } 4) = \frac{1}{6}$$

theoretical probability—when all the outcomes of an experiment that correspond to an event are equally likely, the probability of the event is the ratio of the number of outcomes that make up that event to the total number of possible outcomes

The resulting value is called the **theoretical probability**. Given a large enough number of trials, the theoretical probability and the experimental probability should be approximately equal.

? Think about Probability

- Why is the minimum value of a probability 0?
- Why is the maximum value of a probability 1?
- Probability is often expressed as a ratio. What other ways can probability be expressed?

sample space—the collection of all possible outcomes of the experiment

event space—the collection of all outcomes of an experiment that correspond to a particular event

Theoretical Probability

Assuming that all outcomes are equally likely, the probability of an event in an experiment is the ratio of the number of outcomes that make up that event to the total number of possible outcomes.

The formula for the probability of an event A is

$$P(A) = \frac{n(A)}{n(S)}$$

where

- S is the collection of all possible outcomes of the experiment—the **sample space**;
- A is the collection of outcomes that correspond to the event of interest—the **event space**; and
- the mathematical notation $n(A)$ means the "number of elements in the set A." Both $n(A)$ and $n(S)$ are the numbers of elements in the two sets.

A Venn diagram can be used to show the relationship between the event space, A, and the sample space, S. The use of Venn diagrams as possible solution tools will be explored in Section 4.3 on page 221.

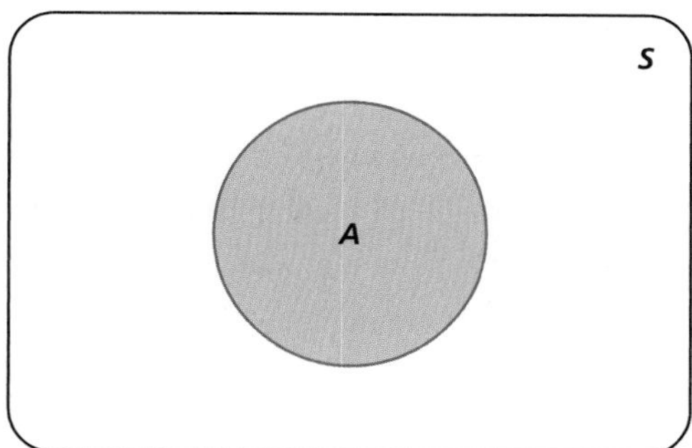

Example 1 Choosing Coloured Marbles From a Bag

A bag contains five red marbles, three blue marbles, and two white marbles. What is the probability of drawing a blue marble?

Solution

The event of selecting a blue marble consists of three possible outcomes (one for each blue marble). Therefore,

$$\begin{aligned} P(\text{blue}) &= \frac{\text{number of blue marbles}}{\text{number of marbles in the bag}} \\ &= \frac{n(A)}{n(S)} \\ &= \frac{3}{10} \end{aligned}$$

Example 2 Rolling a Die

If a single die is rolled, determine the probability of rolling

(a) an even number **(b)** a number greater than 2

Solution

(a) A die has six sides. Each side has a series of dots that represent the numbers 1 to 6. The event of rolling an even number contains the outcomes 2, 4, and 6.

$$P(\text{even number}) = \frac{\text{number of even numbers}}{\text{total number of possible outcomes}}$$
$$= \frac{3}{6} = \frac{1}{2}$$

(b)
$$P(\text{number} > 2) = \frac{\text{number of numbers greater than 2}}{\text{total number of possible outcomes}}$$
$$= \frac{4}{6} = \frac{2}{3}$$

Probability and Complementary Events

In Example 2, $P(\text{number} > 2) = \frac{2}{3}$. What is $P(\text{number} \leq 2)$? The event of a number ≤ 2 contains all outcomes in the sample space that are not in A (number > 2). These numbers are in the complement of A and are represented by A'.

> **Probability and Complementary Events**
>
> The *complement* of a set, A, is written as A' and consists of all the outcomes in the sample space that are not in set A.
>
> $$A' = \{\text{outcomes in } S \text{ that are NOT in } A\}$$

The Venn diagram shows A' as the shaded region within S that is entirely outside of A.

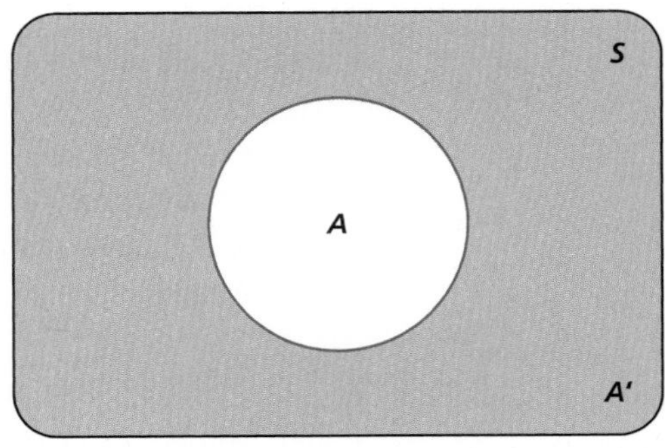

> **Probability of a Complementary Event**
>
> If A is an event in a sample space, the probability of the complementary event, A', is given by
>
> $$P(A') = 1 - P(A)$$

Example 3 Drawing an Ace From a Standard Deck of Cards

A standard deck of cards comprises 52 cards in four suits—clubs, hearts, diamonds, and spades. Each suit consists of 13 cards—ace through 10, jack, queen, and king.

What is the probability of drawing an ace from a well-shuffled deck? What is the probability of drawing anything but an ace?

Solution

> **? Think about The Sample Space**
> - What is the complement of the entire sample space S?
> - What is the value of $P(S)$? Of $P(S')$?

The drawing of any single card from the deck is as likely as the drawing of any other card. There are 4 aces in a deck of 52 cards. The sample space has 52 elements and there are 4 outcomes that correspond to drawing an ace.

Therefore,

$$P(\text{ace}) = \frac{\text{number of aces in the deck}}{\text{number of cards in the deck}}$$
$$= \frac{4}{52}$$
$$= \frac{1}{13}$$
$$P(\text{not an ace}) = 1 - P(\text{ace})$$
$$= 1 - \frac{1}{13}$$
$$= \frac{12}{13}$$

KEY IDEAS

sample space—the collection of all possible outcomes of an experiment

event space—the collection of all outcomes of an experiment that correspond to a particular event

simple event—an event that consists of exactly one outcome

theoretical probability—the ratio of the number of outcomes that make up that event to the total number of possible outcomes

$$P(A) = \frac{n(A)}{n(S)}$$

where

- S is the collection of all possible outcomes of the experiment;
- A is the collection of outcomes that correspond to the event of interest; and
- $n(A)$ and $n(S)$ are the numbers of elements in the two sets.

probability of a complementary event—if A is an event in a sample space, the probability of the complementary event, A', is given by $P(A') = 1 - P(A)$

4.2 Exercises

A

1. Suppose you conduct an experiment in which you draw a card from a standard 52-card deck. List the outcomes in the following event spaces.
   (a) you draw a seven of diamonds
   (b) you draw an ace
   (c) you draw a numbered club
   (d) you draw an even-numbered card of any suit

2. **(a)** Which of the events in Question 1 can be classified as simple events?
   (b) Compute the theoretical probability of each event in Question 1.

3. **Knowledge and Understanding** Three black marbles and two red marbles are in a box. One marble is secretly drawn from the box.
   (a) What is the total number of possible outcomes?
   (b) What is the probability that the marble selected is black?
   (c) What is the probability that the marble selected is red?
   (d) What is the probability that the marble selected is neither red nor black?

4. Suppose the two joker cards are left in a standard deck of cards. One of the jokers is red and the other is black. A single card is drawn from the deck of 54 cards. Determine the probability of drawing
   (a) one of the jokers **(b)** the red joker
   (c) a queen **(d)** any black card
   (e) any card less than 10 (an ace has a value of one)
   (f) the red joker or a red ace

5. Determine the theoretical probability for each of the following events.
   (a) getting tails with a coin toss
   (b) rolling a 3 on a die
   (c) drawing a red card from a well-shuffled deck
   (d) drawing a black seven from a well-shuffled deck
   (e) drawing anything but a face card from a well-shuffled deck

B

6. A spinner is divided into eight equal sectors, numbered 1 through 8.
   (a) What is the probability of spinning an odd number?
   (b) What is the probability of spinning a number divisible by 4?
   (c) What is the probability of spinning a number less than 3?

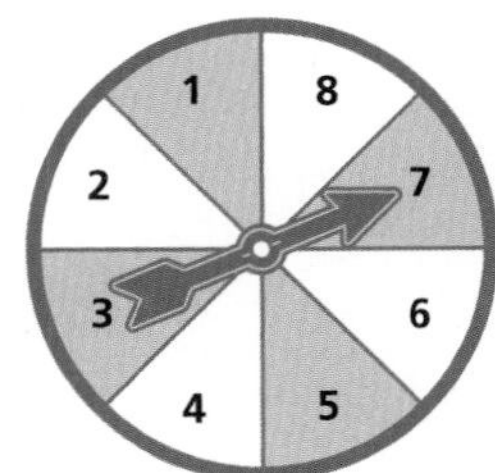

7. A bag contains 12 identically shaped blocks, 3 of which are red and the remainder are green. The bag is well-shaken and a single block is drawn.
   (a) What is the probability that the block is red?
   (b) What is the probability that the block is not red?

8. Each of the letters for the word MATHEMATICS is printed on same-sized pieces of paper and placed in a hat. The hat is shaken and one piece of paper is drawn.
   (a) What is the probability that the letter S is selected?
   (b) What is the probability that the letter M is selected?
   (c) What is the probability that a vowel is selected?

9. **Communication** In the game of Bingo, the numbers 1 to 75 are marked on balls and drawn from a container that constantly mixes the balls. Fifteen balls, numbered 1 to 15, are marked with a B; the next 15 with an I; and so on.

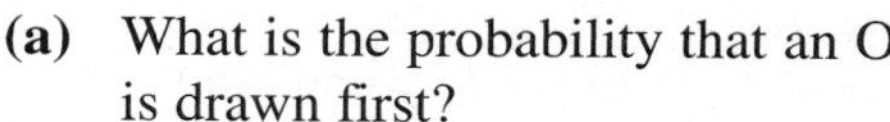

   (a) What is the probability that an O is drawn first?

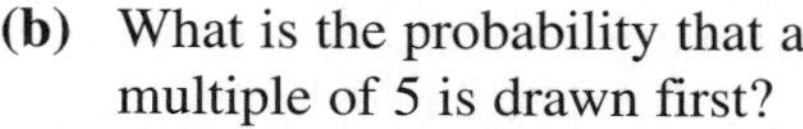

   (b) What is the probability that a multiple of 5 is drawn first?
   (c) Which is more likely to occur when the first ball is drawn, an even number or an odd number? Justify your answer.

10. Three coins are tossed at the same time. Find the probability that
   (a) all come up heads
   (b) at least one comes up tails
   (c) exactly two come up heads

11. **Application** A colour TV is given as a door prize at a dance. A total of 360 tickets are sold and are numbered 1–360. If the winning ticket is drawn at random, find the probability that the winning ticket is between 220 and 280 (excluding 220 and 280).

12. Two dice are rolled: one is red and the other is white.
   (a) How many outcomes are possible?
   (b) Determine the probability that the sum of the two dice totals 7.
   (c) Determine the probability that the sum of the two dice totals anything but 7.

13. You are dialing a friend's phone number but can't remember the last digit. If you guess at the final digit, what is the probability that you dialed the number correctly?

C

14. **Thinking, Inquiry, Problem Solving** A picnic cooler contains different types of cola: 12 regular, 8 cherry, 10 diet, 6 diet cherry, 8 caffeine-free, and some caffeine-free diet. You pick a can of cola without looking at its type. There is a 44% chance that the drink selected is diet. How many caffeine-free diet colas are in the cooler?

15. Studies show that when people are asked to choose one of the integers 1, 2, 3, or 4, more than half of the people choose the same number. Conduct this experiment in your class and determine which number was chosen more often. Explain why asking a person to choose a number is not the same as randomly selecting a number.

ADDITIONAL ACHIEVEMENT CHART QUESTIONS

16. **Knowledge and Understanding** Sarah has five blues CDs, four rap CDs, and nine alternative CDs in the console of her car. If she reaches in and grabs a CD, what is the probability that it is a rap CD?

17. **Communication** What is the difference between an outcome and an event? Use an example in your explanation.

18. **Application** Four students—Mark, Barry, Rita, and Francine—must present their class projects today. The teacher puts their names in a hat and selects the order in which they will present. Determine the probability that the boys will start and end today's presentations.

19. **Thinking, Inquiry, Problem Solving** Find the probability that a number chosen at random between 1 and 100 is divisible by 2 or 7.

Chapter Problem

Analyzing a Traditional Game

CP7. What is the theoretical probability that one of the counters in the game turns up black? Red? What assumptions must you make when calculating these probabilities?

CP8. Based on what you know, is it possible to easily determine the theoretical probability of each outcome in the game? Why or why not?

4.3 Finding Probability Using Sets

COUNTING OUTCOMES WITH VENN DIAGRAMS

Venn diagram—a diagram in which sets are represented by shaded or coloured geometrical shapes

A **Venn diagram**—named after John Venn (1834–1923), a British priest and logician—can be used to graphically describe the relationships between possible results of an experiment (or survey). **Compound events** are shown as combinations of simpler events. All the events exist within the larger collection of all possible outcomes of the experiment. This large set is called the sample space for the experiment. The letter S commonly represents the sample space.

The Master and Fellows of Gonville and Caius College, Cambridge

compound event—consists of two or more simple events

Venn Diagrams and Set Terminology

The following terminology and symbols are used in working with sets.

> **Intersection of Sets**
>
> Given two sets, A and B, the set of common elements is called the *intersection* of A and B, and is written as $A \cap B$.
>
> These common elements are members of set A and are also elements of set B. Consequently,
>
> $$A \cap B = \{\text{elements in both } A \text{ AND } B\}$$

subset—a set whose members are all members of another set

The set $A \cap B$ is represented by the region of overlap of the two sets in the Venn diagram to the right. Sets A and B exist as sets within the larger set S. They are **subsets** of the set S.

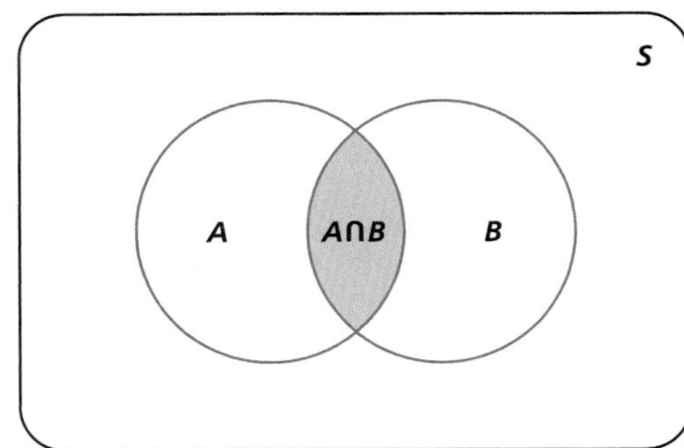

disjoint—two sets that have no elements in common

Disjoint Sets

If A and B have no elements in common (i.e., $n(A \cap B) = 0$), they are said to be **disjoint** and their intersection is the *empty set*, represented by the Greek letter $\varnothing$ (i.e., $A \cap B = \varnothing$).

The Venn diagram to the right shows disjoint sets A and B.

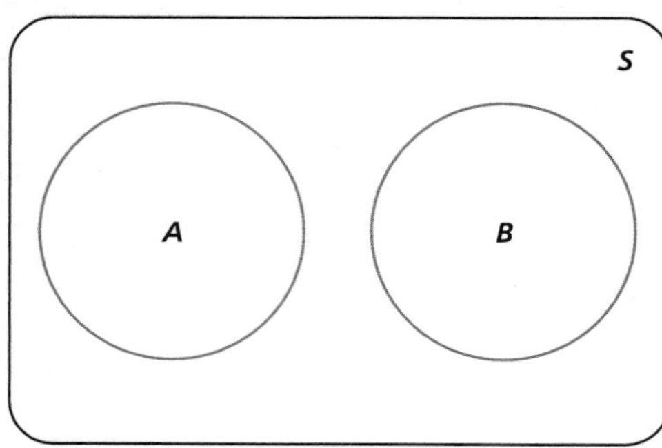

union—the set containing all of the elements in A as well as B

Union of Sets

The set formed by combining the elements of A with those in B is called the **union** of A and B, and is written as $A \cup B$.

The elements in $A \cup B$ are elements of A **or** they are elements of B. Consequently,

$$A \cup B = \{\text{elements in } A \text{ OR } B\}$$

The set $A \cup B$ is represented by the shaded area in the Venn diagram to the right.

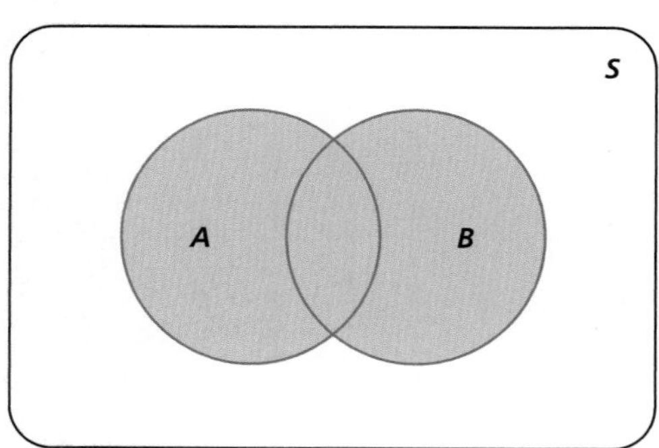

? Think about The Sample Space
What is the value of $P(\varnothing)$? Of $P(\varnothing')$?

Discussion Questions

1. Why is $n(\varnothing') = n(S)$?

2. Why is $n(S') = n(\varnothing)$?

3. If A and B are disjoint, why is $n(A \cup B) = n(A) + n(B)$?

4. If A and B are not disjoint, why is $n(A \cup B) < n(A) + n(B)$?

Example 1 Using a Venn Diagram to Solve a Counting Problem

Suppose a survey of 100 Grade 12 mathematics students in a local high school produced the following results.

Math Course Taken	Number of Students
Advanced Functions and Introductory Calculus (AFIC)	80
Geometry and Discrete Math	33
Data Management	68
Geometry and Discrete Math and AFIC	30
Geometry and Discrete Math and Data Management	6
Data Management and AFIC	50
All three courses	5

How many students are enrolled in AFIC and in no other mathematics course? How many students are enrolled in AFIC? Or Data Management?

Solution

Construct a Venn diagram to represent the three groups of students. For convenience, we can label the sets as C for AFIC, D for Data Management, and G for Geometry and Discrete Math. The entire sample space, S, will consist of all the students in Grade 12.

Think about Completing the Diagram

How could you use the information to complete all the remaining sections of the diagram? Remember, there are 100 students enrolled in Grade 12 math.

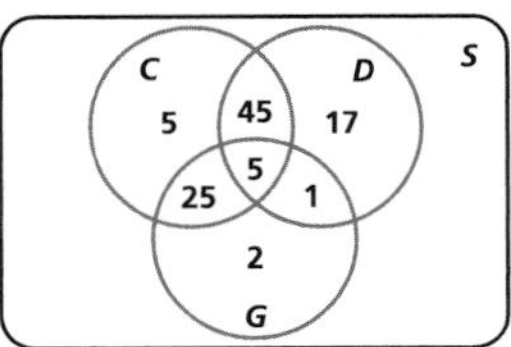

We will use the information in the chart to fill in each region of the Venn diagram. To avoid double-counting, you should start entering information from the chart in the very middle of the diagram and work your way out.

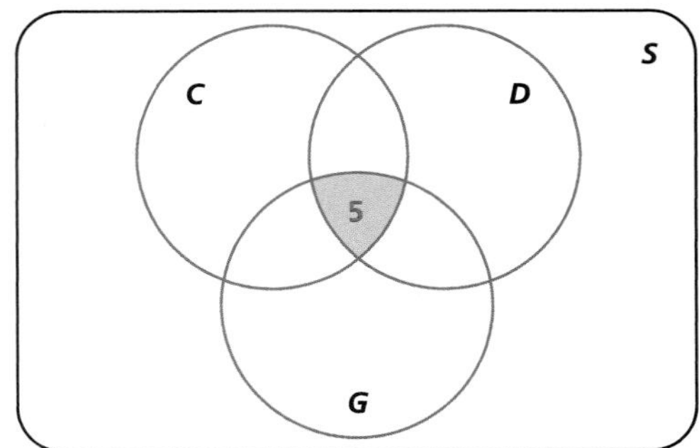

$n(C \cap G \cap D) = 5$, since there are five students in all three courses.

$n(G \cap C) = 30$

Since $n(C \cap G \cap D) = 5$, the number of students who take AFIC and Geometry and Discrete Math, but not Data Management, must be 25.

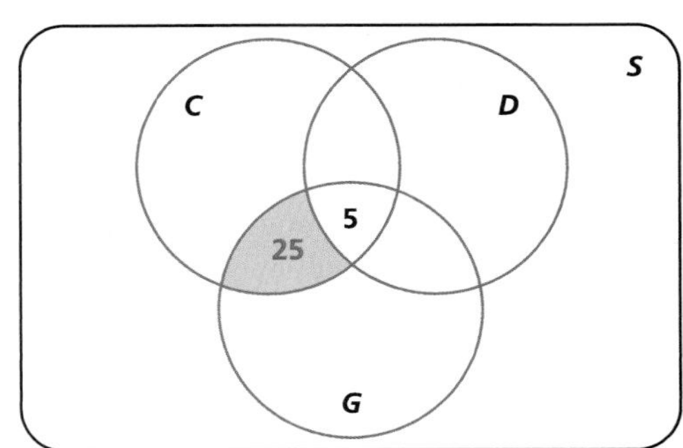

$n(D \cap C) = 50$

Since $n(C \cap G \cap D) = 5$, the number of students who take AFIC and Data Management, but not Geometry and Discrete Math, must be 45.

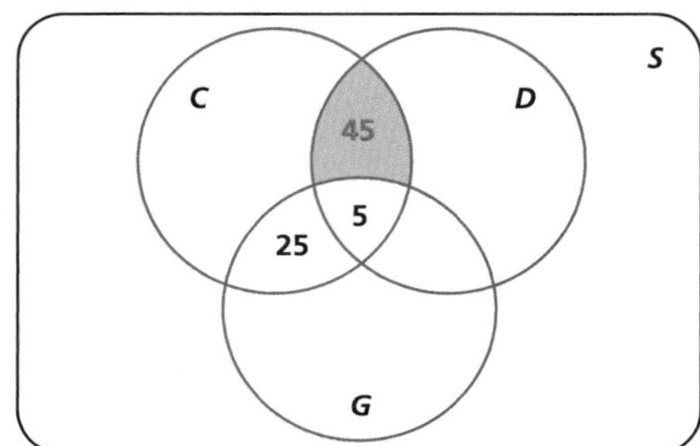

There were 80 students enrolled in AFIC, of which 75 have been accounted for. There must be, therefore, five students who take only AFIC and no other mathematics course.

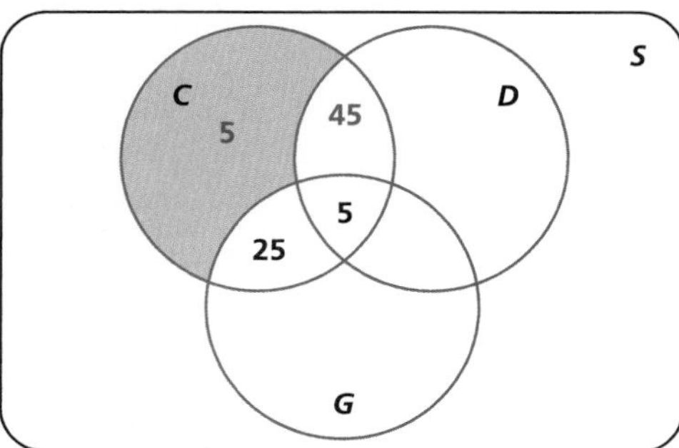

The complete Venn diagram for the math course example is shown on the previous page. If we consider only the students taking AFIC and Data Management, the Venn diagram will have only two sets and one intersection.

The total number of students in both courses is 98.

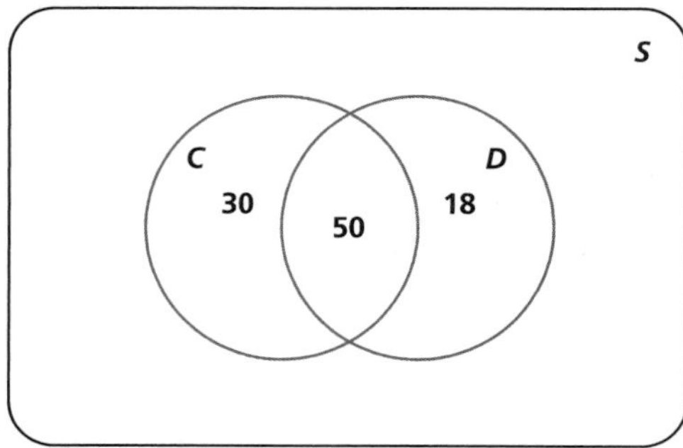

$$\begin{aligned} n(C \cup D) &= n(C) + n(D) - n(C \cap D) \\ &= 80 + 68 - 50 \\ &= 98 \end{aligned}$$

ADDITIVE PRINCIPLE FOR UNIONS OF TWO SETS

The solution to the counting problem above employed a Venn diagram. The counting strategy that was used leads to a more general counting strategy for unions of sets, called the **Additive Principle for unions of two sets**.

Additive Principle for Unions of Two Sets

Given two sets, A and B, the number of elements in $A \cup B$ can be found by totalling the number of elements in both sets and then subtracting the number that have been counted twice. The double-counted elements will be found in the intersection of the two sets.

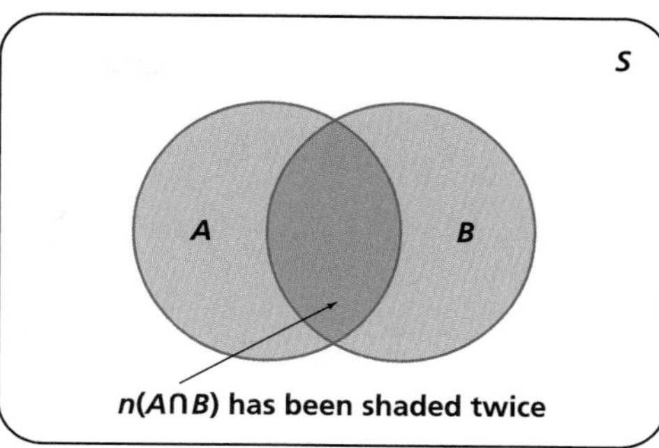

$$n(A \cup B) = n(A) + n(B) - n(A \cap B)$$

? Think about Overlap

- Why is it necessary to subtract $n(A \cap B)$ in the general formula?
- Under what conditions would $n(A \cup B) = n(A) + n(B)$?

Example 2 Applying the Additive Principle

If you were asked to randomly select a student from the group of students described in Example 1, what is the probability that

(a) the student selected is enrolled only in AFIC?

(b) a student was in AFIC *or* in Data Management?

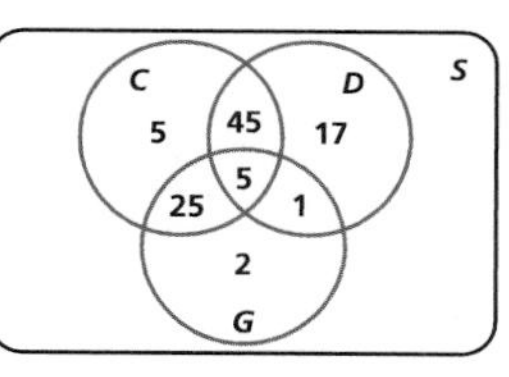

Solution

(a) The event of interest is the selection of a student who takes AFIC and no other course. Using the probability notation introduced earlier,

$$P(\text{student is in AFIC only}) = \frac{\text{number of students in AFIC only}}{\text{total number of students}}$$

$$= \frac{n(\text{AFIC only})}{n(S)}$$

$$= \frac{5}{100} = \frac{1}{20}$$

(b) This will include students enrolled in both courses or in only one of the courses. As a result,

$$P(\text{student is in AFIC } or \text{ in Data Management}) = P(C \cup D)$$

$$= \frac{n(C \cup D)}{n(S)}$$

Using the Venn diagram, we see the following:

- Since $n(C \cap D) = 50$, $P(C \cap D) = \frac{n(C \cap D)}{n(S)} = \frac{50}{100}$
- Since $n(C) = 80$, $P(C) = \frac{n(C)}{n(S)} = \frac{80}{100}$
- Since $n(D) = 68$, $P(D) = \frac{n(D)}{n(S)} = \frac{68}{100}$

Therefore, using the Additive Principle,

$$\begin{aligned} P(C \cup D) &= \frac{n(C \cup D)}{n(S)} \quad \leftarrow \text{Additive Principle} \\ &= \frac{n(C) + n(D) - n(C \cap D)}{n(S)} \\ &= \frac{n(C)}{n(S)} + \frac{n(D)}{n(S)} - \frac{n(C \cap D)}{n(S)} \\ &= P(C) + P(D) - P(C \cap D) \\ &= \frac{80}{100} + \frac{68}{100} - \frac{50}{100} \\ &= \frac{98}{100} = \frac{49}{50} \end{aligned}$$

This principle can also be applied to probabilities.

Additive Principle: Probability of the Union of Two Events

Given two events, A and B, the probability of the event in which A or B occurs is given by

$$P(A \cup B) = P(A) + P(B) - P(A \cap B)$$

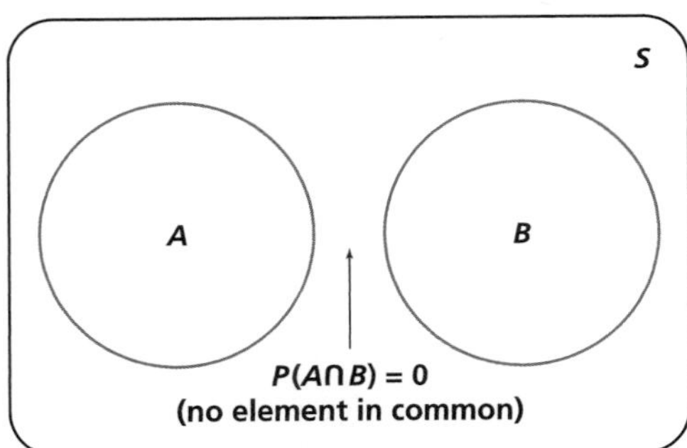

If A and B have no outcomes in common, they are said to be **mutually exclusive events** and $P(A \cup B) = P(A) + P(B)$.

mutually exclusive events—*A* and *B* are mutually exclusive events if $A \cap B = \varnothing$ and, as a result, $P(A \cup B) = P(A) + P(B)$ since $P(A \cap B) = P(\varnothing) = 0$.

Example 3 Additive Principle for Probabilities

If two dice are rolled, one red and one green, find the probability that a total of

(a) 2 or a total of 12 will occur **(b)** 4 or a pair will occur

D_2 \ D_1	1	2	3	4	5	6
1	2	3	4	5	6	7
2	3	4	5	6	7	8
3	4	5	6	7	8	9
4	5	6	7	8	9	10
5	6	7	8	9	10	11
6	7	8	9	10	11	12

Solution

(a) Let A be the event of rolling a total of 2 and B be the event of rolling a total of 12. Then,

$$P(A) = \frac{1}{36} \text{ and } P(B) = \frac{1}{36}$$

D_2 \ D_1	1	2	3	4	5	6
1	2	3	4	5	6	7
2	3	4	5	6	7	8
3	4	5	6	7	8	9
4	5	6	7	8	9	10
5	6	7	8	9	10	11
6	7	8	9	10	11	12

These events are mutually exclusive.

Thus,
$$P(A \cup B) = P(A) + P(B) = \frac{1}{36} + \frac{1}{36} = \frac{1}{18}$$

(b) Let A be the event of rolling a total of 4 (red circle) and B (green circle) be the event of rolling a pair. Then,

$$P(A) = \frac{3}{36} = \frac{1}{12} \quad \text{and} \quad P(B) = \frac{6}{36} = \frac{1}{6}$$

However, these events are not mutually exclusive. The outcome (red 2, green 2) is accounted for in both probabilities, so $P(A \cap B) = \frac{1}{36}$.

Thus,
$$P(A \cup B) = P(A) + P(B) - P(A \cap B) = \frac{3}{36} + \frac{6}{36} - \frac{1}{36} = \frac{2}{9}$$

KEY IDEAS

Venn diagram—a diagram in which sets are represented by geometrical shapes

compound event—consists of two or more simple events

intersection of sets—the set of common elements in two sets, A and B

$$A \cap B = \{\text{elements in both } A \text{ AND } B\}$$

disjoint sets—two sets with no elements or outcomes in common

union of sets—the set formed by combining the elements of A with those in B

$$A \cup B = \{\text{elements in both } A \text{ OR } B\}$$

Additive Principle for unions of two sets—

$$n(A \cup B) = n(A) + n(B) - n(A \cap B)$$

Additive Principle for probabilities—

$P(A \cup B) = P(A) + P(B) - P(A \cap B)$, if A and B are not mutually exclusive

$P(A \cup B) = P(A) + P(B)$, if A and B are mutually exclusive, because $P(A \cap B) = 0$

mutually exclusive events—A and B are mutually exclusive events if $A \cap B = \varnothing$ (no elements in common) and $n(A \cup B) = n(A) + n(B)$

4.3 Exercises

A **1.** Using the Venn diagram below, list the elements (numbers) found in each of the following sets.

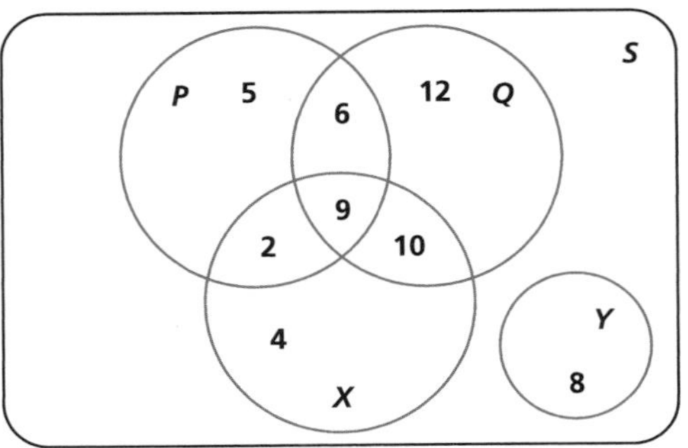

(a) $P \cap Q$ (b) $P \cup Q$ (c) $X \cap Q$
(d) $X \cup Q$ (e) $Y \cap Q$ (f) $P \cap Q \cap X$

2. For each of the following, find the indicated probability and state whether A and B are mutually exclusive.
(a) $P(A) = 0.5$, $P(B) = 0.2$, $P(A \cup B) = 0.7$, $P(A \cap B) = ?$
(b) $P(A) = 0.7$, $P(B) = 0.2$, $P(A \cup B) = ?$, $P(A \cap B) = 0.15$
(c) $P(A) = 0.3$, $P(B) = ?$, $P(A \cup B) = 0.9$, $P(A \cap B) = 0$

3. A sample space contains only three simple events: A, B, and C. If $P(A) = 0.2$ and $P(B) = 0.3$, find
(a) $P(A \text{ and } B)$ if A and B are mutually exclusive
(b) $P(A \text{ or } B)$ if A and B are mutually exclusive
(c) $P(C)$ if A and B are mutually exclusive

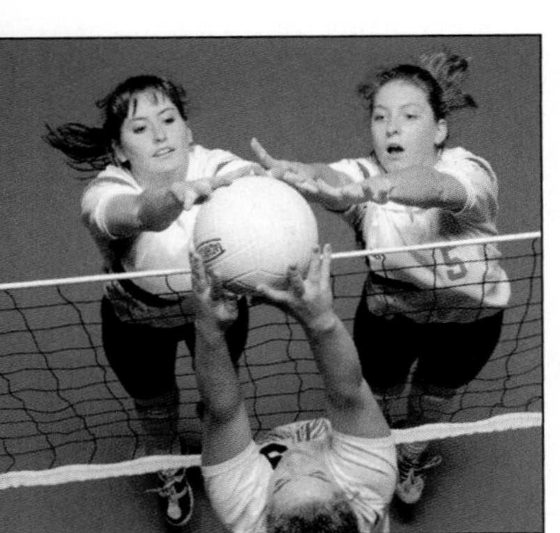

4. The probability that Kelly will make the volleyball team is $\frac{2}{3}$ and the probability that she will make the field hockey team is $\frac{3}{4}$. If the probability that she makes both teams is $\frac{1}{2}$, what is the probability that she makes at least one of the teams?

5. An aquarium at a pet store contains 20 guppies (12 females and 8 males) and 36 tetras (14 females and 22 males). If the clerk randomly nets a fish, what is the probability that it is a female or a tetra?

B

6. **Knowledge and Understanding** A paper bag contains a mixture of three types of candy. There are ten chocolate bars, seven fruit bars, and three packages of toffee.
   (a) Draw a Venn diagram to illustrate the contents of the bag.
   (b) Suppose a child selects one item from the bag at random. Determine the probability that the child chooses
      (i) a chocolate bar
      (ii) a package of toffee
      (iii) something other than a fruit bar

7. An automobile manufacturer estimates the probability of a mechanical defect in the one-year warranty period is 0.65. The probability of any other defect is 0.35. The probability of encountering both types of defect is 0.20. What is the probability of encountering any type of defect?

8. At the start of flu season, Dr. Anna Ahmeed examines 50 patients over two days. Of those 50 patients, 30 have a headache, 24 have a cold, and 12 have neither symptom. Some patients have both symptoms.
   (a) Draw a Venn diagram and determine the number of patients that have both symptoms.
   (b) Find the probability that a patient selected at random
      (i) has just a headache
      (ii) has a headache or a cold
      (iii) does not have cold symptoms

9. Find the probability that, when you draw a single card from a well-shuffled standard deck of 52 playing cards, you choose a 9 or a 10.

10. Find the probability that, when you draw a single card from a well-shuffled standard deck of 52 playing cards, you choose an ace or a club.

11. Find the probability that when you roll two dice, the sum of the outcomes is greater than 6 or you get a 5 on one of the dice.

12. The probability it will rain today is 0.4 and the probability it will rain tomorrow is 0.3. The probability it will rain both days is 0.2. What is the probability it will rain today or tomorrow?

13. **Communication** If events A and B are mutually exclusive, explain why $P(A \cup B)$ is the sum of the probabilities of each event. Use an example in your explanation.

14. **Application** In a group of 45 students, 28 have dark hair, 19 are taller than 185 cm, and 5 neither have dark hair nor are taller than 185 cm. Some have dark hair and are taller than 185 cm. If a student is selected at random, determine the probability that the student is
   (a) taller than 185 cm and has dark hair
   (b) taller than 185 cm or has dark hair
   (c) not taller than 185 cm

C

15. **Thinking, Inquiry, Problem Solving** In 2001, your company paid overtime wages or hired temporary help during 32 weeks of the year. Overtime was paid during 26 weeks and temporary help was hired during 15 weeks. If at year's end an auditor checks your accounting records and randomly selects one week to check the company's payroll, what is the probability that the auditor will select a week in which you paid overtime wages and had hired temporary help?

16. Give an example of two events that are not mutually exclusive and create and solve a probability question using the two events you chose.

ADDITIONAL ACHIEVEMENT CHART QUESTIONS

17. **Knowledge and Understanding** Jarvis High School has 1500 students. The first school dance of the year was attended by 740 students, while only 440 attended the second dance. If 285 students attended both, how many did not go to either dance?

18. **Communication** Give an example and describe a situation in which two events are

(a) mutually exclusive

(b) not mutually exclusive

19. **Application** An advertiser is told that 70% of all adults in the Greater Toronto Area (GTA) read *The Toronto Star* and 60% watch CityTV. She is also told that 40% do both: read *The Toronto Star* and watch CityTV. If she places an advertisement in *The Toronto Star* and runs a commercial on CityTV, what is the probability that a person selected at random in the GTA will see at least one of these?

20. **Thinking, Inquiry, Problem Solving** If A, B, and C are three events that are not mutually exclusive, state the Additive Principle for the union of these three sets.

4.4 Conditional Probability

It is often necessary to know the probability of an event under restricted conditions. Recall the results of a survey of 100 Grade 12 mathematics students in a local high school.

Math Course Taken	Number of Students
Advanced Functions and Introductory Calculus (AFIC)	80
Geometry and Discrete Math	33
Data Management	68
Geometry and Discrete Math and AFIC	30
Geometry and Discrete Math and Data Management	6
Data Management and AFIC	50
All three courses	5

The following example investigates a situation in which the probability of an event is determined under a restricted condition.

Example 1 Conditional Probability

You are asked to determine the probability of selecting a Data Management student, but are first told that the only students from which you can choose are enrolled in AFIC. How does this additional condition affect the probability?

Solution

Without the condition that AFIC students are the only students left from which to select, the Venn diagram would look like the following:

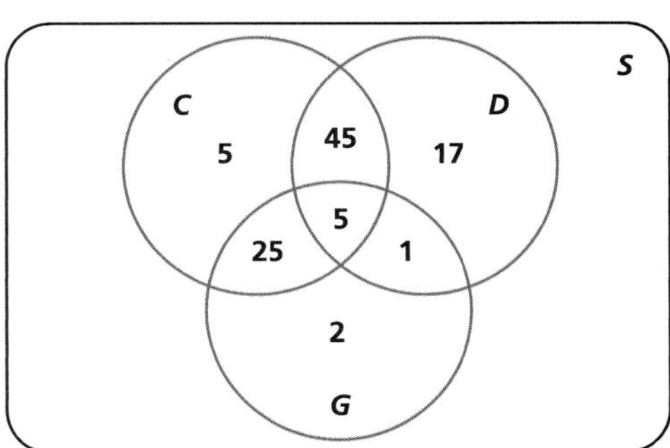

Based on the preceding diagram, the probability of selecting a Data Management student from the entire group is $P(D) = \frac{68}{100}$.

When we add the condition that the students must be enrolled in AFIC, the Venn diagram changes. The sample space S does not consist of all possible students. It includes only those students taking AFIC. In the following Venn diagram, the new restricted sample space corresponds to the area shaded in blue.

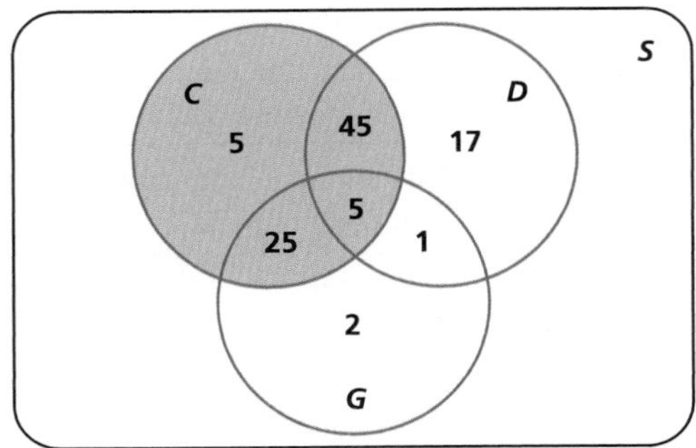

The probability of selecting a Data Management student, given the condition that the student is also enrolled in AFIC, is called a **conditional probability** and is written as $P(D \mid C)$. The revised Venn diagram shows that the probability of D given that C has occurred is

$$P(D \mid C) = \frac{n(\text{students enrolled in Data Management AND AFIC})}{n(\text{students in AFIC})}$$

$$= \frac{n(D \cap C)}{n(C)} = \frac{50}{80} = \frac{5}{8}$$

We can use some simple algebra to convert this to a general statement about probabilities.

$$P(D \mid C) = \frac{n(D \cap C)}{n(C)}$$

$$= \frac{\left(\frac{n(D \cap C)}{n(S)}\right)}{\left(\frac{n(C)}{n(S)}\right)} \quad \text{Divide the numerator and the denominator by } n(S).$$

$$= \frac{P(D \cap C)}{P(C)}$$

For example, you can determine the probability of selecting a Data Management student as follows:

$$P(D \mid C) = \frac{P(D \cap C)}{P(C)}$$

$$= \frac{\frac{50}{100}}{\frac{80}{100}}$$

$$= \frac{50}{80}$$

$$= \frac{5}{8}$$

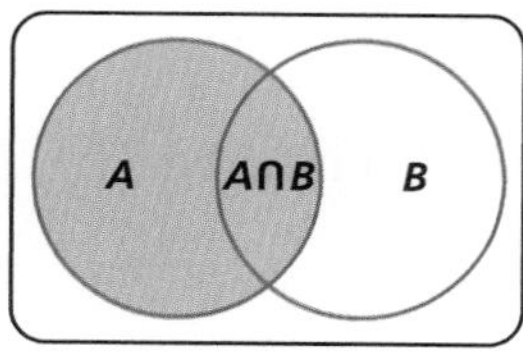

Conditional Probability

The conditional probability of event B, given that event A has occurred, is given by

$$P(B \mid A) = \frac{P(A \cap B)}{P(A)}$$

Example 2 Conditional Probability in Weather Forecasting

Suppose that in Vancouver the probability that a day will be both cloudy and rainy is 25%. Suppose further that 50% of all days are cloudy. Determine the probability that it will rain given it is a cloudy day in that city.

Solution

If C is the event that it is a cloudy day and R is the event that it is raining, the required probability is given by $P(R \mid C)$. This can be represented using the following Venn diagram that represents 100 days of Vancouver weather.

Cloudy 50
Not Cloudy 50
Rainy 25

Therefore,

$$\begin{aligned} P(R \mid C) &= \frac{P(R \cap C)}{P(C)} \\ &= \frac{\frac{25}{100}}{\frac{50}{100}} \\ &= \frac{0.25}{0.5} \\ &= 0.5 \end{aligned}$$

There is a 50% chance of rain on a cloudy day. Rearranging the conditional probability formula results in another important relationship.

Multiplication Law for Conditional Probability

The probability of events A and B occurring, given that event A has occurred, is given by

$$P(A \cap B) = P(B \mid A) \times P(A)$$

because $$P(B \mid A) = \frac{P(A \cap B)}{P(A)}$$

multiply both sides by $P(A)$ $$P(B \mid A) \times P(A) = P(A \cap B)$$

Example 3 Multiplication Law for Conditional Probability

What is the probability of drawing two aces in a row from a well-shuffled deck of 52 playing cards? The first card drawn is not replaced.

Solution

We want to know the probability that the first card is an ace and the second card is an ace. For the first card, there are 4 aces in the deck of 52 cards, so

$$P(\text{first ace}) = \frac{4}{52}$$

For the second card, given that the first is an ace, there are 3 aces remaining in the deck of 51 cards, so

$$P(\text{second ace} \mid \text{first ace}) = \frac{3}{51}$$

Using the multiplication law, we get

$$\begin{aligned} P(\text{first ace and second ace}) &= P(\text{second ace} \mid \text{first ace}) \times P(\text{first ace}) \\ &= \frac{3}{51} \times \frac{4}{52} \\ &= \frac{12}{2652} \\ &= \frac{1}{221} \end{aligned}$$

KEY IDEAS

conditional probability—the conditional probability of event B, given that event A has occurred, is given by $P(B \mid A) = \frac{P(A \cap B)}{P(A)}$

Multiplication Law for conditional probability—the probability of events A and B occurring, given that event A has occurred, is given by

$$P(A \cap B) = P(B \mid A) \times P(A)$$

4.4 Exercises

A

1. Joel surveyed his class and summarized responses to the question, "Do you like school?"

	Liked	Disliked	No Opinion	Total
Males	12	5	2	19
Females	10	3	1	14
Total	22	8	3	33

Find each of the following probabilities.
(a) P(likes school | student is male)
(b) P(student is female | student dislikes school)

2. A person is chosen at random from shoppers at a department store. If the person's probability of having blonde hair and glasses is $\frac{2}{25}$ and the probability of wearing glasses is $\frac{9}{25}$, determine P(blonde hair | wears glasses).

3. Tia and Jerry are tossing two coins. Tia wins when both coins turn up tails. The coins are tossed but roll under a chair. Jerry looks under the chair and, seeing both coins, says, "At least one of them is tails." What is the probability that Tia wins?

4. What is the probability of being dealt two clubs in a row from a well-shuffled deck of 52 playing cards without replacing the first card drawn?

B

5. **Knowledge and Understanding** From a medical study of 10 000 male patients, it was found that 2500 were smokers; 720 died from lung cancer and of these, 610 were smokers. Determine
(a) P(dying from lung cancer | smoker)
(b) P(dying from lung cancer | non-smoker)

6. A bag contains three red marbles and five white marbles. What is the probability of drawing two red marbles at random if the first marble drawn is not replaced?

7. A road has two stop lights at two consecutive intersections. The probability of getting a green light at the first intersection is 0.6, and the probability of getting a green light at the second intersection, given that you got a green light at the first intersection, is 0.8. What is the probability of getting a green light at both intersections?

8. A survey of 1000 people asked whether they wear eyeglasses while driving. These people were also tested to see whether they need to wear eyeglasses while driving. The results are displayed in the table below.

		Wear Eyeglasses While Driving	
		YES	NO
Need to Wear Eyeglasses While Driving	YES	440	140
	NO	20	400

If a person is selected at random from this group, determine the probability he or she

(a) should wear eyeglasses while driving
(b) wears eyeglasses while driving
(c) wears eyeglasses while driving even though he or she does not need to
(d) does not wear eyeglasses while driving even though he or she needs to

9. Suppose the two joker cards are left in a standard deck of cards. One of the jokers is red and the other is black. A single card is drawn from the deck of 54 cards but not returned to the deck, and then a second card is drawn. Determine the probability of drawing

(a) one of the jokers on the first draw and an ace on the second draw
(b) a numbered card of any suit on the first draw and the red joker on the second draw
(c) a queen on both draws
(d) any black card on both draws
(e) any numbered card below 10 on the first draw and the same number on a card on the second draw
(f) the red joker or a red ace on either draw

10. Helena Maksimovik, the human resources director for a company, is given the task of hiring two salespeople from four candidates. From their résumés, the candidates could be ranked as follows: 1. Noel; 2. Sara; 3. Emil; 4. Fran. It is two days before Helena's scheduled vacation and she does not want to take the time to go through a formal interview process. Instead, she decides to hire two of the candidates at random.

(a) List all the possible pairings that would make up the possible selections.
(b) Determine the probability the selection will include
  (i) at least one of the top two candidates
  (ii) both of the top two candidates
  (iii) neither of the top two candidates
  (iv) Emil, if you know Sara has been selected
  (v) either Emil or Fran, if you know Sara has been selected

11. A union and the management of a company are negotiating a new contract. History shows the following:

Event *A*: Contract settlements are reached within two weeks 50% of the time.

Event *B*: The union strike fund is large enough to support a strike 60% of the time.

Events *A* and *B*: Both of the above conditions are satisfied 30% of the time.

Determine the probability of each of the following.

(a) A contract is settled in two weeks given that the strike fund is large enough to support a strike.

(b) The union strike fund is large enough to support a strike given that a contract will be negotiated within two weeks.

12. **Communication**

(a) With the aid of a Venn diagram, explain why the events in Question 11 are not mutually exclusive.

(b) Explain why the answers to Question 11 suggest that event *A* and event *B* have no influence on one another.

13. **Application** Gwen has recently purchased a cottage. She has arranged to have a well dug on the property. One in five wells that were dug recently in the vicinity were dry, and 30% of the others are contaminated. Find the probability of each of the following.

(a) Gwen's well will not be dry.

(b) Gwen's well will be uncontaminated, given that it is not dry.

(c) Gwen will have safe-drinking water from her well.

(d) Gwen will not have safe-drinking water from her well.

14. A survey of readers of *The News* indicated that 40% of them also read *The Chronicle*, 32% read *Info*, and 11% read both publications. Find the probability that a reader of *The News*

(a) also reads *Info*

(b) reads *Info*, but not *The Chronicle*

C **15.** There are three cards in a hat. One card is black on both sides and the other two cards are black on one side and white on the other. If a card is drawn randomly from the hat and placed on a table so that the underside is not visible, determine the probability that the back of the card is black if the front is showing black.

16. **Thinking, Inquiry, Problem Solving** The quality-control inspector for a computer company either accepts or rejects shipments of microprocessors as a result of testing a sample of the items in a shipment. The inspector's previous performance indicates that she has

- accepted 98% and rejected 2% of all shipments that turned out to be good
- accepted 94% of all shipments even though 5% of the shipments are known to be inferior

(a) Find the probability that a good shipment is rejected.
(b) Find the probability that an inferior shipment is accepted.

ADDITIONAL ACHIEVEMENT CHART QUESTIONS

17. **Knowledge and Understanding** A die is rolled twice. Determine the probability that the sum of the two rolls is greater than 6, given that the first roll is a 4.

18. **Communication** A poll was taken to see how people felt about a plan to build a new community centre in town. Use the results to create a conditional probability question.

	In`Favour	Opposed	Total
Retired	105	67	172
Non-Retired	49	97	146
Student	17	12	29
Total	171	176	347

19. **Application** A jar contains six red marbles and four green ones. If two marbles are drawn at random from the jar, and the first marble is not returned to the jar, find the probability of each of these events.
(a) the second marble is green, given that the first is red
(b) both marbles are red
(c) both marbles are green
(d) the second marble is red

20. **Thinking, Inquiry, Problem Solving** Prove that
$P(A \mid B) = \frac{P(A)}{P(B)} \times P(B \mid A)$.

4.5 Finding Probability Using Tree Diagrams and Outcome Tables

Games of chance often involve combinations of random events. These might involve drawing one or more cards from a deck, rolling two dice, or tossing coins. How do you find the probability that a particular sequence of these events will occur?

This section will show you some strategies for listing the outcomes of an experiment in an organized way so that you can find the probability of a particular compound event.

TREE DIAGRAMS AND THE MULTIPLICATIVE PRINCIPLE FOR COUNTING OUTCOMES

A tree diagram is often used to show how simple experiments can be combined one after the other to form more complex experiments. The successive branches of the tree each correspond to a step required to generate the possible outcomes of an experiment. The tree diagram and outcome table that correspond to tossing two coins appear below.

Tree Diagram

First Coin	Second Coin	Outcome
Heads	Heads	HH
	Tails	HT
Tails	Heads	TH
	Tails	TT

Outcome Table

Coin 1	Coin 2	Simple Event
H	H	HH
H	T	HT
T	H	TH
T	T	TT

Think about Tree Diagrams

How would the tree diagram differ if the experiment consisted of rolling a die twice instead of tossing a coin twice?

Consider an experiment in which you first roll a six-sided die and then toss a coin. What is the probability of tossing tails and rolling an even number?

The following tree diagram can be used to represent the possible results.

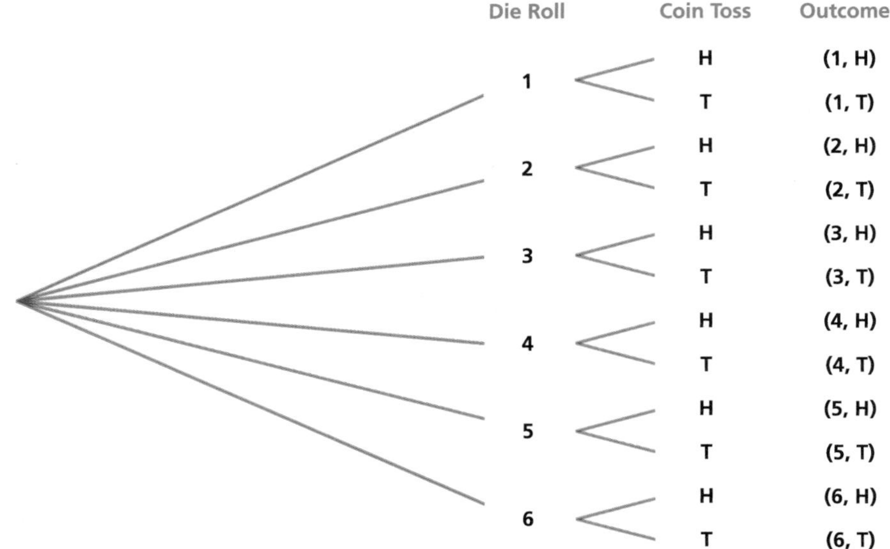

Think about The Outcomes

- Why would writing the ordered pairs as (*c*, *d*) instead of (*d*, *c*) have no effect on the total number of outcomes?
- Does the result of the roll of the die have any influence on the result of tossing the coin?
- What would the tree diagram look like if the coin were tossed before the die is rolled?

The sample space for this experiment consists of ordered pairs of the form (d, c), where d is the result of a roll of the die and c is the result of the toss of a coin. The tree diagram for the experiment clearly shows the 12 possible outcomes.

For each roll of the die (the first entry in the ordered pair), we have a choice of six possible outcomes. For each of these, there are two choices for the coin toss (the second entry of the ordered pair). As a result, there are $6 \times 2 = 12$ possible outcomes.

There are three outcomes that correspond to the event of an even roll of the die followed by a toss of tails. They are (2, T), (4, T), and (6, T). Therefore, $P(\text{even roll, tails}) = \frac{3}{12}$, or $\frac{1}{4}$.

In this case, the event of getting an even roll of the die and the event of getting tails on a coin toss have no influence on each another.

The following Venn diagram shows the relationship between the events.

Think about Representing the Outcomes

- Construct an outcome table for this experiment. Use it to find $P(\text{roll} < 4, \text{heads})$.
- How does a Venn diagram represent the events in an experiment differently from a tree diagram? From an outcome table?
- For what kind of event is it more appropriate to use a Venn diagram or a tree diagram to represent the outcomes from an experiment?

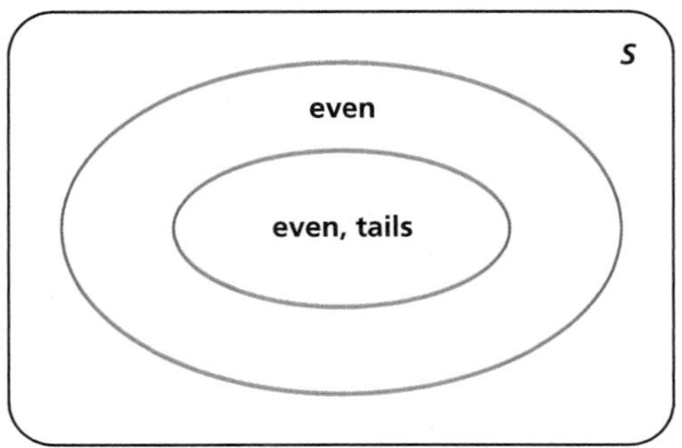

Multiplicative Principle for Counting Ordered Pairs, Triplets, etc.

A tree diagram is used to represent the outcomes of an experiment that are the result of a sequence of simpler experiments. Assume that an outcome for each experiment has no influence on the outcome of any other experiment.

The total number of outcomes is the *product* of the possible outcomes at each step in the sequence. If a is selected from A and b is selected from B, $n((a, b)) = n(A) \times n(B)$.

INDEPENDENT AND DEPENDENT EVENTS

In the die roll/coin toss experiment,

$$\begin{aligned}
P(\text{even roll, tails}) &= \frac{n(\text{even roll, tails})}{n(\text{ordered pairs})} \\
&= \frac{n(\text{even roll}) \times n(\text{tails})}{n(\text{die rolls}) \times n(\text{coin tosses})} \\
&= \frac{n(\text{even roll})}{n(\text{die rolls})} \times \frac{n(\text{tails})}{n(\text{coin tosses})} \\
&= P(\text{even roll}) \times P(\text{tails}) \\
&= \frac{3}{6} \times \frac{1}{2} \\
&= \frac{3}{12} \\
&= \frac{1}{4}
\end{aligned}$$

Project Connection

The purpose of your project may be to determine whether or not some variable has a significant effect on another variable, or using the language of probability, you may want to know whether the variables are dependent or not.

What is the probability of tossing the coin and getting tails if you know in advance that the die will show an even number?

The rolling of the die and the tossing of the coin are independent events. Knowing the outcome of the die roll has no effect on the probability of getting tails.

Consider the conditional probability $P(\text{tails} \mid \text{even})$. From the previous section, we know that

$$\begin{aligned}
P(\text{tails} \mid \text{even}) &= \frac{P(\text{tails} \cap \text{even})}{P(\text{even})} \\
&= \frac{\left(\frac{3}{12}\right)}{\left(\frac{3}{6}\right)} \\
&= \frac{1}{2}
\end{aligned}$$

We also know that $P(\text{tails}) = \frac{1}{2}$. Therefore, $P(\text{tails} \mid \text{even}) = P(\text{tails})$.

independent events—events *A* and *B* are independent if the occurrence of one event does not change the probability of the occurrence of the other event

Conditional Probability for Independent Events

If A and B are **independent events**, then

$$P(B \mid A) = P(B)$$

If this is not the case, the events are **dependent**.

Recall that the conditional probability of event B given event A has occurred is

$$P(B \mid A) = \frac{P(B \cap A)}{P(A)}$$

If events A and B are independent, then $P(B \mid A) = P(B)$. Therefore, $P(B) = \frac{P(B \cap A)}{P(A)}$ and $P(B \cap A) = P(B) \times P(A)$.

Multiplicative Principle for Probabilities of Independent Events

If A and B are independent events, then

$$\begin{aligned} P(A \text{ and } B) &= P(A \cap B) \\ &= P(A) \times P(B) \end{aligned}$$

Example 1 The Even–Odd Game

The Even–Odd game is a game that can be played by two players using two coins. One of the players assumes the Even role; the other, Odd. Each player tosses a coin. If the two coins show an even number of heads, Even wins. If the coins show an odd number of heads, Odd wins. A tie is declared if no heads show.

Draw a tree diagram to represent the possible events.

Solution

The result of the game—Even wins, Odd wins, or they tie—is a random variable since it depends on the outcomes of the coin tosses.

Consider the following tree diagram showing the probabilities of the simple and compound events.

Think about The Diagram

Which diagram is more useful for finding the probabilities of the various possible events: Venn diagrams or tree diagrams?

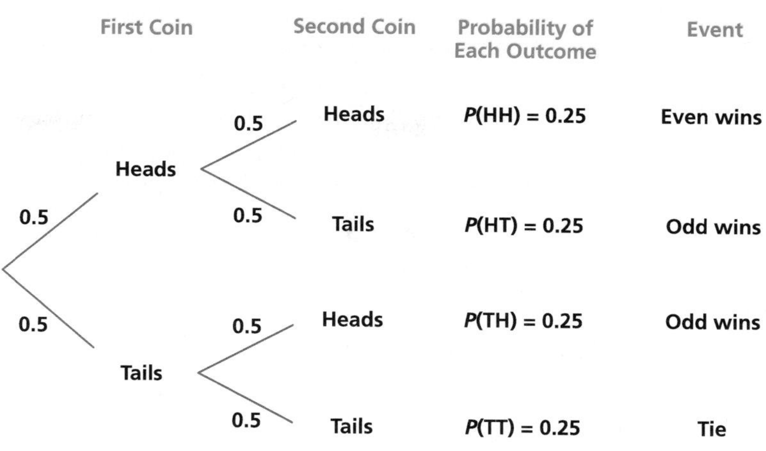

Example 2 Rolling Two Dice

Suppose you are playing a game in which you roll a red and a black six-sided die at the same time. Consider the event that the sum of the dice is 3. Is this event independent of the red die showing 1?

Solution

A sum of 3, with the red die showing 1, can only happen in one way, if the black die shows 2. There are 36 possible outcomes with the two dice. Therefore,

$$P(\text{red die shows 1 and sum is 3}) = \frac{1}{36}$$

However,

$$P(\text{red die shows 1}) = \frac{1}{6} \text{ and } P(\text{sum is 3}) = \frac{2}{36} \text{ or } \frac{1}{18}$$

Therefore,

$$P(\text{red die shows 1}) \times P(\text{sum is 3}) = \frac{1}{6} \times \frac{1}{18} \text{ or } \frac{1}{108}$$

As a result,

$$P(\text{red die shows 1 and sum is 3}) \neq P(\text{red die shows 1}) \times P(\text{sum is 3})$$

and the events must be dependent.

Example 3 Predicting Soccer Results

Suppose that a school's female soccer team has a history of winning 50% of the games it plays on rainy days and 60% of the games it plays on fair days. The weather forecast for the next game day calls for an 80% chance of rain. What is the probability that the team will win the game?

Solution

Draw a tree diagram that represents the sequence of outcomes as ordered pairs in the form (weather, game result).

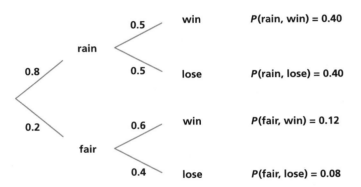

Weather		Game Result		Probability
0.8	rain	0.5	win	**P(rain, win) = 0.40**
		0.5	lose	**P(rain, lose) = 0.40**
0.2	fair	0.6	win	**P(fair, win) = 0.12**
		0.4	lose	**P(fair, lose) = 0.08**

There are two simple events that result in a win. The probabilities for these events are as follows:

$$\begin{aligned} P(\text{rain, win}) &= P(\text{rain}) \times P(\text{win} \mid \text{rain}) \\ &= 0.8 \times 0.5 \\ &= 0.4 \end{aligned}$$

$$\begin{aligned} P(\text{fair, win}) &= P(\text{fair}) \times P(\text{win} \mid \text{fair}) \\ &= 0.2 \times 0.6 \\ &= 0.12 \end{aligned}$$

The probability the team will win is, therefore, the sum $0.4 + 0.12 = 0.52$.

? Think about The Probabilities

Why is the probability of the pair (rain, win) equal to the product 0.8×0.5?

KEY IDEAS

independent events—two events are independent of each other if the occurrence of one event does not change the probability of the occurrence of the other event

conditional probability for independent events—if A and B are independent events, then $P(A \mid B) = P(A)$; if this is not the case, the events are **dependent** and the formula for conditional probability must be applied

Multiplicative Principle for probabilities of independent events—if A and B are independent events, then

$$\begin{aligned} P(A \text{ and } B) &= P(A \cap B) \\ &= P(A) \times P(B) \end{aligned}$$

4.5 Exercises

1. **Knowledge and Understanding** A truck driver, Andrea Ortiz, has a choice of routes as she travels among four cities. She can choose from four routes between Toronto and Oakville, two between Oakville and Hamilton, and three between Hamilton and Guelph. Find the total number of routes possible for complete Toronto–Oakville–Hamilton–Guelph trips.

2. A test has four true/false questions.
   (a) Draw the tree diagram that shows all possible true/false combinations for the answers to the test.
   (b) Determine the probability that a student will get all four correct by guessing.
   (c) Determine the probability that a student will get three questions correct by guessing.

3. Suppose you conduct an experiment in which you draw a card from a standard 52-card deck, return it to the deck, and then draw another card. List the outcomes of the following event spaces.
   (a) You get a seven of diamonds in both draws.
   (b) You get an ace of spades on the first draw and a seven of diamonds on the second.
   (c) You get a numbered club on both draws.
   (d) You get an ace on the first draw and an even club on the second.

B

4. **Communication** The faces of a standard six-sided die represent the numbers 1 through 6. Two of these dice, one red and the other white, are rolled simultaneously.
   (a) If you were to draw a tree diagram showing all possible combinations of the two dice, how many branches would it have?
   (b) Explain why there is only one combination for which the sum is 2.
   (c) Explain why there are two possible combinations for which the sum is 3.
   (d) Complete a chart like the one below for all possible sums of the two dice.

Sum	Required Rolls (Red, White)
2	(1, 1)
3	(1, 2); (2, 1)
4	

   (e) Find the probability of each possible sum.

5. A standard deck of cards has had all the face cards (jacks, queens, and kings) removed so that only the ace through ten of each suit remain. A game is played in which a card is drawn from this deck and a six-sided die is rolled. For the purpose of this game, an ace is considered to have a value of 1.

   (a) Determine the total number of possible outcomes for this game.
   (b) Describe the elements of the sample space for this experiment.
   (c) Find the probability of each of these events.
      (i) an even card and an even roll of the die
      (ii) an even card and an odd roll of the die
      (iii) a card of 3 and a roll of the die of 3 or less
      (iv) the sum of the card and the die is 7
      (v) the sum of the card and the die is 11

6. Suppose the two joker cards are left in a standard deck of cards. One of the jokers is red and the other is black. A single card is drawn from the deck of 54 cards, returned, and then a second card is drawn. Determine the probability of drawing
   (a) one of the jokers on the first draw and an ace on the second
   (b) the red joker on the second draw and a numbered card of any suit on the first
   (c) a queen on both draws
   (d) any black card on both draws
   (e) any numbered card less than 10 on the first draw and a card with the same number on the second
   (f) the red joker or a red ace on either draw

7. **Application** An airplane can make a safe landing if at least half of its engines are working properly. Suppose that engine failures are independent events. Determine whether a two-engine plane is safer than a four-engine plane if the chance that an engine fails is 1 in 2.

8. A health and safety committee is to be selected from all the people who work at a local factory. The committee is to consist of four members selected randomly from a list of ten names submitted by the shop leader. The list has the names of five union members and five workers who are not union members.
   (a) What is the probability that the first person selected from the list is a union member?
   (b) What is the probability that the first two people selected from the list are union members?
   (c) What is the probability that all the committee members are union members?
   (d) What is the probability that three of the four committee members are union members?

9. A paper bag contains a mixture of 3 types of candy. There are ten chocolate bars, seven fruit bars, and three packages of toffee. Suppose a game is played in which a candy is randomly taken from the bag, replaced, and then a second candy is drawn from the bag. If you are allowed to keep the second candy only if it was the same type as the one that was drawn the first time, calculate the probability of each of the following.
   (a) you will be able to keep a chocolate bar
   (b) you will be able to keep any candy
   (c) you won't be able to keep any candy

10. At the beginning of each month, the president of a small manufacturing company decides whether to spend \$1000 or \$2000 on advertising for the month. Suppose she makes her decision by tossing a coin.
    (a) What is the probability that she will spend \$3000 on advertising during the first three consecutive months of this year?
    (b) What is the probability that she will spend more than \$4000 on advertising during the first three consecutive months of this year?
    (c) What is the probability that she will spend more than \$3000 on advertising during the first three consecutive months of this year?

11. **Knowledge and Understanding** A lottery uses a clear plastic drum that contains 100 ping-pong balls numbered from 0 to 9. There are 10 of each number in the drum. A ball is drawn from the drum and then returned after its number is written down. The process is repeated three times. The drawn numbers are used in their order of drawing to create a three-digit number.
    (a) Determine how many three-digit numbers can be created in this way.
    (b) Determine the probability that any number drawn in this way will end in a 5.
    (c) Determine the probability that any number drawn in this way will start with either a 1 or a 2.

12. Postal codes for Canada have the form LDL DLD, where L is any letter from A to Z, and D is any digit from 0 to 9. Some letters may not be permitted in certain positions of the postal code by Canada Post. As a result, the actual number of allowable postal codes will be different from the total number possible.
    (a) Estimate the total number of possible postal codes available for use in Canada.
    (b) Postal codes for Toronto start with the letter M. What is the probability that a postal code selected randomly will represent an area in Toronto?
    (c) Suppose you set up a computer program to generate postal codes randomly in a way such that no two generated postal codes are dependent on each other. What is the probability that your program will generate the same postal code two times in a row?

13. **Thinking, Inquiry, Problem Solving** A basketball player has a success rate of 80% for shooting free throws.
    (a) Calculate the following probabilities.
        (i) She will make three out of five attempts.
        (ii) She will miss five attempts in a row.
        (iii) She will make the first three attempts and miss the next two.
        (iv) She will make at least three out of five attempts.
    (b) Create a computer simulation for the situation in part (a) and use it to find the experimental probability for each event. Evaluate the quality of your simulation by comparing its results to the theoretical probabilities in part (a).

ADDITIONAL ACHIEVEMENT CHART QUESTIONS

14. **Knowledge and Understanding** Draw a tree diagram to list the outcome set for an experiment in which a die is rolled, and then a four-coloured equal-probability spinner (red, blue, green, yellow) is spun. Find each probability.

(a) a 6 is rolled and green is spun

(b) an even number is rolled or red is spun

15. **Application** Joshua and Ravinder are having a video-game competition. Over the course of one week, they play several times. They have decided that the winner will be declared when someone wins three out of five games. Ravinder has had the game longer and his probability of winning each time is $\frac{3}{5}$. Joshua's probability of winning each time is $\frac{2}{5}$. Determine the probability that Joshua will win the weekly competition.

16. **Thinking, Inquiry, Problem Solving** Show that A and B are independent events if, and only if, $P(A \mid B) = P(A \mid B')$.

17. **Communication** Explain the difference between independent and dependent events. Use an example in your explanation.

Chapter Problem

Analyzing a Traditional Game

CP9. Make an outcome table or a tree diagram to model the game.

CP10. How many outcomes are possible if the six counters are distinguishable? Indistinguishable?

CP11. How many ways can the counters produce results that end up in

(a) 5 points awarded?

(b) 1 point awarded?

(c) 0 points awarded?

CP12. Determine the probability that a player earns

(a) 5 points on a turn

(b) 1 point on a turn

(c) 0 points on a turn

CP13. Based on these probabilities, does the point structure seem reasonable? Explain.

4.6 Counting Techniques and Probability Strategies—Permutations

The previous sections showed you that the outcomes of complex experiments can be counted by combining the outcomes of simple experiments. This section will present the mathematical tools and strategies that will allow you to count these outcomes efficiently, and then find the probabilities for these events when the order of the simple events is important.

Example 1 Creating Game Line-Ups

You are trying to put three children—represented by *A, B,* and *C*—in a line for a game.

(a) How many different orders are possible?

(b) What is the probability that a random ordering will produce the order *ABC*?

Solution

(a) Construct a tree diagram for this sequence of choices using *A, B,* and *C* to represent the children.

Think about The Choices

Why is there only one available choice for third after first and second have been determined?

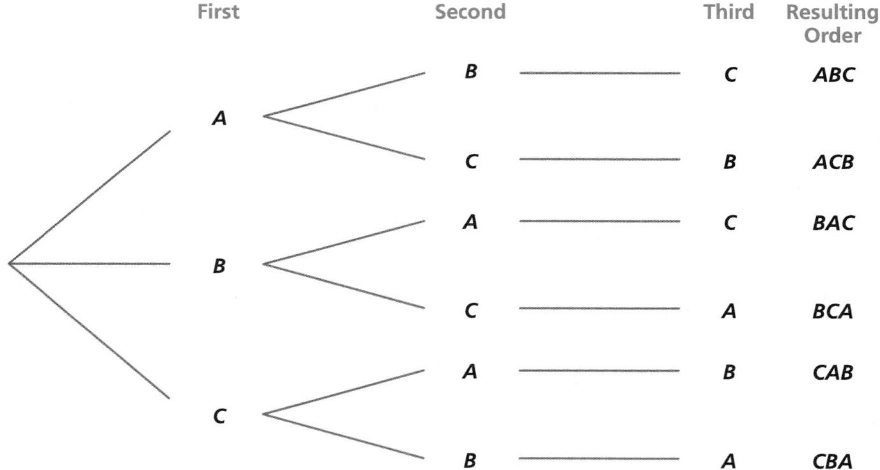

There are six possible arrangements.

Another way of visualizing this problem is to think of placing each child's name into one of three different boxes on a piece of paper.

Think about Order Decisions

Why do the tree diagram and the box diagram represent the same set of choices that can be made?

First	Second	Third

There are three choices for filling in the first box. Once a name has been placed in that box, there are two ways of filling in the second box. Once that has been done, there is one remaining way to fill in the third box. The Multiplicative Principle states that there are $3 \times 2 \times 1$, or six ways of doing this.

(b) Of the six arrangements that are possible, only one of them is the arrangement *ABC*.

$$P(ABC) = \frac{1}{6}$$

Discussion Questions

1. Suppose you have nine players who want to play on the team, but you are allowed to select only three for any game.

(a) How many different three-player line-up orders can you create using the nine available players?

(b) How many different six-player line-up orders can you create using the nine available players?

2. Suppose that you are the manager of a female baseball team with 15 players. During a game, nine players are used. How many different batting orders can you create for the nine players who start the game?

? Think about Question 2

Explain why a tree diagram would not be a very efficient way to solve Question 2.

3. Children frequently play with interlocking plastic blocks. These blocks come in red, blue, white, green, grey, and black. Suppose you have one block of each colour. The position of the locking pegs and holes allows you to determine which block starts a chain.

(a) How many different six-block sequences can be formed?

(b) How many different two-block sequences can be formed?

(c) Why is it important to determine which block starts a chain?

SELECTING OBJECTS WHEN ORDER MATTERS

Factorial Notation

The ordering problem in Example 1 dealt with arranging the names of three children to create sequences with different orders. In the simplest case, we used all the childrens' names to fill the same number of positions. This was done by making a first choice in which all names could be chosen. Then, the second choice had one fewer choice available, since one child's name had already been selected and was no longer available. Finally, the last choice was forced since there was only one remaining name. Thus, there are $3 \times 2 \times 1$ ways of putting the children in a line. This can be written as $3!$.

factorial notation—$n!$ represents the number of ways that n different objects can be selected to create ordered arrangements of size n

Think about The Notation

- Why does each term in the expansion of $n!$ decrease by 1 until the last term is 1?
- 0! is defined to have a value of 1. Why does this definition make sense?

Technolink

Permutations can be computed on a TI-83 Plus calculator using the nPr command. See Appendix C.14 on page 410.

Think about Permutations

Why is the following statement true?

$P(n, n) = n!$

Factorial Notation

$n!$ (read as n factorial) is calculated as

$$n! = n \times (n-1) \times (n-2) \times \ldots \times 2 \times 1$$

For example,

$$\begin{aligned} 5! &= 5 \times 4 \times 3 \times 2 \times 1 \\ &= 120 \end{aligned}$$

Permutations

Suppose you have n objects to choose from, but only want to select some rather than all of them. There is still a sequence of choices to be made. In this case, not all the elements in the set are selected.

Permutation

A *permutation* is an ordered arrangement of objects selected from a set. $P(n, r)$ (sometimes written as ${}_nP_r$) represents the number of permutations possible in which r objects from a set of n different objects are arranged.

$$\begin{aligned} P(n, r) &= n(n-1)(n-2) \ldots (n-r+1) \\ &= [n(n-1)(n-2) \ldots (n-r+1)] \times \left[\frac{(n-r)(n-r-1) \ldots 3 \times 2 \times 1}{(n-r)(n-r-1) \ldots 3 \times 2 \times 1}\right] \\ &= \frac{n(n-1)(n-2)(n-3) \ldots (n-r+1) \times (n-r)(n-r-1) \ldots 3 \times 2 \times 1}{(n-r)(n-r-1) \ldots 3 \times 2 \times 1} \\ &= \frac{n!}{(n-r)!} \end{aligned}$$

For example,

$$\begin{aligned} P(5, 3) &= \frac{5!}{(5-3)!} \\ &= \frac{120}{2} \\ &= 60 \end{aligned}$$

That means there are 60 ways of ordering objects taken three at a time from a set of five different objects.

Example 2 Calculating Permutations

There are 15 players on the school baseball team. How many ways can the coach complete the nine-person batting order?

Solution

Whenever you count the ways that different objects can be put into arrangements of any size, the order in which the objects are selected is an essential consideration. Order matters in this situation. We must calculate the number of arrangements that contain 9 items from a set that contains 15.

$$\begin{aligned}
P(15, 9) &= \frac{15!}{(15-9)!} \\
&= \frac{15!}{6!} \\
&= \frac{15 \times 14 \times 13 \times \ldots \times 2 \times 1}{6 \times 5 \times \ldots \times 2 \times 1} \\
&= 15 \times 14 \times 13 \times \ldots \times 7 \\
&= 1\ 816\ 214\ 400
\end{aligned}$$

CREATING PERMUTATIONS WHEN SOME OF THE OBJECTS ARE ALIKE

How many distinctly different "words" can be formed using the letters of the word OTTAWA?

Suppose it was possible to mark each of the repeated letters so that the two T's and the two A's could be distinguished from one another. By colouring the repeated letters in OTTAWA, we create six letters that are different from one another. These can be arranged in 6! different ways.

One such arrangement is AOTWAT and another is AOTWAT. If the colouring is removed, these two arrangements form the same "word." Since there are 2! ways to arrange the T's, and for each of these there are 2! ways to arrange the A's without actually changing the word, there will be 2! × 2! duplicates of the same word. To correct this overcounting of identical arrangements, divide 6! by the number of ways the duplicate words can be formed for each possible ordering of the letters. Therefore, the number of distinctly different "words" is given by $\frac{6!}{2!2!}$.

Number of Permutations

$\frac{n!}{a!b!c!\ldots}$ represents the number of permutations from a set of n objects in which a are alike, b are alike, c are alike, and so on.

Example 3 Calculating Permutations When Objects Are Alike

Determine the number of arrangements possible using the letters of the word MATHEMATICS.

Solution

There are 11 letters and there are two M's, two A's, and two T's. Therefore, the number of arrangements is $\frac{11!}{2!2!2!} = 4\ 989\ 600$.

SELECTING OBJECTS WITH AND WITHOUT REPLACEMENT

In the situations examined so far, objects were selected from a set and then, once selected, were removed from the collection so that they could not be chosen again. If the object is replaced, how does this affect the possible number of arrangements?

The Problem

How many ways are there to draw two cards from a standard deck of 52 cards?

Analysis and Solution

If you draw the cards without replacement, you draw one card and then, without putting the first card back in the deck, you draw another. You then note what the two cards are. There are 52 ways of selecting the first card, and 51 ways of selecting the second card once the first has been chosen. Therefore, there are $52 \times 51 = P(52, 2)$ or 2652 ways of selecting two cards this way.

If you draw the cards with replacement, you draw a card, note it, and then put it back in the deck. You then shuffle the deck and draw another card. There are 52 ways of selecting the first card. For each possible first card, there are 52 ways of selecting the second card. There are $52 \times 52 = 52^2$ or 2704 ways of selecting the two cards this way.

Replacement increases the number of possible choices.

Example 4 Using Permutations to Determine Probability

Four people are required to help out at a party: one to prepare the food, one to serve it, one to clear the tables, and one to wash up. Determine the probability that you and your three siblings will be chosen for these jobs if four people are randomly selected from a room of 12 people.

Solution

$$
\begin{aligned}
P(\text{you and siblings selected}) &= \frac{n(\text{you and your siblings can be chosen for the four jobs})}{n(\text{12 people can be chosen for the four jobs})} \\
&= \frac{4!}{{}_{12}P_4} \\
&= \frac{4!}{\frac{12!}{(12-4)!}} \\
&= \frac{4!}{\frac{12!}{8!}} \\
&= \frac{4 \times 3 \times 2 \times 1}{12 \times 11 \times 10 \times 9} \\
&= \frac{1}{495}
\end{aligned}
$$

KEY IDEAS

factorial notation ($n!$)

- represents the number of ordered arrangement of n objects

$$n! = n \times (n-1) \times (n-2) \times \ldots \times 2 \times 1$$

- represents the number of permuations possible from a set of n different objects
- $0! = 1$

permutations

- $P(n, r)$ (sometimes written as ${}_nP_r$) represents the number of permutations possible in which r objects from a set of n different objects are arranged.
- $P(n, r) = \frac{n!}{(n-r)!}$
- $\frac{n!}{a!b!c!\ldots}$ represents the number of permutations from a set of n objects in which a are alike, b are alike, c are alike, and so on.
- When order matters in a probability question, use the appropriate formulas for permutations to determine the number of ways the event can occur and the total number of possible outcomes.

4.6 Exercises

1. Evaluate each of the following.

(a) $5!$ **(b)** ${}_5P_3$ **(c)** $8! \times 6!$

(d) $\frac{5!}{4!}$ **(e)** $P(10, 3)$ **(f)** $\frac{16!}{5!\,6!\,8!}$

2. Simplify each of the following.

(a) $\frac{n!}{(n-1)!}$ **(b)** $\frac{(3n)!}{(3n-1)!}$ **(c)** $\frac{(n-r)!}{(n-r-1)!}$

3. Express the following using factorials.

(a) $5 \times 4 \times 3 \times 2 \times 1$ **(b)** $8 \times 7 \times 6$

(c) $\frac{30 \times 29 \times 28}{3 \times 2 \times 1}$ **(d)** 12×11

4. **(a)** In how many ways can 10 students standing in a line be arranged?

(b) In how many ways can 10 students standing in a line be arranged if Jill must be first?

(c) In how many ways can 10 students standing in a line be arranged if Jill must be first and Meera last?

5. In how many ways is it possible to elect a president, a vice-president, and a secretary for a club consisting of 15 members?

6. **Knowledge and Understanding** In how many ways can the letters of the word MONDAY be arranged if

(a) all six letters are used

(b) only four of the letters are used

7. In how many different ways can the letters of the word MISSISSAUGA be arranged?

8. **(a)** Show that ${}_6P_4 = 6({}_5P_3)$.

(b) Solve the equation for n.

(i) $\frac{n!}{(n-1)!} = 5$ **(ii)** $\frac{n!}{(n-2)!} = 90$

(iii) ${}_nP_5 = 14({}_nP_4)$ **(iv)** ${}_nP_3 = 17({}_nP_2)$

9. A standard deck of cards has had all the face cards (jacks, queens, and kings) removed so that only the ace through ten of each suit remains. A game is played in which two cards are drawn (without replacement) from this deck and a six-sided die is rolled. For the purpose of this game, an ace is considered to have a value of 1.

(a) Determine the total number of possible outcomes for this game.

(b) Find the probability of each of the following events.

(i) one even card is drawn and an even number is rolled

(ii) two even cards are drawn and an odd number is rolled

(iii) one card of 3 is drawn and 3 or less is rolled

(iv) the sum of the cards and the die is 7

(v) the sum of the cards and the die is less than 5

10. Repeat Question 9 if the game is played with replacement after the first card is drawn.

11. **Application** A combination lock opens when the right combination of three numbers from 00 to 99 is entered. The same number may be used more than once.

(a) What is the probability of getting the correct combination by chance?

(b) What is the probability of getting the right combination if you already know the first digit?

12. A bag contains four red, three green, and five yellow marbles. Three marbles are drawn, one at time, without replacement. Determine the probability that the order in which they are selected is

(a) yellow, red, green **(b)** yellow, green, green

(c) yellow, yellow, red

13. **Communication** You are taking a chemistry test and are asked to list the first 10 elements of the periodic table in order as they appear in the table. You know the first 10 elements but not the order. Explain why the probability of guessing the correct answer is $\frac{1}{3\,628\,800}$.

C **14. Thinking, Inquiry, Problem Solving** Several years ago, regular motor-vehicle licence plates comprised three letters followed by three numbers. Later, any combination of six characters was permitted in order to provide a greater supply of available licence plates.

(a) By how much did the supply of possible licence-plate numbers increase?

(b) Plates issued by the Motor Vehicle License Office now use four letters followed by three numbers. How many such plates are there now?

(c) For an extra charge, it is possible for car owners to purchase vanity plates that can have up to seven characters on them. How many seven-character plates are possible, excluding those that fit the pattern of the plates described in part (b)? (**Note:** The Ministry of Transportation places some restrictions on the use of characters and words on the licence plates. As a result, the number of allowable licence plates is less than the number of possible plates.)

15. Solve for n: $\frac{(n-1)!}{(n-3)!} = 20$.

ADDITIONAL ACHIEVEMENT CHART QUESTIONS

16. Knowledge and Understanding Twelve students have signed up to serve on the yearbook committee.

(a) How many ways can the staff adviser choose three people to act as publisher, lead photographer, and editor, respectively?

(b) In filling these three positions, what is the probability that Francesca is selected as publisher and Marc is chosen as editor?

17. Application The moderator of a forum discussion is assigning seats to the six participants. If the seats are arranged in a linear fashion, determine the probability that Dr. Eisen and Dr. Bugada are seated next to each other.

18. Thinking, Inquiry, Problem Solving How many three-letter arrangements are possible using the letters of the word CANADA?

19. Communication Create a permutation question that also involves probability. Determine the solution to your problem.

Chapter Problem

Analyzing a Traditional Game

CP14. In this game, all six counters are tossed simultaneously. Does order play a role in determining the number of outcomes? Explain.

CP15. If the rules of the game were changed so that the counters were tossed one at a time, would this affect the probabilities associated with earning points? Explain.

4.7 Counting Techniques and Probability Strategies—Combinations

The previous section showed you that the outcomes of complex experiments can be counted by combining the outcomes of simple experiments when order matters. For many counting problems, order is not important. For example, in most card games, the order in which the cards are dealt is not important. Rearranging the cards that you have been dealt does not change your hand. This section will examine counting techniques and probability problems that involve combinations.

SELECTING OBJECTS WHEN ORDER DOES NOT MATTER

Example 1 Calculating Combinations

Suppose you have nine children who want to play a game that requires three players at a time. In how many ways can you choose a team of three children? The order in which you select the children does not matter.

Solution

? Think about Order
Why doesn't the order in which they are selected matter?

Suppose that teams are selected as follows:

	First Choice	Second Choice	Third Choice
Team A	Ben	Mary	Amir
Team B	Mary	Amir	Ben
Team C	Amir	Ben	Mary

The total number of three permutations of the nine children is $P(9, 3) = 9 \times 8 \times 7$ or 504. This is the number of all possible three-person teams in which order matters.

combination—an unordered selection of elements from a given set

Each of the teams shown above is essentially the same. In total, Ben, Mary, and Amir could be arranged in $P(3, 3) = 3!$ or 6 ways. Therefore, the number of distinct teams, ignoring the order in which players are chosen, is $\frac{P(9, 3)}{3!} = \frac{504}{6}$ or 84. When order does not matter, you divide the total number of permutations by the number of like arrangements. This determines the number of unique combinations.

Technolink

Combinations can be computed on a TI-83 Plus calculator using the nCr command. See Appendix C.14 on page 410.

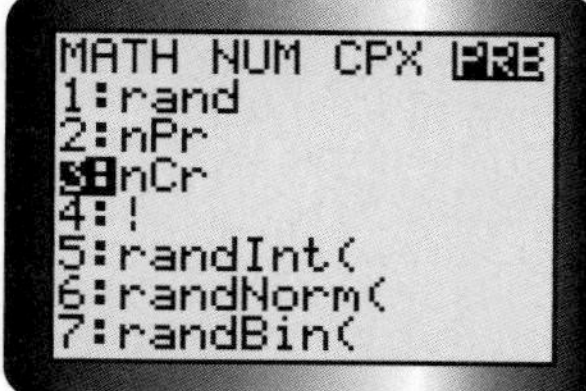

Think about
C(*n*, *r*)

People often read C(*n*, *r*) as "*n* choose *r*." Why does this seem reasonable?

Combination

A combination is a collection of chosen objects for which order does not matter. C(*n*, *r*)—sometimes written as ${}_nC_r$ or as $\binom{n}{r}$—represents the number of combinations possible in which *r* objects are selected from a set of *n* different objects.

$$\begin{aligned} C(n, r) &= \frac{P(n, r)}{P(r, r)} \\ &= \frac{P(n, r)}{r!} \\ &= \frac{n!}{(n-r)!\,r!} \end{aligned}$$

For example,

$$\begin{aligned} C(9, 3) &= {}_9C_3 \\ &= \binom{9}{3} \\ &= \frac{9!}{6!\,3!} \\ &= \frac{9 \times 8 \times \ldots 3 \times 2 \times 1}{6 \times 5 \times 4 \times 3 \times 2 \times 1 \times 3 \times 2 \times 1} \\ &= 84 \end{aligned}$$

Example 2 Calculating the Number of Combinations

From a class of 30 students, determine how many ways a five-person committee can be selected to organize a class party

(a) with no restrictions

(b) with Marnie on the committee

Solution

(a) Each person is not assigned a specific responsibility, so the order does not matter.

$$\begin{aligned} \text{number of committees} &= C(30, 5) \\ &= \binom{30}{5} \\ &= \frac{30!}{25!\,5!} \\ &= 142\ 506 \end{aligned}$$

(b) With Marnie on the committee, there are $\binom{29}{4} = 23\ 751$ ways of choosing the remaining members.

Think about
Restrictions

What restriction must be satisfied before the committee members are selected in part (b)?

Example 3 Calculating the Number of Combinations

Tanya Kozovski, the coach of a co-ed basketball team, must select five players to start the game from a team that consists of six females and five males. How many ways can this be achieved if Tanya must choose three females and two males to start the game?

? Think about The Selections
Why are the number of ways that the coach can pick males and females multiplied?

Solution

Tanya can choose the three females in $\binom{6}{3}$ ways and the males in $\binom{5}{2}$ ways. Thus, the number of ways to choose the starting line-up is as follows:

$$\begin{aligned}\binom{6}{3} \times \binom{5}{2} &= 20 \times 10\\ &= 200 \text{ ways}\end{aligned}$$

Example 4 Calculating the Number of Combinations

In how many ways can 6 people be selected from a group that consists of four adults and eight children if the group must contain at least two adults?

direct reasoning—all suitable outcomes are totalled to arrive at a final answer

Solution 1 *Direct Reasoning*

In this situation, the condition that the group must have at least two adults must be satisfied. This can happen three ways: a group with two adults and four children; three adults and three children; or four adults and two children.

$$\begin{aligned}\text{number of ways} &= \binom{4}{2}\binom{8}{4} + \binom{4}{3}\binom{8}{3} + \binom{4}{4}\binom{8}{2}\\ &= 6 \times 70 + 4 \times 56 + 1 \times 28\\ &= 420 + 224 + 28\\ &= 672\end{aligned}$$

indirect reasoning—undesired outcomes are subtracted from the total to arrive at a final answer

Solution 2 *Indirect Reasoning*

In this situation, the solution can also be found by subtracting the number of ways the condition is not satisfied (0 or 1 adult in the group) from the total number of combinations.

$$\begin{aligned}\text{number of ways} &= \binom{12}{6} - \binom{4}{0}\binom{8}{6} - \binom{4}{1}\binom{8}{5}\\ &= 924 - 1 \times 28 - 4 \times 56\\ &= 924 - 28 - 224\\ &= 672\end{aligned}$$

Example 5 Using Combinations to Find Probabilities

Five cards are dealt at random from a deck of 52 playing cards. Determine the probability that you will have

(a) the 10–J–Q–K–A of the same suit

(b) four of a kind

Solution

(a) The number of five-card hands possible from a deck of 52 cards is $\binom{52}{5} = 2\,598\,960$. There are only four suits, so there are only four hands that are 10–J–Q–K–A of the same suit.

$P(\text{10–J–Q–K–A same suit}) = \frac{4}{2\,598\,960}$ or $\frac{1}{649\,740}$

(b) There are 13 cards in each suit and the hand must contain four of the same card. The remaining card in the hand can be any card of the remaining 48 in the deck.

$$\begin{aligned} P(\text{four of a kind}) &= \frac{13\binom{4}{4}\binom{48}{1}}{\binom{52}{5}} \\ &= \frac{13 \times 1 \times 48}{2\,598\,960} \\ &= \frac{624}{2\,598\,960} \\ &= \frac{1}{4165} \end{aligned}$$

? Think about $\binom{4}{4}$

- Why does $\binom{4}{4} = 1$?
- Why does $\binom{4}{0} = 1$?
- Why are these answers reasonble?

PROBABILITY AND ODDS

The terms *probability* and *odds* are often used interchangeably. However, they mean two different things.

Suppose there are four white balls and seven black balls in a bag. You need to reach into the bag and select one ball.

- The probability that you will select a white ball is $\frac{4}{11}$.
- The odds that you will select a white ball is 4 to 7 or 4:7.

Calculating odds involves comparing the number of favourable outcomes to the number of unfavourable outcomes. This is different from probability, which involves comparing the number of favourable outcomes to the total number of possible outcomes.

KEY IDEAS

combination—a collection of chosen objects for which order does not matter

C(*n*, *r*)—sometimes written as ${}_nC_r$ or as $\binom{n}{r}$—represents the number of combinations possible in which *r* objects are selected from a set of *n* different objects

$$\begin{aligned} C(n, r) &= \frac{P(n, r)}{P(r, r)} \\ &= \frac{P(n, r)}{r!} \\ &= \frac{n!}{(n-r)!\,r!} \end{aligned}$$

When order doesn't matter in a complex probability question, use the appropriate formulas for combinations to determine the number of ways the event can occur and the total number of possible outcomes.

direct reasoning—all suitable outcomes are totalled to arrive at a final answer

indirect reasoning—undesired outcomes are subtracted from the total to arrive at a final answer

odds—number of favourable outcomes: number of unfavourable outcomes

4.7 Exercises

A

1. Evaluate each of the following.

(a) $C(8, 3)$ **(b)** ${}_7C_4$ **(c)** $\binom{12}{11}$

(d) $\binom{5}{2}$ **(e)** $C(10, 3)$ **(f)** $\binom{15}{15}$

2. In how many ways can a team of six female volleyball players be chosen to start the game from a roster of 12 players?

3. In how many ways can a principal select a graduation committee consisting of two teachers and four students if there are six teachers and ten students who are volunteering for the positions?

4. **Knowledge and Understanding** A bag contains 10 red jellybeans and 8 black jellybeans.

(a) Determine the number of ways that 2 jellybeans can be chosen from the 18 that are in the bag.

(b) Determine the number of ways that 2 red jellybeans can be selected.

(c) What is the probability that 2 jellybeans selected at random are red?

5. In the card game Crazy Eights, how many different eight-card hands can be dealt from a standard 52-card deck?

6. Show that

(a) $C(10, 5) = C(9, 4) + C(9, 5)$ **(b)** $5\binom{n}{5} = n\binom{n-1}{4}$

(c) $r\binom{n}{r} = n\binom{n-1}{r-1}$ **(d)** $2\binom{2n-1}{n-1} = \binom{2n}{n}$

7. From a group of five men and four women, determine how many committees of five people can be formed with

(a) no restrictions
(b) exactly three women
(c) exactly four men
(d) no women
(e) at least two men
(f) at least three women
(g) Find the probability of each of parts (b) to (f).

8. **(a)** A rooming house has three rooms that contain four beds, three beds, and two beds, respectively. In how many ways can nine guests be assigned to these rooms?
(b) What is the probability that Renaldo will be assigned to the room with two beds?

9. Three cards are selected at random from a standard deck of 52 playing cards. Determine the probability that all three cards are

(a) hearts
(b) black
(c) aces
(d) face cards

10. A paper bag contains a mixture of three types of candy. There are ten gum balls, seven candy bars, and three packages of toffee. Suppose a game is played in which a candy is randomly taken from the bag and then a second candy is drawn from the bag, without replacement. You are allowed to keep both candies if, and only if, the second is the same type as the first.

(a) Calculate the probability that you will be able to keep a gum ball on the first try.
(b) Calculate the probability that you will be able to keep any candy on the first try.
(c) Calculate the probability that you will not be able to keep any candy on the first try.

A′—the complement of *A*

11. **Application** The odds in favour of an event are expressed as the ratio

$$P(A):P(A') = P(A):(1 - P(A))$$

The winning numbers for the Lotto 6/49 lottery are drawn from a clear plastic drum that contains 49 ping-pong balls numbered from 1 to 49. The order of selection does not matter. Once a ball is drawn from the drum, it is put on display. The process is repeated a total of six times. You can play the lottery by having the computer randomly pick a combination of six numbers for you. What are the odds in favour of you winning the jackpot (matching all six numbers) in this way?

12. A single coin is tossed.

(a) What is the probability of tossing a head? A tail?
(b) What are the odds of tossing a head? A tail?
(c) Describe how the probability of an event is similar to the odds of an event occuring.

13. Melik has five quarters and six dimes in his pocket. He pulls out one coin.

(a) What are the odds of the coin being a quarter?
(b) What are the odds of the coin being a dime?

14. Suppose the probability of rain tomorrow is 80%. What are the odds of rain tomorrow?

15. The coach says that the probability of winning the next game is 40%. What are the odds the team will win?

16. People often talk about the odds *for* or *against* an event. For example, you saw on page 261 that the odds of selecting a white ball were 4:7. The odds against are, thus, 7:4.
   (a) In a horse race, odds are not written in the standard way. For example, a horse with odds 100:1 has little chance of winning. Explain how the odds work.
   (b) Suppose the odds are 100:1 that a horse will win a race. What is the probability the horse will win?

17. **Communication**
   (a) How are combinations and permutations similar? How are they different? Use examples in your answer.
   (b) Explain what ${}_nC_r$ and ${}_nP_r$ represent. How can you find ${}_nC_r$ if you know ${}_nP_r$? Use an example in your answer.

C 18. A CD player can hold five different CDs. The chart below shows the number of songs on each CD in the player.

CD	1	2	3	4	5
Number of Songs	13	15	11	12	16

If the player is set on shuffle and randomly selects songs to play from the five discs, calculate the probability that during the first five songs played
   (a) they will be from CDs 1 and 5
   (b) one song from each of the CDs is played
   (c) your favourite song from each of the five CDs is played

19. **Thinking, Inquiry, Problem Solving**
In a female minor hockey league of 10 teams from different cities, each pair of teams must play three games. Can a schedule be created so that the same number of games is played in each of the 10 cities? Justify your answer.

20. Algebraically prove that the following is true for $n \geq 3$. Why must the condition on the value of n be included?

$$\binom{n}{3} + \binom{n}{2} + \frac{1}{6}\binom{n}{1} = \frac{n^3}{6}$$

ADDITIONAL ACHIEVEMENT CHART QUESTIONS

21. **Knowledge and Understanding** A photographer for an advertising photo shoot has a group of models available consisting of three male adults, four female adults, and five children. In how many ways can the photographer choose four models if there must be one adult male, one adult female, and two children?

22. **Application** Determine the probability that a four-card hand dealt from a standard deck of 52 playing cards contains a card from each suit.

23. **Thinking, Inquiry, Problem Solving** Prove that $\binom{n}{r} + \binom{n}{r+1} = \binom{n+1}{r+1}$.

24. **Communication**

(a) Suppose a commitee of 3 is to be selected from a group of 10 people.

(b) Suppose the committee is actually an executive committee consisting of a president, vice-president, and secretary.

Explain why counting the number of committees described in part (a) will use combinations while those in part (b) will require the use of permutations.

Chapter Problem

Analyzing a Traditional Game

CP16. Use the combination formula to verify that there are 2^6 possible combinations possible when the counters are tossed.

CP17. Copy and complete the table by calculating the probability of each of the following occurring on any random turn and the points to be awarded.

Outcome	Probability	Points
6 Blue, 0 Red		
5 Blue, 1 Red		
4 Blue, 2 Red		
3 Blue, 3 Red		
2 Blue, 4 Red		
1 Blue, 5 Red		
0 Blue, 6 Red		

CP18. Multiply the probability by the number of points, add up the results, and simplify. This is the expected or average number of points you should earn on each turn.

CP19. Based on your findings, how many turns would you expect a typical game to have before someone wins?

Project Connection

Permutations and Combinations

Sanjev was wondering what he could do with his presentation. He was struggling a little bit until he came across the following news headline:

40% of adults feel that winning the lottery is the best way to save for retirement.

This caught his attention. He decided that his presentation would involve calculating the likelihood of being able to use the lottery to save enough money for retirement. He had just finished developing skills with counting techniques, particularly permutations and combinations, and he wondered how he might be able to apply his techniques to help him with his presentation.

First, though, he had to research how to win prizes. He found the information that follows.

Lottery Draws and Prizes

(i) There are six numbers, drawn at random, between 1 and 49. Once a number has been chosen, it no longer can be used again.
(ii) Each ticket has six numbers.
(iii) A ticket wins the grand prize if all its numbers match the six numbers drawn.
(iv) Second prize is won if five numbers on the ticket match any five of the six numbers drawn.
(v) Third prize is won if four numbers on the ticket match any four of the six numbers drawn.
(vi) Fourth prize is won if three numbers on the ticket match any three of the six numbers drawn.

Sanjev decided to use his counting techniques to determine how many ways there are for winning each of the prizes. Help Sanjev complete his calculations by answering the questions that follow.

- How many ways are there for selecting the numbers on a ticket that can win the grand prize?
- How many ways are there for selecting the numbers on a ticket that can win second prize?
- How many ways are there for selecting the numbers on a ticket that can win third prize?
- How many ways are there for selecting the numbers on a ticket that can win fourth prize?

Sanjev was astonished when he saw the number after his calculations. Why do you think that Sanjev was so surprised? What do these numbers indicate to you about the likelihood of being able to win the lottery and save enough money for retirement?

By now, you have probably gathered a lot of data and have done a fair amount of research on your topic. You may be looking for ways to analyze your data. Look at your data.

- Is there any way that your counting techniques can be used on your data to help you interpret it or get more meaning from it?
- What information is gained because of the application of your counting techniques?
- What conclusions can you make because of the application of your counting techniques?
- How does the information that you have gained, and the conclusions you have drawn, fit into your project and presentation?
- Have any new questions been raised that you would like to answer now? Do you feel you should answer these questions?

Chapter 4 Wrap-Up

EXTRA PRACTICE

1. Compute the value of each of the following expressions.

(a) P(4, 4) **(b)** $1! - 0!$ **(c)** $\frac{20 \times 19!}{20!}$

(d) P(5, 0) **(e)** C(5, 5) **(f)** $\binom{18}{2}$

2. Two hundred students have enrolled in at least one Grade 12 university math course this year.

- 68 are in Geometry and Discrete Math
- 78 are in Data Management
- 60 are in Geometry and Discrete Math and AFIC
- 35 are in AFIC and Data Management
- 13 are in Geometry and Discrete Math, and Data Management
- 10 take all three Grade 12 university math courses

(a) Draw a Venn diagram to represent this situation.
(b) Use the Venn diagram to determine the total number of students who take AFIC.

3. A six-sided die is rolled and then a coin is tossed.
(a) Draw the tree diagram that represents all possible results of the two actions taken together.
(b) Determine the number of outcomes in which the roll of the die is an odd number.
(c) Determine the total number of outcomes in which the roll of the die is odd and the coin toss is heads.

4. Design and carry out a simulation to investigate the following situation: If you randomly stop students in the hall and ask them for their birth month, on average, how many students must you ask before you find someone born in the same month as you, assuming birth months are equally likely?

5. Determine the probability of each of the following situations.
(a) a red card is drawn from a standard deck of 52 playing cards
(b) two even numbers are rolled on two consecutive rolls of a die
(c) at least one 3 turns up when three dice are rolled
(d) a five-card poker hand dealt from a standard deck of 52 playing cards results in a full house (three of a kind and two of a kind)
(e) two face cards are drawn in a row (without replacement) from a standard deck of 52 playing cards given that the first card drawn is a king
(f) a committee of six people randomly chosen from seven males and eight females is either all male or all female
(g) in a six-person sprint, Jesse finishes first, Marnie second, and Raul last

6. Use the appropriate counting techniques to answer each of the following.

(a) Twenty books are to be placed on a shelf. Determine the number of ways the first five books can be placed on the shelf.

(b) In how many ways can nine people place themselves in nine seats in a row?

(c) Out of 15 different stores, how many ways can a salesperson visit 10 of the stores once each?

(d) Three identical red blocks, a black block, and two identical blue blocks are to be placed in a row. In how many ways can this be done?

(e) A team consisting of 3 members is to be chosen from a group of 12 people. How many different teams are possible if there must be a chairperson, a secretary, and a treasurer?

(f) The letters of the word STATISTICS are to be arranged among themselves. In how many different ways can this be done?

(g) A class has 12 students. In how many different ways can the students be put into lab groups consisting of 3 students in each group?

(h) How many distinct permutations of the letters of the word OTTAWA begin and end with the letter T?

(i) In how many permutations of the digits 123456789 are the numbers 1 and 2 beside each other?

(j) A school has 480 girls and 520 boys. How many committees of 5 members can be formed if there must be at least 1 boy on each committee?

(k) How many groups consisting of at least 2 people can be chosen from a group of 10 people?

7. Dr. Kai Phoon has found that 25% of her patients have eye problems, 10% have hearing problems, and 5% have both. Are the events "have eye problems" and "have hearing problems" independent? Justify your decision.

8. Toronto is playing Anaheim in the Stanley Cup final. The first team to win four games is the new NHL champion. If the probability that Toronto wins any game is 0.55, determine the probability that

(a) Toronto wins in four straight games

(b) Anaheim wins the Stanley Cup

9. Describe a situation in which two events are

(a) mutually exclusive

(b) independent

(c) not mutually exclusive

(d) dependent

10. Given that $P(A \cap B) = 0.4$, $P(A \cap C) = 0.2$, $P(B \mid A) = 0.6$, and $P(B) = 0.5$, find the following.

(a) $P(A \mid B)$

(b) $P(B')$

(c) $P(A)$

(d) $P(C \mid A)$

(e) the odds in favour of B

11. The student council has 15 members.

(a) Determine the probability that the staff adviser selects Yuko, Luigi, and Justine as treasurer, secretary, and liaison to the principal, respectively.

(b) Determine the probability that the staff adviser randomly selects Yuko, Luigi, and Justine from student council to clean up after the Pep Rally.

Chapter 4 Test

1. Two hundred students have enrolled in at least one Grade 12 university course this year.

   70 are in Chemistry
   110 are in Physics
   76 are in Biology
   60 are in Chemistry and Physics
   35 are in Physics and Biology
   13 are in Biology and Chemistry
   7 are in Chemistry, Biology, and Physics

   (a) Draw a Venn diagram to represent this situation.
   (b) Use the Venn diagram to determine the number of students who take Grade 12 courses but no Grade 12 university science courses.
   (c) Determine the probability that a student selected at random from the group is taking Biology.
   (d) Determine the probability that a student selected at random from the group is taking Chemistry or Physics.

2. Three playing cards—a jack, a queen, and a king—are placed in a box. A card is drawn from the box, its value is recorded, and then the card is put back into the box. The process is then repeated a second time.
   (a) Draw the tree diagram for all possible outcomes of the two draws.
   (b) Determine the number of outcomes in which a king is the first card drawn from the box.
   (c) Find the probability that the first and second cards drawn are the same.

3. **Knowledge and Understanding** A five-card poker hand is dealt and the last card is turned face up. Determine the probability that you have been dealt four aces, given that the card turned over is an ace.

4. In how many ways can a group of 10 people be chosen from 6 adults and 8 children if the group must contain at least 2 adults?

5. **Communication** Mutually exclusive events are always independent. Is this true or false? Why?

6. **Application** Nine horses are entered in a horse race. If you "box" three horses (three are chosen and they can finish in any of the first 3 positions in the race), determine the probability that you will hold the winning ticket.

7. A drawer contains four red socks and five blue socks.
   (a) Three socks are drawn one at a time and then put back before the next selection. Determine the probability that
      (i) exactly two red socks are selected
      (ii) at least two red socks are selected
   (b) Repeat part (a) without replacement

8. **Thinking, Inquiry, Problem Solving** There are 25 students in a Data Management class. Determine the probability that at least two of them share the same birthday. (Assume that every year has 365 days.)

5 Probability Distributions and Predictions

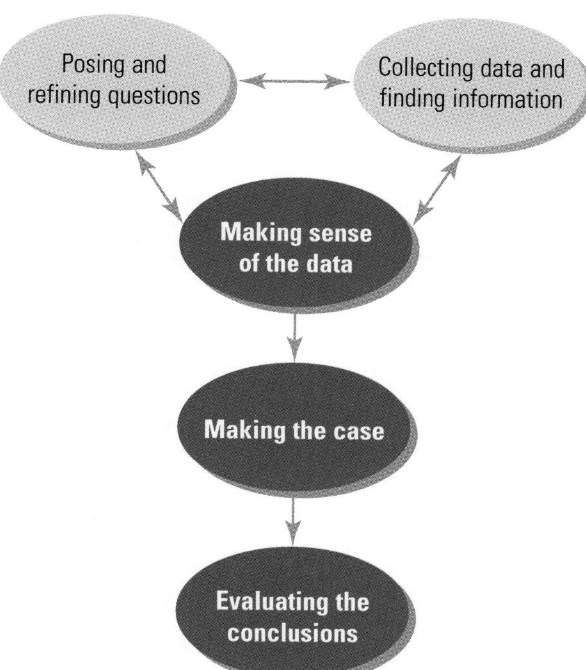

Statistics is the branch of mathematics that makes predictions about a population using data collected from a sample. People who use statistics to make important decisions require a high level of confidence in the predictions. A decision based on poor statistical information can have expensive and sometimes disastrous consequences.

Common sense dictates that the results from a sample may be similar to, but not exactly the same as, those for the entire population. Statisticians are interested in the probability that their predictions are representative of the population they are dealing with. If that probability is high enough, the risk of making a poor decision is minimized.

In this chapter, you will

- create theoretical probability distributions for events
- use simulations to create probability distributions when it is not possible to find the theoretical probability distributions
- analyze simulations that can be modelled using a binomial probability distribution
- determine the likelihood that a particular simulation is representative of a whole population

Chapter Problem

Are Frog Populations Declining?

April 20, 1992 San Francisco Chronicle

Disappearance of toads, frogs has some scientists worried

By Charles Petit, *Chronicle* Science Writer

Gary Fellers, a biologist at Point Reyes National Seashore, hiked into the back country around Mount Lassen recently to scour the ponds and streams for the small, brown Cascades frog that he used to find there by the thousands.

"We looked at 50 localities, including 15 where historically the frogs were always found," he said. "We found two. Not frogs in two places. Two frogs total."

For several years in a row now, similar news of vanishing frogs and toads has come from Australia, Canada, India, Europe, what used to be the Soviet Union, the mountain-hugging rain forest of Central and South America, and most of the western United States.

Now, after a series of meetings to compare fragmentary but worrisome notes, hundreds of scientists and amateur naturalists have joined in an international attempt to find out whether, as so many fear, frog and toad populations are in simultaneous decline around the world.

Environmental scientists believe that there is a decline in the population of frogs around the world. They speculate that declining frog populations are a symptom of deteriorating environmental conditions. How would these scientists gather accurate data about existing frog populations? How would they use these data to speculate on previous or future population levels?

Project Connection

As part of your course project, you will have to discuss the validity of your results. The content of this chapter will provide you with the tools you will need to estimate the probability that your results are a reliable predictor for an entire population. Combined with the material in Chapters 3 and 4, you will have a complete set of statistical tools for analyzing and validating either sample data or simulation data.

5.1 Probability Distributions and Expected Value

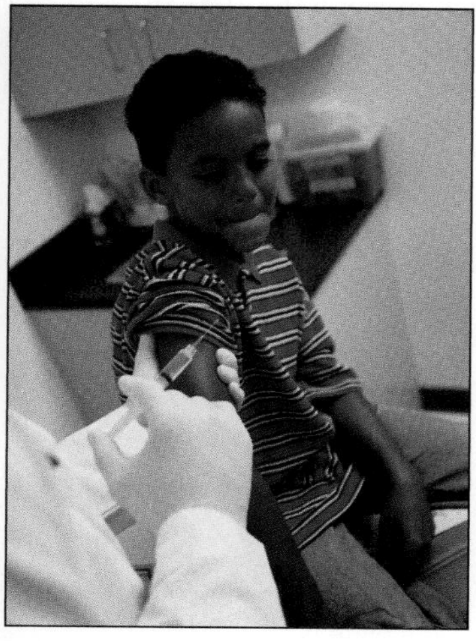

Should you close down a manufacturing plant because 5% of the drills produced during a specific shift were defective? Should you follow a prescribed medical treatment if you are not sure that the test results correctly identified your illness?

Probability distributions (theoretical and experimental) and expected value are significant pieces of information that can be used in making these kinds of decisions.

INVESTIGATION 1: DISTRIBUTION OF DICE SUMS

Consider the experiment in which two six-sided dice are rolled. Suppose one die is red and the other is green.

Purpose

To compute the experimental probability for the sum resulting from the roll of two six-sided dice.

Procedure

discrete random variable—a variable that assumes a unique value for each outcome

The sum on the dice is a *discrete random variable*. It is the result of a random event and can take on any whole number from 2 to 12.

A. Create a table or spreadsheet to record the possible sums that result from rolling the dice. Roll the dice 50 times to record 50 sums.

B. Draw a histogram that indicates the frequency for each sum.

C. Compute the experimental probability (relative frequency) for each possible sum.

? Think about Step C

Why are there 36 possible rolls of the two dice? Refer to the chart on page 226.

Discussion Questions

1. Why do all the experimental probabilities from Step C add to 1?
2. Does a sum of 2 have the same probability as a sum of 12? Why?
3. Which sum has the greatest probability of occurring? Explain why this is so.
4. If you were to roll the dice 360 times, how often would you expect a sum of 7 to occur? How often would you expect a sum of 8? Explain your answers.

PROBABILITY DISTRIBUTION OF A DISCRETE RANDOM VARIABLE

probability distribution—a table, formula, or graph that provides the probabilities of a discrete random variable assuming any of its possible values

A table of probabilities for the possible sums of the dice appears in the margin on the following page. This table is one way to represent the **probability distribution** of the possible sums. After a number of trials of the experiment, the

relative frequency distribution—a table that shows the ratio of the number of times each value of a discrete random variable occurs to the total number of trials

Sum	Theoretical Probability
2	$\frac{1}{36}$
3	$\frac{2}{36}$
4	$\frac{3}{36}$
5	$\frac{4}{36}$
6	$\frac{5}{36}$
7	$\frac{6}{36}$
8	$\frac{5}{36}$
9	$\frac{4}{36}$
10	$\frac{3}{36}$
11	$\frac{2}{36}$
12	$\frac{1}{36}$

number of times each sum occurs is represented in a frequency distribution. The frequency distribution can be converted into a **relative frequency distribution** by dividing each frequency by the total number of trials. Each relative frequency is the observed experimental probability of a particular sum and is an estimate of the theoretical probability of that sum.

The graph below is another way to represent the probability distribution. This graph also provides the probability of each sum occurring when a pair of dice is rolled.

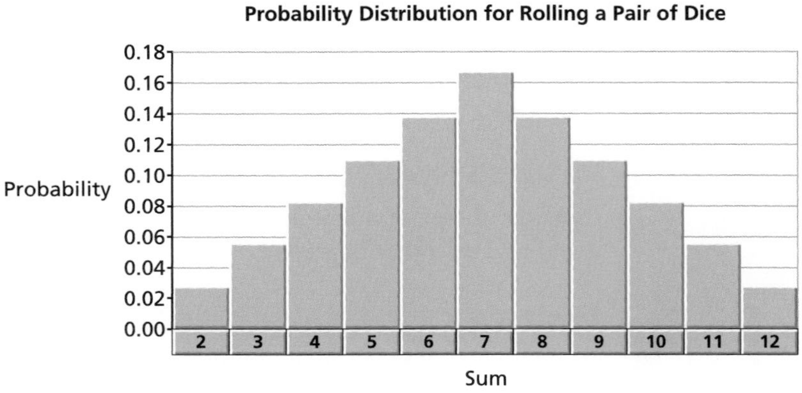

Probability Distribution for Rolling a Pair of Dice

Probability

0.18
0.16
0.14
0.12
0.10
0.08
0.06
0.04
0.02
0.00

2 3 4 5 6 7 8 9 10 11 12

Sum

Probability Distribution of a Discrete Random Variable

The probability distribution of a discrete random variable, X, is a function that provides the probability of each possible value of X. This function may be presented as a table of values, a graph, or a mathematical expression.

Think about Mean and the Expected Value

The expected value of a discrete random variable is often referred to as its **mean**. Why is this an appropriate term?

EXPECTED VALUE OF A DISCRETE RANDOM VARIABLE

An informal definition for the *expected value* of a random variable was given in the previous chapter. After many repetitions of the experiment, the average value of the random variable tends toward the expected value. A more mathematically formal definition of expected value will be introduced in this section.

By analyzing the probabilities of all possible sums when two dice are rolled, the probability distribution above was constructed.

You can see that the theoretical probability of a sum of 7 is $\frac{6}{36} = \frac{1}{6}$. In other words, after many trials of the experiment, you would expect to see 7 close to one-sixth of the time. Similarly, each of the other possible sum values should occur, in the long run, with a relative frequency close to its probability. The expected value of the sum is the result of adding each possible sum value multiplied by its expected relative frequency, or probability.

Therefore, the expected value for the sum of two dice is as follows:

$$\begin{aligned} E(\text{Sum}) &= 2P(\text{Sum} = 2) + 3P(\text{Sum} = 3) + 4P(\text{Sum} = 4) + \ldots \\ &\quad + 12P(\text{Sum} = 12) \\ &= 2 \times \frac{1}{36} + 3 \times \frac{2}{36} + 4 \times \frac{3}{36} + \ldots + 12 \times \frac{1}{36} \\ &= \frac{252}{36} = 7 \end{aligned}$$

Expected Value of a Discrete Random Variable

The expected value of a discrete random variable, X, is the sum of the terms of the form $X \cdot P(X)$ for all possible values of X. In other words, if X takes on the values $x_1, x_2, \ldots, x_n$, then the expected value of X is given by

$$\begin{aligned} E(X) &= x_1P(X = x_1) + x_2P(X = x_2) + \ldots + x_nP(X = x_n) \\ &= \sum_{i=1}^{n} x_iP(X = x_i) \end{aligned}$$

where n represents the number of terms in the sum.

Example 1 Tossing Three Coins

Suppose you were to toss three coins.

(a) What is the likelihood that you would observe at least two heads?

(b) What is the expected number of heads?

Solution

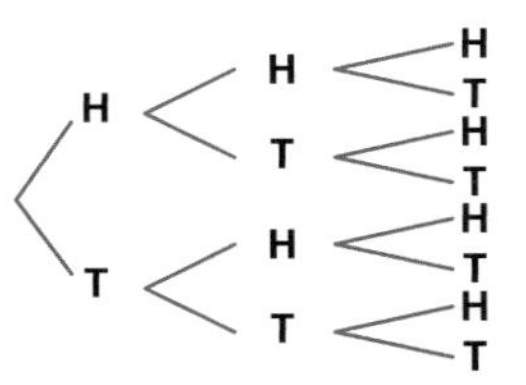

The following table shows the theoretical probability distribution for this experiment. The discrete random variable, X, represents the number of heads observed.

X	0 heads	1 head	2 heads	3 heads
$P(X) = x$	$\frac{1}{8}$	$\frac{3}{8}$	$\frac{3}{8}$	$\frac{1}{8}$

(a) The probability that at least two heads are observed is

$$\begin{aligned} P(X = 2) + P(X = 3) &= \frac{3}{8} + \frac{1}{8} \\ &= \frac{1}{2} \end{aligned}$$

(b) The expected number of heads is

$$\begin{aligned} E(X) &= 0P(X = 0) + 1P(X = 1) + 2P(X = 2) + 3P(X = 3) \\ &= 0\left(\frac{1}{8}\right) + 1\left(\frac{3}{8}\right) + 2\left(\frac{3}{8}\right) + 3\left(\frac{1}{8}\right) \\ &= \frac{0}{8} + \frac{3}{8} + \frac{6}{8} + \frac{3}{8} \\ &= 1\frac{1}{2} \end{aligned}$$

? Think about The Expected Value

- Why is $1\frac{1}{2}$ heads in the toss of three coins not surprising?
- What does this result mean?
- Why is this expected value not a whole number?

Example 2 Selecting a Committee

Suppose you want to select a committee consisting of three people. The group from which the committee members can be selected consists of four men and three women.

(a) What is the probability that at least one woman is on the committee?

(b) What is the expected number of women on the committee?

Solution

There are $C(7, 3)$ or 35 possible committees. Of these, $C(4, 3)$ have no women; $C(4, 2) \times C(3, 1)$ have one woman; $C(4, 1) \times C(3, 2)$ have two women; and $C(3, 3)$ have three women. The probability distribution for the number of women on the committee appears below. The discrete random variable, X, represents the number of women on the committee.

X	0 women	1 woman	2 women	3 women
$P(X)$	$\frac{4}{35}$	$\frac{18}{35}$	$\frac{12}{35}$	$\frac{1}{35}$

(a) The probability that at least one woman will be on the committee is

$$\begin{aligned} P(X = 1) + P(X = 2) + P(X = 3) &= \frac{18}{35} + \frac{12}{35} + \frac{1}{35} \\ &= \frac{31}{35} \end{aligned}$$

(b) The expected number of women on the committee is

$$\begin{aligned} E(X) &= 0P(X = 0) + 1P(X = 1) + 2P(X = 2) + 3P(X = 3) \\ &= 0\left(\frac{4}{35}\right) + 1\left(\frac{18}{35}\right) + 2\left(\frac{12}{35}\right) + 3\left(\frac{1}{35}\right) \\ &= \frac{0}{35} + \frac{18}{35} + \frac{24}{35} + \frac{3}{35} \\ &\doteq 1.3 \end{aligned}$$

KEY IDEAS

discrete random variable—a variable that assumes a unique value for each outcome

probability distribution—a function that gives the probability of each possible value of a discrete random variable, X; this function may be presented as a table of values, a graph, or a mathematical expression

relative frequency distribution—a table that shows the ratio of the frequency of each value of a discrete random variable to the number of trials

expected value—the sum of the terms of the form $X \cdot P(X)$ for all possible values of a discrete random variable, X

$$E(X) = x_1P(X = x_1) + x_2P(X = x_2) + ... + x_nP(X = x_n)$$

5.1 Exercises

1. An experiment is conducted in which two coins are tossed and the number of heads is recorded.
   (a) Explain why the number of heads is a discrete random variable.
   (b) Create a probability distribution table for the number of heads.
   (c) Compute the expected number of heads per trial.

2. Identify which of the following are discrete random variables. Explain each answer.
   (a) the number of job applications received each week by a restaurant
   (b) the time it takes a student to complete math homework
   (c) the number of defective parts in a sample taken from a factory
   (d) the life span of a light bulb observed during a quality-control test
   (e) the total amount of money earned at a movie theatre during a day

3. Why is the sum of all the probabilities in a probability distribution for a discrete random variable equal to 1?

4. **Knowledge and Understanding** Which of the following are valid probability distributions? Explain your answers.

(a)

X	$P(X)$
0	0.5
1	0.25
2	0.25

(b)

X	$P(X)$
0.5	0.2
0.2	0.3
0.3	0.25

(c)

X	$P(X)$
0	0.3
1	0.25
2	0.25
3	0.2

5. What is the expected value of the random variable representing the number observed on a single roll of a six-sided die? Explain why the answer is *not* an integer.

6. What is the expected value of the random variable representing the number observed on a single roll of an eight-sided die?

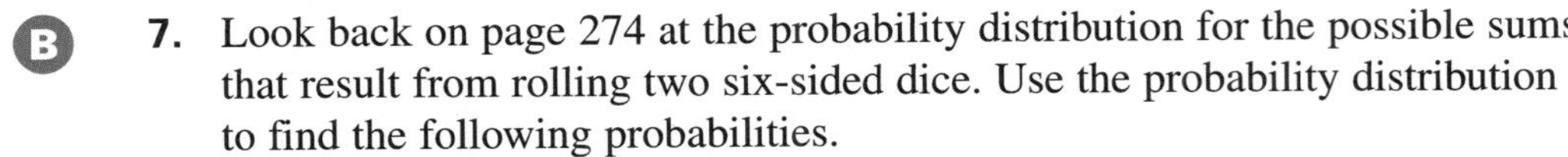

B

7. Look back on page 274 at the probability distribution for the possible sums that result from rolling two six-sided dice. Use the probability distribution to find the following probabilities.

(a) $P(\text{sum} \leq 5)$ **(b)** $P(\text{sum is even and sum} > 8)$

(c) $P(\text{sum is not } 7)$ **(d)** $P(\text{sum is even and sum} \leq 8)$

8. Create a probability distribution for the results of rolling a single die with eight faces numbered 1 through 8.

9. Create a probability distribution for all the sums of two eight-sided dice.

10. A customer randomly selects two RAM modules from a shipment of six known to contain two defective modules.

(a) Find the probability distribution for n, the number of defective modules in the purchase.

(b) Use labelled pieces of paper to simulate this situation. Carry out 50 trials and compare your simulation's experimental probability distribution with the theoretical distribution you obtained in part (a).

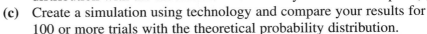

(c) Create a simulation using technology and compare your results for 100 or more trials with the theoretical probability distribution.

(d) Compute the expected number of defective RAM modules the customer would purchase.

11. **Application** A study of consumer habits indicates that 20% of all shoppers in a certain city read the unit-pricing labels on product packages before deciding which product to buy. Two customers are observed shopping in a food store in the city. Consider the discrete random variable, u, the number of shoppers who use the unit-pricing information.

(a) Use five pieces of paper, cards, or coloured marbles to create a simulation of the situation with 30 trials. Record the experimental probability distribution for u from your results.

(b) Create a simulation using appropriate technology and compare your results for 1000 trials with your answer in part (a).

(c) Create the theoretical probability distribution for u and compare the results of your simulations to the theoretical values.

(d) Compute the expected number of shoppers in the sample of two customers who would use the unit-pricing information.

12. **Communication** If a construction company wins a bid for a project, it will earn \$50 000. The bid preparation will cost the company \$5000. The president feels that the company's probability of winning the bid is 0.4. The company has a policy of submitting a bid on any project for which the expected return is \$12 000 or more. Should the president submit a bid?

13. Suppose a marketing manager wishes to know which of two package designs, A or B, the general public will prefer. He decides to survey 20 randomly selected people. Assume that the probability of someone selecting design A is $\frac{1}{2}$. Consider the value a, the number of people in a group of 20 who select package design A.

(a) Construct a non-technology-based simulation of the situation. Generate an experimental probability distribution for a based on several trials of your simulation. Estimate the probability that more than 15 people in a random sample of 20 would choose package design A.

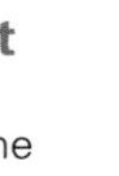

(b) Use a technology-based simulation to generate more trials and refine the estimated values for the probability distribution of a.

(c) Determine the theoretical probability distribution for a and compare the values with the results of your simulations in parts (a) and (b).

(d) What is the probability that, in a group of 20 randomly selected people, 15 or more will select package design A?

C **14.** **Thinking, Inquiry, Problem Solving** An insurance company's statistical records indicate that a particular type of automobile accident has occurred nearly three times per 10 000 drivers. The company wants to break even on policies that pay out $100 000 in the event of this particular type of accident. Find the premium that the insurance company must charge customers for insurance against this type of accident.

? Think about Question 14
How would you find the expected value of the insurance company's costs on the policy?

ADDITIONAL ACHIEVEMENT CHART QUESTIONS

15. **Knowledge and Understanding** The manager of a telemarketing firm conducted a time study to analyze the length of time his employees spent engaged in a typical sales-related phone call. The results are shown in the table below, where time has been rounded to the nearest minute.

Time (min)	1	2	3	4	5	6	7	8	9	10
Frequency	15	12	18	22	13	10	5	2	2	1

(a) Define the random variable X.

(b) Create a probability distribution for these data.

(c) Determine the expected length of a typical sales-related call.

16. **Application** A drawer contains four red socks and two blue socks. Three socks are drawn from the drawer without replacement.

(a) Create a probability distribution in which the random variable represents the number of red socks.

(b) Determine the expected number of red socks if three are drawn from the drawer without replacement.

17. **Thinking, Inquiry, Problem Solving** Do some research to find a set of data that meets the following two conditions:

- The data are represented by a frequency table.
- A discrete random variable can be used to represent the outcomes.

(a) Create a probability distribution for your data set.

(b) Use your data set to determine the expected value.

18. **Communication** The graph to the right shows the probabilities of a variable, N, for the values $N = 0$ to $N = 4$. Is this the graph of a valid probability distribution? Explain.

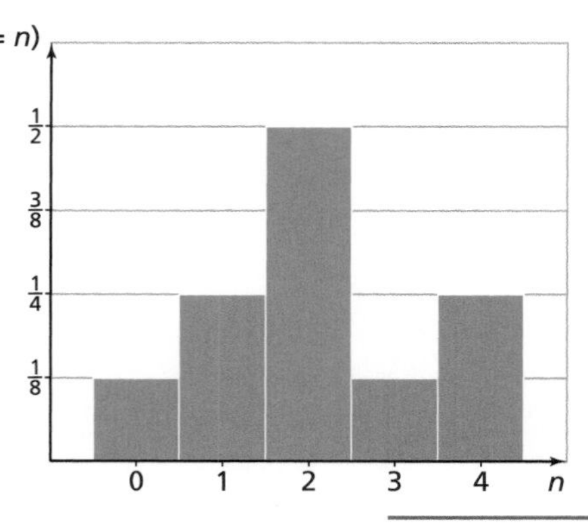

Chapter Problem

Are Frog Populations Declining?

CP1. Imagine that a wetland you are studying has a population of 5000 frogs, including bullfrogs, spring peepers, and mink frogs. The populations of the three species are shown below.

Species	Percent of Total Marsh Population	Species Gender Ratio	
		Males	Females
Bullfrog	30%	60%	40%
Spring peeper	50%	55%	45%
Mink frog	20%	52%	48%

Determine the probability that the first two frogs captured are

(a) bullfrogs
(b) female bullfrogs
(c) females of any species
(d) frogs that are not spring peepers

CP2. **(a)** Design and describe a simulation that will allow you to construct a probability distribution for the number of bullfrogs in a sample of 30 frogs. Use it to predict the probability that the sample will have eight or more bullfrogs.

(b) Compute the theoretical probability distribution for the number of bullfrogs in the sample, and then compare your simulation results with the predicted theoretical values.

(c) Design and describe a simulation that will allow you to construct a probability distribution for the number of female frogs of each species in a sample of 30 frogs. Use it to predict the probability that the sample will have eight or more females.

(d) Compute the theoretical probability distribution for the number of females in the sample, and then compare your simulation results with the predicted theoretical values.

5.2 Pascal's Triangle and the Binomial Theorem

What does computing the expansion of an algebraic expression such as $(a + b)^4$ have in common with finding the number of pathways through a city's street system? It turns out that both depend on calculating combinations. In fact, the two problems are similar.

Example 1 Paths Through a Map Grid

The streets of a city are laid out in a rectangular grid, as shown. By travelling either east or north along the streets, how many possible routes lead from start to finish?

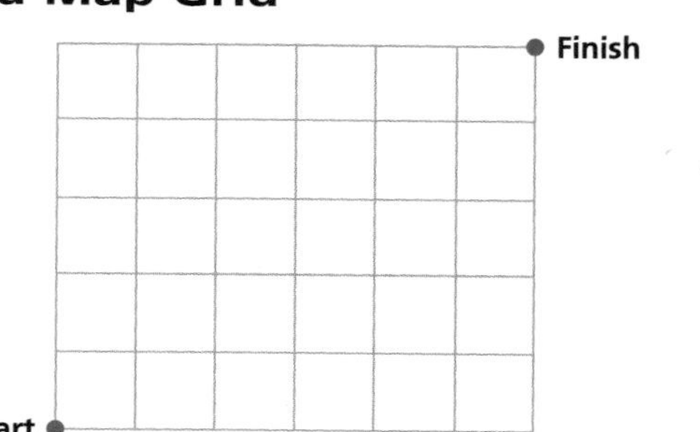

Solution

You must move 6 streets east and 5 streets north to get from start to finish. Therefore, every possible route requires 11 steps. Of these steps, 5 will move you north and 6 will move you east. You can record a route by filling in 11 spaces with 6 E's (east) and 5 N's (north) in a route record. An example of such a route record, as well as a diagram of the corresponding route map, appears below.

E	N	N	E	E	N	E	E	N	N	E

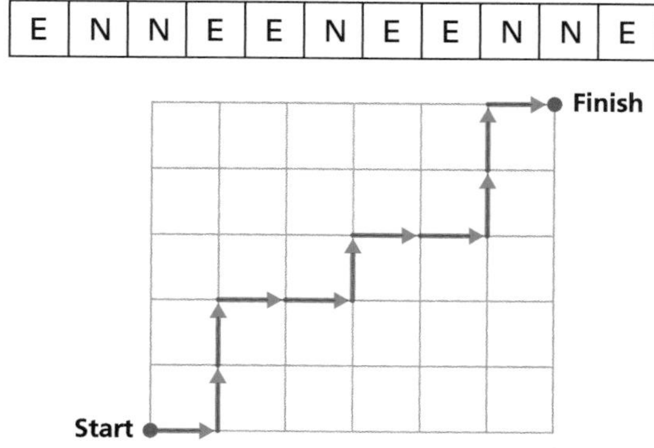

Think about The Route Record
Why does knowing the number of E's in the record automatically tell you the number of N's?

Calculating the number of routes is equivalent to determining the number of ways E can be inserted into 6 positions selected from the 11 available positions. This can be done using combinations in $C(11, 6)$ or $\binom{11}{6} = 462$ ways.

Think about Counting the Placement of E's
Why does it not matter whether you count the number of ways the E's can be placed or the ways the N's can be placed?

BINOMIAL THEOREM

The expansions for several different powers of $(a + b)$ are listed below. The French mathematician Blaise Pascal noted a pattern in the expansion of these powers. As a result, the triangular array of coefficients of these expansions became known as *Pascal's Triangle*.

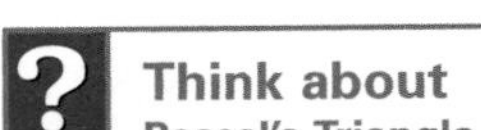

Think about Pascal's Triangle

The first five rows are

1

1 1

1 2 1

1 3 3 1

1 4 6 4 1

Determine the sixth and seventh rows.

$$(a + b)^0 = 1$$
$$(a + b)^1 = a + b$$
$$(a + b)^2 = a^2 + 2ab + b^2$$
$$(a + b)^3 = a^3 + 3a^2b + 3ab^2 + b^3$$
$$(a + b)^4 = a^4 + 4a^3b + 6a^2b^2 + 4ab^3 + b^4$$
$$(a + b)^5 = a^5 + 5a^4b + 10a^3b^2 + 10a^2b^3 + 5ab^4 + b^5$$

The values of the coefficients in the expansions can be determined using a strategy very similar to the one used previously to analyze paths through a map grid. For example, consider the term that includes a^3b in the expansion of $(a + b)^4$. It is the result of multiplying the a-term from three of the factors with the b-term from the remaining factor. The product, $aaab$, is illustrated below.

$$(a + b)^4 = (a + b)(a + b)(a + b)(a + b)$$

a	a	a	b
a	a	b	a
a	b	a	a
b	a	a	a

Think about The Coefficients of a^3b

Does it matter whether you count the ways the three *a*'s can be placed or the ways the one *b* can be placed?

The four ways that this can be done appear here.

There are four available places to record a's and b's. For the term a^3b, one space has to be occupied by a b. Therefore, there are $C(4, 1)$ ways of doing this. Hence, the coefficient of the a^3b term is $C(4, 1) = \binom{4}{1}$ or 4. As a result, the coefficients of the general binomial expansion $(a + b)^n$ can be represented by Pascal's Triangle in terms of the combination formula $\binom{n}{r}$. The numerical values appear to the right.

Pascal's Triangle Using $\binom{n}{r}$

Value of n	
0	$\binom{0}{0}$
1	$\binom{1}{0}$ $\binom{1}{1}$
2	$\binom{2}{0}$ $\binom{2}{1}$ $\binom{2}{2}$
3	$\binom{3}{0}$ $\binom{3}{1}$ $\binom{3}{2}$ $\binom{3}{3}$
4	$\binom{4}{0}$ $\binom{4}{1}$ $\binom{4}{2}$ $\binom{4}{3}$ $\binom{4}{4}$
5	$\binom{5}{0}$ $\binom{5}{1}$ $\binom{5}{2}$ $\binom{5}{3}$ $\binom{5}{4}$ $\binom{5}{5}$
6	$\binom{6}{0}$ $\binom{6}{1}$ $\binom{6}{2}$ $\binom{6}{3}$ $\binom{6}{4}$ $\binom{6}{5}$ $\binom{6}{6}$

r = 0, r = 1, r = 2, r = 3, r = 4, r = 5, r = 6

Pascal's Triangle Numerically

Value of n	
0	1
1	1 1
2	1 2 1
3	1 3 3 1
4	1 4 6 4 1
5	1 5 10 10 5 1
6	1 6 15 20 15 6 1

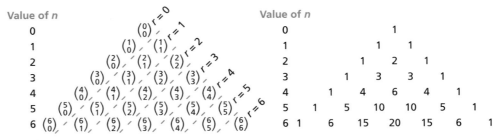

In both representations, n represents a row in the triangle as well as the exponent in the expansion of $(a + b)^n$. We can generalize the results of the expansions above $[(a + b)^n$, where $n = 0, 1, 2, \ldots, 5]$ and Pascal's Triangle with the Binomial Theorem, as stated on the following page.

Think about $\binom{n}{r}a^{n-r}b^r$

If n is the exponent in $(a + b)^n$, what does r represent?

Binomial Theorem

$$(a + b)^n = \binom{n}{0}a^n + \binom{n}{1}a^{n-1}b + \binom{n}{2}a^{n-2}b^2 + \dots + \binom{n}{r}a^{n-r}b^r + \dots + \binom{n}{n}b^n$$

The coefficients of the form $\binom{n}{r}$ are called binomial coefficients.

Example 2 Using the Binomial Theorem

Expand using the Binomial Theorem.

(a) $(a + b)^8$ **(b)** $(2x - 3)^5$

Solution

(a)
$$(a + b)^8 = \binom{8}{0}a^8 + \binom{8}{1}a^7b + \binom{8}{2}a^6b^2 + \binom{8}{3}a^5b^3 + \binom{8}{4}a^4b^4 + \binom{8}{5}a^3b^5 + \binom{8}{6}a^2b^6 + \binom{8}{7}ab^7 + \binom{8}{8}b^8$$
$$= a^8 + 8a^7b + 28a^6b^2 + 56a^5b^3 + 70a^4b^4 + 56a^3b^5 + 28a^2b^6 + 8ab^7 + b^8$$

(b) In $(2x - 3)^5$, let $n = 5$, $a = 2x$, and $b = -3$.

Therefore,

$$(2x - 3)^5 = \binom{5}{0}(2x)^5 + \binom{5}{1}(2x)^4(-3) + \binom{5}{2}(2x)^3(-3)^2 + \binom{5}{3}(2x)^2(-3)^3 + \binom{5}{4}(2x)(-3)^4 + \binom{5}{5}(-3)^5$$
$$= 32x^5 - 240x^4 + 720x^3 - 1080x^2 + 810x - 243$$

Think about **Pascal's Triangle**

A version of Pascal's Triangle was known to the Chinese long before the birth of Blaise Pascal. This diagram comes from Chu Shih-Chieh's *Precious Mirror of the Four Elements,* published in 1303.

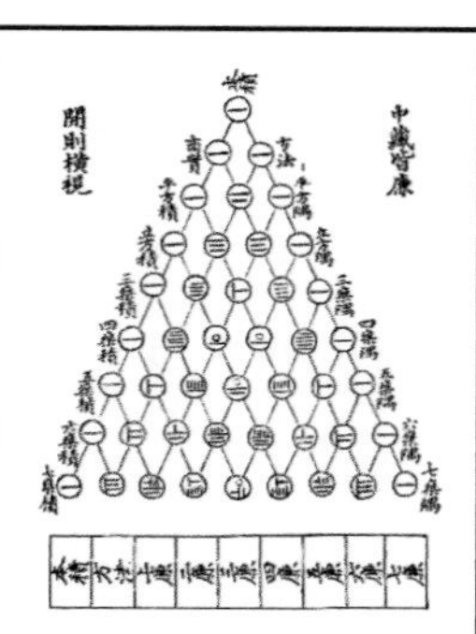

INVESTIGATION 2: BINOMIAL THEOREM

Numerous patterns can be found in the expansion of a binomial.

Purpose

To identify patterns in the binomial coefficients using the Binomial Theorem.

Procedure

A. Write the expansion of $(x + y)^6$ using the Binomial Theorem.

B. Write the expansion of $(x + y)^9$ using the Binomial Theorem.

Discussion Questions

1. Using the expansion of $(x + y)^6$, answer the questions that follow.
   (a) In the term containing x^5, what is the exponent of the y-term? What is the coefficient of this term?

(b) Why is the value of the coefficient of the term containing x^5 the same as the coefficient of the term containing y^5?
(c) How is finding the coefficient in part (a) similar to finding routes through a street grid following a five-east, one-north path?

2. Using the expansion of $(x + y)^9$, answer the questions that follow.
(a) In the term containing x^5, what is the exponent of the y-term? What is the coefficient of this term?
(b) Why is the value of the coefficient of the term containing x^5 the same as the coefficient of the term containing y^5?

? Think about The Exponents over *a* and *b*

If the exponent over a is r, why is the exponent over b always $n - r$?

PASCAL'S TRIANGLE

Blaise Pascal discovered many interesting patterns in the coefficients in the expansions of $(a + b)^n$. Some of the patterns become easier to see when the triangle is arranged as it is to the right.

	$r = 0$	$r = 1$	$r = 2$	$r = 3$	$r = 4$	$r = 5$	$r = 6$
$n = 0$	1						
$n = 1$	1	1					
$n = 2$	1	2	1				
$n = 3$	1	3	3	1			
$n = 4$	1	4	6	4	1		
$n = 5$	1	5	10	10	5	1	
$n = 6$	1	6	15	20	15	6	1

As discussed previously, the entry in the $n = 4$ row and $r = 3$ column corresponds to the coefficient of a^3b in the expansion of $(a + b)^4$ and has a value of $C(4, 1)$, or 4.

Perhaps the most famous pattern in Pascal's Triangle stems from the relationship between the sum of consecutive values in one row and the value found in the next row immediately beneath.

The diagram suggests that $\binom{4}{1} + \binom{4}{2} = \binom{5}{2}$. This can be verified by direct computation.

$$\begin{aligned}\binom{4}{1} + \binom{4}{2} &= \frac{4!}{1!\,3!} + \frac{4!}{2!\,2!}\\ &= 4 + 6\\ &= 10\end{aligned}$$

$$\begin{aligned}\binom{5}{2} &= \frac{5!}{2!\,3!}\\ &= 10\end{aligned}$$

	$r = 0$	$r = 1$	$r = 2$	$r = 3$	$r = 4$	$r = 5$	$r = 6$
$n = 0$	1						
$n = 1$	1	1					
$n = 2$	1	2	1				
$n = 3$	1	3	3	1			
$n = 4$	1	**4**	**6**	4	1		
$n = 5$	1	5	**10**	10	5	1	
$n = 6$	1	6	15	20	15	6	1

Think about The Steps in the Proof

- Where in the proof is a common denominator used to add fractions?
- How is the fact that for any value of k, $k!(k + 1) = (k + 1)!$ used in the proof?
- Where is common factoring used to simplify an expression in the proof?

Pascal's Identity

As a result of the importance of this particular relationship in Pascal's Triangle, it has become known as Pascal's Identity. An identity is a relationship that is true for all possible values of the variables involved.

$$\binom{n}{r} + \binom{n}{r+1} = \binom{n+1}{r+1}$$

Proof

$$\begin{aligned}
\binom{n}{r} + \binom{n}{r+1} &= \frac{n!}{r!(n-r)!} + \frac{n!}{(r+1)![n-(r+1)]!} \\
&= \frac{n!}{r!(n-r)!} + \frac{n!}{(r+1)!(n-r-1)!} \\
&= \frac{(r+1)n!}{(r+1)r!(n-r)!} + \frac{(n-r)n!}{(r+1)!(n-r)(n-r-1)!} \\
&= \frac{(r+1)n!}{(r+1)!(n-r)!} + \frac{(n-r)n!}{(r+1)!(n-r)!} \\
&= \frac{(r+1)n! + (n-r)n!}{(r+1)!(n-r)!} \\
&= \frac{n!(r+1+n-r)}{(r+1)!(n-r)!} \\
&= \frac{n!(n+1)}{(r+1)!(n-r)!} \\
&= \frac{(n+1)!}{(r+1)!(n-r)!}
\end{aligned}$$

$$\begin{aligned}
\binom{n+1}{r+1} &= \frac{(n+1)!}{(r+1)![(n+1)-(r+1)]!} \\
&= \frac{(n+1)!}{(r+1)!(n-r)!}
\end{aligned}$$

Example 3 Using Pascal's Triangle to Analyze Routes on a Checkerboard

A checker is placed on a game board as shown below. Determine the number of paths the checker may take to get to each allowable square on the board if it can move only diagonally forward one square at a time.

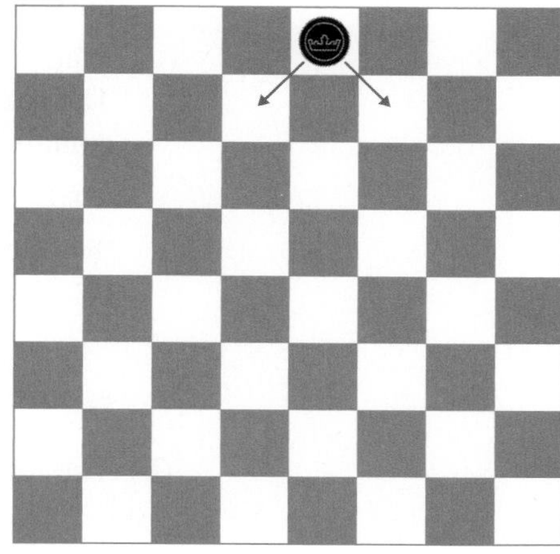

Solution

Indicate in each square the cumulative number of possible routes that led to it. Note the pattern that results. The squares shaded in blue show values found in Pascal's Triangle. The other squares contain values that have been adjusted for terms that were cut off by the edges of the board.

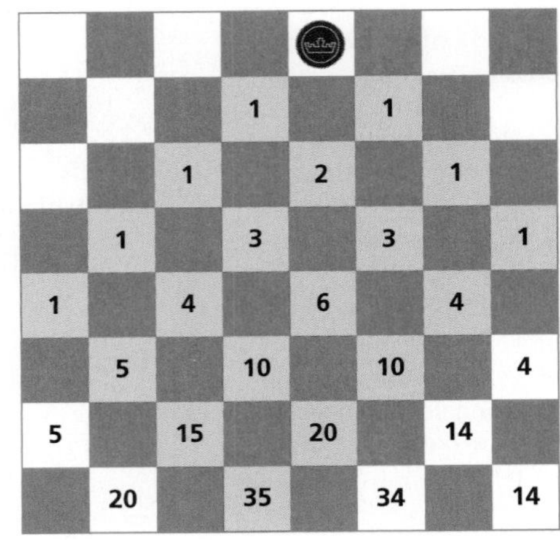

Example 4 Finding the Number of Routes Through a City Street Grid

Suppose that you travel without backtracking through the following city street grid, moving only north and east.

Label the bottom left corner as (0, 0) and the top right corner as (7, 7).

(a) How many routes pass through (2, 2)?

(b) How many routes avoid (2, 2)?

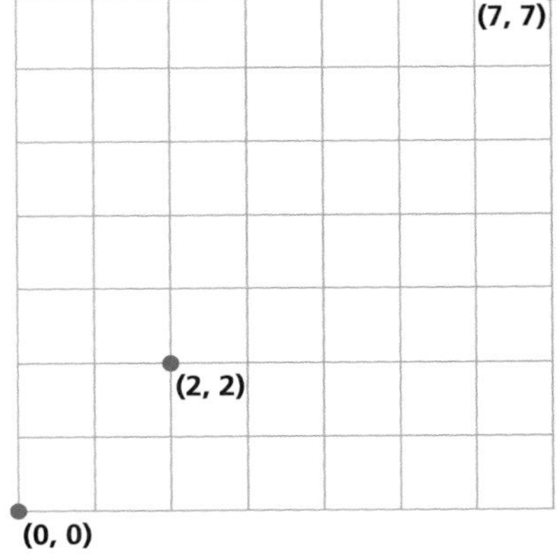

Solution

(a) The routes that lead to (2, 2) from (0, 0) must each contain 2 north and 2 east passages. There are $\binom{4}{2}$ of these. An example appears in red in the diagram. The routes from (2, 2) to (7, 7) must contain 5 north and 5 east passages. There are $\binom{10}{5}$ of these. As a result, the total number of routes from (0, 0) to (2, 2) and then on to (7, 7) is the product $\binom{4}{2} \times \binom{10}{5}$, or 1512 routes. One example appears in red in the diagram.

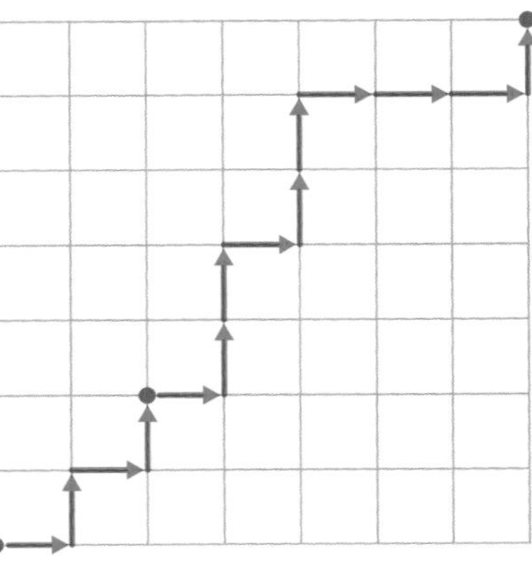

(b) The total number of routes from (0, 0) to (7, 7) without restrictions is $\binom{14}{7}$.

The number of routes that avoid (2, 2) is equal to $\binom{14}{7}$ minus the number of routes that pass through (2, 2) from part (a). Therefore, there are $\binom{14}{7} - \binom{4}{2} \times \binom{10}{5}$, or 1920 routes.

Example 5 Finding a Sum Using the Binomial Theorem

Evaluate $\binom{7}{0} + \binom{7}{1} + \binom{7}{2} + \binom{7}{3} + \binom{7}{4} + \binom{7}{5} + \binom{7}{6} + \binom{7}{7}$.

Solution

The sum is the expanded version of $(x + y)^7$ when $x = 1$ and $y = 1$.

$$(1 + 1)^7 = \binom{7}{0}(1)^7 + \binom{7}{1}(1)^6(1) + \binom{7}{2}(1)^5(1)^2 + \binom{7}{3}(1)^4(1)^3$$
$$+ \binom{7}{4}(1)^3(1)^4 + \binom{7}{5}(1)^2(1)^5 + \binom{7}{6}(1)(1)^6 + \binom{7}{7}(1)^7$$

Therefore,
$$2^7 = \binom{7}{0} + \binom{7}{1} + \binom{7}{2} + \binom{7}{3} + \binom{7}{4} + \binom{7}{5} + \binom{7}{6} + \binom{7}{7}$$
$$128 = \binom{7}{0} + \binom{7}{1} + \binom{7}{2} + \binom{7}{3} + \binom{7}{4} + \binom{7}{5} + \binom{7}{6} + \binom{7}{7}$$

The expansion of $(a + b)^n$ can be written in a more compact form $(a + b)^n = \sum_{r=0}^{n} \binom{n}{r} a^{n-r}b^r$, where $n \in$ N. In this form, individual terms of any binomial expansion can be determined.

> **General Term of a Binomial Expansion**
>
> The general term in the expansion of $(a + b)^n$ is
>
> $$t_{r+1} = \binom{n}{r} a^{n-r}b^r \qquad (r = 0, 1, 2, \ldots, n)$$
>
> This formula can be used to determine the $(r + 1)^{\text{st}}$ term in a binomial expansion.

Example 6 Finding the Term in the Expansion of a Binomial That Is Independent of *x*

Is there a constant term in the expansion of $\left(x + \frac{1}{x}\right)^{10}$ that is independent of x?

Think about The Algebra of Exponents

What properties of exponents are used to simplify the expression to the right?

Solution

The general term in the expansion of this binomial is

$$\begin{aligned} t_{r+1} &= \binom{10}{r}x^{10-r}\left(\frac{1}{x}\right)^r \\ &= \binom{10}{r}x^{10-r}(x^{-1})^r \\ &= \binom{10}{r}x^{10-r}x^{-r} \\ &= \binom{10}{r}x^{10-2r} \end{aligned}$$

For a constant term, the exponent on x must be 0.

Therefore, $10 - 2r = 0$

$r = 5$

Thus, the constant term in this expansion is $\binom{10}{5}$, or 252.

KEY IDEAS

Binomial Theorem

$$\begin{aligned} (a + b)^n &= \binom{n}{0}a^n + \binom{n}{1}a^{n-1}b + \binom{n}{2}a^{n-2}b^2 + \ldots + \binom{n}{r}a^{n-r}b^r + \ldots \\ &\quad + \binom{n}{n}b^n \\ &= \sum_{r=0}^{n}\binom{n}{r}a^{n-r}b^r, \text{ where } n \in \mathrm{W} \end{aligned}$$

General Term of a Binomial Expansion—in the expansion of $(a + b)^n$, the general term is of the form $\binom{n}{r}a^{n-r}b^r$, providing the $(r + 1)^{\text{st}}$ term in the expansion of $(a + b)^n$; the coefficients of these terms are often termed **binomial coefficients**

Pascal's Triangle—the coefficients in the expansion of $(a + b)^n$ form a triangular array of numbers known as Pascal's Triangle. These numbers are the binomial coefficients that result from the Binomial Theorem. Problems involving routes through rectangular grid systems and checkerboards or chessboards can be analyzed using the binomial coefficients that appear in Pascal's Triangle.

Pascal's Identity—the coefficients in Pascal's Triangle obey the identity

$$\binom{n}{r} + \binom{n}{r+1} = \binom{n+1}{r+1}$$

5.2 Exercises

A

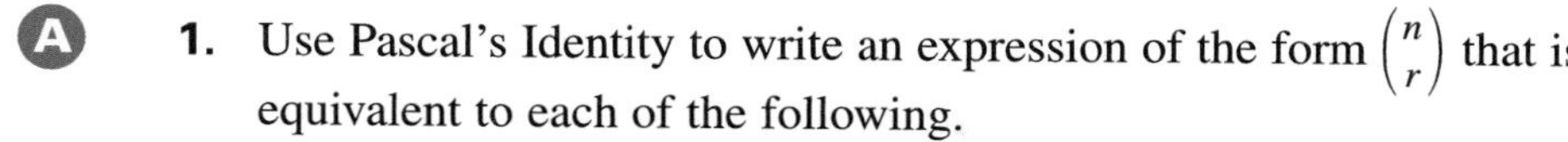

1. Use Pascal's Identity to write an expression of the form $\binom{n}{r}$ that is equivalent to each of the following.

(a) $\binom{10}{2} + \binom{10}{3}$ **(b)** $\binom{20}{18} + \binom{20}{19}$

(c) $\binom{15}{14} + \binom{15}{13}$ **(d)** $\binom{n}{r-2} + \binom{n}{r-1}$

2. Write an expression that is equivalent to each of the following.

(a) $\binom{10}{2}$ **(b)** $\binom{20}{18}$ **(c)** $\binom{15}{14}$ **(d)** $\binom{100}{98}$

(e) $\binom{7}{7}$ **(f)** $\binom{20}{0}$ **(g)** $\binom{25}{1}$ **(h)** $\binom{100}{93}$

3. Write the terms in the expansions of the following. Do not simplify your answer.

(a) $(x + y)^6$ **(b)** $(a + b)^5$ **(c)** $(1 - 2)^4$ **(d)** $\left(\frac{2}{3} + \frac{1}{3}\right)^5$

4. **Knowledge and Understanding** In the expansion of $(x + y)^{10}$, write the value of the exponent k in the term that contains

(a) x^4y^k **(b)** x^ky^8 **(c)** x^ky^{4k} **(d)** $x^{k-2}y^{3k}$

5. Express the following in the form $(x + y)^n$.

$$\binom{7}{0}a^7 + \binom{7}{1}a^6b + \binom{7}{2}a^5b^2 + \binom{7}{3}a^4b^3 + \binom{7}{4}a^3b^4 + \binom{7}{5}a^2b^5 + \binom{7}{6}ab^6 + \binom{7}{7}b^7$$

B

6. If $\binom{n}{0} + \binom{n}{1} + \binom{n}{2} + \ldots + \binom{n}{n} = 256$, find the value of n.

7. Using the arrangement of letters in the margin, compute the number of paths that spell the word MATHEMATICS if all paths must start at the top and move diagonally down through the letters.

M
A A
T T T
H H H H
E E E
M M M M
A A A
T T
I I I
C C
S

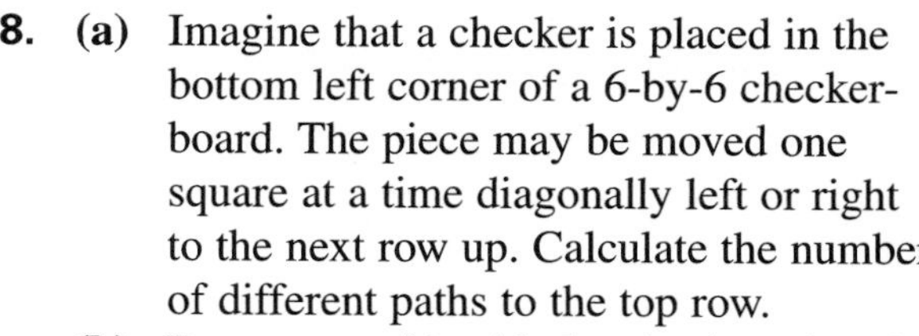

8. **(a)** Imagine that a checker is placed in the bottom left corner of a 6-by-6 checkerboard. The piece may be moved one square at a time diagonally left or right to the next row up. Calculate the number of different paths to the top row.

(b) Repeat part (a) with the checker placed in the bottom right corner.

(c) Suppose the checker began in the third square from the left in the bottom row. Calculate the number of possible paths to the top row from this position.

9. Imagine that the terms in each row of Pascal's Triangle had alternating signs.

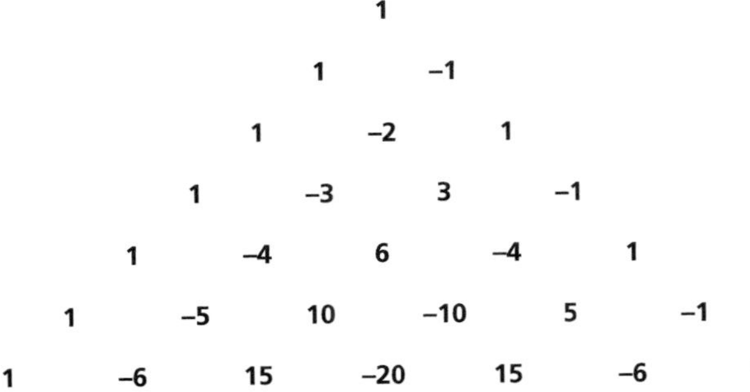

(a) Find the sum of the entries in each row.
(b) Predict the sum for the rows corresponding to $n = 7$, 8, and 9.
(c) Generalize your results to show the value of the sum of $\binom{n}{0} - \binom{n}{1} + \binom{n}{2} - \dots + (-1)^n\binom{n}{n}$.

10. **Application** Triangular numbers are based on the figures shown in the margin. Each triangular number corresponds to the number of discs required to construct a triangular pile.
(a) Determine the number of discs in the fourth, fifth, and sixth triangular numbers.
(b) Locate the triangular numbers in Pascal's Triangle.
(c) Find an expression in the form $\binom{n}{r}$ for the nth triangular number.
(d) Use your results to evaluate $1 + 2 + 3 + \dots + 100$.

11. Using the arrangement of letters to the right, compute the number of paths that spell the word MATH if all paths must start at the top and move diagonally down through the letters.

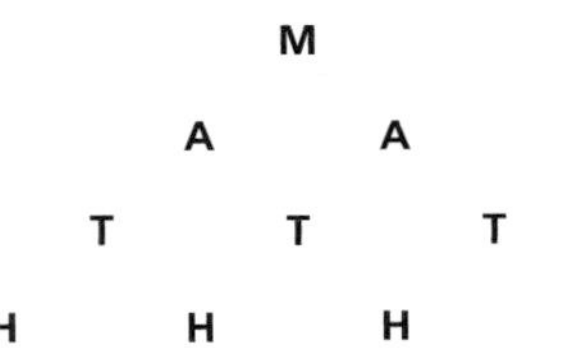

12. **Thinking, Inquiry, Problem Solving** Faizel wants to travel from his house to the hardware store that is six blocks east and five blocks south of his home. If he walks east and south, how many different routes can he follow from his home to the store?

13. Expand and simplify each of the following using the Binomial Theorem.
(a) $(a + 2b)^4$
(b) $(x - y)^6$
(c) $\left(c + \frac{1}{c}\right)^4$
(d) $\left(d - \frac{1}{d}\right)^5$

14. Find an expression for the general term, in simplified form, for each of the following.
(a) $(x + y)^{10}$
(b) $(x - y)^{10}$
(c) $\left(z + \frac{1}{z}\right)^8$
(d) $\left(w^2 + \frac{1}{w}\right)^9$

15. Find an expression for the indicated term in the expansion of each of the following.

(a) $(x^2 - 2)^7$	third term
(b) $(c - d)^8$	middle term
(c) $\left(\frac{x}{3} - \frac{3}{x}\right)^{12}$	tenth term
(d) $\left(y + \frac{1}{y}\right)^{15}$	term independent of y
(e) $(0.25 + 0.75)^6$	fifth term

C 16. **Communication** Examine each step in the proof of Pascal's Identity. Explain the algebraic operations used in each step and the purpose of each step.

17. Why is the identity

$$\binom{n}{r} + \binom{n}{r+1} = \binom{n+1}{r+1}$$

equivalent to the identity

$$\binom{n-1}{r} + \binom{n-1}{r+1} = \binom{n}{r+1}?$$

18. Why are both identities in Question 17 equivalent to

$$\binom{n-1}{r-1} + \binom{n-1}{r} = \binom{n}{r}?$$

19. In the expansion of $(ax + by)^n$, the coefficients of the first three terms are 6561, 34 992, and 81 648. Find the values of a, b, and n.

ADDITIONAL ACHIEVEMENT CHART QUESTIONS

20. **Knowledge and Understanding**
(a) How many terms are there in the expansion of $(3x + 2y)^6$?
(b) Expand $(3x + 2y)^6$.

21. **Application** In the expansion $\left(4x - \frac{2}{x}\right)^8$, find the following.
(a) the term containing x^6
(b) the constant term

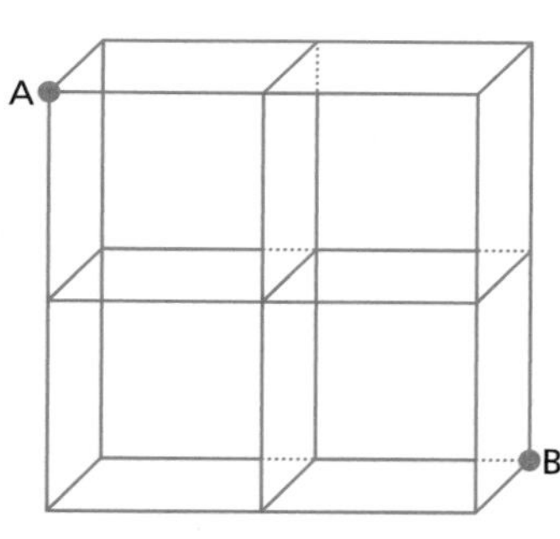

22. **Thinking, Inquiry, Problem Solving** Determine the number of possible paths from point A to point B in the diagram to the left if travel may occur only along the edges of the cubes and if the path must always move closer to B.

23. **Communication** Describe the relationship that exists between Pascal's Triangle and the binomial expansion of $(a + b)^n$. Use an example to help illustrate this relationship.

5.3 Binomial Distributions

Project Connection
If your project involves analyzing a process in which the results have two possible outcomes only—success or failure—then the probability distribution described in this section will apply to your analysis.

Parvin Das is a quality-control engineer. One of his responsibilities is to monitor the defect rate of a production line. Probability distributions based on the results of the Binomial Theorem can be used as mathematical models to do this.

Binomial Experiments

Each time a quality-control inspector chooses an item to test, there are two possible outcomes for the test. The item either passes the test and is used, or it fails and does not get used. Each of these outcomes has a probability associated with it.

To guarantee consistency, the quality-control process is based on certain assumptions. These assumptions form the formal definition of a **binomial experiment**.

Binomial Experiment

A binomial experiment is any experiment that has the following properties:

1. There are n identical trials. Together, these form a **binomial experiment**.
2. The purpose of the experiment is to determine the number of successes that occurs during the n trials.
3. There are two possible outcomes for each trial. These are usually termed *success* and *failure*. The probability of a *success* is usually denoted p and the probability of a failure is q or $1 - p$.
4. The probability of the outcomes remains the same from trial to trial. The values of p and $1 - p$ do not change from one trial to the next because the value of p is the same for each trial.
5. The trials are independent of one another.

binomial event—an experiment in which each outcome is the result of Bernoulli trials (defined in the box to the right)

Think about The Value of q
Why does $q = 1 - p$?

Bernoulli trial—an independent trial that has two possible outcomes: success or failure

Repeated trials, which are independent and have two possible outcomes (success and failure) are called **Bernoulli trials**. They are named after Daniel Bernoulli, a member of a remarkable family of mathematicians and scientists. Daniel's grandfather Nicolaus Sr., his uncles Jacob I and Nicolaus I, his father John I, his brothers Nicolaus III and John II, and his nephews John III and Jacob II all made significant contributions to mathematics and science. Each member of the Bernoulli family was known for his keen intellect and fiery temper. After winning the French Academy of Science Prize, which his father had unsuccessfully tried to win, Daniel was thrown out of the house!

INVESTIGATION: THE DISTRIBUTION OF THE NUMBER OF HEADS IN FOUR COIN TOSSES

Suppose you were to simulate sampling a production line known to have a 50% defect rate. You do this by tossing coins. Calculate the probability distribution for selecting four items from this production line.

The tossing of a coin is an example of a Bernoulli trial. An experiment in which each trial requires the toss of a coin several times and the recording of the number of heads is an example of a binomial experiment.

Purpose

To investigate the results of a binomial experiment.

Procedure

Think about Step A
Why is tossing one coin four times equivalent to tossing four coins once?

A. Work with a partner and record the results of tossing four coins simultaneously. Alternatively, you could create a simulation of the coin toss using a spreadsheet, a TI-83 Plus calculator, or Fathom™.
B. Record the number of heads. A head will represent a defective item.
C. Repeat until you have completed 100 repetitions of the experiment.
D. Create a relative frequency distribution for the number of heads (defects) in the toss of four coins.
E. Either repeat Steps A through C, or combine results with other students to increase the number of trials.
F. Create a new relative frequency distribution using the larger data set.

Discussion Questions

Technolink
Using technology to record your data and generate a histogram will save time.

1. How did increasing the number of repetitions of the experiment affect the shape of the distribution?
2. Why is tossing a single coin once a trial?
3. Why is each trial a Bernoulli trial?
4. Why is the number of heads obtained in each repetition a discrete random variable?

THE PROBABILITY DISTRIBUTION FOR A DIE-ROLL SIMULATION

In a binomial experiment, the number of successes in n repeated Bernoulli trials is a discrete random variable, usually represented by the letter X. X is termed a **binomial random variable** and its probability distribution is called a **binomial distribution**.

binomial random variable—the number of successes in n repeated trials of a binomial experiment

binomial distribution—the probability distribution of a binomial random variable

Rolling a Die

Suppose a cereal company puts one of six possible prizes in each cereal box. You can use a simulation involving rolling a six-sided die to determine the probability distribution for getting a particular prize in four purchased boxes of cereal.

Roll 1	Roll 2	Roll 3	Roll 4	Count of 1s
1	5	5	5	1
5	4	4	3	0
2	5	4	2	0
1	1	6	4	2
6	6	1	3	1
4	2	1	6	1
1	6	5	5	1
4	3	4	6	0
3	3	4	2	0
6	4	5	1	1
3	3	6	5	0
2	4	6	5	0
6	2	3	6	0
5	3	1	6	1
3	3	4	4	0
3	3	5	2	0
6	1	1	5	2
1	2	3	3	1
6	2	2	4	0
6	5	4	5	0
6	3	5	1	1
6	3	3	5	0
5	4	2	6	0
2	2	1	5	1
3	5	4	5	0
3	3	4	1	1
2	4	5	2	0
6	5	2	2	0
1	6	3	2	1

Define a success as the appearance of a 1. What is the probability for one, two, three, four, or zero 1s showing?

The table in the margin shows the results of 30 repetitions of a simulation of this experiment using a spreadsheet. The frequency and experimental probability distribution for all 100 repetitions of the simulation appear below.

Number of 1s	Frequency
0	54
1	38
2	7
3	1
4	0

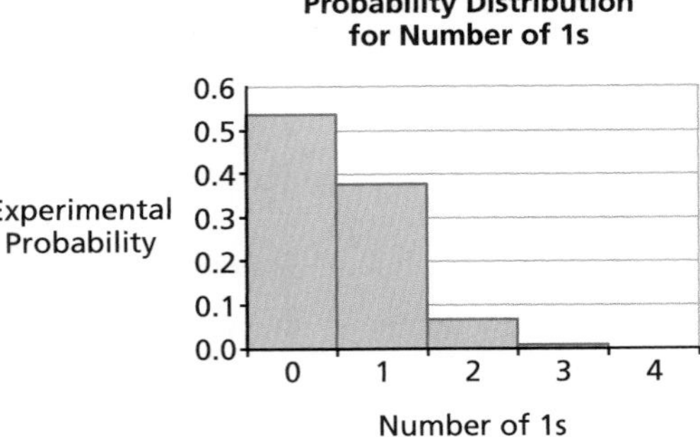

Analysis of the Simulation as a Counting Problem

Verify that the die-roll simulation is a binomial experiment by checking that it has all the required properties. Then, conduct the experiment yourself or do a simulation to see if your experimental probability distribution is the same.

1. There were four identical trials in which a die was rolled. A trial involves rolling a die one time. Each repetition of the experiment consists of four trials. You would then count the number of trials that produces a number 1, in each of the 100 repetitions of the experiment.
2. The trials were Bernoulli trials because
   - there were only two possible outcomes—a success is a roll of 1, and a failure is a roll that is not a 1. In this case, $p = \frac{1}{6}$ and $1 - p = \frac{5}{6}$;
   - the probability of success is the same for every roll;
   - the trials are independent of one another; and
   - the purpose of the experiment is to determine the number of 1s that occurs in four rolls. That is the binomial random variable.

Think about how to record the possible outcomes of the four rolls of the die. For each repetition of the experiment, record the outcome of each of the four trials in a table similar to the following example.

Roll 1	Roll 2	Roll 3	Roll 4
?	?	?	?

Example 1 Rolling 1s

(a) What is the probability that the first roll will be a 1 and all the others will be something other than a 1?

(b) Find the probability of the combined event that the roll of 1 will appear in any of the four available positions in the table.

(c) What is the probability that exactly two 1s show in the four rolls of the die?

(d) Complete the theoretical probability distribution for the number of 1s showing in four rolls.

Solution

(a) Consider the following:

Roll 1	Roll 2	Roll 3	Roll 4
1	?	?	?

$P(\text{Roll } 1 = 1) = \frac{1}{6}$ $P(\text{Roll } 2 \neq 1) = \frac{5}{6}$

$P(\text{Roll } 3 \neq 1) = \frac{5}{6}$ $P(\text{Roll } 4 \neq 1) = \frac{5}{6}$

Thus, $P([\text{Roll } 1 = 1] \text{ AND } [\text{Roll } 2 \neq 1] \text{ AND } [\text{Roll } 3 \neq 1] \text{ AND } [\text{Roll } 4 \neq 1])$

$= \frac{1}{6} \times \frac{5}{6} \times \frac{5}{6} \times \frac{5}{6}$

$= \frac{1}{6}\left(\frac{5}{6}\right)^3$

(b) The number of ways that 1 can be placed in one of the four entries of the table is the same as counting the number of ways one object can be selected from four available objects. This can be done in $\binom{4}{1} = 4$ ways. Therefore, the probability that only one of the rolls will result in a 1 showing is the sum of the four individual probabilities, all of which are $\frac{1}{6}\left(\frac{5}{6}\right)^3$. Therefore,

$$P(\text{one 1 in four trials}) = \binom{4}{1}\left(\frac{1}{6}\right)\left(\frac{5}{6}\right)^3$$
$$= \frac{500}{1296} \text{ or about } 0.39$$

(c) Suppose the two 1s appeared in Roll 1 and Roll 2. The probability of this event is

Roll 1	Roll 2	Roll 3	Roll 4
1	1	?	?

$P([R1 = 1] \text{ AND } [R2 = 1] \text{ AND } [R3 \neq 1] \text{ AND } [R4 \neq 1])$

$= \left(\frac{1}{6}\right)\left(\frac{1}{6}\right)\left(\frac{5}{6}\right)\left(\frac{5}{6}\right)$

$= \left(\frac{1}{6}\right)^2\left(\frac{5}{6}\right)^2$

The number of ways that exactly two of the entries can be filled in with 1s is $\binom{4}{2} = 6$.

Therefore, $P(\text{two 1s in four trials})$

$= \binom{4}{2}\left(\frac{1}{6}\right)^2\left(\frac{5}{6}\right)^2$ or about 0.12.

Number of 1s	Probability
0	$\binom{4}{0}\left(\frac{1}{6}\right)^0\left(\frac{5}{6}\right)^4 \doteq 0.4823$
1	$\binom{4}{1}\left(\frac{1}{6}\right)^1\left(\frac{5}{6}\right)^3 \doteq 0.3858$
2	$\binom{4}{2}\left(\frac{1}{6}\right)^2\left(\frac{5}{6}\right)^2 \doteq 0.1157$
3	$\binom{4}{3}\left(\frac{1}{6}\right)^3\left(\frac{5}{6}\right)^1 \doteq 0.0154$
4	$\binom{4}{4}\left(\frac{1}{6}\right)^4\left(\frac{5}{6}\right)^0 \doteq 0.0008$

? Think about The Sum of the Probabilities in the Table

Why do the probabilities add to 1?

? Think about The Coefficients

- What is the relationship between these probabilities and the Binomial Theorem?
- How does the expansion of $(p + q)^n$ relate to the binomial probability distribution?

(d) Each row of the probability distribution for this experiment can be found using reasoning similar to that on the previous page.

The probability that the four rolls of the die will show k 1s is given by the formula $P(k \text{ 1s in four trials}) = \binom{4}{k}\left(\frac{1}{6}\right)^k\left(\frac{5}{6}\right)^{4-k}$.

This formula is another way to express the probability distribution of the binomial random variable that indicates the number of 1s showing in four trials. Remember that a probability distribution can be represented by a graph, a table of values, or a formula.

BINOMIAL PROBABILITY DISTRIBUTION

In general, the probability of k successes in n trials of a binomial experiment corresponds to finding the number of ways the k successes can be recorded in the n available recording slots in the outcome table for the event. There are $\binom{n}{k}$ ways of selecting the locations in which to record the successes. The probability of each of these is $(p)^k(q)^{n-k} = (p)^k(1 - p)^{n-k}$. Using the Additive Principle for Probabilities, the probability of the event corresponding to k successes is the sum of all the individual probabilities for the outcomes that make up the event.

Binomial Probability Distribution

Consider a binomial experiment in which there are n Bernoulli trials, each with a probability of success of p. The probability of k successes in the n trials is given by

$$P(X = k) = \binom{n}{k}(p)^k(1 - p)^{n-k}$$

where X is the discrete random variable corresponding to the number of successes.

Example 2 Cost of Coffee

In Section 4.1, you investigated the amount you could expect to pay for coffee if you and a friend tossed a coin to determine who would pay each day. Coffee costs \$1.00 a cup. Determine the expected cost to you each week.

Solution

Assume that each coin toss is a Bernoulli trial. Your correct call is defined as a success for which $p = \frac{1}{2}$. The experiment consists of five trials (one for each day of the week). Consider the number of successes. The discrete random variable, X, represents the number of wins in five tosses. This is a binomial experiment for which the binomial probability distribution formula yields

$$\begin{aligned} P(X = k) &= \binom{5}{k}\left(\frac{1}{2}\right)^k\left(\frac{1}{2}\right)^{5-k} \\ &= \binom{5}{k}\left(\frac{1}{2}\right)^5 \end{aligned}$$

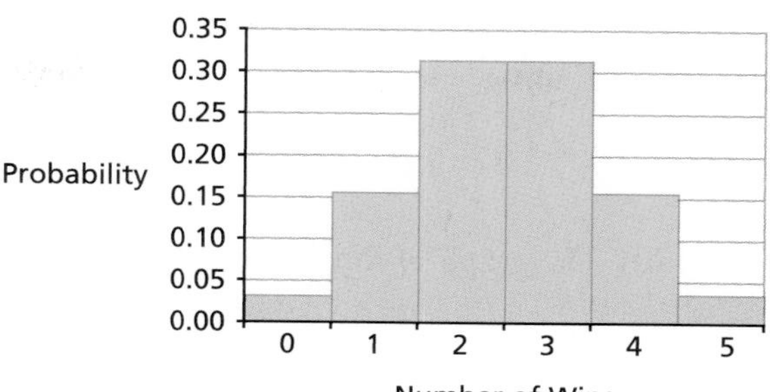

$$E(X) = 1\binom{5}{1}\left(\frac{1}{2}\right)^5 + 2\binom{5}{2}\left(\frac{1}{2}\right)^5 + \ldots + 5\binom{5}{5}\left(\frac{1}{2}\right)^5$$
$$= 2.5$$

If we examine the expected cost of the coffee game, we also observe the following:

$$E(X) = 5\left(\frac{1}{2}\right)$$
$$= 2.5$$

In this case, the number of trials multiplied by the probability of success results in the expected value.

Expected Value of a Binomial Experiment

The expected value of a binomial experiment that consists of n Bernoulli trials with a probability of success, p, on each trial is

$$E(X) = np$$

Example 3 Probability of a Hit

In Section 4.1, you considered a baseball player who had a batting average of 0.320. You created a simulation to predict the likelihood that he could have a game in which he has no hits in three times at bat.

(a) Determine the theoretical probability of this event.

(b) Determine the probability distribution for the number of hits per game.

(c) Calculate the batter's expected number of hits per game.

Solution

Assume that each time at bat is a Bernoulli trial for which a success is a hit and for which $p = 0.320$. The experiment consists of three trials in which the number of hits is considered a success. For the calculation of the theoretical probability, the number of games played during the season is not relevant.

? Think about
The Probability of No Hits

Why is it reasonable for a batter with a 0.320 average to have a relatively small probability of getting no hits in three times at bat?

The discrete random variable, X, represents the number of hits in three times at bat.

(a) This is a binomial experiment for which the binomial distribution formula yields

$$P(X = 0) = \binom{3}{0}(0.320)^0(1 - 0.320)^3$$
$$= 0.314\ 432$$

(b) The graph of the distribution is shown below.

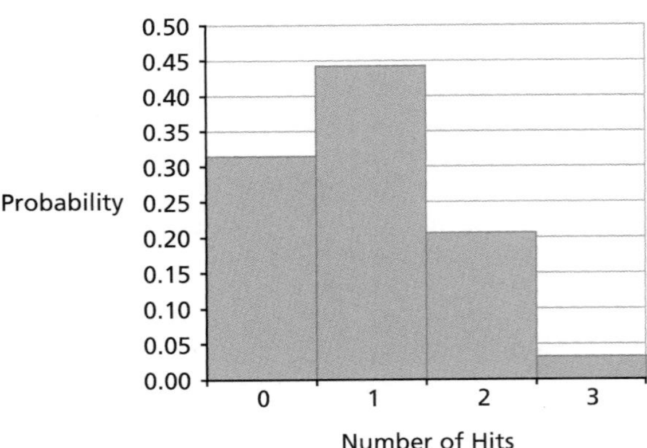

If X is the number of hits in three times at bat, the general formula for this distribution is

$$P(X = k) = \binom{3}{k}(0.320)^k(0.680)^{3-k}$$

? Think about
The Expected Value

- Why does a batter with a hitting average of 0.320 have an expected number of hits in three times at bat that is almost 1?
- What would the batter's average be to make the expected value exactly 1?

(c) Method 1

$$E(X) = \sum_{i=1}^{n} X_i P(X_i)$$
$$= 0P(X = 0) + 1P(X = 1) + 2P(X = 2) + 3P(X = 3)$$
$$\doteq 0.96$$

Method 2

$$E(X) = np$$
$$= 3 \times (0.32)$$
$$= 0.96$$

KEY IDEAS

binomial experiment—any experiment that consists of n Bernoulli trials and for which the purpose of the experiment is to determine the number of successes that occurs during the n trials

Bernoulli trial—Bernoulli trials have the following properties:

- There are two possible outcomes for each trial, which are usually termed *success* and *failure*. The probability of a success is usually denoted p and the probability of a failure is q or $1 - p$.
- The probability of the outcomes remains the same from trial to trial. The values of p and $1 - p$ do not change from one trial to the next.
- The trials are independent of one another.

binomial probability distribution—consider a binomial experiment in which there are n Bernoulli trials, each with a probability of success of p. The probability of k successes in the n trials is given by

$$P(X = k) = \binom{n}{k}(p)^k(1 - p)^{n-k}$$

where X is the discrete random variable corresponding to the number of successes

expected value of a binomial experiment—in any binomial experiment, the expected number of successes is given by

$$E(X) = \sum_{i=1}^{n} x_i P(X = x_i) = np$$

where n is the number of trials and p is the probability of success on each trial

5.3 Exercises

A

1. For each term, identify

(i) the number of trials

(ii) the probability p of a success

(iii) the number of successes

(a) $\binom{10}{6}\left(\frac{1}{2}\right)^6\left(\frac{1}{2}\right)^4$

(b) $\binom{7}{3}\left(\frac{1}{3}\right)^3\left(\frac{2}{3}\right)^4$

2. Evaluate the following sum.

$\binom{3}{0}\left(\frac{1}{4}\right)^3 + \binom{3}{1}\left(\frac{1}{4}\right)^2\left(\frac{3}{4}\right) + \binom{3}{2}\left(\frac{1}{4}\right)\left(\frac{3}{4}\right)^2 + \binom{3}{3}\left(\frac{3}{4}\right)^3$

B

3. Suppose $p = \frac{1}{2}$. Simplify this expression.

$\binom{n}{k}(p)^k(1 - p)^{n-k}$

4. Explain why this sum is equal to 1.

$\binom{n}{0}(p)^0(1 - p)^{n-0} + \binom{n}{1}(p)^1(1 - p)^{n-1} + \ldots + \binom{n}{n}(p)^n(1 - p)^{n-n}$

5. Look back at Example 1 in this section. Use it to answer the following questions.
   (a) The expression for the probability of the specific event that a 1 appears only in the first row of the outcome table has a probability $\left(\frac{1}{6}\right)^1\left(\frac{5}{6}\right)^3$. Explain.
   (b) Why is the probability in part (a) multiplied by $\binom{4}{1}$ to find the probability of getting a single 1?
   (c) Determine the probability that an even number shows in only the second and third of four rolls of a six-sided die.
   (d) Determine the probability for an even number showing in exactly two of the four rolls of a six-sided die.
   (e) Determine the probability distribution for the number of times an even number shows in four rolls of a six-sided die.
   (f) Suppose you were tossing a coin four times instead of rolling a die. What is the probability of getting a head on the first toss only?

6. **Communication** Explain why the problems in parts (a) and (b) can be modelled using a binomial distribution, but the problems in parts (c) and (d) cannot.
   (a) Find the probability that a customer will seek a refund because of a defective product when traditionally 10% of all customers have requested such a refund.
   (b) Find the probability that 3 defective parts will show up in a sample of 10 parts selected randomly from a manufacturing process that the plant knows has a 5% defect rate.
   (c) Find the probability that 3 defective parts will show up in a sample of 10 parts selected randomly from a manufacturing process when it is known that there are 3 defective machines out of 10.
   (d) A hockey goaltender has stopped 387 of 400 shots. Find the probability that she will stop the next 3 shots in a row.

Design simulations for Questions 7 to 11. Compare the probability distribution resulting from your simulation with the theoretical distribution in each question.

7. **Knowledge and Understanding** Mail-order marketing companies have a response rate of 15% to their advertising flyers.
   (a) Compute the probability that exactly 3 people out of a sample of 20 respond to the flyers they receive.
   (b) Find the expected number of people in a sample of 20 who will respond to the flyers.
   (c) Compute the probability that at least 3 people out of a sample of 20 respond to the flyers they receive.

8. A family hopes to have six children. Assume boys and girls are born with the same probability.
   (a) Determine the probability that four of the children will be boys.
   (b) Determine the probability that at least two of the children will be girls.
   (c) Determine the probability that all six children will be girls.

9. **Thinking, Inquiry, Problem Solving** A study published in a consumer magazine indicated that when a husband and a wife shop for a car, the husband exerts the primary influence in the decision 70% of the time. Five couples who will be purchasing a car are selected at random. Determine the probability of each of the following.
   (a) In exactly two of the couples, the husband will exert the primary influence on the decision.
   (b) In all five couples, the husband will exert the primary influence on the decision.
   (c) Find the expected number of couples in which the husband will exert primary influence.
   (d) Determine the probability that in all five couples, the wife will exert the primary influence on the decision.

10. A baseball player has a batting average of 0.280.
   (a) Find the probability that the player will get
      (i) at least 3 hits in her next 5 times at bat
      (ii) at least 3 hits in her next 10 times at bat
      (iii) at least 6 hits in her next 10 times at bat
   (b) What is the player's expected number of hits in her next 10 times at bat?

11. In a large manufacturing plant, random samples of 10 final products are taken each hour. When an hourly defect rate exceeding 3 out of 10 items is detected, production is shut down.
   (a) If a production lot has a 10% defect rate, what is the probability that production will be shut down?
   (b) What is the probability that production will be shut down if the actual defect rate is 30%?
   (c) What is the expected number of defective items in a sample of 10 for each defect rate in parts (a) and (b)?

Questions 12, 13, and 14 also appeared in Section 4.1. For each question, compare the simulation results you obtained in Section 4.1 with the theoretical probability that you find here.

12. A field-goal kicker for a high school football team has an 80% success rate based on his attempts this year. Determine the probability that he will miss three field goals in a row.

13. Ten percent of the keyboards a computer company manufactures are defective. Determine the probability that one or more of the next three keyboards to come off the assembly line will be defective.

14. **Application** Imagine that the first traffic light you encounter on your way to school each morning has a 60-s cycle in which it is green for 20 s. What is the probability that you will get a green light on the next three morning trips to school?

ADDITIONAL ACHIEVEMENT CHART QUESTIONS

15. **Knowledge and Understanding** Determine the probability, correct to four decimal places, that a die rolled six times in a row will produce the following.
    (a) one 3 **(b)** five 3s **(c)** at least two 3s

16. **Application** A multiple-choice quiz has 10 questions. Each question has four possible answers. Sam is certain that he knows the correct answer for Questions 3, 5, and 8. If he guesses on the other questions, determine the probability that he passes the quiz.

17. **Thinking, Inquiry, Problem Solving** In the dice game *Yahtzee*, a player has three tries at rolling some or all of a set of five dice. Each player is trying to achieve results such as three of a kind, two pairs, full house, so on. A yahtzee occurs when a player rolls five of a kind. If Cheryl rolls a pair of 2s on the first toss, and then rolls only the non-2s showing on the subsequent two tosses, find the probability that she gets a yahtzee.

18. **Communication** What conditions must be satisfied in order for an experiment to be considered a binomial experiment? Describe a situation that meets these conditions.

Chapter Problem

Are Frog Populations Declining?

CP3. Suppose that the populations of the three species are distributed as shown in the following table. You capture a frog, note its species and gender, and then release it. This process is repeated until you have captured and recorded 50 frogs.

Species	Percent of Total Marsh Population	Species Gender Ratio	
		Males	Females
Bullfrog	30%	60%	40%
Spring peeper	50%	50%	50%
Mink frog	20%	50%	50%

(a) Determine the probability that there will be at least five female bullfrogs in the sample.
(b) Determine the probability that there will not be any mink frogs in the sample.
(c) Suppose that there were 30 spring peepers in the sample. Determine whether this is unusual enough to cause you to reconsider your original estimate of their proportion of the frog population.

Project Connection

Permutations, Combinations, and Probability

By now, you should have completed most (if not all) of your research, and you should now be analyzing the data. One way to look at your data is to determine whether or not the skills associated with probability can be used to help in your analysis. You can use calculated probabilities to help support the point of your presentation.

Fingerprint Data

Rohan is interested in how fingerprints are used in criminal cases to convict a defendant. He decided that his presentation would be about why fingerprint testing is effective in placing someone at the scene of a crime.

Rohan researched his topic and discovered that Sir Francis Galton established, mathematically, that one can assume each person's fingerprints are unique. Rohan decided to use fingerprints from two different people to show that the probability of the fingerprints being the same is quite small.

Simulation

The process Rohan followed in his presentation is outlined below. It is similar to the steps first used by Galton in 1892.

Purpose

To use probability to show that two people's fingerprints are unlikely to be identical.

Procedure

A. Obtain two fingerprints. (Two fingerprints are shown below in case you are having difficulty obtaining others.)

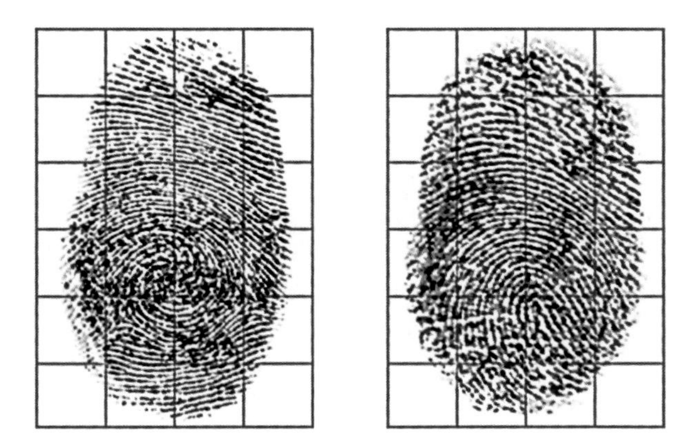

B. Galton wanted to find the probability that two fingerprints are identical. To do so, he separated each fingerprint into 24 equal squares, as shown on the preceding page. He then defined three different events, as shown below.

W: The same number of lines (ridges) pass through two corresponding squares.

X: The lines (ridges) in two corresponding squares have the same general direction.

Y: Two corresponding squares match (both in number of lines and direction).

Estimate each of the following probabilities.

(i) $P(W)$ **(ii)** $P(X)$ **(iii)** $P(Y)$

C. Using your results in part B, what is the probability of two people's fingerprints being the same?

D. Answer each of the following.

- How does the probability in Step C show that the probability of two fingerprints being identical is very small?
- Is each event that Galton defined above an independent event? Why or why not?

Now take a look at the data that you have collected for your project.

- Should you be calculating any probabilities based on your data? If so, what are they?
- When you calculate the probabilities using your data, what do you think you will find? Is this to be expected? What does this mean for your data and your conclusions?
- Calculate any probabilities you need to find. Interpret each probability for your data. Does this help support any conclusions that you wish to make?

5.4 Normal Approximation of the Binomial Distribution

You have seen that probabilities can be calculated using the formula for a binomial distribution provided that

- each trial in the experiment is identical
- the outcomes of each trial can be classified as a success or failure

For example, you can calculate the probability of tossing a coin many times and finding a certain number of heads.

Example 1 Number of Heads

What is the probability of getting exactly 30 heads if a coin is tossed 50 times?

Solution

To calculate the probability, remember that $P(k \text{ successes in } n \text{ trials})$ is $\binom{n}{k}(p)^k(1 - p)^{n-k}$, where p is the probability of success.

$$P(30 \text{ heads in } 50 \text{ trials}) = \binom{50}{30}(0.5)^{30}(1 - 0.5)^{50-30}$$
$$\doteq 0.042$$

There is about a 4.2% chance of tossing exactly 30 heads in 50 tosses.

While the calculation in this activity involves very large or very small numbers, it is not difficult or time-consuming to perform on a calculator.

The real problem occurs with more complex situations; for example, finding the probability of tossing between 20 and 30 heads in 50 tosses of a coin. You would be faced with 11 such calculations.

$$P(20 \leq X \leq 30) = P(20 \text{ heads in } 50 \text{ trials}) + P(21 \text{ heads in } 50 \text{ trials}) + P(22 \text{ heads in } 50 \text{ trials}) + \ldots + P(30 \text{ heads in } 50 \text{ trials})$$

This calculation would be time-consuming even though these numbers are not very large. To help simplify the calculation and make these probabilities easier to calculate, look at the graphical representation of the binomial distribution for this situation on the following page.

GRAPHING THE BINOMIAL DISTRIBUTION

The graph of the binomial distribution where $n = 50$ and $p = 0.5$ is shown on the following page. Notice that it approximates a normal distribution. This suggests that a binomial distribution can be approximated by a normal distribution as long as the number of trials is relatively large.

Think about The Graph
Describe the features of a normal probability distribution that are displayed by this binomial distribution.

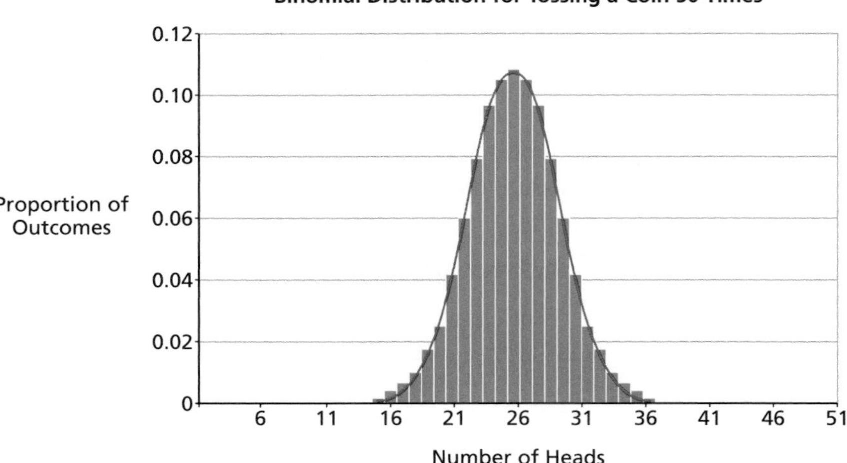

Notice how this binomial probability distribution appears mound-shaped. A normal curve (shown in blue) can be superimposed over the histogram with a pretty close fit. French mathematician Abraham De Moivre first discovered this relationship in 1718. Under certain conditions, a normal curve can be used to approximate a binomial probability distribution. First, we must find values for the mean and the standard deviation.

MEAN AND STANDARD DEVIATION OF THE NORMAL APPROXIMATION TO THE BINOMIAL DISTRIBUTION

If you were to toss a coin 50 times, you would probably expect to get approximately 25 heads since $n = 50$ and $P(\text{heads}) = 0.5$. It is calculated as $\bar{x} = np$, where n represents the number of trials and p represents the probability of success on each trial. In any binomial distribution, the standard deviation of the binomial random variable can be approximated by using the formula.

$$\begin{aligned}\sigma &= \sqrt{np(1 - p)}\\ &= \sqrt{50(0.5)(1 - 0.5)}\\ &= \sqrt{12.5}\\ &= 3.54\end{aligned}$$

Using these formulas, we can determine that the normal curve shown above has a mean of 25 and a standard deviation of 3.54.

FROM DISCRETE TO CONTINUOUS

The important difference between the binomial and the normal distribution is that the binomial distribution represents a discrete random variable, which is always represented with a whole number (e.g., number of heads).

A normal distribution is continuous, and can be used to display continuous values (e.g., height in centimetres). In order to use the normal distribution to approximate the binomial distribution, consider a range of values rather than specific discrete values. The range of continuous values between 4.5 and 5.5 can, therefore, be used to represent the discrete value 5.

In order to use the normal approximation of $X = 20$, we need to consider all the values of X that round to 20. On the graph below, we can see that the bar centred at $X = 20$ contains all the values from 19.5 to 20.5. The area of this bar is approximated by the area under the normal curve between $X = 19.5$ and $X = 20.5$. Similarly, if we wanted to estimate the probability of X being 20, 21, or 22, in the binomial distribution, we would evaluate $P(19.5 < X < 22.5)$ for the normal distribution.

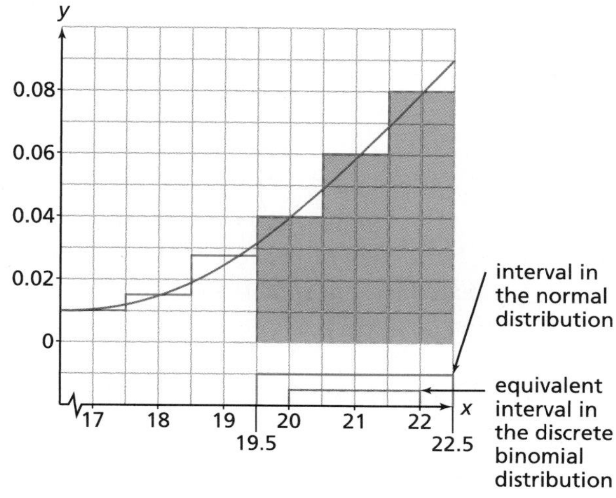

Example 2 Approximating Probability Using the Normal Distribution

Fran tosses a fair coin 50 times. Estimate the probability that she will get tails less than 20 times.

Solution

Let a success be a toss of tails. Thus, $n = 50$ and $p = 0.5$.

$$\bar{x} = 50(0.5) = 25 \qquad \sigma = \sqrt{50(0.5)(1 - 0.5)} = \sqrt{12.5} = 3.54$$

You want to evaluate $P(X < 20)$, where the data are normally distributed with $N(25, 3.54^2)$. Using z-scores, this distribution can be standardized to $N(0, 1)$. Continuous values from 0 to 19.5 will be considered less than 20. Calculating your z-score for 19.5 yields

$$z = \frac{19.5 - 25}{3.54} = -1.55$$

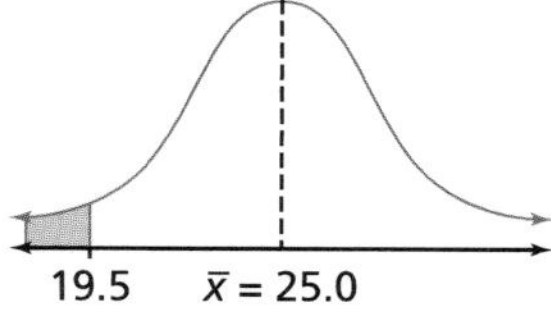

Therefore, $P(X < 19.5) = P(z < -1.55) = 0.0606$

There is a 6% chance that Fran will toss less than 20 tails in 50 attempts.

Not all binomial distributions can be approximated using the normal distribution. As you will recall from Chapter 3, some distributions are left-skewed or right-skewed and do not fit within a normal distribution. Use the following rule when considering whether or not a binomial distribution is "symmetrical enough" to be approximated by the normal distribution.

> If X is a binomial random variable of n independent trials, each with probability of success p, and if
>
> $$np > 5 \qquad \text{and} \qquad n(1 - p) > 5$$
>
> then the binomial random variable can be approximated by a normal distribution with $\bar{x} = np$ and $\sigma = \sqrt{np(1 - p)}$.

Example 3 Testing Binomial Distributions for Symmetry

Check each of the following binomial distributions to see if they can be approximated by a normal distribution.

(a) $n = 10, p = 0.3$ **(b)** $n = 14, p = 0.5$

Solution

(a) $np = 10(0.3)$
$= 3.0$

$nq = 10(0.7)$
$= 7.0$

Here, $np < 5$. A normal approximation would not be accurate.

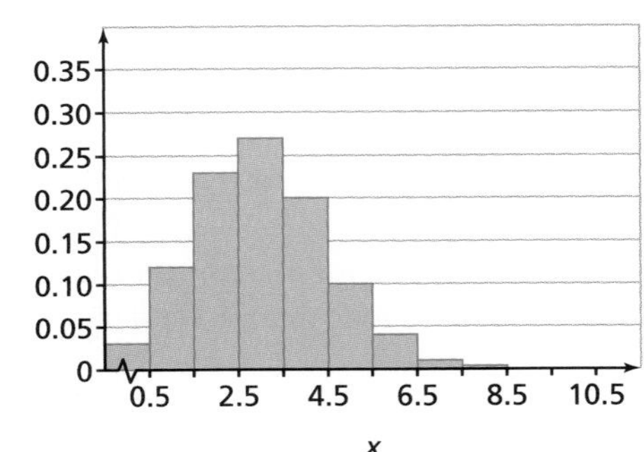

(b) $np = 15(0.5)$
$= 7.5$

$nq = 15(0.5)$
$= 7.5$

Here, both np and nq are greater than 5. A normal approximation would be valid.

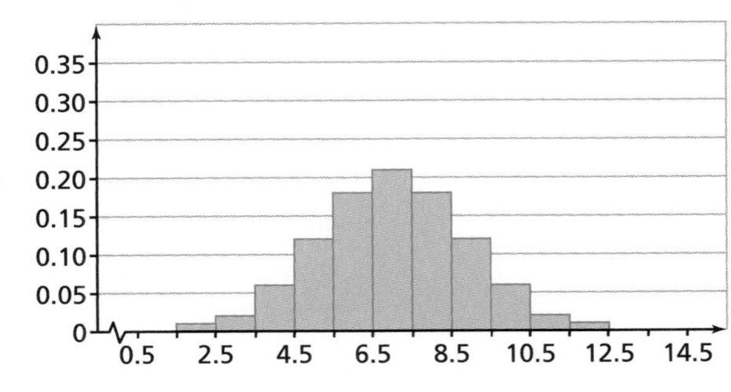

Example 4 Approximating Probabilities in a Range

Calculate the probability that, in 100 rolls of a fair die, a 6 appears between 10 and 20 times, inclusive.

Solution 1 *No technology required*

Let a success be rolling a 6. Then, $n = 100$ and $p = \frac{1}{6}$.

First, check to see if the normal approximation to the binomial distribution can be used.

$$np = 100\left(\frac{1}{6}\right) \qquad n(1-p) = 100\left(1 - \frac{1}{6}\right)$$
$$\doteq 16.67 \qquad \doteq 83.33$$

Since $np > 5$ and $n(1 - p) > 5$, the binomial distribution can be approximated by the normal curve. Find the mean and the standard deviation for the normal approximation.

$$\bar{x} = np = 100\left(\frac{1}{6}\right) \doteq 16.67$$

$$\sigma = \sqrt{np(1-p)} = \sqrt{100\left(\frac{1}{6}\right)\left(1 - \frac{1}{6}\right)} \doteq 3.73$$

We want to determine $P(10 \le X \le 20)$, where the data are normally distributed with $N(16.67, 3.73^2)$. This can be standardized to $N(0, 1)$. Values between 9.5 and 20.5 will be rounded to discrete values between 10 and 20, inclusive. Calculating z-scores for 9.5 and 20.5 yields the following:

N(16.67, 3.73²)

10 20

5.48 9.21 12.94 16.67 20.4 21.13 27.86

$$z = \frac{x - \bar{x}}{\sigma} = \frac{9.5 - 16.67}{3.73} = -1.92 \qquad z = \frac{x - \bar{x}}{\sigma} = \frac{20.5 - 16.67}{3.73} = 1.03$$

Therefore, $P(10 \le X \le 20) = P(-1.92 \le z \le 1.03)$.

From the tables, the area to the left of $z = -1.92$ is 0.0274. The area to the left of 1.03 is 0.8238. The area between the z-scores is $0.8238 - 0.0274 = 0.7964$. Therefore, the probability of rolling between 10 and 20 sixes on a fair die rolled 100 times is almost 80%.

Solution 2 *Using a TI-83 Plus calculator*

Technolink

For more information on using the **normalcdf(** command on a TI-83 Plus calculator, see Appendix C.8 on page 406.

A TI-83 Plus calculator can be used to calculate the area under the normal distribution. The command for this purpose is **normalcdf(** (normal cumulative density function). To select this function, press [2nd] [DISTR] [2]. You will then enter the lower X value, the upper X value, the mean, and the standard deviation, each separated by a comma.

The calculator will return the area between the lower and upper values. Enter the mean and standard deviation as shown in the calculator screen above.

The result is slightly different because the calculator computes z-scores exactly, and doesn't round them to two decimal places.

Example 5 Quality-Control Decisions

A hamburger-patty producer claims that its burgers contain 400 g of beef. It has been determined that 85% of burgers contain 400 g or more. An inspector will only accept a shipment if at least 90% of a sample of 250 burgers contain more than 400 g. What is the probability that a shipment is accepted?

Solution

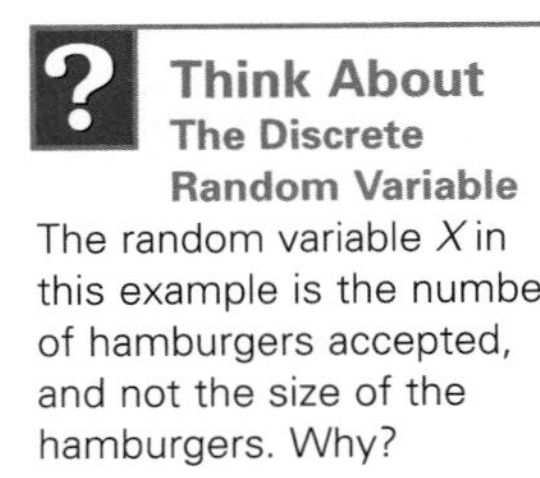

Think About The Discrete Random Variable

The random variable X in this example is the number of hamburgers accepted, and not the size of the hamburgers. Why?

The testing of an individual burger may be treated as a Bernoulli trial with a probability of success of $p = 0.85$. The inspector performs $n = 250$ independent trials.

Check to see if the normal approximation to the binomial distribution can be used.

$$\begin{aligned} np &= 250(0.85) \\ &= 212.5 \end{aligned} \qquad \begin{aligned} n(1 - p) &= 250(1 - 0.85) \\ &= 37.5 \end{aligned}$$

Since $np > 5$ and $n(1 - p) > 5$, the binomial distribution can be approximated by the normal curve.

Find the mean and the standard deviation for the normal approximation.

$$\begin{aligned} \bar{x} &= 250(0.85) \\ &= 212.5 \end{aligned} \qquad \begin{aligned} \sigma &= \sqrt{np(1 - p)} \\ &= \sqrt{250(0.85)(0.15)} \\ &\doteq 5.646 \end{aligned}$$

We want to determine the probability that at least 90% of the 250 samples are acceptable. Given that 90% of 250 is 225, we need to determine $P(X > 224.5)$.

The corresponding z-score is

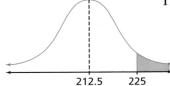

$$\begin{aligned} z &= \frac{x - \bar{x}}{\sigma} \\ &= \frac{224.5 - 212.5}{5.646} \\ &= 2.12 \end{aligned}$$

212.5 225

Therefore,
$$\begin{aligned} P(X > 224.5) &= P(z > 2.12) \\ &= 1 - P(z < 2.12) \\ &= 1 - 0.9830 \\ &= 0.017 \end{aligned}$$

There is only a 1.7% chance that the shipment will be accepted.

KEY IDEAS

- A **normal distribution** may be used to approximate a binomial distribution. This is useful if the number of binomial calculations is large.
- The approximation is only valid if both np and $n(1 - p)$ are greater than 5, where n is the number of independent trials, p is the probability of success in a single trial, and $(1 - p)$ is the probability of failure.
- The normal parameters $\bar{x}$ and σ are calculated as follows:

$$\bar{x} = np \text{ and } \sigma = \sqrt{np(1 - p)}$$

- The normal approximation of the binomial probability disribution may be calculated on a TI-83 Plus calculator using the **normcdf(** command. See Appendix C.8 on page 406 for more details.

5.4 Exercises

1. A coin is tossed four times. Find the probability of each of the following.
(a) P(exactly 1 head) **(b)** P(exactly 2 heads)
(c) P(exactly 3 heads) **(d)** P(exactly 4 heads)
(e) P(exactly 0 heads)

2. A die is rolled 10 times. Calculate the probability of each of the following events, correct to six decimal places.
(a) one 1 appears **(b)** two 2s appear **(c)** three 3s appear
(d) four 4s appear **(e)** five 5s appear **(f)** six 6s appear

3. A bag contains 20 yellow marbles and 80 blue marbles. The bag is shaken so that the marbles are thoroughly mixed. Marbles are then removed from the bag one at a time, the colour is recorded, and the marble is returned to the bag. This process is done a total of four times. Find the probability of each of the following.
(a) P(exactly three blue marbles are drawn)
(b) P(at least three blue marbles are drawn)

4. A student guesses all 10 answers on a multiple-choice test. There are 5 choices for each of the questions. Find the probability (correct to 6 decimal places) that the student scores exactly 50% on the test (gets 5 correct answers).

B

5. **Knowledge and Understanding** If 20 coins are dropped on a table, what is the probability (correct to three decimal places) that
   (a) exactly 12 coins are heads   (b) at least 12 coins are heads

6. A card is drawn from a standard deck and replaced. If this experiment is repeated 30 times, what is the probability that
   (a) exactly 10 of the cards are spades
   (b) no more than 5 cards are spades

7. It is known that approximately 90% of the population is right-handed. In a sample of 100 people, what is the probability that
   (a) exactly 10 people are left-handed
   (b) more than 10 people are left-handed
   (c) less than 5 people are left-handed

8. **Application** A drug has a 70% success rate. What is the probability that 80 or more people out of 100 will be cured by the drug?

9. **Communication** A pair of six-sided dice is rolled 50 times. Which is more likely?
   (a) exactly 8 doubles are rolled   (b) 10 or more doubles are rolled

10. A test consists of 50 questions. What is the probability that you can
    (a) pass
    (b) get more than 40% correct if
        (i) it is a true/false test
        (ii) it is a multiple-choice test with four possible choices

11. The probability of engine trouble on a jet airplane is relatively small. Suppose a jet has a $\frac{1}{30}$ chance of having at least one engine fail on any flight. (The jet can fly with the other engines working normally.) The jet has just flown its fiftieth flight. Find the probability that the plane has experienced engine trouble on at least two flights.

12. Singh Textiles produces computer chips. On average, 2% of all computer chips produced are defective. In a sample of 500 chips, the quality-control inspector accepts the batch only if fewer than 1% of the chips tested are defective. Determine the probability that a batch is accepted.

C

13. **Thinking, Inquiry, Problem Solving** An airline has determined that 4% of people do not show up for their flights. To avoid having empty seats, the flight is overbooked. A large jet holds 300 people.
    (a) What is the probability that some travellers will not get a seat if 310 tickets are sold? 305 tickets?
    (b) How many tickets could be oversold in order to be 98% sure that everyone gets a seat?

14. Xiau and Kim interviewed 175 people and found that 75 were in favour of raising funds for a new arena by increasing property taxes. The question will be decided in a referendum in which it is expected that all of the 26 076 eligible voters will vote. Over half the votes must be in favour of raising property taxes for the new arena to be built. How likely is it that there will be a new arena?

15. An election is being held at your school to determine who will be treasurer of the student council. Teresa and Elisabete are the candidates. The day before the election, Elisabete takes a poll of 74 students and finds that 30 will vote for her. There are 1148 students in the school and all are expected to vote in the election. How likely is it that Elisabete will win?

ADDITIONAL ACHIEVEMENT CHART QUESTIONS

16. **Knowledge and Understanding** A student guesses all 15 answers on a multiple-choice test. There are 5 choices for each of the questions. Find the probability (correct to 6 decimal places) that the student passes the test.

17. **Applications** On average, Mike Weir scores a birdie on about 20.9% of all the holes he plays. Mike is in contention to win a PGA golf tournament but he must birdie at least four of the last six holes he plays. Find the probability, as a percent correct to one decimal place, that Mike will win.

18. **Thinking, Inquiry, Problem Solving** An insurance company has said that "the probability of your having an accident while travelling on a stretch of road at night is $\frac{1}{500}$." Find the probability that you will have at least one accident on the stretch of road if you travel the road 350 times.

19. **Communication** As a shoe salesperson paid on commission, it is important for Devica to close a sale. She knows that the probability of closing a sale with any one customer who tries on shoes is about 26%. She predicts that she will help about 220 customers try on shoes each month. She says she can expect to sell shoes to between 40 and 90 customers each month. Should you believe this claim?

5.5 Using Simulations and Samples to Estimate Probability in the Real World

Project Connection

If your project uses data from a random sample of a population, you can construct a simulation based on your data. Several repetitions of your simulation will show you whether your particular sample results are unique or could simply have happened by chance.

SIMULATING A WORLD SERIES

Suppose that the Toronto Blue Jays and the New York Mets will play each other in the World Series. Imagine that the Blue Jays had a slightly better regular-season record and have a probability of 0.6 of winning any given game in the series. The first team to win four games in the series becomes world champion. What is the expected number of games required before a winner of the series is declared?

Analysis of the Problem

The World Series final can be thought of as a probability experiment in which each game is a trial. Each trial has one of two possible outcomes—a Blue Jays win (success with $p = 0.6$) or a Met win (failure with $q = 0.4$). Assume that the result of one game has no influence over the results of future games, so each trial is independent of the others. In this experiment, each trial is a Bernoulli trial. However, the series cannot be thought of as a binomial experiment because the random variable is not the number of successes in seven trials. This type of problem is called a *waiting-time* problem, and the random variable is the number of games that need to be completed before one team wins.

INVESTIGATION 1: SIMULATION DESIGN WITHOUT TECHNOLOGY

The mathematical tools used so far are not appropriate for a theoretical analysis of this waiting-time situation. We will estimate the probability with a simulation.

? Think about The Need for a Simulation

Why is it necessary to do a simulation for this problem rather than use the strategies presented in earlier sections?

If you were to use a spinner, the sector angles should be 216° (for 60%) and 144° (for 40%).

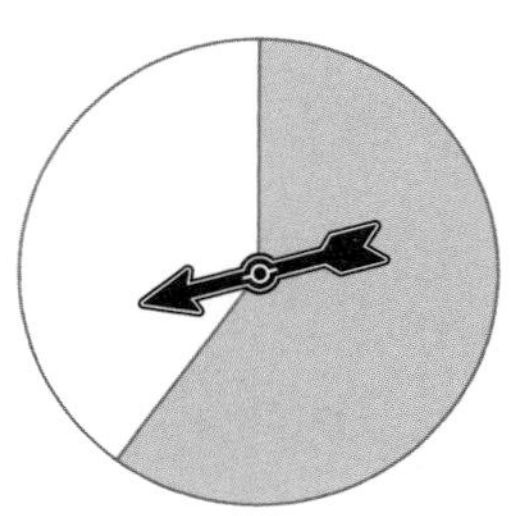

Purpose

To design a simulation of the World Series.

Procedure

A. The Blue Jays are expected to win 6 out of 10 games. Create a simulation using numbered slips of paper, playing cards (an ace and numbered cards 2 through 10), or a spinner. Randomly generate a number between 1 and 10. If its value is 1 through 6, record a Blue Jays win; otherwise, record a Mets win.

B. Repeat this process up to seven times, stopping as soon as one team has won four games.

C. Repeat the experiment several times (at least 100) and use the results to create a probability distribution. (The class could be divided into 10 groups and each group conducts the experiment 10 times. The results of each group are then combined to create 100 simulations.)

Think about **The Frequency Distribution**

- Should you be surprised if your simulation differs widely from this example?
- How much of a difference would cause you to think that your simulation produced typical results or unexpected results?

The results of one such simulation are displayed below.

Number of Games	4	5	6	7
Frequency	16	28	30	26
Experimental Probability	0.16	0.28	0.30	0.26

Using this probability distribution, the expected number of games required before a winner is declared is

$$\begin{aligned} E(X) &= 4(0.16) + 5(0.28) + 6(0.30) + 7(0.26) \\ &= 5.66 \end{aligned}$$

INVESTIGATION 2: USING A TI-83 PLUS CALCULATOR

The simulation above generates 10 random integers between 1 and 10 for each trial and conducts up to 7 trials.

Purpose

To design a simulation of the World Series using a TI-83 Plus calculator.

Procedure

Technolink For more information on using **randInt** with a TI-83 Plus calculator, see Appendix C.11 on page 408.

```
randInt(1,10,7)
{9 7 2 4 5 10 4}
{9 8 1 2 5 6 7}
{6 6 7 5 1 1 7}
{8 1 4 4 5 7 2}
{6 4 1 3 10 4 8}
{1 4 3 5 1 4 4}
```

The **randInt** function on a TI-83 Plus calculator generates lists of seven random integers with values between 1 and 10. Use this to simulate one World Series. Pressing ENTER allows you to simulate as many series as you wish.

The sample screen in the margin represents the following win sequences.

Simulation	Winning Teams						
1	M	M	J	J	J	M	J
2	M	M	J	J	J	J	
3	J	J	M	J	J		
4	M	J	J	J	J		
5	J	J	J	J			
6	J	J	J	J			

INVESTIGATION 3: USING A SPREADSHEET

Purpose

To design a simulation of the World Series using a spreadsheet.

Procedure

Spreadsheet software was used to create the following 10-series simulation. Repeat this simulation to give at least 100 trials.

Technolink The formula =INT(RAND()*10+1) was used to generate the random integers in this spreadsheet. See Appendix E.3 on page 426.

Game 1	Game 2	Game 3	Game 4	Game 5	Game 6	Game 7	Games Required
8	6	10	9	4	9	6	6
8	8	8	8	1	5	3	4
6	9	2	5	6	3	4	5
4	2	2	3	3	4	10	4
10	4	1	6	2	8	7	5
7	6	5	6	8	1	9	6
3	2	9	5	8	9	8	7
8	3	6	1	1	6	10	5
7	6	1	8	2	6	3	6
9	8	8	8	9	2	5	4
2	2	2	1	4	10	8	4
10	2	3	2	1	5	2	5
8	5	4	8	10	9	4	6
10	9	4	2	8	10	4	6
3	2	6	7	8	3	3	6
1	10	3	4	10	10	9	7
8	7	10	6	9	6	1	5
5	1	8	8	5	5	7	6
7	8	8	2	2	7	9	6
9	8	10	6	1	5	8	7

The probability distribution resulting from this simulation appears below.

Number of Games	4	5	6	7
Frequency	4	5	8	3
Experimental Probability	0.20	0.25	0.40	0.15

Using this probability distribution, the expected number of games required before a winner is declared is

$$E(X) = 4(0.20) + 5(0.25) + 6(0.40) + 7(0.15)$$
$$= 5.5$$

Discussion Questions

1. How does the number of repetitions affect the probability distribution?
2. How does the number of repetitions affect the expected value?

3. Repeat your simulation several times. (If other students have carried out the same simulation, you could combine the results.) Describe the distribution of the expected values. Do they appear to be normally distributed? Explain your answer.

? Think about The Effectiveness of Two Drugs
Why do the sample results not provide absolute evidence that one drug is actually more effective than the other?

SIMULATIONS BASED ON SAMPLE RESULTS

Drug A has been in use for a number of years and has an observed success rate of 80% when used to treat a particular illness. In an experimental trial group of 100 patients suffering from the same medical condition, 90 showed improvement using drug B. How likely is it that drug B is really more effective than drug A?

Analysis of the Problem and Simulation Design

No theoretical probability is associated with the success rate of either drug. If the entire population of people with that particular medical condition were given drug A, a certain proportion would show improvement. Assume the same for drug B. Those proportions are unknown.

Suppose that the effectiveness of drug B were the same as that for drug A. It is possible that a larger group of people who improved were selected by chance in the sample. If the probability of this happening is low, then drug B can be said to be more effective than drug A. If the probability of this happening is high, then it cannot be said with certainty that drug B is more effective.

In statistics, if the probability of an event happening by chance is small (the cutoff of 5% is commonly used), it is considered that the event does not happen by chance. Thus, there is a high level of confidence that when the event occurs, it does not occur by chance and is, therefore, noteworthy.

INVESTIGATION 4: SAMPLE RESULTS

Design a simulation of the sampling process for drug B assuming that it has the same effectiveness as drug A, namely 80%.

Purpose

To design a simulation to compare the effectiveness of drugs A and B without the use of technology.

Procedure

A sample spinner for drug A is shown below.

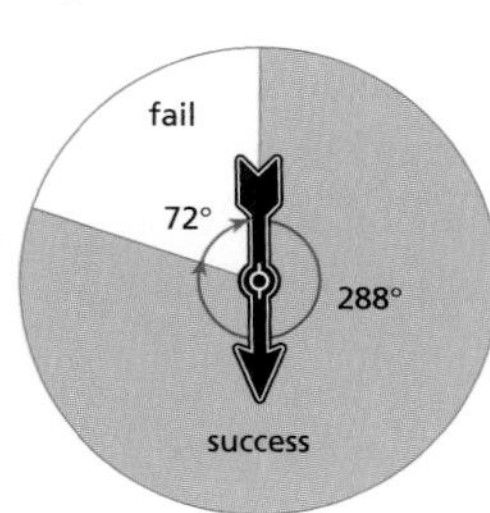

A. One way to carry out this simulation is to use a large number of pieces of paper, 100 for example. Label 80% of them with the letter B to indicate that drug B caused significant improvement.

B. Randomly draw a sample of 10 and record the number of papers that have the letter B.

C. Repeat the experiment at least 200 times.

D. Create a probability distribution for the number of B's in a sample of 10.

While it would work, this simulation is very impractical to carry out. It would be simpler to use a spinner set to reflect the 80% success rate, and spin it 100 times repeatedly.

If P is small, there is a small chance that this happened as a result of a random selection of patients. Therefore, the difference in the results of the two drugs is significant and not due to chance. The assumption that drug B was only as effective as drug A is rejected.

Technolink
The screen image below shows the simulation steps as they are carried out one step at a time using a TI-83 Plus calculator.

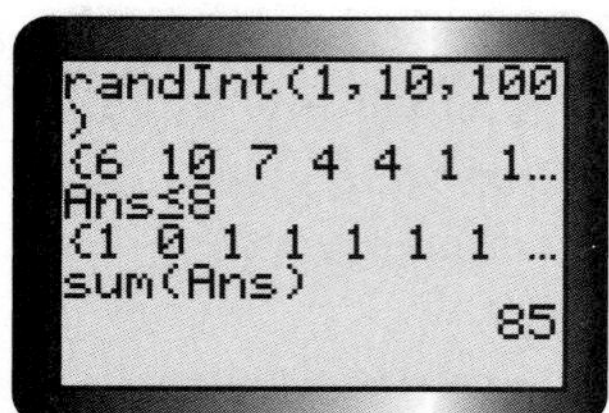

INVESTIGATION 5: USING A TI-83 PLUS CALCULATOR

It may not be practical to approach this problem using labelled pieces of paper. Simulate the sampling process by generating random numbers as described below.

Purpose

To design a simulation to compare the effectiveness of drugs A and B using a TI-83 Plus calculator.

Procedure

A. Generate single-digit random integers between 1 and 10. The numbers 1 through 8 will represent a patient for whom drug B had a strong effect. The numbers 9 and 10 represent a patient for whom the drug had no significant effect.

B. Generate 100 of these random numbers. This will correspond to one trial in the simulation.

C. The trial is considered an indication that drug B has a stronger effect if 90 or more of the numbers are between 1 and 8. For the manufacturer of drug B, this would be a success.

D. Perform many trials and use the results to construct a probability distribution for the number of patients for whom drug B has been effective.

E. Use the probability distribution to determine *P*(number of patients for whom drug B is effective).

Technolink
Sample results of combining these into a single command are shown below.

The following steps can be used with a TI-83 Plus calculator to carry out one trial of this simulation.

1. **randInt(1,10,100)** will generate a list of 100 random integers between 1 and 10.

2. **randInt(1,10,100)≤8** will create a list of 1s and 0s. A 1 will appear in each position in which the original random number was less than 8. A 0 will appear in each position in which this was not the case. The ≤ test can be found using [2nd] [MATH] **6:≤**.

3. **sum(randInt(1,10,100)≤8)** will add up the entries in the list in Step 2. This will indicate how many 1s were in this list and will correspond to the number of random numbers in Step 1 that were less than 8. This will count the number of patients for whom drug B was successful. The **sum** function can be found using [2nd] [STAT] [MATH] **5:sum(**.

INVESTIGATION 6: USING A SPREADSHEET PROGRAM

Spreadsheet software can also be used to generate several simulations. Below is part of a spreadsheet that shows 150 trials with 100 random integers each. The command required to generate each random integer is the same as that used in the World Series simulation.

	A	B	C	D	E	F	G	H	I	J	K	L	M	N	O	P	Q	R	S	T	U	V	W	X	Y	Z
82	7	6	5	1	5	2	4	8	7	8	7	2	6	3	10	3	10	4	7	1	4	1	9	9	9	1
83	4	3	6	7	9	9	6	8	8	9	2	8	3	4	6	7	6	4	2	10	7	2	3	5	2	8
84	6	8	1	3	4	3	5	1	9	2	3	5	4	9	7	9	8	2	4	6	4	8	3	6	8	2
85	6	3	3	10	5	1	5	4	9	6	4	2	7	8	8	9	9	1	1	5	2	6	1	7	2	3
86	10	3	7	8	2	4	9	5	2	13	7	8	4	9	10	10	6	1	5	4	6	7	7	2	6	3
87	4	3	9	1	3	7	3	3	3	5	4	5	9	7	6	5	4	10	7	4	10	3	2	7	7	6
88	8	2	2	4	4	8	2	3	2	5	6	10	5	9	9	3	3	7	7	6	4	8	1	9	2	8
89	8	8	7	9	7	8	3	3	3	1	1	8	3	8	5	8	7	4	8	2	3	6	10	7	10	5
90	5	1	7	7	10	4	7	6	10	1	7	9	9	9	7	9	1	2	6	3	7	5	5	8	2	1
91	7	6	2	5	2	6	5	9	7	6	1	3	6	1	1	1	8	2	1	1	9	6	6	4	8	8
92	6	8	10	1	1	1	9	5	3	4	10	7	3	6	6	9	2	8	8	4	2	9	6	2	2	5
93	1	5	10	7	2	1	9	7	9	7	3	3	8	7	6	7	5	3	10	2	4	8	5	1	8	8
94	7	2	9	9	8	2	3	1	4	7	7	5	9	1	4	4	4	8	8	10	3	8	6	3	3	9
95	2	1	3	6	10	5	10	8	8	1	5	3	1	6	8	4	9	2	9	4	3	9	2	1	9	7
96	10	2	7	4	9	5	5	2	7	4	5	3	8	8	5	4	6	4	6	6	10	4	7	3	7	5
97	2	6	3	3	3	4	2	6	1	9	9	9	8	8	5	9	2	1	8	2	2	9	8	2	5	6
98	3	5	4	5	3	5	8	4	6	1	5	1	1	2	8	7	10	2	9	1	5	5	6	3	6	5
99	4	10	6	7	6	4	3	7	4	9	4	3	9	1	3	7	6	2	8	9	7	3	4	7	4	8
100	3	2	1	3	2	9	2	7	8	4	2	6	1	9	5	9	8	10	9	8	8	9	2	3	6	7
101	86	84	82	85	82	85	86	87	77	81	88	82	86	75	84	74	83	79	77	79	72	75	82	82	75	76

Successes	Frequency	Probability
70	1	0.67%
71	1	0.67%
72	2	1.33%
73	3	2.00%
74	9	6.00%
75	4	2.67%
76	6	4.00%
77	11	7.33%
78	17	11.33%
79	12	8.00%
80	15	10.00%
81	13	8.67%
82	13	8.67%
83	19	12.67%

Successes	Frequency	Probability
84	7	4.67%
85	5	3.33%
86	2	1.33%
87	4	2.67%
88	2	1.33%
89	3	2.00%
90	1	0.67%
91	0	0.00%
92	0	0.00%
93	0	0.00%
94	0	0.00%
95	0	0.00%
96	0	0.00%

Each column represents one trial with 100 random numbers. The last row of the spreadsheet shows the count of the numbers less than 8. The simulation's probability distribution appears below.

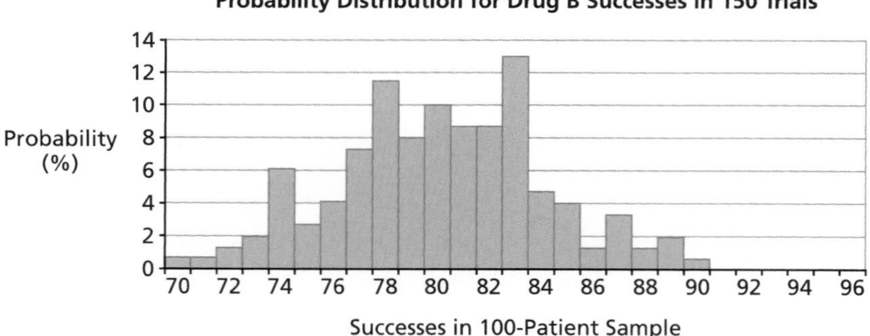

There was one trial in which the number of successes was 90 or more. The probability of this happening was less than 0.67%—very small. As a result, it is appropriate to reject the assumption that the 90% success rate for drug B reported in the sample was only a chance result.

The conclusion is that there is strong evidence that drug B is more effective than drug A. You can be confident that this is a correct conclusion at least 95% of the time.

KEY IDEAS

using simulations to estimate probability distributions—We have dealt exclusively with the binomial distribution in this text. Many probability experiments can be best described using other types of distributions that you have not yet encountered. Other situations are so complex that it may be practical to determine a theoretical probability distribution for them.

A simulation can be used to estimate the probability distribution when it is not possible or it is impractical to determine the theoretical probability distribution.

using samples to estimate the probability distribution for a population—Often, the results of an experiment or a survey provide evidence that a particular characteristic occurs within a sample of the overall population with a certain relative frequency. The relative frequency value can be used as an estimate for the proportion of the entire population that possesses the characteristic. This estimate can be used to design a simulation and to estimate the probability distribution of the characteristic for the entire population.

5.5 Exercises

A

1. Calculate the experimental probability for each outcome in the following frequency tables.

(a)

X	7	8	9	10	11	12	13
Frequency	15	19	12	7	5	2	1

(b)

X	1	2	3	4	5	6	7	8
Frequency	1	7	11	13	9	5	2	0

(c)

X	3	4	5	6	7	8
Frequency	1	1	5	8	15	12

(d)

X	10	11	12	13	14	15
Frequency	2	7	10	6	8	5

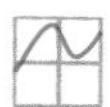

2. Use technology to generate 50 random numbers between 1 and 10, and record the results in a frequency table.

3. Calculate the experimental probability for each outcome in the frequency table you created in Question 2.

4. **Knowledge and Understanding** Design a simulation that will give you an estimate of the number of people in a group of 20 who have the same birthday. For the purposes of this problem, ignore the year of birth and assume that there are only 365 days per year.

5. Suppose you have a container in which there are 13 balls numbered 1 through 13. Design a simulation to determine the probability that no ball is drawn in numerical order (ball 1 is not drawn first, ball 2 is not drawn second, and so on).

B

6. Raymond recorded the number of people at his office building that were sick each day for two months (61 days) and summarized his findings in the following frequency table, where the random variable, X, represents the number of sick people each day.

X	0	1	2	3	4	5	6	7
Frequency	44	8	4	2	1	0	1	1

(a) Calculate the experimental probability for each of the outcomes.
(b) Using the experimental results, calculate the probability that no one will be sick during the next 5 work days.
(c) Calculate the expected value of the discrete random variable, X.

7. Twenty-five trials of an experiment produce the following values for the discrete random variable, X: 4, 2, 4, 3, 4, 2, 2, 3, 3, 4, 2, 4, 3, 2, 4, 1, 2, 3, 3, 4, 3, 3, 3, 1, 1.
   (a) Create a frequency table for these experimental results.
   (b) Calculate the experimental probability for each outcome.
   (c) Calculate the expected value for the discrete random variable, X.

8. Suppose the Blue Jays and the Mets each has a probability of 0.5 of winning any game of the World Series. Design a simulation that will allow you to determine the probability that the Blue Jays win the series given that the Mets win the first game. (**Remember**: To win the World Series, you need 4 wins.)

9. A baseball player has a batting average of 0.300. Consider his next 20 at-bats. Design a simulation that will allow you to estimate the probability that he will have a run of 7 at-bats in a row without a hit.

10. You toss a coin 20 times and it comes up tails 18 times. Use a simulation that assumes the coin is unbiased to find evidence that it is a biased coin.

11. **Communication** A well-known basketball player has a career success rate of 80% when shooting free throws. He has missed four out of his last five attempts. Write a report, based on the results of a simulation, that discusses whether or not the coach should be concerned about this.

12. **Application** An experiment is conducted to determine whether a subject has extrasensory perception (ESP). The experimenter tosses a coin and the subject, seated in another room, states what he or she thinks the result is. Should a subject who correctly guesses 7 out of 10 tosses be considered to have ESP?

13. In a jar of 100 jellybeans, 90 are green and 10 are yellow. Five jellybeans are selected at random.
   (a) Determine the probability that there are exactly 2 yellow jellybeans in the sample.
   (b) Explain why this situation cannot be represented by a binomial distribution.
   (c) Determine the probability distribution for the discrete random variable, X, the number of yellow jellybeans in a sample of 5 jellybeans.
   (d) Design a simulation to verify the probability distribution you determined in part (c).
   (e) Determine the expected number of yellow jellybeans in a sample of 5 jellybeans.

14. A survey was taken of 100 potential voters from a population of 10 000 voters. If 60% of the actual population will vote in the election, determine the probability of the following.
   (a) All 100 in the sample will vote.
   (b) None of the 100 in the sample will vote.
   (c) At least 10 in the sample will vote.

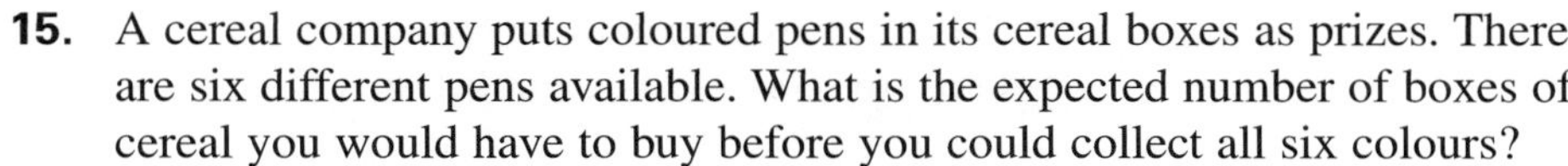

Think about Question 15

Rolling a die provides a good simulation for Question 15. Why?

15. A cereal company puts coloured pens in its cereal boxes as prizes. There are six different pens available. What is the expected number of boxes of cereal you would have to buy before you could collect all six colours?

C

16. **Thinking, Inquiry, Problem Solving** Recall the birthday problem in Question 4. Use a simulation to determine the number of people needed so that the probability that at least two of them have the same birthday is more than 0.5.

ADDITIONAL ACHIEVEMENT CHART QUESTIONS

17. **Knowledge and Understanding** Design a simulation that will give you an estimate of the number of people in a group of 30 who were born in June.

18. **Application** A small convenience store throws away milk that has expired. At this store, 75% of the 1-L milk cartons are sold before they expire. The store receives 12 new cartons every week. Design and conduct a simulation to determine the probability of throwing out three or more of these cartons.

19. **Thinking, Inquiry, Problem Solving** A newspaper poll of 50 voters showed that 30 approved a proposal for constructing a new expressway around the city. Mayor Haviva Lieberthal, however, says his mail is running against this proposal. Can the mayor be correct? What is the probability that a sample of 50 voters from a population that is equally split could produce 30 *yes* votes?

20. **Communication** Describe a real-world situation for which determining the theoretical probability distribution is impractical or impossible. Describe a simulation that you could use to provide an estimate for the probability distribution of this situation.

Chapter Problem

Are Frog Populations Declining?

CP4. In phase 2 of your study, suppose you capture 100 frogs:

Species	Number in Sample
Bullfrog	35
Spring peeper	50
Mink frog	15

Design a simulation to determine whether or not the distribution in your sample indicates that the number of mink frogs is seriously reduced relative to the number of spring peepers.

Chapter 5 Wrap-Up

EXTRA PRACTICE

Outcome	Winnings ($)
HH	5
HT	0
TH	0
TT	2

1. A game is played by tossing two coins. Each toss costs $2.00. The player wins when both coins turn up the same and loses when they differ. The payouts are given in the table in the margin.
   (a) Create a probability distribution for this game.
   (b) What can a player expect to win playing this game?
   (c) Is this a fair game? Explain.

2. Four teachers and five students have volunteered to serve on the school's fundraising committee, which is chaired by the principal. The principal wishes to select the committee using a random draw. He places each person's name on a slip of paper and draws four names.
   (a) What is the probability that there is a teacher on the committee?
   (b) What is the expected number of students on the committee?

3. The streets of a city are laid out in a rectangular grid, as shown below.

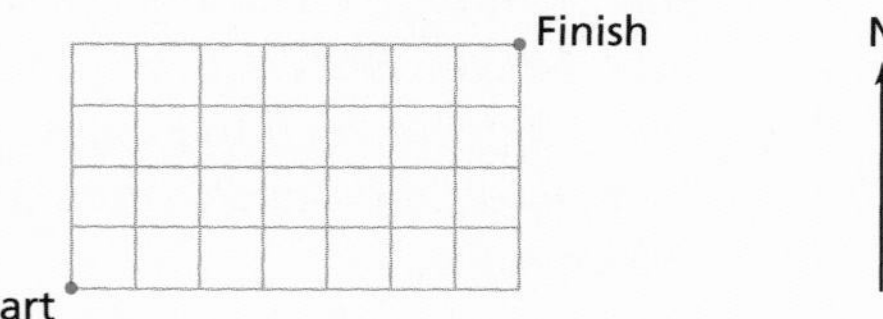

   (a) Determine the total number of routes through the grid that lead from start to finish if you travel only north or east.
   (b) How many routes begin with three north steps in a row?

4. Expand each of the following.
   (a) $(3x + 4y)^5$ **(b)** $(2x^3 - 3x^2)^6$
   (c) $\left(5 - \frac{2}{x}\right)^3$ **(d)** $(x + \sqrt{x})^4$

5. In the expansion of $\left(\frac{3}{x} - x^3\right)^8$, find
   (a) the number of terms **(b)** the constant term
   (c) the term containing x^{12}

6. Simplify.
   (a) $\dfrac{\binom{74}{21}}{\binom{73}{20}}$ **(b)** $\binom{20}{15} + \binom{20}{16}$

7. Find the probability that in 10 tosses of a fair coin,
   (a) there will be exactly 5 heads **(b)** there will be exactly 8 heads
   (c) there will be exactly 2 heads **(d)** there will be at least 2 heads

8. (a) An experiment is designed in which a ball is drawn from a box containing three red balls, a blue ball, and a green ball, and then a coin is tossed to determine if the ball is to be kept (heads = keep the ball, tails = put it back). Draw a tree diagram to represent the possible outcomes of one trial of this experiment.
   (b) Design a simulation using technology that will provide an estimate of the probability of drawing a red ball and tossing a head to keep it using at least 100 repetitions of the experiment.
   (c) Determine the probability that a red ball will be kept.
   (d) Explain whether or not the experiment qualifies as a binomial experiment.

9. A student is selling chocolates to raise money for school athletics. She has found that she is able to sell to one in every three people she calls on. Determine the probability that she will have at least two sales in an evening in which she calls on four homes.

10. A multiple-choice test has 10 questions, each of which has 4 possible answers. If a student guesses the answers, determine the probability of getting exactly
   (a) 5 answers correct
   (b) 6 answers correct
   (c) 1 answer correct
   (d) all answers correct

11. A pair of dice is rolled 30 times. Determine the probability that
   (a) double 3s are rolled exactly five times
   (b) double 3s are rolled at least once

12. In a manufacturing process, 0.2% of the brake pads that come off the production line are considered defective.
   (a) Determine the probability that at least one brake pad is defective in an order of 200 pads.
   (b) What is the expected number of defective brake pads in an order of 200?

13. In a bag, there are 10 white marbles and 6 red ones. Four are selected at random.
   (a) Determine the probability that there are exactly 3 white marbles in the sample.
   (b) Can this situation be represented by a binomial distribution? Explain.
   (c) If the discrete random variable, X, is defined as the number of white marbles in a sample of 4, determine the probability distribution.
   (d) Design a simulation to verify the probability distribution you determined in part (c).
   (e) Determine the expected number of white marbles in the sample of 4.

14. You roll a die 10 times and 6 times it comes up showing 5.
   (a) What is the probability of this occurring?
   (b) Conduct a simulation to show that this is an unfair die.

Chapter 5 Test

1. **Knowledge and Understanding** At several branches of the Trillium Bank, transaction times with tellers during a two-hour period were recorded. Time, in the table, has been rounded to the nearest minute.

Time (min)	1	2	3	4	5	6 or more
Frequency	20	12	9	5	3	1

   (a) Define the random variable, X.
   (b) Create a probability distribution from these data.
   (c) Determine the expected transaction time at the Trillium Bank.

2. A baseball player has a batting average of 0.275. In most games, a player has four at-bats. Determine the probability that the player gets
   (a) exactly three hits in a game **(b)** at least one hit in a game
   (c) the expected number of hits in a game

3. DZ Technical, a small electronics firm, produces microprocessors for a large computer manufacturer. The computer manufacturer samples 12 microprocessors from each shipment and will reject the entire shipment if there are 2 or more defective units in the sample. Determine the probability that the shipment will be accepted if DZ Technical knows that 10% of its units are defective.
   (a) Design and carry out a simulation to estimate the probability.
   (b) Compute the theoretical probability.

4. **Communication** What is a Bernoulli trial? Describe a situation that is representative of a Bernoulli trial.

5. Determine the 10th term in the expansion of $\left(x^2 + \frac{2}{\sqrt{x}}\right)^{15}$.

6. **Application** A penny is placed in the bottom row of an eight-by-eight grid, as shown. If the penny can be moved one square at a time to the row above, either diagonally or straight ahead, how many paths will lead to the square in the top left-hand corner?

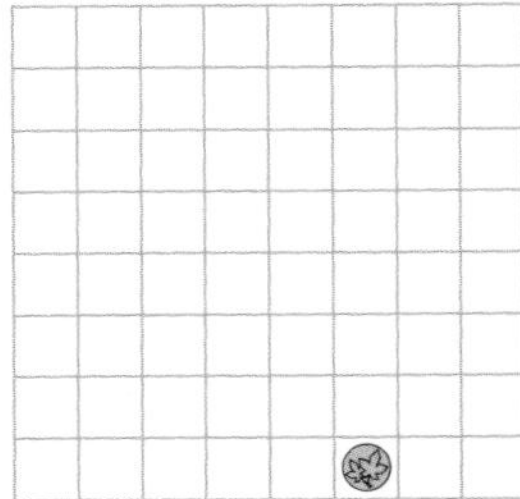

7. **Thinking, Inquiry, Problem Solving** Use the Binomial Theorem to determine an expansion of $(a + b + c)^3$. (**Hint:** Express the trinomial as a binomial and expand.)

8. Which technique yields the most reliable results: a probability distribution determined using theoretical probabilities or a probability distribution determined through simulation? Explain.

6 Solving Problems with Matrices, Graphs, and Diagrams

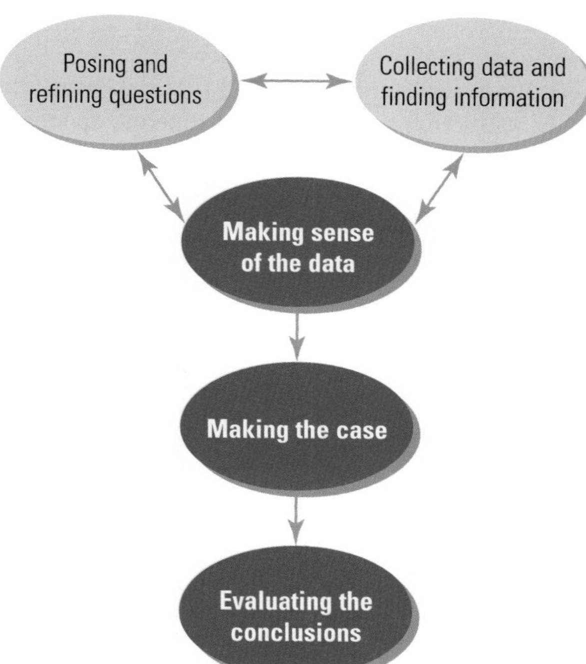

Frequently, in the worlds of business, science, and politics, decisions must be made based on large amounts of raw data. In order to make sense of the data, they have to be put into a form that can be readily manipulated by computer software. Often, the data are entered in the form of a matrix: a rectangular array of numbers for which the rows and columns have specific meanings.

Matrix methods can also be used to analyze and solve problems such as scheduling events, allocating resources efficiently, making manufacturing processes more efficient, building communication networks, or planning delivery routes. The first step in solving these kinds of problems is to use a diagram or graph, and then to translate the information from the diagram into matrix form.

In this chapter, you will

- represent simple and complex processes using diagrams
- solve network problems associated with scheduling events or with efficiently planning routes using simple graph theory
- represent and carry out computations on numerical data using matrices
- use matrix methods to solve problems drawn from a variety of applications

Chapter Problem

How Much Time Will It Take to Build This House?

For the construction of a house to be completed on time and on budget, Bombay Construction must develop a schedule of all the different tasks, arranged in the proper order. Having highly paid tradespeople and expensive, specialized equipment, such as backhoes and steam shovels, on site sitting idle is not ideal. Nor is having supplies delivered so early as to risk getting damaged or stolen, or worse, having to shut down the site because supplies have not yet arrived.

Although some tasks depend on others being completed first, other tasks can occur simultaneously. Bombay Construction must take all of this into account when drawing up the schedule.

How does Bombay Construction schedule all the different tasks to ensure the equipment and personnel are used most efficiently and with the least cost?

Project Connection

This chapter will introduce tools you will need to help you solve problems associated with your course project. You may need to organize and carry out computations with a large amount of data, and will likely have to represent relationships among interacting variables using a diagram. This diagram, and the analysis of the data associated with it, will become a key component of your final project presentation. The methods presented in this chapter may even help you plan and monitor your progress on your project.

6.1 Using Diagrams to Represent and Analyze Processes

An ecosystem, which can involve a large combination of smaller systems, can be quite difficult to analyze. Researchers will often use a diagram to clarify the processes involved and to discover how the variables interact. In this section, you will use flow charts and other diagrams to simplify complex systems.

flow chart—a representation of a process using symbols and directed line segments

A **flow chart** is a diagram in which symbols are used to represent specific activities or events. Directed line segments are also used to indicate the sequence in the process. Flow charts are read by following the direction of the line segments from one event to the next.

Example 1 Representing a Process

Because Noel finds it difficult to get to school on time, his math teacher suggests Noel create a flow chart to illustrate the process he follows each morning. Then, using the flow chart, Noel could identify those parts of his morning routine that might be simplified or streamlined.

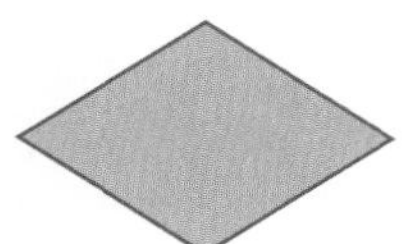

A rectangle represents a step in which an action takes place.

A diamond represents a step in which a test or a decision is carried out. The result of the test determines the next step.

Solution

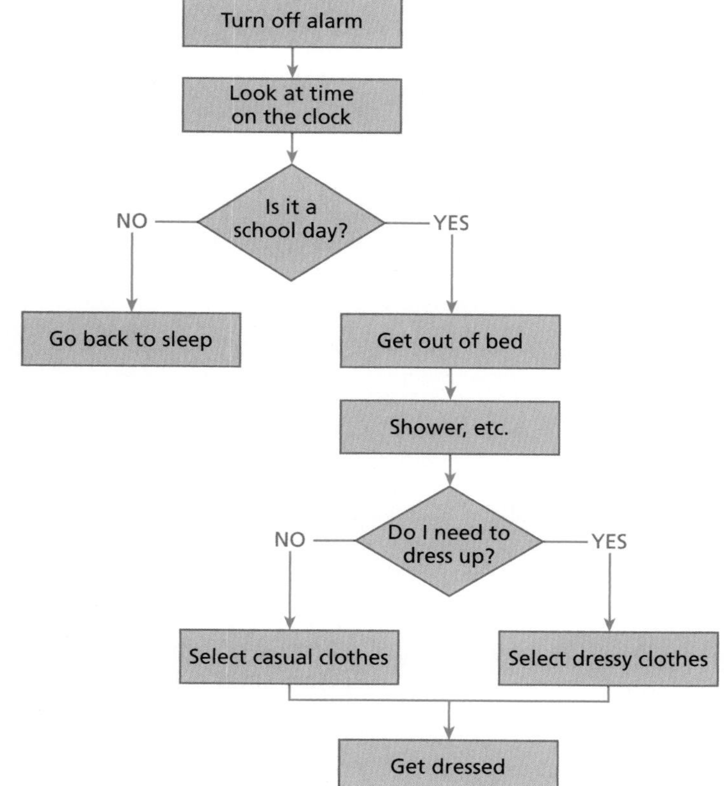

From the flow chart, Noel determines that he may be able to streamline his shower routine, or shower the night before to save time. Selecting clothes is something else that Noel could do the night before.

Another visual display that can simplify information is a picture, which is the focus of the next example.

Project Connection

If your project involves analyzing a process, you may want to construct a flow chart to help you understand the components of the process or identify the variables and how they interact.

Example 2 Representing the Water Cycle

Create a picture illustrating the water cycle. Show how water moves above, on, and below the surface of the earth. Use the verbal description that follows as a reference.

> The water cycle begins with the evaporation of water from the ground, or the surface of any other large body of water. As moist air is lifted, it cools and water vapour condenses to form clouds. Moisture is then transported by wind and returns to the surface as precipitation. Once the water reaches the ground, it either evaporates back into the atmosphere or penetrates the surface and becomes groundwater. Groundwater either seeps its way to the oceans, rivers, and streams, or is released back into the atmosphere through transpiration. The rest of the surface water empties into lakes, rivers, and streams, and is carried back to the oceans, where the cycle begins again.

Solution

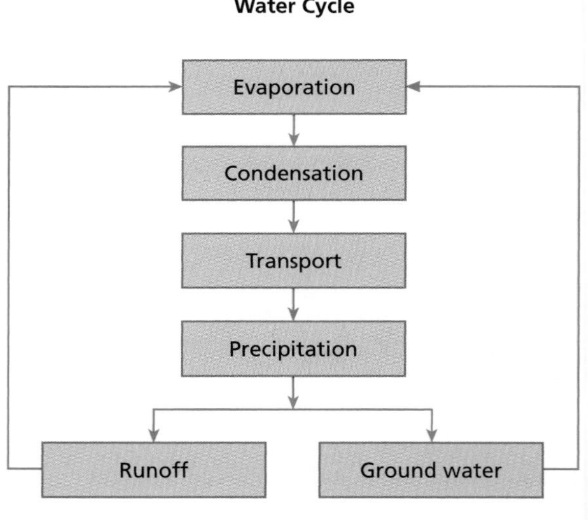

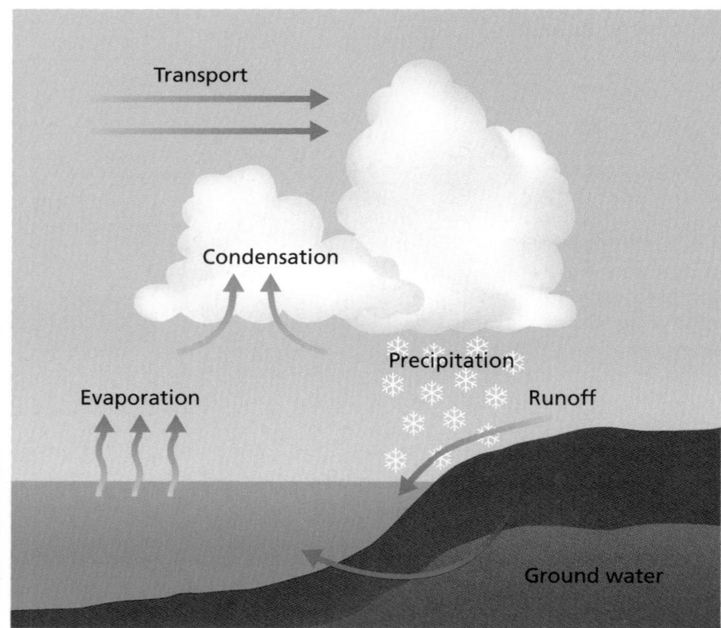

A flow chart is less visually appealing; however, it can contain the same information. A flow chart is shown to the left of the picture above.

Diagrams make it easier to identify unnecessary steps or spot possible interactions and dependencies between the variables in the system. For example, when exploring changes in the current water supply, environmental events can be investigated as possible causes. A diagram would identify the data that are to be examined. Precipitation rates could be compared with historical data and, if the changes were recent, factors that might affect runoff, groundwater, or evaporation could be isolated.

NEWTON'S METHOD

Today, any inexpensive calculator will calculate the square root of a number. However, before calculators were readily available, tables, slide rules, or pencil-and-paper procedures were used to find the square root of a number.

algorithm—a step-by-step procedure for solving a problem or carrying out a process

Newton's Method is an **algorithm** for finding the square root of any number. The following description shows the step-by-step process that uses Newton's Method to compute $\sqrt{5}$.

Description of Steps	Mathematical Result
A. Set up the equation $x = \frac{x_0^2 + a}{2x_0}$ in which a is the number whose root you are trying to find and x_0 is any reasonable estimate of the root's value. Calculate x.	Since the value of $\sqrt{5}$ is to be calculated, $a = 5$. A reasonable estimate of the value of $\sqrt{5}$ is 2, so $x_0 = 2$. From the equation, $x = \frac{2^2 + 5}{2(2)} = \frac{9}{4}$.
B. Calculate x^2.	$x^2 = \left(\frac{9}{4}\right)^2 = 2.25^2 = 5.0625$
C. If the value for x^2 is close enough to 5, stop. Otherwise go to Step D.	This is reasonably close to the desired result, but it can be improved.
D. Substitute the result for x into x_0 and repeat the process.	$x = \frac{x_0^2 + a}{2x_0}$ $= \frac{2.25^2 + 5}{2(2.25)}$ $\doteq 2.236111$
E. Repeat Steps B and C with this new value of x.	$2.236\,111^2 \doteq 5.000\,193$ This is very close to the desired result, so stop.

iterative process—a process in which an algorithm is repeated using a previous result

This algorithm is an example of an **iterative process**. In an iterative process, a series of steps is repeated using the previously computed approximation to calculate the next approximation. The flow chart for this process appears on the following page.

Example 3 Newton's Method

Create a flow chart that illustrates Newton's Method for finding the square root of a number.

Solution

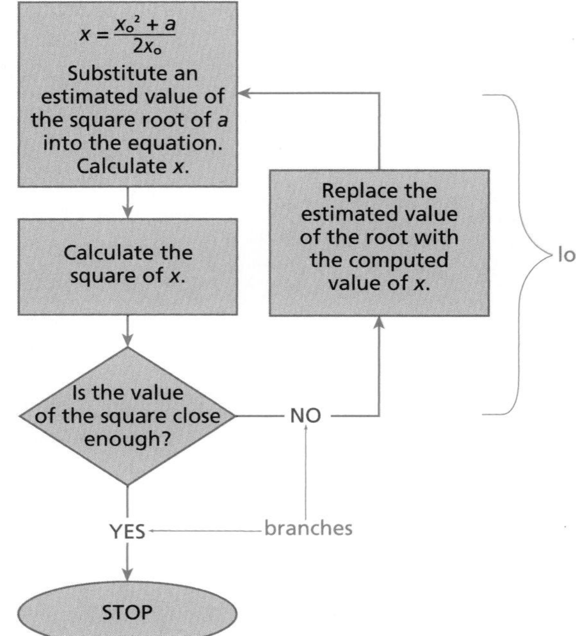

The sequence of steps that are repeated as a result of the decision made in the diamond is called a **loop**. Other paths that may be selected as a result of the decision are called **branches**.

loop—a part of an algorithm that is to be repeated

branches—a part of an algorithm that follows a decision

Computer programmers frequently use flow charts to assist in troubleshooting or debugging programs. It is common during the development process to make a simple, logical error in the order in which the commands are executed. If the commands are spelled properly, using the correct syntax, a computer will be unable to identify the problem. Only a human being, with the use of a flow chart, will be able to identify and correct the problem.

KEY IDEAS

flow chart—a representation of a process using symbols and directed line segments. Each step is represented by either

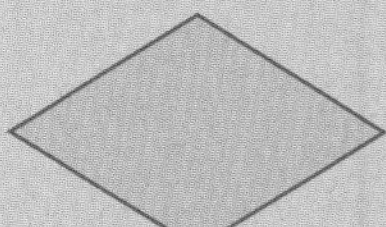

a rectangle, which contains a description of the step, or,

a diamond, which contains a decision to be made.

algorithm—a step-by-step procedure for solving a problem or carrying out a process

iterative process—a process in which an algorithm is repeated using a previous result

loop—steps in a process that are repeated

branch—a place in a process where one of several alternative paths is chosen, depending on the result of some test or condition

6.1 Exercises

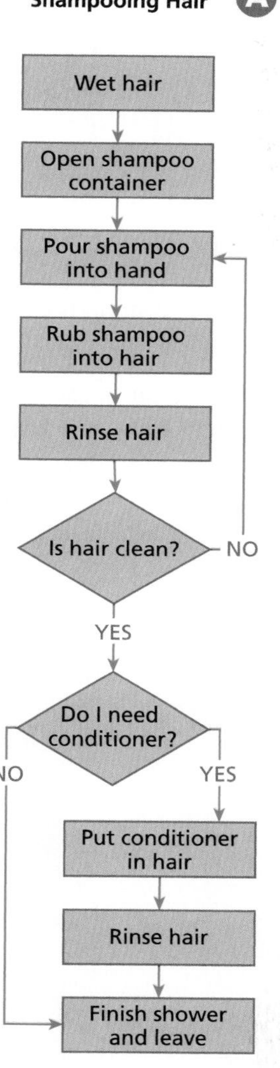

1. **Knowledge and Understanding** The flow chart in the margin represents the activities and decisions a person might make when shampooing hair.
   (a) Copy the flow chart and circle the branching points in the process.
   (b) Identify the loops in the process.
   (c) Modify the flow chart to include any additional steps or decisions you make when you shampoo your hair.
2. Draw a flow chart to represent the process you use to purchase a soft drink from a vending machine.
3. **Communication** Draw a flow chart to represent the process of filling an automobile with gasoline.
4. What do the diamond shapes in a flow chart represent?
5. Create a verbal description of the steps outlined in each of the following flow charts.
   (a)

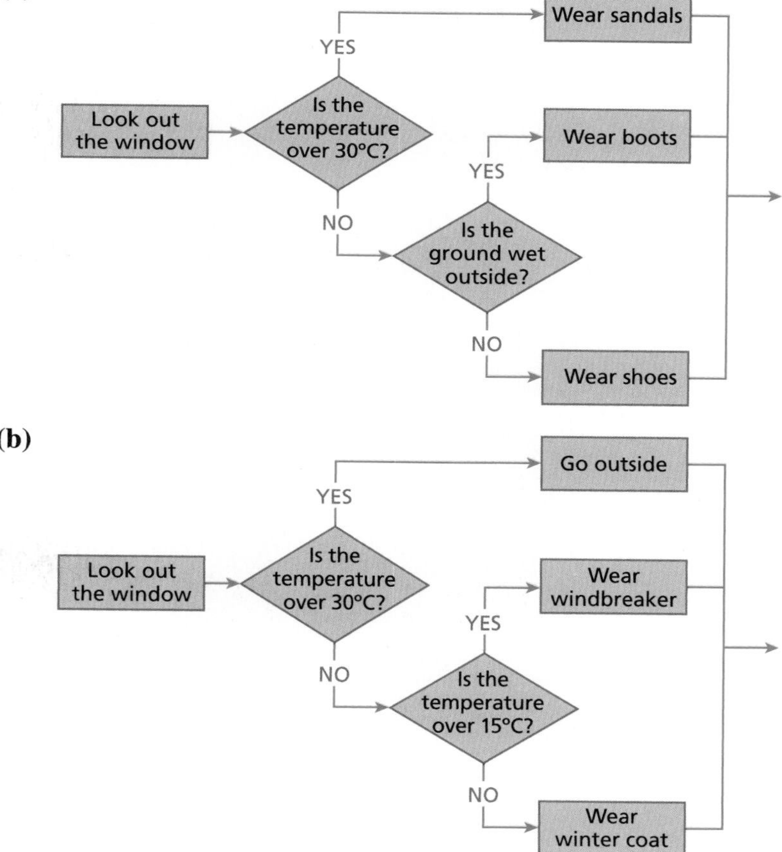

(c)

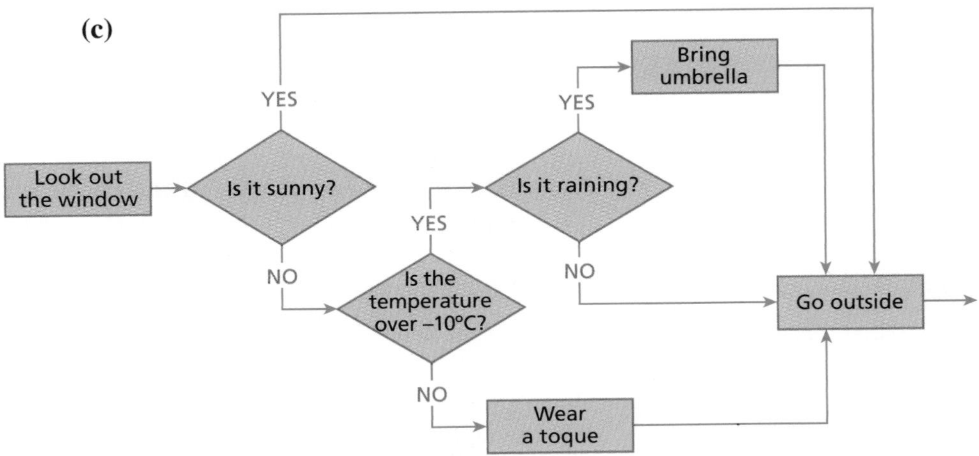

B **6.** Combine the three flow charts in Question 5 into one chart, eliminating any unnecessary steps.

7. **Application** Nitrogen is a large component of the breathable air in the atmosphere and is essential for life on Earth. However, excessive or inadequate supplies of nitrogen can be harmful. The following picture illustrates the cycle by which nitrogen is absorbed and released in the closed environmental system of an aquarium. Construct a flow chart to represent this nitrogen cycle.

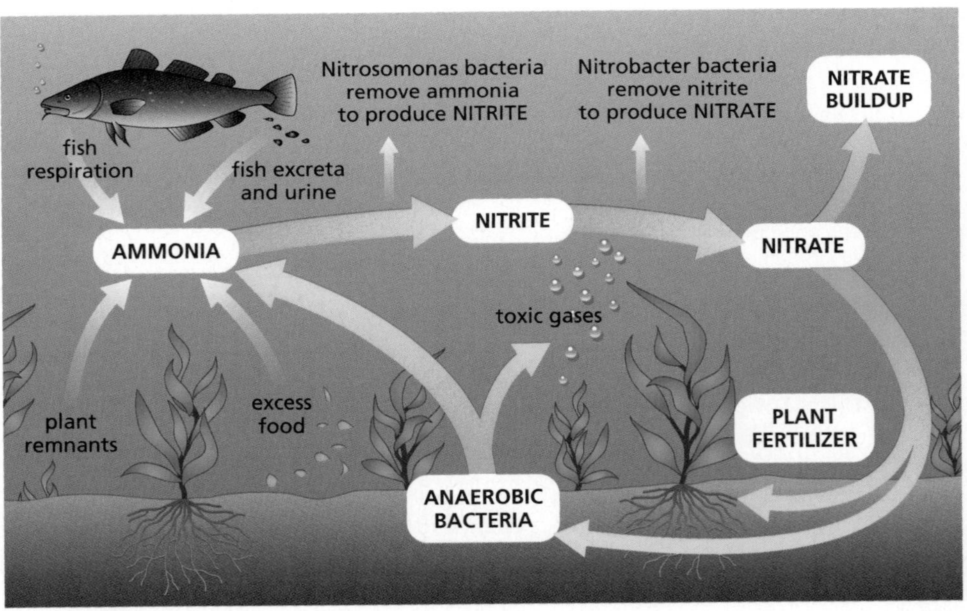

8. Create a flow chart that illustrates the steps a bank machine (ATM) performs in processing a cash withdrawal.

Think about Question 9

Can you find any flaws with this algorithm? How could they be corrected?

9. The following algorithm can be used to find the smallest divisor of an integer. Draw a flow chart to represent it.

(i) If the integer is even, the divisor is 2.
(ii) If it is not even, compute the square root of the integer.
(iii) Set the guess for the divisor to 3.
(iv) If the guess is not an exact divisor, add 2 to the guess and check again.
(v) If the guess for the divisor is an exact divisor, you are done. If the guess is greater than the square root of the integer, indicate that the number is prime.

10. Draw a flow chart to represent the process you would use to look up the term *flow chart* in a dictionary.

11. A Sierpinski Gasket is a fractal constructed from a triangle. The triangle is divided into fourths by joining the midpoints of the sides, as shown in the diagram below. The middle triangle is then removed. The process is then repeated for each of the remaining triangles, continuing indefinitely. Draw a flow chart that illustrates this process being repeated a total of six times.

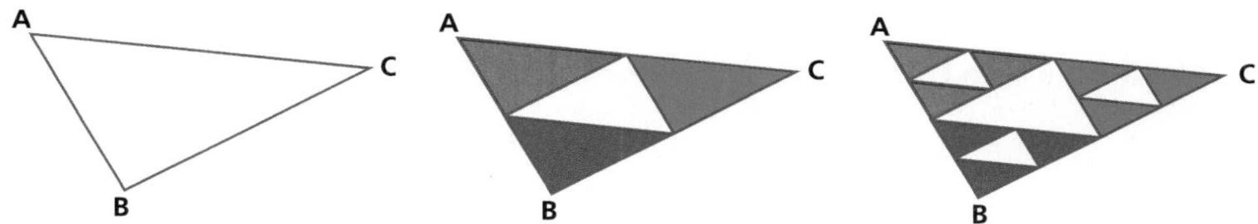

12. Another algorithm for producing a Sierpinski Gasket begins with a square. The square is divided into four congruent smaller squares. The bottom left square is removed. This process is repeated for each of the remaining small squares.

(a) Construct a flow chart to illustrate this process being repeated a total of 10 times.
(b) **Thinking, Inquiry, Problem Solving** Modify the flow chart to include a calculation of the total area removed from the original square following each iteration.

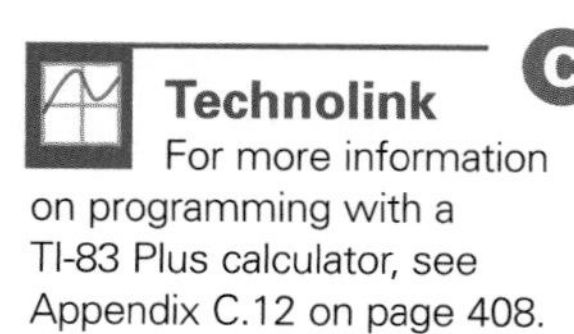

Technolink For more information on programming with a TI-83 Plus calculator, see Appendix C.12 on page 408.

13. Use the programming language on a TI-83 Plus calculator, or any other suitable language that will execute the task illustrated in the flow chart that follows.

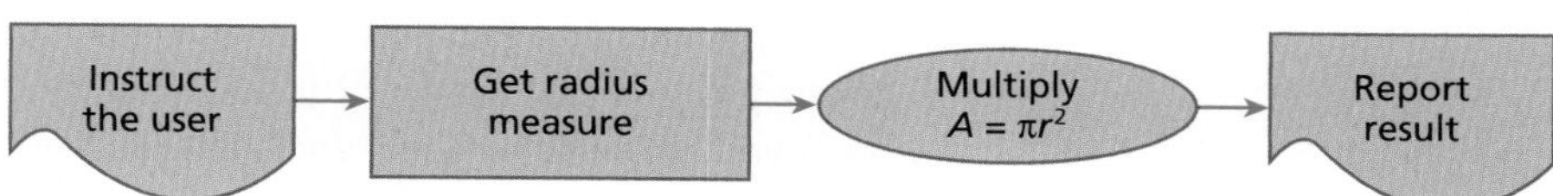

14. To further outline the procedure illustrated in Question 13, create a flow chart for each of the four steps of the program. Be sure to use the appropriate element for each step in the flow chart.

15. Programmers frequently use flow charts to summarize the function of a program or routine. Take the following code and create a flow chart that summarizes its function.

```
void check_noise(void)
{int noise;

/*Collect Data*/
    printf("Enter noise level in decibels: ");
    scanf ("%d", &noise);

/*Classify noise levels */
if (noise <=50)
    printf("At %d decibels a noise seems quiet.\n",
    noise);
else if (noise <= 70)
    printf("At %d decibels a noise is distracting.\n",
    noise);
else if (noise <= 90)
    printf("At %d decibels a noise is loud.\n", noise);
else if (noise <= 110)
    printf("At %d decibels a noise is very loud.\n",
    noise);
else
    printf("At %d decibels a noise is painful and will
    cause permanent damage.\n", noise);}
```

Think about Computer Programming

Flow charts for computer programs use the following conventions:

Writing that is sent to the screen or printer is contained in a square with a curled bottom

Decisions are written in diamonds

Functions and procedures are written in rectangles

Instructions to start or stop are written in ovals

ADDITIONAL ACHIEVEMENT CHART QUESTIONS

16. **Knowledge and Understanding** Create a flow chart that illustrates the following process.

    To heat a can of tomato soup, open the can and pour the contents into a large microwavable bowl. Mix in one can of milk and stir well. Place the bowl of soup in the microwave and heat at high power for 90 seconds. Stir the soup and then heat at high power for another 90 seconds. Pour into individual bowls and serve.

17. **Application** Create a flow chart that illustrates the process of playing a videotape in a TV/VCR. Allow for rewinding the tape, if necessary, checking if there is already a cassette in the VCR, and so on.

18. **Thinking, Inquiry, Problem Solving** Eduardo has to buy solution for his contact lenses and diapers for his baby brother; he has to drop off a film to be developed in one hour, and then pick up the pictures; and he has to buy a newspaper, drop off dry cleaning, and eat lunch.
    (a) Does the order in which he completes these tasks matter? Explain.
    (b) How could Eduardo streamline the completion of these tasks?
    (c) Draw a flow chart illustrating the optimal arrangement.

19. **Communication** In what way(s) is a family tree similar to a flow chart? How is it different? Explain.

Chapter Problem

How Much Time Will It Take to Build This House?

Part of the planning associated with building a house involves creating a detailed list of activities that have to take place before, during, and after the construction process.

CP1. The table below lists a series of tasks and decisions associated with the construction of a house. Draw a flow chart to illustrate the process.

Task	Description	Prerequisite Task(s)
Start	Acquire land	
A	Stake lines and grades	none
B	Clear site of trees, etc., and do rough grading	A
C	Install service for all utilities	B
D	Excavate	A
E	Lay foundation, pour basement, and then backfill	D
F	Frame doors, walls, and roof	C, E
G	Shingle roof	F
H	Install doors and windows	F
I	Build exterior wall surfaces	G, H
J	Rough-in ductwork, plumbing, and electrical	F
K	Install drywall	J
L	Paint	H, K, N
M	Do finish carpentry	K, L
N	Do plumbing, heating, and electrical finish work	J
O	Install flooring	M
P	Complete legal work and transfer of ownership	O
Finish		

6.2 Using Diagrams to Represent and Analyze Relationships

In addition to flow charts, there are other visual tools that can be used to represent interactions. In this section, you will learn about more sophisticated tools for summarizing and analyzing relationships.

CAUSE-AND-EFFECT DIAGRAMS

Why do students occasionally get questions on a test wrong? There are many factors that might be at work for any particular student. Here is a partial list:

- The student experienced a conflict with another person that led to an inability to concentrate on the test.
- The student had poor study habits and was not well-prepared for the test.
- The test required technology with which the student was unfamiliar.
- The student had difficulty understanding the textbook.
- The student suffered from test anxiety and simply "blanked out" during the test.

In 1943, Kaoru Ishikawa developed the following **cause-and-effect (CE) diagram** to list the causes and sub-causes of a student missing questions on a test. This diagram was used to analyze the results of a brainstorming session during which possible causes of student test failure were explored.

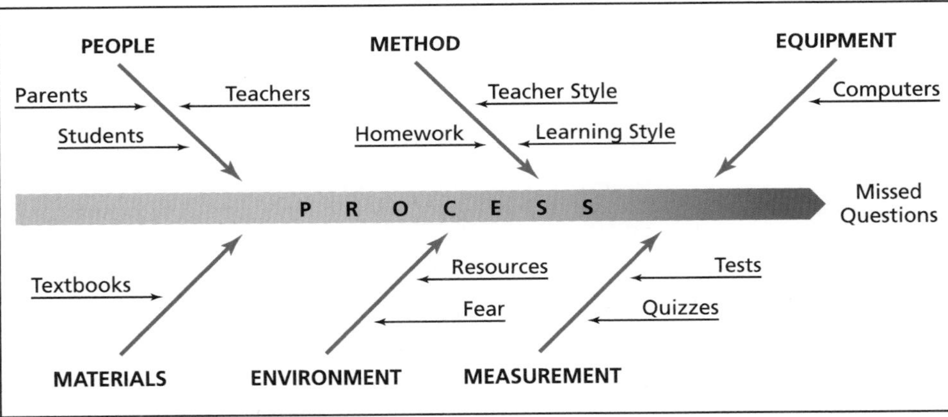

Because of its resemblance to the skeleton of a fish, a cause-and-effect diagram is sometimes called a *fishbone diagram.*

Example 1 Analyzing Causes

Suppose you noticed that the leaves on some of the nearby trees were turning yellow in mid-summer. What might cause this to happen? Create a cause-and-effect diagram to show possible causes.

Solution

There are three steps to the construction of a cause-and-effect diagram.

Step 1 Write down the particular event that is to be investigated. Then, draw the main arrow, or *backbone*, leading to the event. In this case, the event is Leaf Yellowing.

Leaf Yellowing

Step 2 List all the broad categories for further research. First, brainstorm a substantial list of possible causes. Then, develop a list of potential causes.

- flooding
- an insect
- animals
- tree age
- insufficient moisture
- drought
- chemicals in the soil
- a bacterium
- insufficient sunlight
- a fungus
- soil quality
- insecticide use

It appears that the causes fall under the general categories of sunlight, moisture, chemicals, animals, infection, and age. These categories form the first level of connections.

? Think about Categories

How does stating a set of categories influence the research you would carry out to determine the real cause of leaf yellowing?

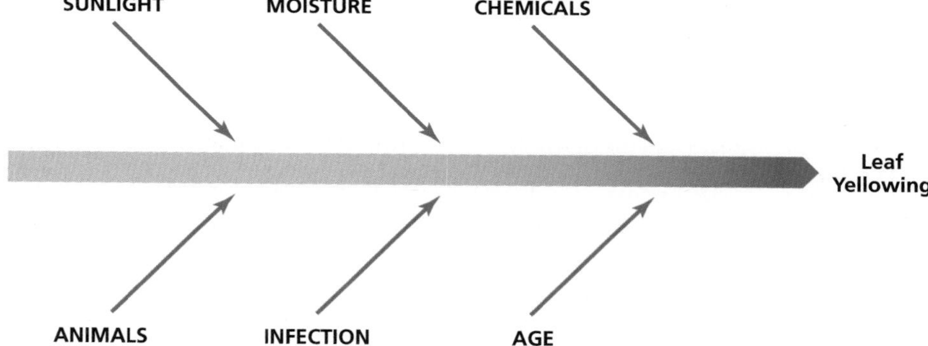

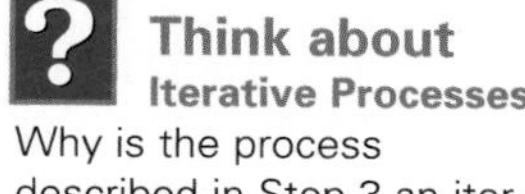

Why is the process described in Step 3 an iterative process?

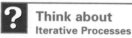

Project Connection

If your course project involves trying to identify the causes of a particular event, one of the first things you should do is brainstorm possible causes and then use a cause-and-effect diagram to categorize, group, and display these possible causes.

Step 3 Organize all the detailed potential causes under each of the broad categories you identified in the previous step. Explore each cause to see if there are any underlying sub-causes that could connect to it. The following partially completed cause-and-effect diagram shows how some of the sub-causes related to sunlight can be added to the diagram.

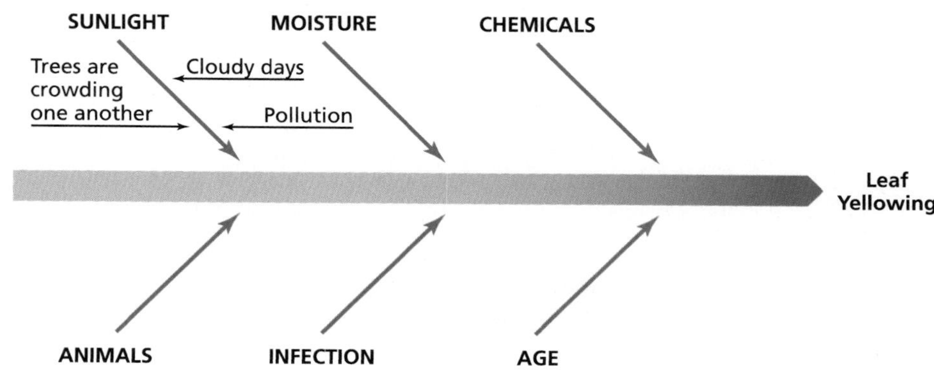

? Think about The Cause-and-Effect Diagram
Brainstorm some additional possible causes. Do all the possible causes fit into the existing broad categories?

Now copy and complete the cause-and-effect diagram. Add to the diagram as you feel it is necessary. For example, you might consider the sub-cause "Trees are crowding one another," identify possible causes for this, and add them to the diagram.

NETWORK DIAGRAMS

network diagram—a picture representation of relationships made of nodes (points), edges (branches), and contained regions

Special diagramming methods have been developed to help in visualizing systems such as the flow of information within an organization, the interconnections among people, and the hierarchy of responsibility within a company or government. These diagrams are called **network diagrams**.

Example 2 Using Network Diagrams

A teacher asked students in a class to list the other students with whom each would like to work. Suppose the following table reflects the results.

Would work with ...	Barb	Amir	Ken	Rene	Sean
Barb		+	+	–	+
Amir	–		+	+	–
Ken	+	–		–	–
Rene	+	+	+		+
Sean	+	–	+	+	

A "+" indicates that the person whose name appears at the start of a row would work with the person listed at the top of a column. A "–" indicates an unwillingness to work with that person. The table shows that Barb will work with Amir, Ken, and Sean, but not with Rene. Create a network diagram to analyze the results.

Solution

directed graph—a graph with arrowheads to assign direction to the edges (**digraph**)

node—a vertex of a graph

A special network diagram called a **directed graph** can be constructed to graphically depict the preferred partnerships. Place the name of each student at a **node** on the graph and connect the names using edges with arrowheads to indicate who "would work with" whom.

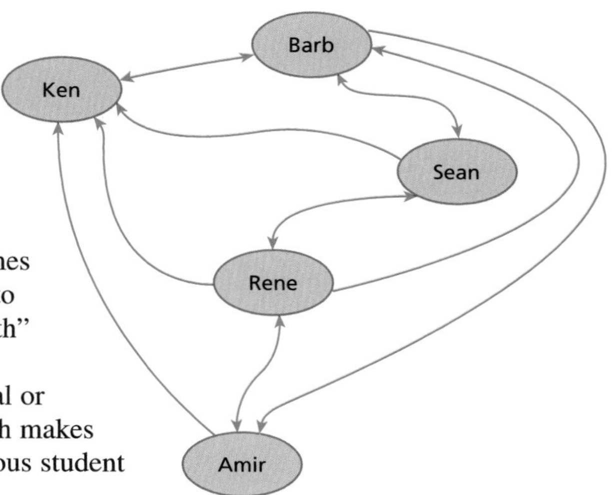

The following more formal or systematic version of the graph makes it a little easier to see the various student preferences.

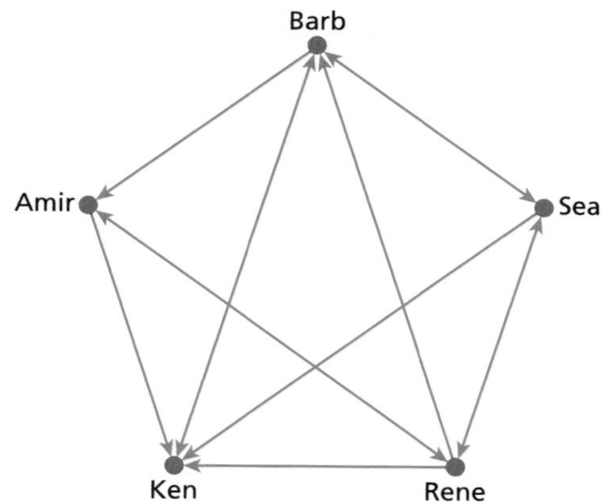

It is easy to see from the graph or from the table that everyone is willing to work with Ken, but that he is willing to work only with Barb. The graph is actually superior to the table since it readily shows four edges directed to Ken's node, but only one going out from that node. This would suggest that the teacher should initially pair Ken with Barb, and then work out other possible groupings afterward.

Project Connection

If your course project involves working with a complex system, a digraph may help you identify and analyze the existence and the strength of relationships, connections, or dependencies within the system. It may also help you present a convincing argument for your thesis question.

Example 3 Using Tree Diagrams

The fact that you are enrolled in this math course suggests you did some research into the courses you need for acceptance into a post-secondary program. Each year, you make a decision about which courses to take. Create a tree diagram to represent the decision criteria you could use to plan mathematics course selections from Grades 10 to 12.

Solution

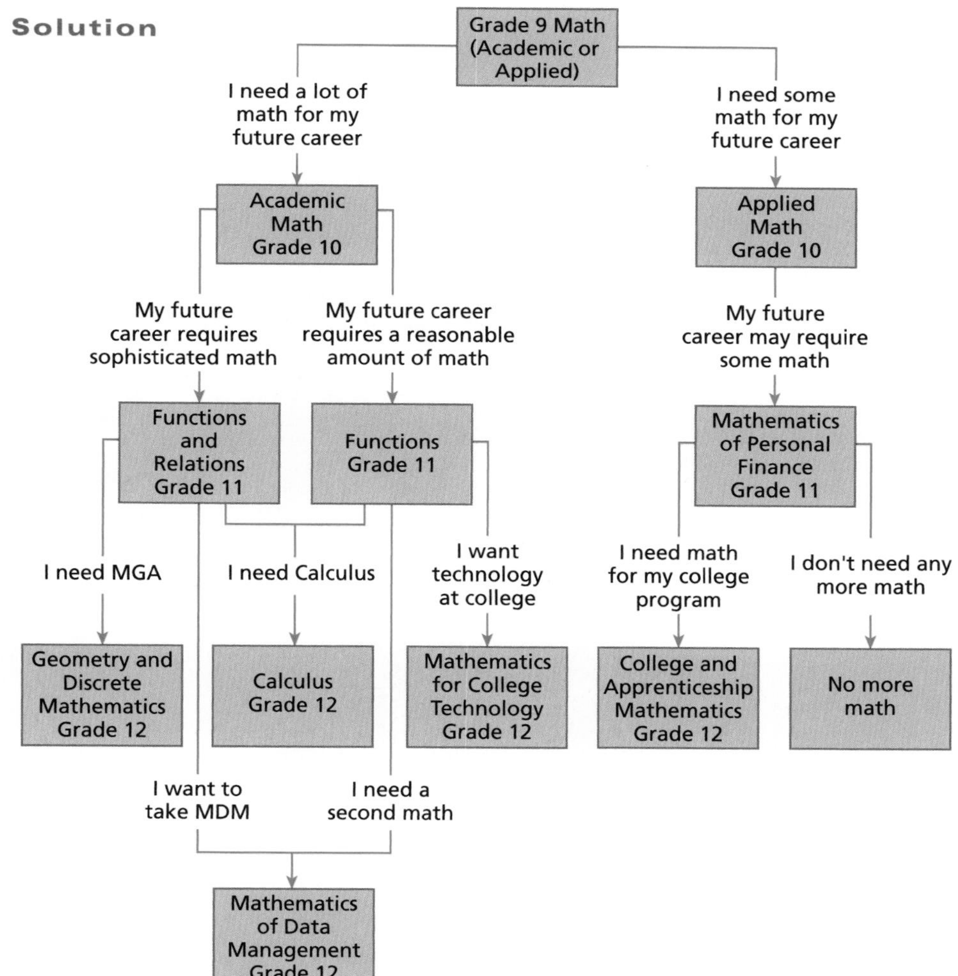

Think about Tree Diagrams

Why is a tree diagram considered a digraph?

Project Connection

If your course project involves analyzing the impact of a series of decisions, analyzing the overall effect of a series of dependent events, or examining a system that has a hierarchical order, a tree diagram will help you see, and demonstrate to others, the structure in the system.

Think about Organizational Charts

To whom is the Minister of Natural Resources responsible? In what way can this organization chart be considered a digraph?

Example 4 Using Organization Charts

A special kind of tree diagram is often used to represent the flow of information or the hierarchy of responsibility within an organization. When a tree diagram is used this way, it is called an **organization chart**.

The Government of Canada published the following organization chart to help citizens understand the structure of responsibility within the Ministry of Natural Resources. Individuals or departments report, and are accountable, to the people or departments above them in the chart.

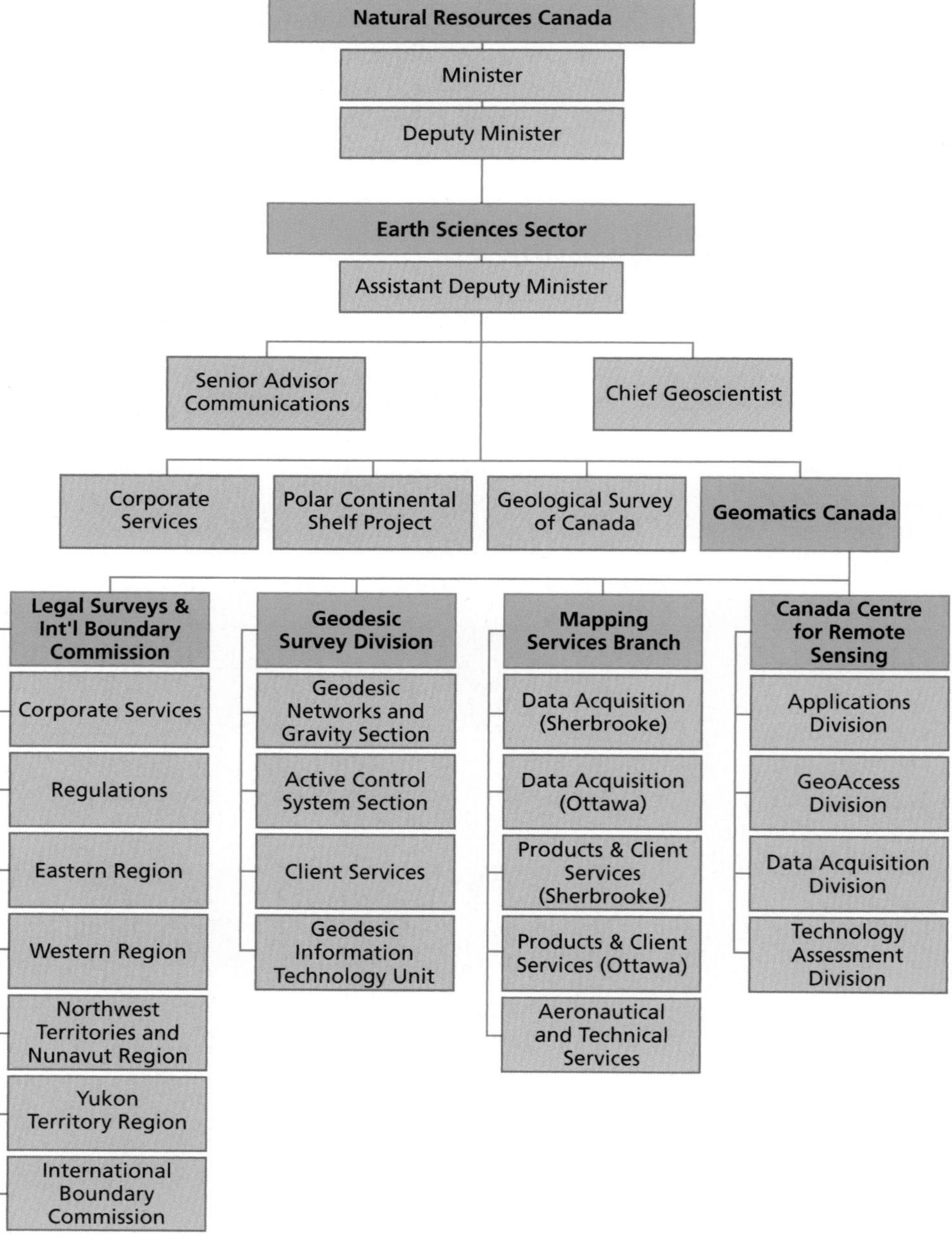

KEY IDEAS

Cause-and-Effect Diagrams

- Helps group the underlying causes of an event into categories.
- Often employed after brainstorming sessions during which all possible causes have been explored.
- Creating a cause-and-effect diagram usually involves three steps:
  - Use the effect to form the backbone of the diagram.
  - Organize the possible causes into broad categories, and then use these categories to form the first level of connections.
  - Connect the detailed possible causes to the categories in which they are best placed to complete the diagram, thus forming a second level of connections. If the detailed possible causes can be broken down into sub-causes, connect these to their more general causes, thus forming a third level of connections.

Network Diagram or Graph

- A picture representation of relationships made of nodes (points) that represent entities, and edges (branches) that represent relationships.
- Arrowheads are used to show the directions of the relations whenever present. The resulting graph is called a directed graph or digraph.

Tree Diagrams and Organization Charts

- Digraphs are used to represent a hierarchical organization or the sequential flow through a series of decisions.
- Steps or objects higher on the diagram are assumed to take precedence over those that appear below them.

6.2 Exercises

1. Brainstorm at least six different factors that may affect the following topics.
(a) your health
(b) the price of gasoline
(c) your class grade
(d) box office success of a major motion picture
(e) your choice of a new car
(f) the winner of the student council presidential elections

2. **Application** Using each topic in Question 1 as a backbone, create a cause-and-effect diagram showing the factors you collected as the first level of connections.

3. **Communication** Explain the difference between a tree diagram and a cause-and-effect diagram.

4. An e-mail virus was first received by Elliot. His computer sent it to Jeri and Hanne. Jeri sent it to Kofi, Giovanni, Quentin, and Amy, while Hanne sent it to Devin and Jacob.
   (a) Illustrate this scenario with a diagram.
   (b) If Hanne also sent the virus back to Elliot, what kind of diagram would be needed?

5. A box of candy has two cherry-filled, two caramel-filled, and two coconut-filled chocolates. Draw a tree diagram that illustrates the first three possible selections from the box.

B

6. **Knowledge and Understanding** A typical secondary school has a principal, one or two vice-principals, secretaries, custodians, heads of departments, teachers, and students. Construct an organization chart to represent the structure of responsibilities in your school.

7. Suppose your school's student council showed you the following list of causes for poor attendance at school dances.
   - ticket price
   - loudness
   - quality of posters
   - transportation
   - music selection
   - time of dance
   - student interest
   - location
   - quality of DJ
   - promotion
   - other non-school activities
   - supervision

   Develop categories for the factors listed above, and then construct a cause-and-effect diagram to help the student council analyze the possible causes. Add any additional causes you think are possible.

8. The chart shows the available daily connections between cities offered by a regional airline. Draw a digraph to represent the available routes.

From/To	Calgary	Hamilton	Edmonton	Regina	Ottawa
Calgary		N	Y	Y	Y
Hamilton	N		N	N	Y
Edmonton	Y	N		N	Y
Regina	N	N	N		Y
Ottawa	Y	Y	Y	Y	

9. A family tree is a kind of tree diagram that shows the line of descent from an ancestor. Research your relatives as far back as you are able and construct a family tree based on your data.

10. Application

(a) This textbook is organized into several chapters. Each chapter is further organized into several sections. Draw a tree diagram using the chapter and section titles to illustrate the organization of the text.

(b) The work in some of the chapters depends on the completion of the work in other chapters. Other chapters are independent. Modify the tree diagram to create a digraph or organization chart that represents the dependencies between the chapters.

11. Draw a network diagram to represent the tasks that you must finish in order to complete your course project. Remember to use directed edges to illustrate their interconnections.

12. Visit an Internet Web site related to your course project's topic. Follow the links and construct a tree diagram that illustrates the organization of the various Web pages and their links.

C **13. Thinking, Inquiry, Problem Solving** Brainstorm the possible causes for the lateness or incompletion of your final course project. Categorize these causes and construct a cause-and-effect diagram. Use the cause-and-effect diagram to form a plan to complete your project on time.

ADDITIONAL ACHIEVEMENT CHART QUESTIONS

Employees at MNO Wholesale can transfer merchandise from warehouses as follows: A to F, B to E, F to D, C to E, D to F, E to G , F to A, and E to B.

14. Knowledge and Understanding Draw a digraph of these relationships.

15. Application

(a) Can the employees send merchandise from A to B?

(b) Can they send merchandise from B to G?

(c) If they have merchandise in warehouse E, which warehouses can they move it to?

16. Thinking, Inquiry, Problem Solving Which links need to be added so that merchandise can be moved between any two warehouses in no more than two steps?

17. Communication

(a) Which warehouse would originally serve best as a central headquarters? Explain.

(b) To which warehouse is it most difficult to send merchandise? Explain.

(c) From which warehouse is it most difficult to send merchandise? Explain.

Chapter Problem

How Much Time Will It Take to Build This House?

CP2. Draw a digraph to represent the relationships between the various jobs listed in the builder's task list for the construction of a house.

Task	Description	Prerequisite Task(s)
Start	Acquire land	
A	Stake lines and grades	none
B	Clear site of trees, etc., and do rough grading	A
C	Install service for all utilities	B
D	Excavate	A
E	Lay foundation, pour basement, and then backfill	D
F	Frame doors, walls, and roof	C, E
G	Shingle roof	F
H	Install doors and windows	F
I	Build exterior wall surfaces	G, H
J	Rough-in ductwork, plumbing, and electrical	F
K	Install drywall	J
L	Paint	H, K, N
M	Do finish carpentry	K, L
N	Do plumbing, heating, and electrical finish work	J
O	Install flooring	M
P	Complete legal work and transfer of ownership	O
Finish		

6.3 Organizing Information with Matrices

The following table shows the breakdown by grade of student enrolment in Ontario schools in the school year 1998–99.

Grade/Age	Public Schools	Separate Schools
JK	66 113	43 734
K	91 149	47 813
Grade 1	96 878	49 834
Grade 2	96 618	48 832
Grade 3	97 185	49 182
Grade 4	94 650	47 169
Grade 5	91 885	45 150
Grade 6	91 812	44 482
Grade 7	93 309	44 403
Grade 8	92 778	44 336
Ungraded (elementary)	1 274	117
Special Education (elementary)	29 755	5 328
Pre-Grade 9 (secondary)	1 444	298
Grade 9	110 437	44 131
Grade 10	113 379	41 939
Grade 11	107 250	40 296
Grade 12	162 147	64 202
Age 21+	11 139	1 174

Source: Web site of Ontario Ministry of Education

DEFINITION OF A MATRIX

The meaning of a value in the table depends on its row and column position. For example, the number circled in red in the table above tells you there were 110 437 Grade 9 students enrolled in public schools in 1998–99.

While the row and column headings are useful, the real information in the table consists of the numbers themselves. The numbers remaining after the row and column headings are removed form a rectangular array of numbers. Such an array is called a **matrix**.

matrix—a rectangular array of numbers set out in rows and columns

The matrix formed from the table appears to the right. A matrix is always bordered by square brackets to distinguish it from other rectangular arrays of information. Columns indicate public and separate schools.

For convenience, a matrix is labelled with a single capital letter, in this case, P. The lowercase letter p is used to refer to the individual entries in the matrix. Subscripts indicate the row and column position. For example, the number circled in red is in the fourteenth row and first column. Thus, $p_{14\,1} = 110\,437$. The number circled in blue is referred to as $p_{3\,2} = 49\,834$. It is in row 3, column 2.

Since this matrix has 18 rows and 2 columns, it is called an 18-by-2 matrix; these numbers are known as the dimensions of the matrix.

columns indicate public and separate schools

$$P = \begin{bmatrix} 66\,113 & 43\,734 \\ 91\,149 & 47\,813 \\ 96\,878 & \boxed{49\,834} \\ 96\,618 & 48\,832 \\ 97\,185 & 49\,182 \\ 94\,650 & 47\,169 \\ 91\,885 & 45\,150 \\ 91\,812 & 44\,482 \\ 93\,309 & 44\,403 \\ 92\,778 & 44\,336 \\ 1\,274 & 117 \\ 29\,755 & 5\,328 \\ 1\,444 & 298 \\ \boxed{110\,437} & 44\,131 \\ 113\,379 & 41\,939 \\ 107\,250 & 40\,296 \\ 162\,147 & 64\,202 \\ 11\,139 & 1\,174 \end{bmatrix}$$

rows indicate grade and age

? Think about Matrix Labels

The elements in the enrolment matrix would be labelled as follows:

$$P = \begin{bmatrix} p_{1\,1} & p_{1\,2} \\ p_{2\,1} & p_{2\,2} \\ p_{3\,1} & p_{3\,2} \\ \cdot & \cdot \\ \cdot & \cdot \\ \cdot & \cdot \\ p_{17\,1} & p_{17\,2} \\ p_{18\,1} & p_{18\,2} \end{bmatrix}$$

Explain how the letters and numbers are used.

Matrix Terminology

In general, if a matrix A has m rows and n columns, it is called an m-by-n matrix. The variables m and n represent the dimensions of the matrix.

The entry, a, in row i and column j is represented as $a_{i\,j}$.

Example 1 Row and Column Operations

What was the total number of Ontario students in each grade or age category in 1998–99?

Solution 1 *No technology required*

Since each row in the matrix corresponds to one of the grade/age categories, each **row sum** will provide the total number of students enrolled at each grade/age level. Similarly, each **column sum** will provide the total enrolment for either the public or separate school systems.

row sum—the sum of the elements in one row of a matrix

column sum—the sum of the elements in one column of a matrix

Solution 2 *Using spreadsheet software*

For simple computations with large matrices, a spreadsheet is a useful tool. The spreadsheet that follows shows the formulas required to calculate the row sums and the column sums for the 1998–99 matrix of student enrolments.

Think about Spreadsheets
What formula would find the combined total of all students enrolled in both school systems for 1998–99?

	A	B	C
1	66113	43734	=SUM(A1:B1)
2	91149	47813	=SUM(A2:B2)
3	96878	49834	=SUM(A3:B3)
4	96618	48832	=SUM(A4:B4)
5	97185	49182	=SUM(A5:B5)
6	94650	47169	=SUM(A6:B6)
7	91885	45150	=SUM(A7:B7)
8	91812	44482	=SUM(A8:B8)
9	93309	44403	=SUM(A9:B9)
10	92778	44336	=SUM(A10:B10)
11	1274	117	=SUM(A11:B11)
12	29755	5328	=SUM(A12:B12)
13	1444	298	=SUM(A13:B13)
14	110437	44131	=SUM(A14:B14)
15	113379	41939	=SUM(A15:B15)
16	107250	40296	=SUM(A16:B16)
17	162147	64202	=SUM(A17:B17)
18	11139	1174	=SUM(A18:B18)
19	=SUM(A1:A18)	=SUM(B1:B18)	

Technolink
For more information on using formulas in spreadsheets, see Appendix E.1 on page 425.

Solution 3 *Using a TI-83 Plus calculator*

Use the following procedure to find the row sums:

- Enter the values from the matrix columns into $\mathbf{L_1}$ and $\mathbf{L_2}$ using the **STAT EDIT** command.
- Use the arrow-up key to move the insertion point to the top of $\mathbf{L_3}$.
- Enter the formula $\mathbf{L_1 + L_2}$ into the top of $\mathbf{L_3}$. This tells the calculator to add the elements in each row and enter the sums in the same row of $\mathbf{L_3}$.

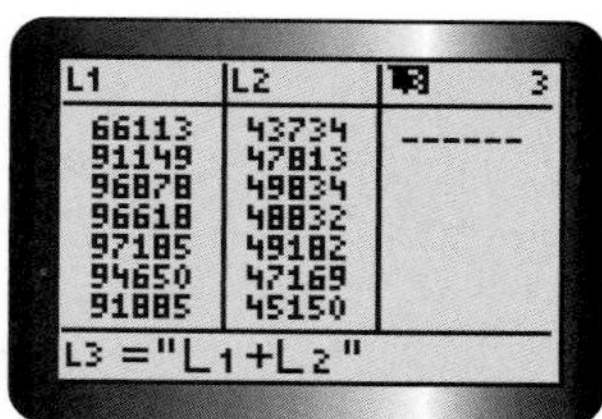

To find the column sums, you must return to the home screen and use the **sum** command. It is found by pressing [2nd] [LIST] and using the arrow keys to scroll over to the **MATH** menu.

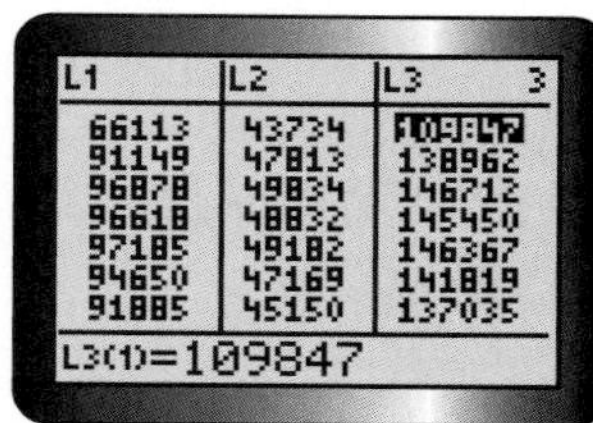

Technolink
To update a column result, enclose the formula in L_3 in quotes (SHIFT+); otherwise, you will need to re-enter the formula to recalculate the column.

Example 2 Multiplying by a Scalar

Suppose the government spent an average of $1500 per student for education. Calculate the expenditure for each grade/age category and school system.

Solution 1 *No technology required*

scalar—a quantity with magnitude but no direction

Multiply each entry in the enrolment matrix by 1500, a **scalar** quantity, to create a new matrix that shows the expenditures. Manually, for this matrix, this would be a very tedious operation.

$$\begin{bmatrix} 1500 \times 66\,113 & 1500 \times 43\,734 \\ 1500 \times 91\,149 & 1500 \times 47\,813 \\ 1500 \times 96\,878 & 1500 \times 49\,834 \\ \cdot & \cdot \\ \cdot & \cdot \\ \cdot & \cdot \end{bmatrix}$$

Technolink For more information on using a TI-83 Plus calculator to work with matrices, see Appendix C.15 on page 411.

Solution 2 *Using a TI-83 Plus calculator*

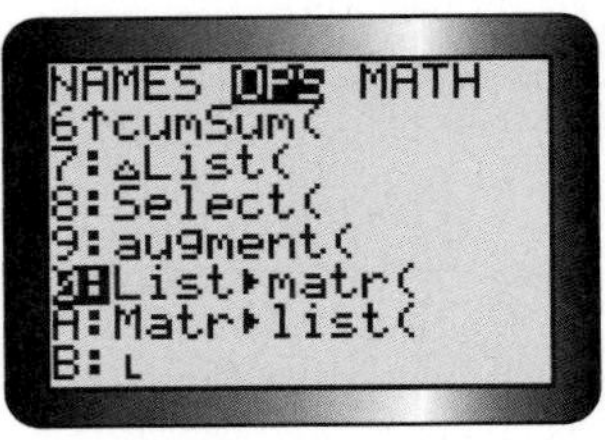

A TI-83 Plus calculator will multiply the elements of a matrix by a scalar. You can create a new matrix and enter the elements into it, or you can create a matrix from the elements in the two separate lists L_1 and L_2. This is done using the [2nd] [LIST] **OPS List▸ matr(** command.

Immediately following the left parenthesis, enter the names, separated by commas, of the lists that will form the columns of the matrix.

To identify the matrix in which the results will be stored, use the **MATRIX NAMES** command. In this case, matrix **[A]** was selected.

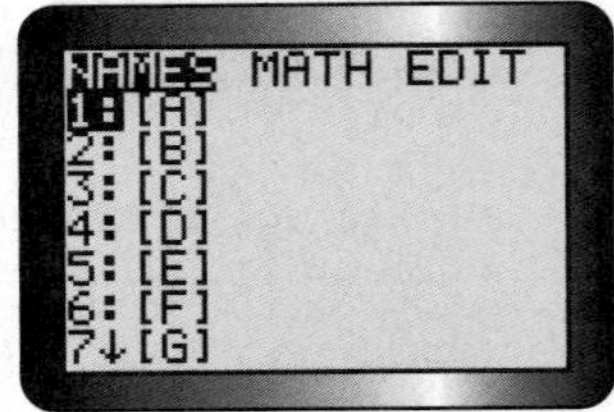

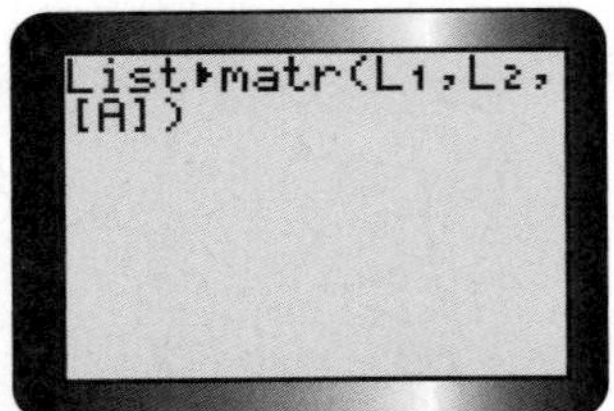

The original matrix **[A]** and the matrix produced by entering the calculation **1500*[A]** appear below. The arrow keys are used to scroll vertically or horizontally so that all the entries can be viewed.

Technolink You may store the results of your matrix calculation in any of the matrices in the NAMES list by using the [STO▸] key.

The multiplication could have been entered as 1500[A]. The use of the * is not required.

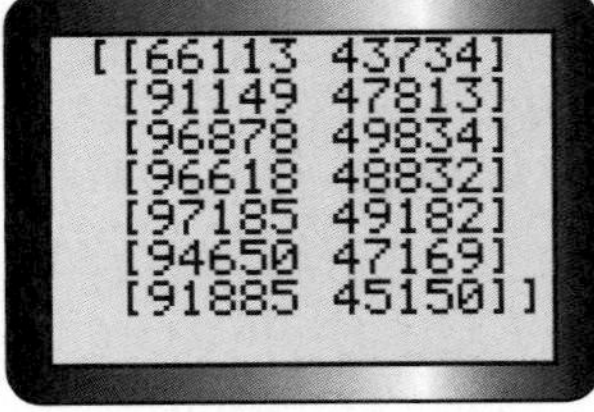

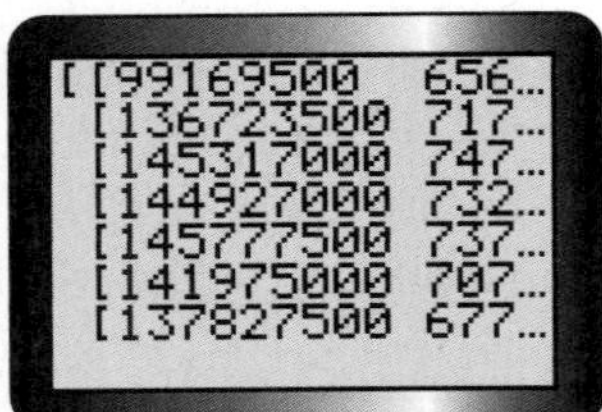

Example 3 Subtracting Matrices

Use the data in the following tables to compute the changes in Ontario student enrolment from 1997–98 to 1998–99.

Student Enrolment in Ontario (1997–1998)		
	Elementary	Secondary
Public Schools		
Male	477 349	266 694
Female	448 599	246 679
Separate Schools		
Male	238 426	93 242
Female	230 065	94 576

Student Enrolment in Ontario (1998–1999)		
	Elementary	Secondary
Public Schools		
Male	486 350	263 190
Female	457 056	242 606
Separate Schools		
Male	239 104	95 159
Female	231 276	96 881

Solution

The changes in enrolment for each category in the table can be calculated by subtracting the values in the 1997–98 table from the corresponding values in the 1998–99 table. Matrices can be used to help you.

Create a matrix for each table. Matrix A contains the data for 1998–99 and matrix B contains the data for 1997–98.

$$A = \begin{bmatrix} 486\ 350 & 263\ 190 \\ 457\ 056 & 242\ 606 \\ 239\ 104 & 95\ 159 \\ 231\ 276 & 96\ 881 \end{bmatrix} \qquad B = \begin{bmatrix} 477\ 349 & 266\ 694 \\ 448\ 599 & 246\ 679 \\ 238\ 426 & 93\ 242 \\ 230\ 065 & 94\ 576 \end{bmatrix}$$

The enrolment changes can be found by creating a new matrix $C = A - B$. To subtract matrices, each element in the second matrix (matrix B) is subtracted from the corresponding element in the first matrix (matrix A) as shown below.

? Think about Subtracting Matrices
Why must the matrices being subtracted have the same dimensions?

$C = A - B$

$$= \begin{bmatrix} 486\ 350 & 263\ 190 \\ 457\ 056 & 242\ 606 \\ 239\ 104 & 95\ 159 \\ 231\ 276 & 96\ 881 \end{bmatrix} - \begin{bmatrix} 477\ 349 & 266\ 694 \\ 448\ 599 & 246\ 679 \\ 238\ 426 & 93\ 242 \\ 230\ 065 & 94\ 576 \end{bmatrix}$$

$$= \begin{bmatrix} 486\ 350 - 477\ 349 & 263\ 190 - 266\ 694 \\ 457\ 056 - 448\ 599 & 242\ 606 - 246\ 679 \\ 239\ 104 - 238\ 426 & 95\ 159 - 93\ 242 \\ 231\ 276 - 230\ 065 & 96\ 881 - 94\ 576 \end{bmatrix}$$

$$= \begin{bmatrix} 9001 & -3504 \\ 8457 & -4073 \\ 678 & 1917 \\ 1211 & 2305 \end{bmatrix}$$

Technolink
For more information on using a TI-83 Plus calculator to add, subtract, or multiply matrices, see Appendix C.16 on page 412.

The calculation can be carried out on a TI-83 Plus calculator.

The enrolment changes are displayed in the table to the right.

Changes in Ontario Student Enrolment from 1997–1998 to 1998–1999		
	Elementary	**Secondary**
Public Schools		
Male	9001	–3504
Female	8457	–4073
Separate Schools		
Male	678	1917
Female	1211	2305

Sum and Difference of Matrices

If matrices A and B have the same dimensions, then

- the sum $S = A + B$ is the matrix formed by adding the entries of matrix A to the corresponding entries of matrix B
$$s_{ij} = a_{ij} + b_{ij}$$
- the difference $D = A - B$ is the matrix formed by subtracting the entries of matrix B from the corresponding entries of matrix A
$$d_{ij} = a_{ij} - b_{ij}$$

Project Connection
You may be gathering large amounts of information for your course project. Much of these data may be in the form of tables of numbers. Matrix operations using spreadsheets or calculators will make computations with these data easier.

KEY IDEAS

matrix—a rectangular array of numbers set out in rows and columns

- The entries or elements in the matrix are labelled according to the row and column in which each appears. For example, the element $a_{3\,7}$ is the value found in row 3 and column 7 of matrix A.
- The dimensions of a matrix correspond to the number of rows and the number of columns in the matrix. For example, a 3-by-5 matrix has 3 rows and 5 columns.

Simple Matrix Operations

- The entries in a row or column of a matrix may be added to form a row sum or a column sum.
- Two matrices of equal dimension may be added or subtracted by adding or subtracting the corresponding entries within each matrix.
- A matrix may be multiplied by a scalar. Each entry in the matrix is multiplied by the same number.

6.3 Exercises

A

1. Given matrices A and B below, find

$$A = \begin{bmatrix} 2 & 4 & 9 \\ 3 & 10 & 0 \\ 4 & 11 & 5 \end{bmatrix} \quad B = \begin{bmatrix} 3 & 5 & 7 & 9 \\ 9 & 25 & 49 & 81 \end{bmatrix} \quad C = \begin{bmatrix} 1 & 2 & 3 \\ 0 & 5 & -1 \\ 1 & 8 & 4 \end{bmatrix}$$

$$D = \begin{bmatrix} -1 & 0 \\ 0 & 3 \end{bmatrix} \quad E = \begin{bmatrix} 2 & 5 \\ 5 & 1 \end{bmatrix} \quad F = \begin{bmatrix} 5 & 2 & -7 & 0 \\ 3 & 9 & 6 & 4 \end{bmatrix}$$

(a) $a_{2\,3}$ **(b)** $c_{3\,2}$ **(c)** $b_{1\,3}$ **(d)** $d_{2\,2}$
(e) the dimensions of matrix A and matrix B
(f) the row sums for the matrix A
(g) the column sums for the matrix B

2. Knowledge and Understanding Using the matrices from Question 1, determine the following if possible.
(a) $3A$ **(b)** $E \times 0.10$ **(c)** $A + C$ **(d)** $A - B$
(e) $D + E$ **(f)** $F - B$ **(g)** $2E - D$ **(h)** $5F - B$

3. Communication Explain why matrices A and B in Question 1 may not be added or subtracted, while matrices A and C may.

4. For matrix A in Question 1, determine the position in the form $a_{i\,j}$ of each of these numbers.
(a) 2 **(b)** 3 **(c)** 0 **(d)** 10 **(e)** 11

B

5. Application Use matrix operations to get career totals for Bobby Orr from the following regular season data. (G: goals, A: assists, Pts: points, PIM: penalties in minutes)

Year	Games	G	A	Pts	PIM
1966–67	61	13	28	41	102
1967–68	46	11	20	31	63
1968–69	67	21	43	64	133
1969–70	76	33	87	120	125
1970–71	78	37	102	139	91
1971–72	76	37	80	117	106
1972–73	63	29	72	101	99
1973–74	74	32	90	122	82
1974–75	80	46	89	135	101
1975–76	10	5	13	18	22
1976–77	20	4	19	23	25
1978–79	6	2	2	4	4

Source: Orr Fan (**http://www.orrfan.com/stats.htm**)
© H. Holman

	Employment		
	Sept. '01	Oct. '01	% Change
Total	15 093.6	15 095.4	0.0
NF & L	212.0	212.9	0.4
PEI	66.0	66.0	0.0
NS	425.6	429.7	1.0
NB	333.8	336.6	0.8
PQ	3 497.1	3 501.7	0.1
ON	5 958.6	5 955.7	0.0
MB	558.7	562.9	0.8
SK	468.9	468.0	–0.2
AB	1 638.9	1 641.3	0.1
BC	1 934.1	1 920.6	–0.7

Source: Statistics Canada, *The Daily,* Nov. 2, 2001

6. **Knowledge and Understanding** In the table to the left, the first column contains the number of people employed in September 2001, the second column contains the data for October 2001, and the third column contains the percent increase from September to October.
   (a) Write matrix E that would contain these data.
   (b) Which number would be found in $e_{6\,1}$? Which province corresponds to this employment data?
   (c) Which element $e_{j\,k}$ in matrix E would contain the October employment statistics for Alberta?

7. The following table lists the number of Canadians 15 years of age or older by their highest degree or certificate.

Definitions and notes	1986	1991	1996
Total	19 634 100	21 304 740	22 628 925
No degree, certificate, or diploma	9 384 100	8 639 900	8 331 615
Secondary (high) school graduation certificate	3 985 820	4 967 325	5 217 205
Trades certificate or diploma	1 989 850	2 342 105	2 372 000
Other non-university certificate or diploma	2 034 485	2 494 460	3 181 840
University certificate or diploma below bachelor level	381 580	441 205	525 560
Bachelor's degree	1 254 250	1 585 775	1 979 460
University certificate or diploma above bachelor level	189 000	264 845	310 820
Medical degree	74 945	90 835	105 050
Master's degree	293 335	394 750	501 505
Earned doctorate	66 955	83 545	103 855

Source: Statistics Canada, 1996 Census *Nation* tables

Use matrix operations to
(a) find the change from 1986 to 1991 in the number who earned a doctorate
(b) verify that the number in the Total row for each year is correct
(c) compute the total amount of money spent obtaining a Bachelor's degree in 1991 and 1996, if the average degree costs $50 000.

8. **Application** The following table summarizes the number of Canadians 15 years of age and older who were involved in a variety of sports activities in 1998.

Sports Activity	Males (1000s)	Females (1000s)
Golf	1325	476
Hockey (ice)	1435	65
Baseball	953	386
Swimming	432	688
Basketball	550	237
Volleyball	394	350
Soccer	550	189
Tennis	434	224
Skiing, downhill/alpine	342	315
Cycling	358	250
Skiing, cross-country/nordic	208	304
Weightlifting	294	140
Badminton	199	204
Football	347	40
Curling	179	133
Bowling, 10 pin	132	150
Softball	118	92
Bowling, 5 pin	78	122

Source: Statistics Canada

(a) Use matrix methods to calculate
  (i) the total number of Canadians who played each sport
  (ii) the total number of males involved in sports activities
  (iii) the total number of females involved in sports activities

(b) Canadians played sports other than those shown in the table above. The total number of males in the original data was 11 937 000 and the total number of females was 12 323 000. Use matrix methods to determine the percent of total males and the percent of total females involved in each of the sports activities reported above.

C **9.** Ever-Green Pine Trees has compiled the following sales data:

	1998	1999	2000	2001
Scotch Pine	58	44	51	39
Douglas Fir	13	15	19	22
Blue Spruce	25	30	22	24

(a) Using matrix methods, determine which year was the best year for sales.
(b) If Scotch Pine were sold for \$25, Douglas Fir for \$40, and Blue Spruce for \$20, which year generated the most revenue?
(c) For every tree that is cut down, the company must plant three in its place. How many of each species of tree needs to be planted to replace the trees sold in the four years recorded above?

10. Consider the following results from the 2000 Summer Olympic Games in Sydney, Australia:

Country	Gold	Silver	Bronze
United States	39	25	33
Russia	32	28	28
China	28	16	15
Australia	16	25	17
Germany	14	17	26
France	13	14	11
Italy	13	8	13
The Netherlands	12	9	4
Cuba	11	11	7
Great Britain	11	10	7

Source: British Broadcasting Corporation (BBC)

(a) Record the results in matrix form.
(b) If a gold medal were worth 5 points, a silver worth 3 points, and a bronze worth 1 point, which country would receive the most points?

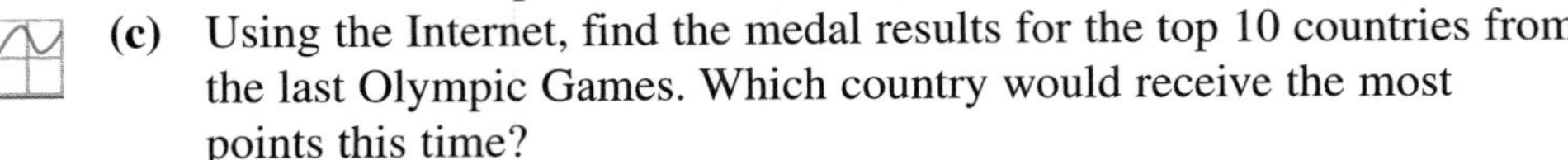

(c) Using the Internet, find the medal results for the top 10 countries from the last Olympic Games. Which country would receive the most points this time?

ADDITIONAL ACHIEVEMENT CHART QUESTIONS

The following chart lists VGY Toy Company's inventory of their top-selling toys in their four local warehouses.

		Warehouses			
		N	E	S	W
Toy	Fizzie Ball	34	40	37	25
	Quaterno	15	22	10	13
	The Baffo Game	27	34	13	22

11. **Knowledge and Understanding** For quality control purposes, the company has decided to select 5% of their inventory for inspection. Using matrix multiplication, determine the number of each kind of toy at each location that is to be selected for inspection.

12. **Application** Using matrix methods, determine the number of toys at each warehouse, as well as the total number of each toy in all four warehouses.

13. **Thinking, Inquiry, Problem Solving** Head office has ordered that no more than 50% of the inventory of any warehouse is to be made up of Fizzie Balls. What exchanges of merchandise are necessary to comply with this directive?

14. **Communication** The following matrix contains the retail price in dollars of the Fizzie Ball, Quaterno, and The Baffo Game, respectively:

$[17.99 \quad 27.95 \quad 22.88]$

Describe how you would determine the value of the inventory in warehouse N.

Chapter Problem

How Much Time Will It Take to Build This House?

CP3. The contractor has determined the number of days and the number of workers required to complete each task in the construction of the house. Use the information in the table below to construct a matrix showing the number of days and workers.

(a) Use the matrix to determine the total number of person days required for each task, as well as the total number of person days needed to complete the project.

(b) If each worker is paid $15/h, estimate the total labour cost for the project.

Task	Description	Duration (days)	Workers
Start	Acquire land	0	2
A	Stake lines and grades	5	2
B	Clear site of trees, etc., and do rough grading	5	4
C	Install service for all utilities	7	3
D	Excavate	6	3
E	Lay foundation, pour basement, and then backfill	8	5
F	Frame doors, walls, and roof	19	6
G	Shingle roof	7	2
H	Install doors and windows	5	2
I	Build exterior wall surfaces	13	3
J	Rough-in ductwork, plumbing, and electrical	17	3
K	Install drywall	20	2
L	Paint	11	1
M	Do finish carpentry	14	1
N	Do plumbing, heating, and electrical finish work	9	3
O	Install flooring	9	2
P	Complete legal work and transfer of ownership	7	1
Finish			

6.4 Matrix Multiplication

Imagine that a builder constructs four different house models in three different cities. The following table shows the number of each model being built in each community.

	Deerfield	Cambridge	Exeter	Lansdowne
Oshawa	11	4	1	3
Milton	6	9	3	4
Port Credit	5	5	5	0

Each model has different design requirements. The number of windows and exterior doors required for each model is summarized below.

	Windows	Doors
Deerfield	16	3
Cambridge	20	4
Exeter	20	4
Lansdowne	12	2

How many windows and doors does the contractor need to order for all the houses that are to be built in each community? First, examine the requirements for the homes to be built in Oshawa. The total number of windows and doors required can be found by calculating the sum of the number of windows and doors required for each model of house being built. The calculations appear below.

Model	Windows	Doors
Deerfield	$11 \times 16 = 176$	$11 \times 3 = 33$
Cambridge	$4 \times 20 = 80$	$4 \times 4 = 16$
Exeter	$1 \times 20 = 20$	$1 \times 4 = 4$
Lansdowne	$3 \times 12 = 36$	$3 \times 2 = 6$
TOTAL	312	59

For the homes in Oshawa, the contractor must order 312 windows and 59 doors. This process would need to be repeated for the homes in Milton and Port Credit. To perform the calculations this way would be rather tedious. Instead, you can simplify it with the use of matrices.

Example 1 Using Matrix Multiplication

Recall that a matrix is a rectangular array of numbers with the row and column headings removed. The tables used to display the information on the previous page can each be written as a matrix. The matrix that provides the number of house models built in each city is a 3-by-4 matrix.

	Deerfield	Cambridge	Exeter	Lansdowne
Oshawa	11	4	1	3
Milton	6	9	3	4
Port Credit	5	5	5	0

$$C = \begin{bmatrix} 11 & 4 & 1 & 3 \\ 6 & 9 & 3 & 4 \\ 5 & 5 & 5 & 0 \end{bmatrix}$$

The information for the window and door requirements for each model can be placed in a 4-by-2 matrix.

	Windows	Doors
Deerfield	16	3
Cambridge	20	4
Exeter	20	4
Lansdowne	12	2

$$W = \begin{bmatrix} 16 & 3 \\ 20 & 4 \\ 20 & 4 \\ 12 & 2 \end{bmatrix}$$

? Think about Matrix Multiplication

- How were the entries in matrices C and W combined to find the total number of windows for Oshawa?
- How were they combined to find the total number of doors for Oshawa?

The results can then be placed in a 3-by-2 matrix.

$$R = \begin{bmatrix} 312 & 59 \\ ? & ? \\ ? & ? \end{bmatrix}$$

Product of Matrices

Matrix R is called the product of matrices C and W. The mathematical symbolism for this is $R = C \times W$.

Each entry in matrix R is calculated using the entries in the other two matrices. The process used to calculate the number of windows and the number of doors for the house to be built in Oshawa will be used to calculate the remainder of the entries.

Recall that the number of windows is $11 \times 16 + 4 \times 20 + 1 \times 20 + 3 \times 12 = 312$. Compare the entries in matrix R to the product of matrices C and D. This shows how the calculation was done.

$$\text{Compare } R = \begin{bmatrix} 312 & 59 \\ ? & ? \\ ? & ? \end{bmatrix} \text{ to } \begin{bmatrix} 11 & 4 & 1 & 3 \\ 6 & 9 & 3 & 4 \\ 5 & 5 & 5 & 0 \end{bmatrix} \times \begin{bmatrix} 16 & 3 \\ 20 & 4 \\ 20 & 4 \\ 12 & 2 \end{bmatrix}.$$

Symbolically, you have the following situation:

$$\begin{bmatrix} r_{1\,1} & r_{1\,2} \\ r_{2\,1} & r_{2\,2} \\ r_{3\,1} & r_{3\,2} \end{bmatrix} = \begin{bmatrix} c_{1\,1} & c_{1\,2} & c_{1\,3} & c_{1\,4} \\ c_{2\,1} & c_{2\,2} & c_{2\,3} & c_{2\,4} \\ c_{3\,1} & c_{3\,2} & c_{3\,3} & c_{3\,4} \end{bmatrix} \times \begin{bmatrix} w_{1\,1} & w_{1\,2} \\ w_{2\,1} & w_{2\,2} \\ w_{3\,1} & w_{3\,2} \\ w_{4\,1} & w_{4\,2} \end{bmatrix}$$

? Think about Matrix Multiplication
Why must the number of entries of each row of matrix *C* be equal to the number of entries of each column of matrix *W*?

The number of windows required for Oshawa is the entry $r_{1\,1}$ and it was calculated as follows:

$$r_{1\,1} = c_{1\,1}\,w_{1\,1} + c_{1\,2}\,w_{2\,1} + c_{1\,3}\,w_{3\,1} + c_{1\,4}\,w_{4\,1}$$

The number of doors required for Oshawa is the row entry $r_{1\,2}$ and it was calculated as $r_{1\,2} = c_{1\,1}\,w_{1\,2} + c_{1\,2}\,w_{2\,2} + c_{1\,3}\,w_{3\,2} + c_{1\,4}\,w_{4\,2}$.

$$\begin{bmatrix} 312 & 59 \\ ? & ? \\ ? & ? \end{bmatrix} = \begin{bmatrix} 11 & 4 & 1 & 3 \\ 6 & 9 & 3 & 4 \\ 5 & 5 & 5 & 0 \end{bmatrix} \times \begin{bmatrix} 16 & 3 \\ 20 & 4 \\ 20 & 4 \\ 12 & 2 \end{bmatrix}$$

inner product—the number that is the sum of the products of each row entry from one matrix with its corresponding column entry from the other matrix.

One entry in the product matrix *R* is the **inner product** of a row from matrix *C* and the corresponding column from matrix *W*.

Matrix Dimensions

In general, if a matrix *A* with *m* rows and *k* columns is multiplied by a matrix *B* with *k* rows and *n* columns, the product will be a matrix *P* with *m* rows and *n* columns.

$$\begin{matrix} \boldsymbol{A} & \times & \boldsymbol{B} & = & \boldsymbol{P} \\ m \times k & & k \times n & & m \times n \end{matrix}$$

same

product dimensions

The remaining elements of the product matrix can be found using similar computations. For example, the total number of doors required for the house to be built in Port Credit is calculated using the following inner product:

? Think about Matrix Multiplication
Why can the matrix product *CW* ($C \times W$) be calculated, but not the product *WC* ($W \times C$)?

$$\begin{bmatrix} 11 & 4 & 1 & 3 \\ 6 & 9 & 3 & 4 \\ 5 & 5 & 5 & 0 \end{bmatrix} \times \begin{bmatrix} 16 & 3 \\ 20 & 4 \\ 20 & 4 \\ 12 & 2 \end{bmatrix} = \begin{bmatrix} 312 & 59 \\ ? & ? \\ ? & ? \end{bmatrix}$$

The value of $r_{3\,2}$ is the result of finding the inner product of row 3 of matrix *C* with column 2 of matrix *W*.

Example 2 Using a TI-83 Plus Calculator

Calculate the number of doors and windows required using matrix multiplication on a TI-83 Plus calculator.

Solution

To edit matrices, press [2nd] [MATRIX] and use the arrow keys to scroll over to the EDIT menu. Press [1] to edit [A].

- Change the dimensions of [A] to 3 × 4.
- Enter the values one at a time, pressing [ENTER] after each. To view the entire matrix, you can use the arrow keys to scroll left or right, up or down.

Technolink For more information on using a TI-83 Plus calculator to work with matrices, see Appendix C.15 and C.16 on pages 411 and 412.

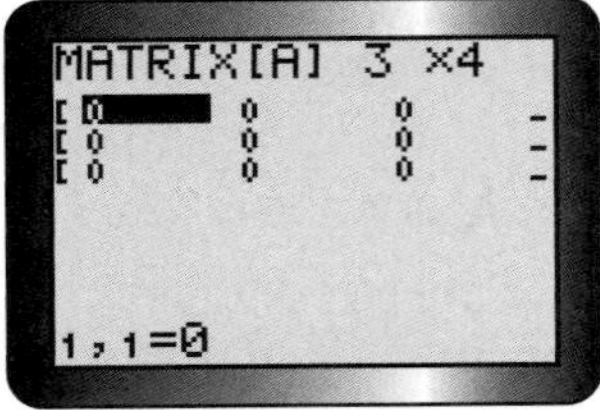

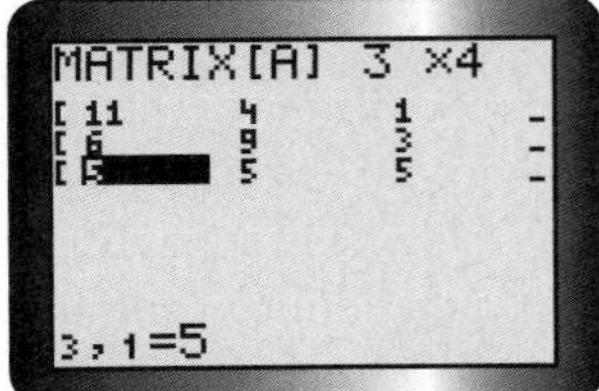

- Use a similar sequence of steps to enter the window/door requirement information from matrix W into matrix [B].

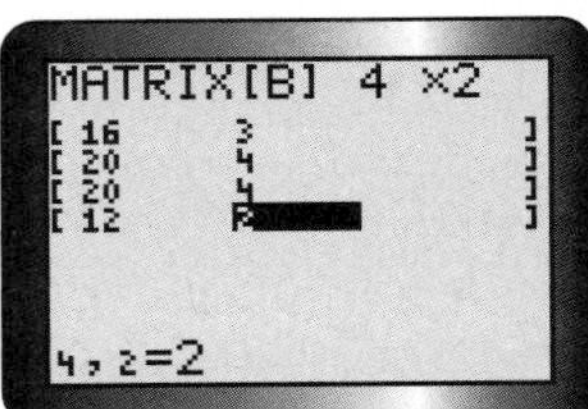

You may now return to the home screen and carry out the product. Press [2nd] [MATRIX] [1] and [2nd] [MATRIX] [2] to make [A] and [B] appear on the screen.

The final results are as follows:

City	Windows	Doors
Oshawa	312	59
Milton	384	74
Port Credit	280	55

MATRICES AND GRAPHS

The Thamesville Maize, home of Ken and Ingrid Dieleman, **www.cornfieldmaze.com**. Photo taken by Austin Wright.

This aerial photograph shows a cornfield maze constructed in Thamesville, Ontario. A person enters the maze and tries to find a route that leads from the entrance to the exit. Because walls prevent the traveller from seeing the entire maze, the ability to make direction decisions at the end of each path intersection is limited.

INVESTIGATION: ESCAPING A MAZE

Examine the following maze. Is it possible to find a route through the maze that requires no backtracking?

A. Copy the maze into your notebook. Label the places in the maze where a traveller would have to make a direction decision. Use the letters A, B, C, and so on. How many direction choices are there at each decision point?

B. Think of each decision point as a gate. The route through the maze consists of a sequence of paths that lead from one gate to the next. How many of these gate-to-gate paths are required for the shortest route through the maze?

REPRESENTING PATHS USING GRAPHS AND MATRICES

> **? Think about Mazes**
> Graphs and networks were introduced in Section 6.1. How is the path through the maze like a graph?

The individual pathways that lead from one point to the next, along with the points themselves, form a graph or network. The graph showing all possible routes in the maze from the Investigation is shown below.

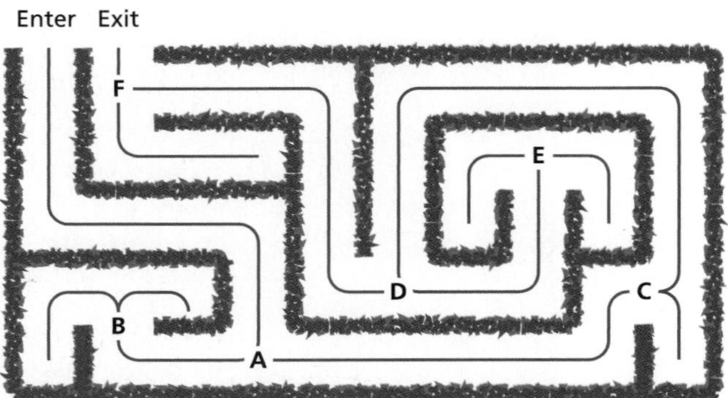

A table can be used to show the number of one-step paths that link the lettered gates in this maze. These are called one-step paths because they join a gate to the next with only a single link.

In the table below

- the enter point, the lettered decision points, and the exit are shown down the side, and across the top.
- each cell in the table contains a 1 or a 0.
- a 1 shows that a link can be made directly from one point to the next. For example, if you read across the table from B, there is a "1" in column A. This means there is a link that goes from B to A.
- a 0 shows that there is no link.

> **? Think About Tables**
> Why does the table show that there is a path from A to B and also a path from B to A?

TO

FROM	Enter	A	B	C	D	E	F	Exit
Enter	0	1	0	0	0	0	0	0
A	1	0	1	1	0	0	0	0
B	0	1	0	0	0	0	0	0
C	0	1	0	0	1	0	0	0
D	0	0	0	1	0	1	1	0
E	0	0	0	0	1	0	0	0
F	0	0	0	0	1	0	0	1
Exit	0	0	0	0	0	0	1	0

transition matrix—a matrix that shows the number of edges that connect the vertices of a graph

The information contained in this table can be modelled using the 8-by-8 **transition matrix** A shown below. Each row corresponds to a gate in the maze. Each column indicates whether or not a path exists directly from one gate to another.

$$A = \begin{bmatrix} 0 & 1 & 0 & 0 & 0 & 0 & 0 & 0 \\ 1 & 0 & 1 & 1 & 0 & 0 & 0 & 0 \\ 0 & 1 & 0 & 0 & 0 & 0 & 0 & 0 \\ 0 & 1 & 0 & 0 & 1 & 0 & 0 & 0 \\ 0 & 0 & 0 & 1 & 0 & 1 & 1 & 0 \\ 0 & 0 & 0 & 0 & 1 & 0 & 0 & 0 \\ 0 & 0 & 0 & 0 & 1 & 0 & 0 & 1 \\ 0 & 0 & 0 & 0 & 0 & 0 & 1 & 0 \end{bmatrix}$$

ANALYZING ROUTES USING A TRANSITION MATRIX

The transition matrix A (above) shows the number of paths joining vertices of the graph that are one edge in length. Now, consider paths that are two edges in length.

For example, there is a two-step path from Enter to B that passes through A, and also one from Enter to C. There is also a two-step path that goes from Enter to A and back to Enter. There are no two-step paths from Enter to A because the line must first pass through A.

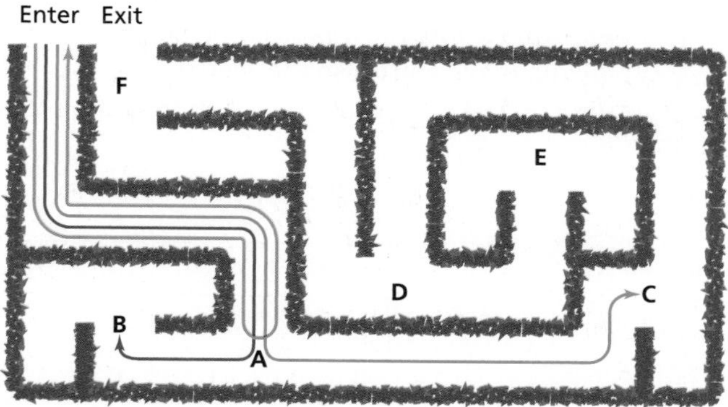

Suppose you begin at A. There are three two-step paths that begin at A and end at A:

- A to Enter to A
- A to B to A
- A to C to A

There is also a two-step path from A to D through C, but no others.

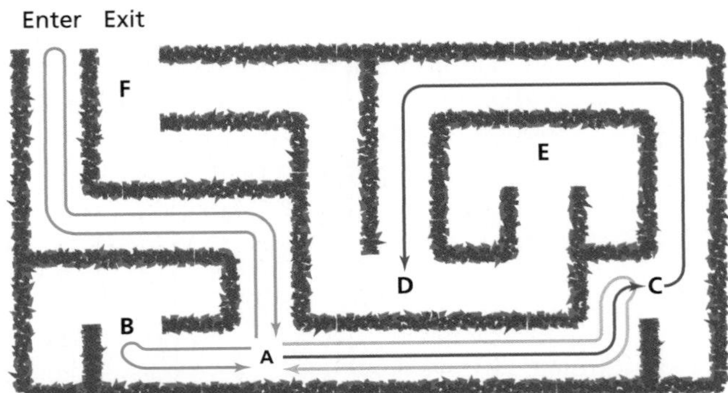

The partially completed transition matrix for two-step paths would have the following entries:

TO (in two steps)

FROM	Enter	A	B	C	D	E	F	Exit
Enter	1	0	1	1	0	0	0	0
A	0	3	0	0	1	0	0	0
B								
C								

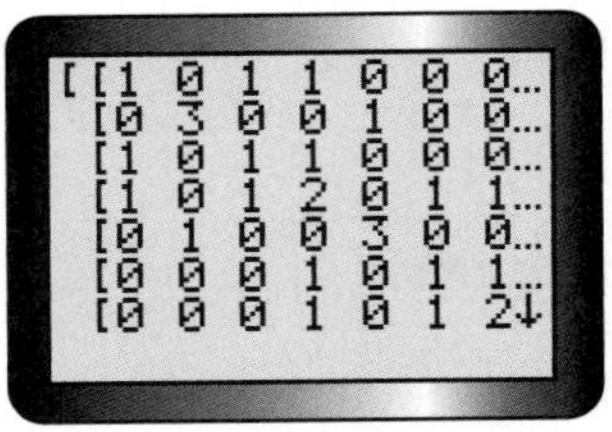

Computing the remaining entries would be time-consuming. However, this two-step transition matrix turns out to be the product matrix $A^2 = A \times A$. Once the matrix entries have been entered into a TI-83 Plus calculator, the computation requires just pressing [A]*[A] or [A]^2. Use the arrow keys to scroll through the other entries in the matrix.

The completed two-step transition matrix is shown below.

TO (in two steps)

FROM	Enter	A	B	C	D	E	F	Exit
Enter	1	0	1	1	0	0	0	0
A	0	3	0	0	1	0	0	0
B	1	0	1	1	0	0	0	0
C	1	0	1	2	0	1	1	0
D	0	1	0	0	3	0	0	1
E	0	0	0	1	0	1	1	0
F	0	0	0	1	0	1	2	0
Exit	0	0	0	0	1	0	0	1

? Think about Transition Matrices

For what value of n does A^n show that an n-step route exists going from Enter to Exit? What does this mean?

A Food Chain

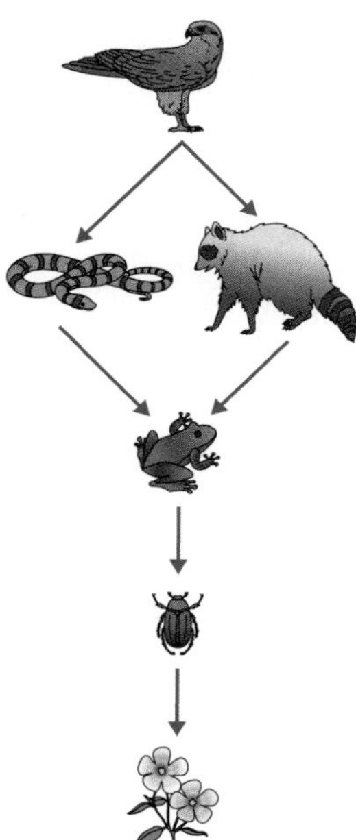

USING MATRICES TO ANALYZE A FOOD CHAIN

Chemical contaminants in the environment are passed up the food chain. For example, when the insecticide DDT is used, insects ingest it and pass it up the food chain to frogs and toads, who feed on the insects. It is then passed up the chain to snakes and racoons, who eat the toads and frogs. This continues until the animal at the top of the chain (often humans) is reached.

The simple food chain in the margin illustrates how a food chain can be thought of as a digraph in which the direction of the edge means "preys upon." In table form, this becomes the following:

	hawk	snake	raccoon	frog	beetle	plant
hawk		Yes	Yes			
snake				Yes		
raccoon				Yes		
frog					Yes	
beetle						Yes
plant						

The predator–prey relationship in this diagram can be represented using a matrix. For example, the 1s in $m_{1\,2}$ and $m_{1\,3}$ represent the fact that the hawk preys upon the snake and the raccoon. The 1 in $m_{3\,4}$ indicates that the raccoon preys upon the frog.

$$M = \begin{bmatrix} 0 & \textcircled{1} & \textcircled{1} & 0 & 0 & 0 \\ 0 & 0 & 0 & 1 & 0 & 0 \\ 0 & 0 & 0 & \textcircled{1} & 0 & 0 \\ 0 & 0 & 0 & 0 & 1 & 0 \\ 0 & 0 & 0 & 0 & 0 & 1 \\ 0 & 0 & 0 & 0 & 0 & 0 \end{bmatrix}$$

This matrix can be interpreted in a manner similar to the way a transition matrix models a maze. Each entry indicates whether or not a one-step path (or direct connection) exists between a predator and its prey. Each step represents the passing of DDT contamination along the food chain to a predator.

By examining the various powers of M, you can determine the number of steps required before the contamination reaches the top predator in the chain.

$$M^2 = \begin{bmatrix} 0 & 0 & 0 & 2 & 0 & 0 \\ 0 & 0 & 0 & 0 & 1 & 0 \\ 0 & 0 & 0 & 0 & 1 & 0 \\ 0 & 0 & 0 & 0 & 0 & 1 \\ 0 & 0 & 0 & 0 & 0 & 0 \\ 0 & 0 & 0 & 0 & 0 & 0 \end{bmatrix}$$

The 2 in row 1, column 4 of M^2 indicates that the hawk has indirectly fed on the frog by consuming one of two frog predators: the snake or the raccoon.

$$M^3 = \begin{bmatrix} 0 & 0 & 0 & 0 & 2 & 0 \\ 0 & 0 & 0 & 0 & 0 & 1 \\ 0 & 0 & 0 & 0 & 0 & 1 \\ 0 & 0 & 0 & 0 & 0 & 0 \\ 0 & 0 & 0 & 0 & 0 & 0 \\ 0 & 0 & 0 & 0 & 0 & 0 \end{bmatrix}$$

The 2 in row 1, column 5 of M^3 indicates that the hawk has indirectly fed on the bug via the frog and then the snake or the raccoon.

$$M^4 = \begin{bmatrix} 0 & 0 & 0 & 0 & 0 & 2 \\ 0 & 0 & 0 & 0 & 0 & 0 \\ 0 & 0 & 0 & 0 & 0 & 0 \\ 0 & 0 & 0 & 0 & 0 & 0 \\ 0 & 0 & 0 & 0 & 0 & 0 \\ 0 & 0 & 0 & 0 & 0 & 0 \end{bmatrix}$$

The hawk will receive the DDT contamination when a non-zero entry appears in $m_{1\,6}$ since that indicates a path connecting the hawk to the plant. This occurs in M^4, indicating that four steps are required before the contamination reaches the top of the food chain.

KEY IDEAS

Product Matrix

- The product $P = A \times B$ of two matrices A and B is the matrix for which each entry $p_{r\,c}$ is the inner product of row r from matrix A with column c of matrix B.
- For the product to exist, the matrices must be compatible; that is, the number of columns of matrix A must equal the number of rows of matrix B.

Transition Matrix

- A transition matrix represents the number of edges that connect the vertices of a directed graph.

- Transition matrices may be used to represent paths through a maze, predator–prey relationships, or any other interrelationships that can be represented by a digraph.
- If T is a transition matrix for a digraph, then T^n shows all paths of length n between the vertices of the graph.

6.4 Exercises

1. Consider the following matrices.

$$A = \begin{bmatrix} 1 \\ 2 \\ 3 \end{bmatrix} \qquad B = \begin{bmatrix} 10 & 20 & 30 \end{bmatrix} \qquad C = \begin{bmatrix} 2 & 4 & 6 \\ 3 & 6 & 9 \\ 4 & 8 & 12 \end{bmatrix}$$

(a) Why is the matrix product BC possible, but the product CB is not?
(b) Find the dimensions of BA.
(c) Evaluate BA. Show your work.
(d) Evaluate the product AC or BC, whichever is possible.

2. If X is a 5-by-3 matrix and Y is a 3-by-5 matrix, what dimensions will the products XY and YX have? Explain your answer.

3. Perform the following matrix multiplications.

(a) $\begin{bmatrix} 1 & 2 & 3 \end{bmatrix} \times \begin{bmatrix} 10 \\ 20 \\ 30 \end{bmatrix}$ **(b)** $\begin{bmatrix} 1 & 0 \\ 0 & 1 \end{bmatrix} \times \begin{bmatrix} 2 & 4 & 6 \\ 1 & 3 & 5 \end{bmatrix}$

4. **Knowledge and Understanding** Write the transition matrix that represents each of the following digraphs.

(a)

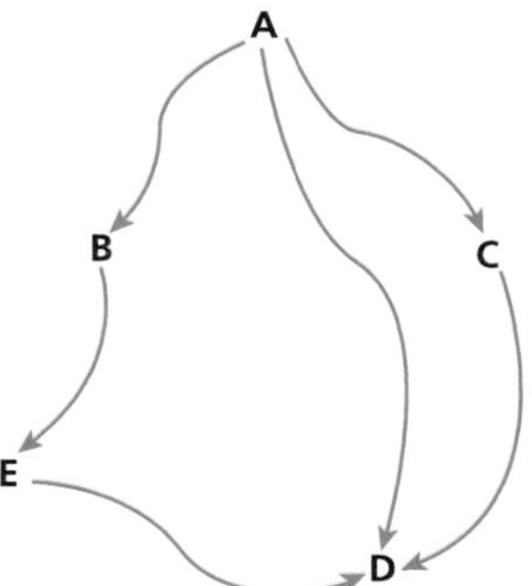

(b)

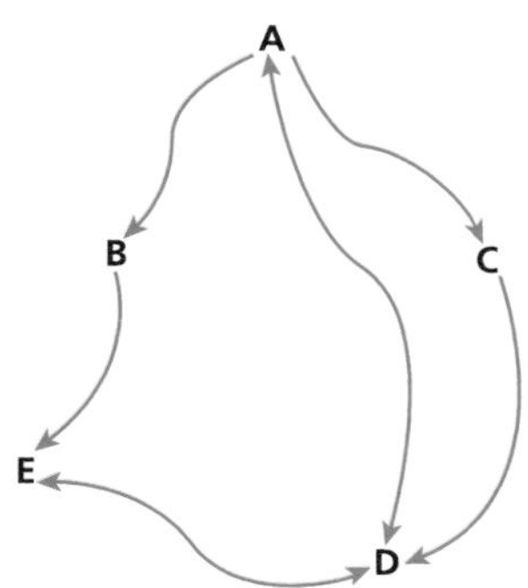

5. Draw the digraph that corresponds to this transition matrix.

$$A = \begin{bmatrix} 0 & 1 & 1 & 0 \\ 1 & 0 & 1 & 1 \\ 1 & 0 & 0 & 1 \\ 1 & 1 & 0 & 0 \end{bmatrix}$$

B

6. Knowledge and Understanding

For $A = \begin{bmatrix} 1 & -1 \\ 0 & 2 \end{bmatrix}$, $B = \begin{bmatrix} 2 & 4 \\ 3 & 5 \end{bmatrix}$, and $C = \begin{bmatrix} 1 & 1 \\ 1 & 1 \end{bmatrix}$,

(a) show that $(A \times B) \times C = A \times (B \times C)$
(b) show that $A \times B \neq B \times A$
(c) show that $(A - B) \times C = A \times C - B \times C$
(d) show that $(A + B) \times C = A \times C + B \times C$

7. For $A = \begin{bmatrix} 1 & -1 & 2 \\ 2 & 1 & 1 \\ -1 & 3 & 2 \end{bmatrix}$, $B = \begin{bmatrix} 1 & 0 & 1 \\ 0 & 1 & 1 \\ 1 & 1 & 0 \end{bmatrix}$, and $C = \begin{bmatrix} 1 & 1 & 1 \\ 1 & 1 & 1 \\ 1 & 1 & 1 \end{bmatrix}$,

(a) show that $(A \times B) \times C = A \times (B \times C)$
(b) show that $A \times B \neq B \times A$
(c) show that $(A - B) \times C = A \times C - B \times C$
(d) show that $(A + B) \times C = A \times C + B \times C$

8. Show that $AB = AC$.

$$A = \begin{bmatrix} 2 & 4 \\ 1 & 2 \end{bmatrix} \qquad B = \begin{bmatrix} 1 & 2 \\ 1 & -1 \end{bmatrix} \qquad C = \begin{bmatrix} 5 & 6 \\ -1 & -3 \end{bmatrix}$$

9. Thinking, Inquiry, Problem Solving Find examples of two 2-by-2 matrices A and B for which $AB = BA$.

10. A bicycle manufacturer has tracked the time required for each stage of the manufacturing process for each of two models. The times required for each bike model are shown below.

Model	Assembly Time (min)	Painting Time (min)	Packing Time (min)
Kiddie	20	5	10
Adult	30	10	10

Assemblers earn \$20/h, painters earn \$15/h, and packers earn \$10/h. Use matrix methods to determine the total labour cost associated with each bike.

11. **Application** To make the manufacturing process efficient, a window supplier has designed windows so that each style can be made using the same-sized frame pieces and the same-sized glass sections. The requirements for each style are listed below.

Style	Frame Pieces	Glass Sections
A	4	1
B	7	2
C	13	4
D	16	5

A builder has several different models of homes for which she has ordered windows. The requirements for each model are listed in the following table.

	Window Styles			
Model	A	B	C	D
Descartes	5	2	0	1
Gauss	4	4	2	0
Fermat	4	1	3	2

Find the total number of frame pieces and glass sections the manufacturer will need to use for each model.

12. Bombay Pacific airlines charges different amounts based on the class of ticket purchased. For a flight from Toronto to Vancouver, the price schedule is $750 for first class, $625 for business class, and $500 for economy. In one week of travel, the number of tickets sold for each class is shown in the table below. Use matrix methods to calculate the daily total revenue for the airline.

	First Class	Business Class	Economy
Monday	10	15	130
Tuesday	12	17	140
Wednesday	11	20	150
Thursday	15	15	200
Friday	20	11	210
Saturday	8	0	220
Sunday	2	0	165

13. The window supplier described in Question 11 knows that each frame piece costs \$2.00 and each glass section costs \$15.00.
    (a) Use matrix methods to determine the cost of each window.
    (b) Use matrix methods to determine the total cost to the window supplier for the windows needed for each model of home.

14. The following chart indicates the routes flown by a small airline.

From/To	Calgary	Hamilton	Edmonton	Regina	Ottawa
Calgary		N	Y	Y	Y
Hamilton	N		N	N	Y
Edmonton	Y	N		N	Y
Regina	N	N	N		Y
Ottawa	Y	Y	Y	Y	

    (a) Use matrix methods to determine if a passenger can reach Hamilton in a round-trip flight from Calgary.
    (b) It is not possible for a passenger to fly directly from Edmonton to Regina. Use matrix methods to determine if it is possible to do so using two flights.
    (c) How many different routes are possible for a passenger to fly from Ottawa and return using three flights? Show your work.

C 15. Five friends communicate by telephone. However, not all of them will speak to one another directly.
    - Della will phone Billy, Ahmed, and Dahlia, but not David.
    - Billy will phone only Ahmed and Della.
    - Dahlia will phone only David and Della.
    - David will phone only Billy and Dahlia.
    - Ahmed won't phone anybody.

    (a) How many calls are needed for Billy to send a message to David?
    (b) Show whether it is possible for Dahlia to send a message and get it back in three phone calls.

16. A baker is planning her next day's production requirements. She knows that a loaf of cottage bread requires 1.5 L of flour, two packages of yeast, and 100 mL of oil. Each loaf of white bread requires 2 L of flour, two packages of yeast, and 75 mL of oil. Each loaf of buttermilk bread requires 1.25 L of flour, two packages of yeast, and 60 mL of oil.

    Flour costs \$1.25 per litre, oil costs \$0.30 per 100 mL, and yeast costs \$0.25 a package.
    (a) Use matrix methods to compute the cost of the ingredients for each type of bread.
    (b) Use matrix methods to determine the cost of the ingredients for an order consisting of 30 cottage loaves, 120 white loaves, and 50 loaves of buttermilk bread.

ADDITIONAL ACHIEVEMENT CHART QUESTIONS

In Section 6.2 you were introduced to a friendship matrix that led to a graph of student relationships.

Would work with ...	Barb	Amir	Ken	Rene	Sean
Barb		+	+	–	+
Amir	–		+	+	–
Ken	+	–		–	–
Rene	+	+	+		+
Sean	+	–	+	+	

17. **Knowledge and Understanding** Write this chart as matrix F in which "would work with" is represented by a 1 and "would not work with" is represented by a 0. Assume that students would work with themselves.

18. **Application** Compute F^2 and F^3.

19. **Thinking, Inquiry, Problem Solving** Imagine that the five students were asked to rate the others as follows: most-wanted partner (1) to least-wanted partner (5). Create a way of recording this result in a matrix R. What does R^2 mean?

20. **Communication** What information about the working relationships among students does F^2 provide?

6.5 Solving Problems with Graphs

When planning the construction of a house, a contractor has to schedule a complicated series of events. Land has to be purchased, and plans have to be finalized and approved by the municipal building department. Carpenters, plumbers, electricians, and other skilled trades have to be hired. Materials have to be delivered and equipment has to be available on site when they are needed.

Single Family Home
Nov 00
Dec 00
Jan 01
Feb 01
Mar 01
Apr 01
May 01
Activity
Start Date
Finish Date
Duration
1 Acquire land Ready to build from land developer 11/06/00
2 Stake lines and graces 11/06/00 11/10/00 5.00
3 Clearing and rough gracing 11/13/00 11/17/00 5.00
4 Utilities 11/18/00 11/28/00 7.00
5 Excavation 11/22/00 11/29/00 6.00
6 Foundation, basement and backfill 12/02/00 12/13/00 8.00
7 Frame floors, walls, and roof 12/16/00 01/11/01 19.00
8 Roofing 01/13/01 01/23/01 7.00
9 Doors and windows 01/22/01 01/26/01 5.00
10 Exterior wall surfaces... 02/03/01 02/21/01 13.00
11 Rough in ductwork, plumbing, and electrical... 01/22/01 02/13/01 17.00
12 Drywall... 02/03/01 03/02/01 20.00
13 Painting... 03/03/01 03/19/01 11.00
14 Finish carpentry... 03/10/01 04/05/01 14.00
15 Plumbing, heating, and electrical finish work... 03/25/01 04/05/01 9.00
16 Flooring... 04/06/01 04/18/01 9.00
17 Landscaping... 04/04/01 04/27/01 18.00
18 Punchlist 05/01/01

Many builders use a graphical tool called a Gantt chart to help them schedule the activities, equipment, materials, and personnel in the most efficient and least costly manner. A sample Gantt chart is shown below.

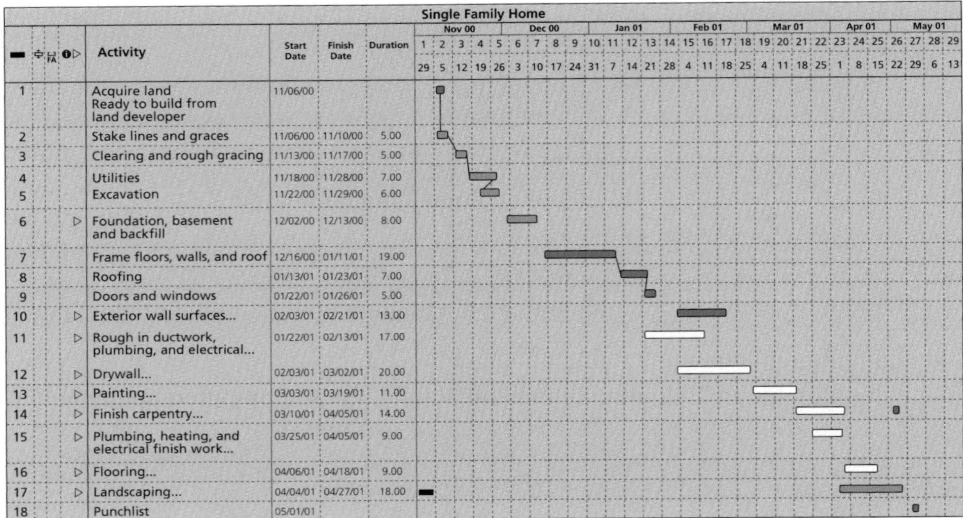

sequential tasks—tasks that are dependent on each other and must be performed in order

project graph—a digraph on which each task that must be completed as part of the project is a vertex. Vertices that are dependent are connected with an edge

weight of an edge—the duration a preceding task takes to complete

parallel tasks—tasks that are independent and can be performed at the same time

This Gantt chart shows a simplified version of the activities that must occur, the order in which they must take place, and the duration of each activity. Some of the tasks listed depend on other activities being completed before they can begin. These tasks are called **sequential tasks**. For example, the land must be purchased before anything else can occur. The foundation cannot be poured until the hole for the foundation has been excavated.

Tasks that are dependent in this way have a directed line segment that links them on a **project graph**. Often there is a number, or **weight**, associated with each edge. This typically represents the duration of the preceding task.

On the other hand, some activities are independent of one another. Landscaping, for example, can occur at the same time that the drywall is being installed. These tasks are called **parallel tasks**.

The tasks required to complete the construction of a home can be extensive. The chart above was created with a specialized computer program called *FastTrack Schedule*. This software allows contractors to manage the resources and people, and also allows them to track the cost of the project so they can stay within their budget.

CRITICAL PATH ANALYSIS

critical path analysis—finding the optimal way to complete a complex task

earliest start time—the earliest that a task can begin if all the tasks on which it depends begin as early as possible

task table—a table that lists all the tasks associated with a project, including the duration of each task and the tasks on which each depends

In the middle of the twentieth century, the U.S. government developed methods to monitor complex military construction projects. The branch of mathematics that evolved became known as Operations Research. One of the tasks of Operations Research was **critical path analysis**, which was involved in identifying tasks in a process that were critical to the earliest completion of the project.

One of the most useful applications of critical path analysis is determining the **earliest start time (EST)** for each task. By comparing the weights of each edge in a project graph, you can find the time at which all prerequisite tasks have been completed (the earliest start time).

Example 1 Using Graphs to Schedule a Project

Using the **task table** shown below, determine the minimum amount of time required to complete the construction of a home. (The prerequisite tasks are those jobs that need to be completed before the indicated task can start.)

Project Connection

Setting up a task table for your final project will help you determine all the tasks you need to complete.

Task	Description	Duration (days)	Prerequisite Task(s)
Start	Acquire land	0	
A	Stake lines and grades	5	none
B	Clear site and do rough grading	5	A
C	Install service for all utilities	7	B
D	Excavate	6	A
E	Lay foundation, pour basement, and then backfill	8	D
F	Frame doors, walls, and roof	19	C, E
G	Shingle roof	7	F
H	Install doors and windows	5	F
I	Build exterior wall surfaces	13	G, H
J	Rough-in ductwork, plumbing, and electrical	17	F
K	Install drywall	20	J
L	Paint	14	K, N
M	Do finish carpentry	14	K, L
N	Do plumbing, heating, and electrical work	9	J
O	Install flooring	9	M
P	Complete legal work to transfer ownership	7	I, O
Finish			

Solution

Drawing a project graph of the various tasks makes it easier to see how the tasks relate to one another. Each vertex corresponds to one of the tasks. The arrow on each edge indicates that a task depends on another to be completed before it can start. The number on the edge is the time required for the preceding task to be completed.

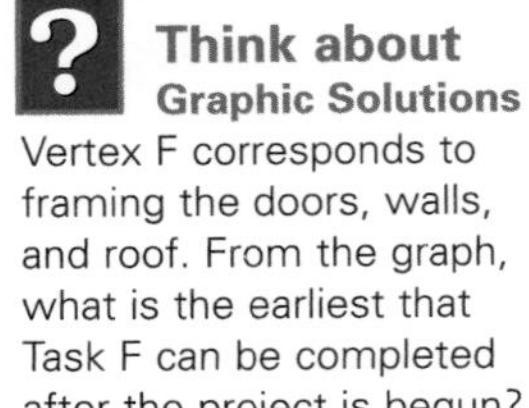
Think about
Graphic Solutions
Vertex F corresponds to framing the doors, walls, and roof. From the graph, what is the earliest that Task F can be completed after the project is begun?

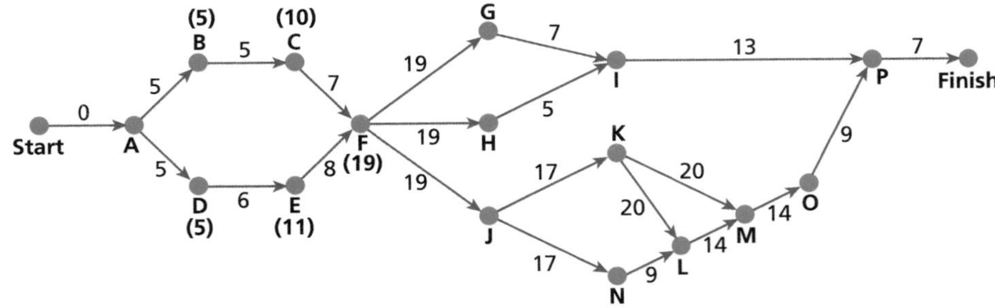

In calculating the EST, we can see that

- Task B depends on Task A being completed, so (5) is indicated above B for 5 days on the graph
- Task C requires Task B to be completed, so (10) is indicated above C $(5 + 5 = 10)$
- Task E requires Task D to be completed, so (11) is indicated below E $(5 + 6 = 11)$
- Task F cannot begin until 19 days have elapsed because both Tasks C and E must be completed first $(11 + 8 = 19)$

Think about
Earliest Start Time
The first few ESTs are shown on the graph. Complete the graph before reading the rest of this page.

The least number of days in which the house can be completed is the time it takes to complete all the tasks in the project. This corresponds to the total time represented by the longest path from start to finish on the project graph. That path is shown in red on the following graph. The earliest the job can be completed is 119 days.

The critical path for this project is

Start – A – D – E – F – J – K – L – M – O – P – Finish.

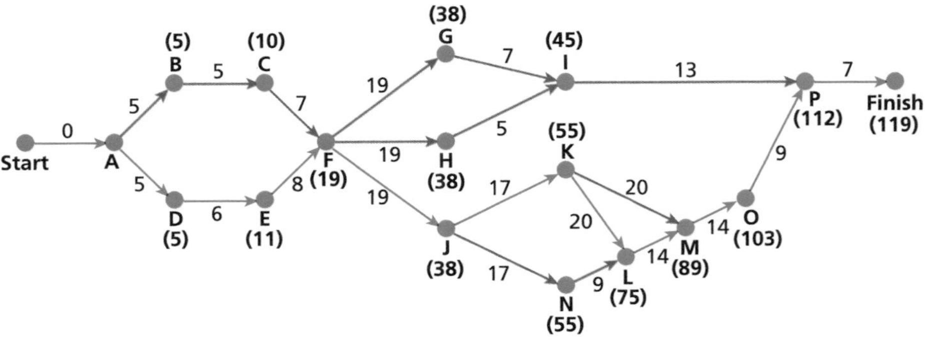

Example 2 **Using an ATM**

Each week Vasundhara deposits her paycheque, keeping $40 for herself. In an effort to be more organized, she times each part of her weekly routine at the bank machine and creates the following task table.

Task	Description	Time (s)	Prerequisite
A	Enter bank	35	
B	Insert bank card	8	A
C	Type in PIN	7	B
D	Select deposit	7	C
E	Key in amount	4	D
F	Put cheque in envelope	9	
G	Insert envelope	5	E, F
H	Select withdrawal	7	C
I	Type in amount	4	H
J	Collect money	5	I
K	Press DONE	6	G, J
L	Retrieve bank card	2	K
M	Exit bank	35	L

Create a project graph and use critical path analysis to determine the optimal order in which to perform this transaction. Find the EST.

Solution

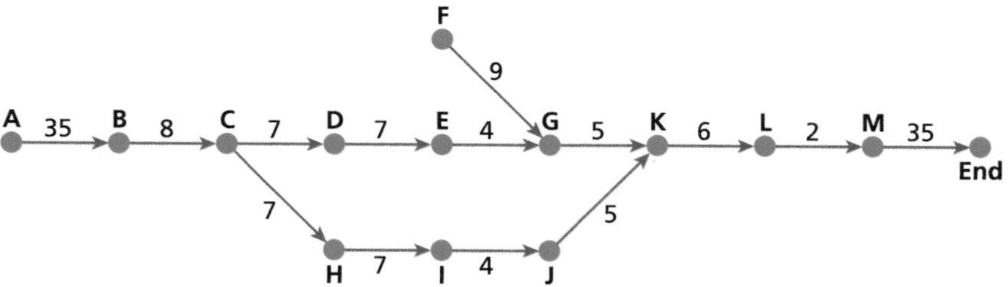

After creating a graph, Vasundhara notices the following facts:

- As long as she can remember the amount the cheque is made out for, Task F can be done any time.
- Since her account balance is greater than $40 on a regular basis, she can do either the deposit or the withdrawal first.
- The graph makes a critical error. It implies that Tasks D, E, and G can be done at the same time as H, I, and J. While the order doesn't matter, Vasundhara must choose one of the two series of tasks to do first.

Vasundhara decides to streamline her transaction. She decides to have her cheque already in an envelope and will deposit it first. Her corrected graph is shown below.

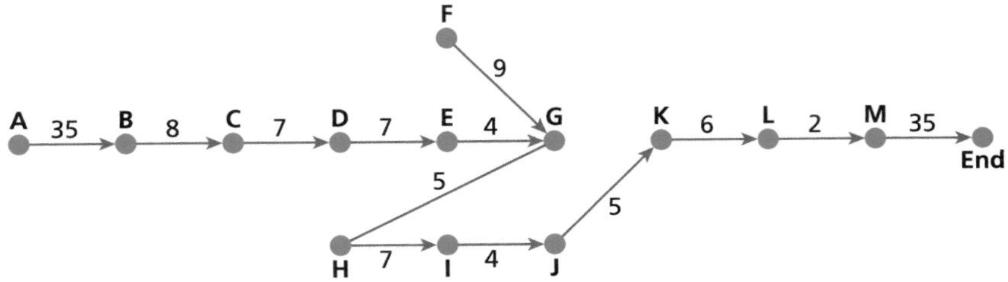

The minimum amount of time the transaction will take is 125 s (2 min, 5 s), assuming there is no line-up!

KEY IDEAS

task table—a table that lists all the tasks required to complete a project. For each task entry, it includes the duration of each task and a list of tasks that must be finished before that task may be started.

sequential tasks—tasks that are dependent on each other and must be performed in order

project graph—a digraph on which each task that must be completed as part of the project is a vertex. Task vertices are joined to those vertices that depend on their prior completion.

weight of an edge—the number associated with an edge; typically represents the time needed to accomplish the preceding task

parallel tasks—tasks that are independent and can be performed at the same time

critical path analysis—finding the optimal way to complete a complex task

earliest start time—the time required for the latest completion of its prerequisite tasks

critical path—the longest path (in terms of completion times) from start to finish through the project graph

graph theory—the study of graphs and their application in solving puzzles

6.5 Exercises

1. Take the following sequential tasks and put them in an appropriate order.
   (a) click OK, turn off computer, turn on computer, click on Shortcut, turn on printer, enter password, exit program, click Start, turn off printer, click Shut Down, click Print, turn on monitor, turn off monitor
   (b) get plate from cupboard, get two slices of bread, push down toaster switch, spread peanut butter on bread, get knife from drawer, get peanut butter from shelf, eat peanut butter on toast
   (c) go to third class, drive to school, go to fourth class, eat lunch, park the car, drive home, go to second class, go to first class, go to after-school practice
   (d) select CD, press Play, turn on stereo receiver, adjust volume, turn on CD player
2. For each list in Question 1, create a task table listing the dependencies.
3. **Communication** Explain the difference between parallel tasks and sequential tasks. Give two examples of each.

4. List, in order, five sequential tasks that are part of washing a car.
5. **Knowledge and Understanding** For each of the project graphs below, do the following. (Assume all times are in days.)
   (i) Complete the graph by adding the earliest start times for each task.
   (ii) Identify the critical path for the project.
   (iii) Determine the least amount of time required for the project.
   (a)

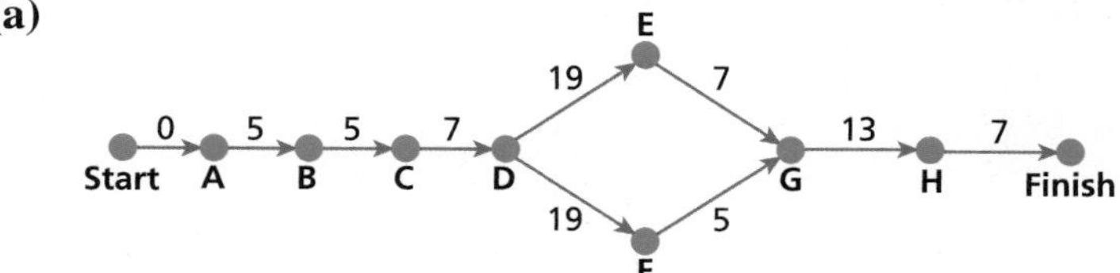

   (b)

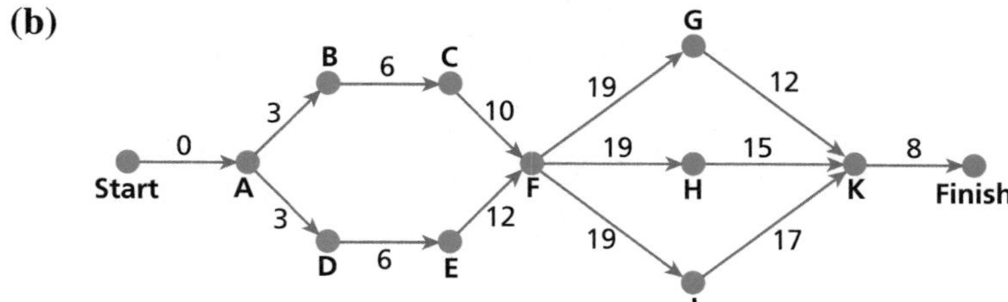

   (c)

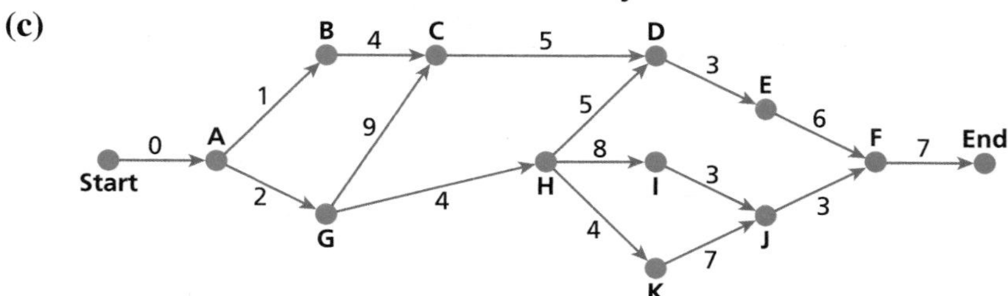

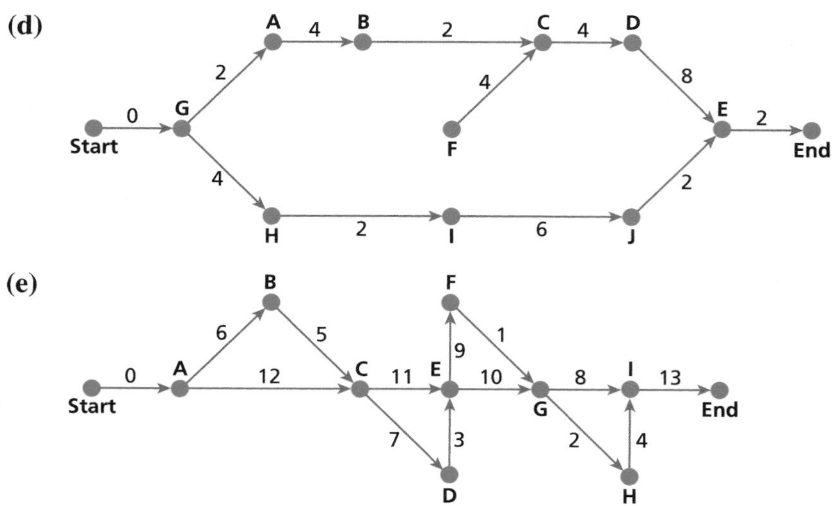

6. Application A shipyard is working on the construction of a passenger ship.

Task	Task Description	Duration (in months)	Prerequisite Task(s)
A	Create initial design	1	none
B	Prepare detailed design	2.5	A
C	Order steel	1.5	A
D	Lay keel	1	B, C
E	Build hull	2	D
F	Order and build engines	2	B, C
G	Build superstructure	2	B, C
H	Install engines	2	E, F
I	Order and build navigation equipment	2.5	B
J	Install superstructure	1	G
K	Install navigation and other equipment	1	I, J
L	Trial runs	1.5	H, K
M	Install furniture, heating, lighting, etc.	2.5	J

(a) Construct a project graph for this project.
(b) Determine the least time in which the project can be completed.

7. A bicycle is to be completely dismantled and carefully packaged prior to shipping it to an overseas buyer. The following table provides estimates of the time required to remove or disassemble each part. Determine the least completion time for this project.

Task	Description	Time (min)	Prerequisites
A	chain	5	I
B	crank	30	A, I
C	fork	35	G, E
D	frame	30	C, F, J, K, N
E	front brake	10	G
F	front gear sprocket	10	A, B, G
G	front wheel	5	I
H	hand control levers	10	E
I	pedals	20	none
J	rear brake	10	L
K	rear gear sprocket	20	A, B, L
L	rear wheel	5	A
M	saddle	1	none
N	handle bars	5	H

C

8. **Thinking, Inquiry, Problem Solving** Create a task table and project graph for all the tasks you need to complete prior to the final presentation of your course project. Use critical path analysis to determine the earliest completion time for your project.

9. Consider the following recipe.

Mexican Party Pie

Put 2 lb of ground beef in a frying pan and fry it until it is browned (about 10 min). Then mix in 2 tbsp of vegetable oil, $\frac{1}{2}$ of a chopped onion, 1 clove of garlic, 14 oz. of tomato sauce, 19 oz of kernel corn, 1 chopped green pepper, 1 tsp of sugar, 1 tsp of salt, and 1 tsp of chili powder. Stir for 5 min and pour into a 13×9 inch baking dish. Add topping and put it into the oven for 45 min.

To make the topping, combine 1 cup of cornmeal with $\frac{3}{4}$ cup of milk, mix, and let stand for 10 min. While you are waiting, mix $1\frac{1}{4}$ cups of flour with 1 tsp of salt, $2\frac{1}{2}$ tsp baking powder, and $\frac{1}{2}$ cup of sugar. Stir for 2 min and then add $\frac{1}{2}$ cup of vegetable shortening, 1 egg, and $\frac{3}{4}$ cup of milk. Mix for 5 min, and then add the cornmeal.

Make sure to preheat the oven to 375°F.

Assuming it takes 2 min to chop one kind of vegetable, 9 min for the oven to heat up, and 15 min for the dish to cool after baking,

(a) create a task table that lists the prerequisite tasks
(b) use your task table to create a project graph with weighted edges
(c) use the critical path to determine how long it will take to prepare this dish from start to serve

ADDITIONAL ACHIEVEMENT CHART QUESTIONS

10. **Knowledge and Understanding** Consider the following list of tasks associated with a male student getting dressed for a winter school day. Which groups of tasks are sequential? Which groups of tasks are parallel?

put on socks	put on boxer shorts
put on T-shirt	put on watch
put on jeans	put on shoes
put on sweater	put on belt
put on coat	put on scarf
put on toque	put on gloves

11. **Application** Using the list of tasks from Question 10, create a task table that specifies which tasks are dependent on which tasks.

12. **Thinking, Inquiry, Problem Solving** Use the task table from Question 11 and create a project graph.

13. **Communication** What decisions need to be made before a critical path can be determined? (**Hint**: Does it matter what series of tasks get performed first?) Choose a critical path and explain why you think it is the optimal way to get dressed.

Chapter Problem

How Much Time Will It Take to Build This House?

CP4. The critical path for the Chapter Problem was provided as a solved example in this section. How would the time required to complete the project change if the contractor could convince the painter to complete that job in 11 d instead of 14 as originally scheduled? Explain.

Project Connection

The Final Product and Presentation

Your final presentation should be more than just a factual, written report of the information you have found. To make the most of your hard work to this point, you need to select a format for the final presentation that will suit your strengths as well as the nature of your topic.

Presentation Styles

In your presentation, you could use

- a report on an experiment or an investigation
- a summary of a detailed written product, such as a newspaper article or an editorial with commentary
- a case study
- a pamphlet
- a short story, musical performance, or play
- a Web page
- a PowerPoint® presentation
- a video or slide show
- a debate
- an advertising campaign or well-designed logo
- a demonstration or the teaching of a lesson

What follows are some of the decisions that others have made about the presentation of their project.

Project 1 *Weather Predictions*

Muhamud has done a project on the mathematics of weather predictions. He decides that his presentation will be a demonstration of how a weather report is prepared, including the mathematics used, followed by an actual TV weather report. He also plans to hand in a written report on his research and conclusions.

Project 2 Gender Differences

Ming has studied the differences between the responses of females and males on cognitive aptitude tests. To illustrate her findings, she will have the class complete one of the assessment tasks during her presentation and then compare the results with standardized norms. Ming's project will also include testing she has done on randomly selected students at her school.

Project 3 *Sleep Patterns and Academic Success*

Laura studied the relationship between the number of hours of sleep students get and their academic performance. During her presentation, Laura will summarize the regressions she has performed and present her position that a student must get seven hours of sleep to be successful in school. At the end of her presentation, the class will spend a few minutes debating her thesis.

Learning Styles

People have different learning styles and these styles dictate how the presentation is delivered as well as received. For example, some people understand best by listening. Their best presentation style will involve the use of words, music, and so on. Other people are visual learners; they learn best from visual aids like overhead transparencies, videos, and pictures. Finally, kinesthetic learners need to do and touch before understanding is reached. Their best presentation style will involve movement, such as a play or a performance.

To help you decide on the type of presentation you want to create, try answering the following questions:

1. **(a)** Do you think you learn best by hearing, seeing, or doing? Explain.
(b) How might your answer to part (a) influence the type of presentation you create?
(c) From which type of presentation do you think you will gain the greatest understanding? Why?

2. Before giving your presentation, make sure that you answer these questions about your presentation:
- Did I define my topic well? What is the best way to define my topic?
- Is my presentation focused? Will others in the class find it focused? Did I organize my information effectively?
- Did I summarize relevant information?
- Is it obvious that I am following a plan in my presentation?
- Am I satisfied with the presentation? What might make it more effective?
- What unanswered questions do I still have?

Executive Summary

Sometimes, it is effective to give your audience an executive summary of your presentation. This is a one-page summary of your presentation that includes the reason for having the presentation and the conclusions you make. Ask your teacher about making copies of your summary for the class.

Chapter 6 Wrap-Up

EXTRA PRACTICE

1. Thailand Gourmet Sauces pays its employees $11.50/h for any hours worked per week up to 40 h. For over 40 h of work per week, an employee receives overtime pay at the rate of 1.5 times the regular hourly rate. Construct a flow chart that describes the process by which an employee's weekly pay is calculated.

2. The manager, Adnan Omar, received complaints about employees not returning clients' phone calls. After a brainstorming session, the following list of possible causes was created: line was busy, employee was on another line, employee forgot to return the call, call was sent to the wrong extension, call came in before or after office hours, employee chose not to return the call, employee was at lunch, switchboard staff lost the call, call was directed to the wrong employee, employee was at a meeting, phone message server was full, and employee did not know how to pick up the call.

The group studying the problem then developed the following broad categories for the causes: technical problems, employee error, directory/database error, and employee judgement. Construct a cause-and-effect chart to organize and present the results of the cause–effect analysis.

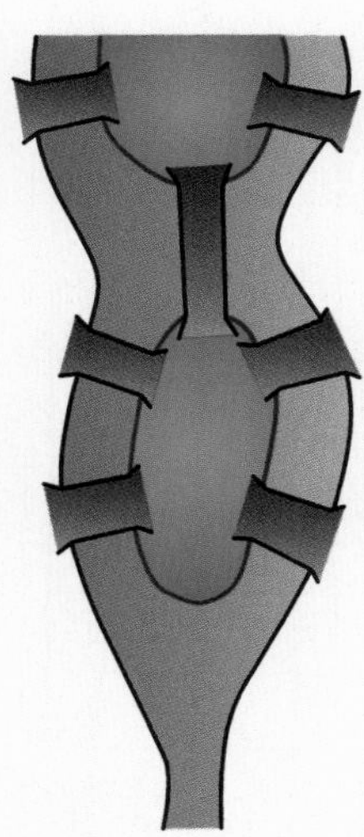

3. In 1736, Leonhard Euler solved the following problem and invented the branch of mathematics now known as Graph Theory. The people of Konigsberg loved to walk about their town and particularly enjoyed the bridges that crossed the river, which flowed through the town. Euler wondered if it was possible to traverse each bridge exactly once on a stroll through town. Create a graph that shows each bridge as an edge to represent the town and use your graph to determine if it is possible to cross each bridge only once.

4. Use the matrices below to answer the questions that follow.

$$A = \begin{bmatrix} 1 & 2 & 5 \end{bmatrix} \quad B = \begin{bmatrix} -1 \\ 2 \\ 10 \end{bmatrix} \quad C = \begin{bmatrix} 1 & 2 & 4 \\ 4 & 5 & 1 \\ 0 & 1 & 3 \end{bmatrix} \quad D = \begin{bmatrix} 1 & 0 & 0 \\ 0 & 1 & 0 \\ 1 & 0 & 1 \end{bmatrix}$$

(a) State the dimensions of A, B, and C.
(b) Calculate $C + D$.
(c) Calculate $C - D$.
(d) Calculate $2C$.
(e) Calculate $-3B$.
(f) Calculate AC.
(g) Calculate BC and CB.
(h) Explain why the product AC is possible but the product CA is not.
(i) Show that $A(D + C) = AD + AC$.

5. The following project graph indicates the duration (in days) of a project that has already been broken down into tasks numbered 1 to 11. Create a task table, and identify the project's critical path and earliest completion time.

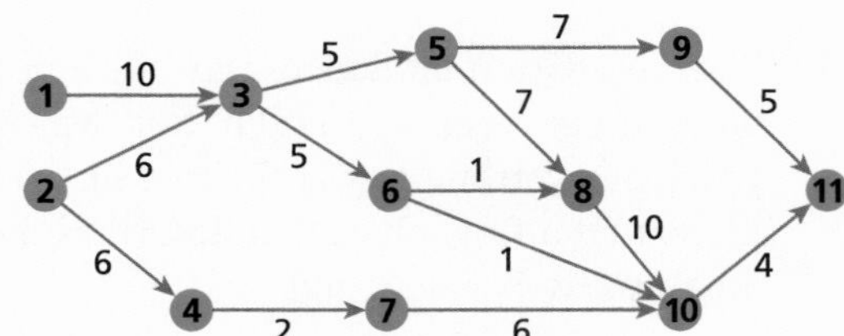

6. Consider the following task table.

Task	Description	Duration (in days)	Prerequisite Task(s)
A	Decide on date for party	1	none
B	Reserve karaoke machine	1	A
C	Send invitations	4	A
D	Receive replies	21	C
E	Buy toys and balloons	2	D
F	Buy food	3	D
G	Blow up balloons	1	E
H	Prepare food	3	F
I	Decorate room	1	H, G
J	Pick up karaoke machine	1	B
K	Have party	1	J, I
L	Clean up	1	K
M	Return karaoke machine	1	K
N	Send out thank-you letters	3	L
O	Give extra food to food bank	1	K

Your class has decided to hold a surprise birthday party for your mathematics teacher. This task table represents the results of your planning.

(a) Draw a project graph for this party and the subsequent clean-up.

(b) Determine the critical path.

(c) Use the critical path to determine the earliest completion time.

Chapter 6 Test

1. Draw the flow chart that represents the following algorithm for finding $n!$.

A: Enter the value of n.
B: Store the value of n into k.
C: Reduce the value of n by 1.
D: Multiply k by the new value of n.
E: If n is greater than 1, go to Step C; otherwise, stop.

2. Use the matrices below to answer the questions that follow.

$$A = \begin{bmatrix} -4 & 0 & 5 \end{bmatrix} \quad B = \begin{bmatrix} -2 \\ 3 \\ -7 \end{bmatrix} \quad C = \begin{bmatrix} 2 & 2 & 4 \\ 4 & 0 & 1 \\ 5 & 1 & 3 \end{bmatrix} \quad D = \begin{bmatrix} 2 & 0 & 0 \\ 3 & 1 & 0 \\ 1 & 0 & 4 \end{bmatrix}$$

(a) State the dimensions of A, B, and C.
(b) Calculate $C + D$.
(c) Calculate $C - D$.
(d) Calculate $2C$.
(e) Calculate $-3B$.
(f) Calculate AC.
(g) Calculate BC and CB.
(h) Explain why the product AC is possible but the product CA is not.
(i) Show that $A(D + C) = AD + AC$.

3. A teacher surveyed the students in a class to find out who would like to sit beside whom. The results for part of the class are shown.

Student	Would sit beside ...
Ellia	Paul, Ramzia, Kaethe, Wendy
Paul	Ellia, Roger, Ramzia
Ramzia	Kaethe, Roger
Kaethe	Wendy, Ramzia
Wendy	any student
Roger	anyone but Ramzia

(a) Draw a directed graph to represent the seating preferences among this group of students.
(b) Write out the relationship matrix that describes the seating preferences for this group.
(c) Suppose the students passed a note from one to another. Use matrix methods to determine the number of different ways there are for Paul to send a note and get it back in four passes.

4. Create a task table and calculate the earliest start time. (Assume that all times are in days.) Identify the critical path in the following graph.

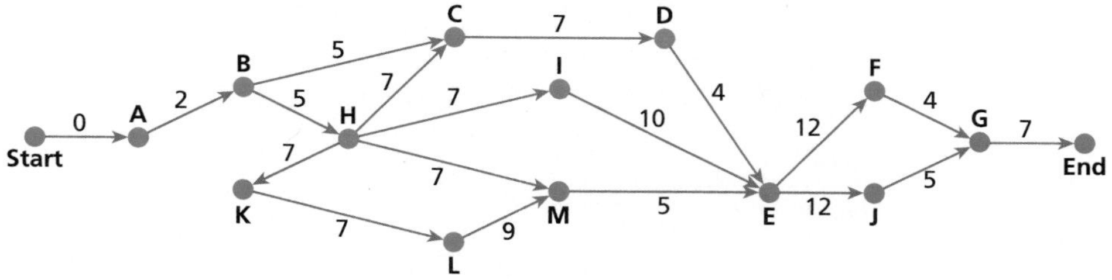

Appendix A: Data Sets

A.1 Men's Summer Olympics Gold Medal Results

Year	High Jump (m)	Discus Throw (m)	Long Jump (m)
1896	1.81	29.15	6.35
1900	1.90	36.04	7.19
1904	1.80	39.28	7.34
1908	1.91	40.89	7.48
1912	1.93	45.21	7.60
1920	1.94	44.68	7.15
1924	1.98	46.15	7.45
1928	1.94	47.32	7.74
1932	1.97	49.49	7.64
1936	2.03	50.48	8.06
1948	1.98	52.78	7.82
1952	2.04	55.04	7.57

Year	High Jump (m)	Discus Throw (m)	Long Jump (m)
1956	2.11	56.35	7.83
1960	2.16	59.18	8.12
1964	2.18	61.00	8.07
1968	2.24	64.78	8.90
1972	2.23	64.39	8.24
1976	2.25	67.50	8.34
1980	2.36	66.65	8.54
1984	2.35	66.60	8.54
1988	2.38	68.82	8.72
1992	2.34	65.12	8.67
1996	2.39	69.40	8.50
2000	2.35	69.30	8.55

For more Olympic results, see **www.ex.ac.uk/cimt/data/olympics/olymindx.htm**.

A.2 TV Advertising Spending

The following data is a sample taken from a 1983 study by a New York ad-testing company. It is based on interviews with 20 000 adults who were asked to name the most outstanding TV commercial they had seen that week. **Spend** lists the annual advertising spending for the company in 1983. **Milimp** is an index that measures millions of retained impressions per week.

Firm	Spend ($)	Milimp
Miller Lite	50.1	32.10
Pepsi	74.1	99.60
Crest	32.4	71.10
Federal Express	22.9	21.90
Burger King	82.4	60.80
Coca-Cola	40.1	78.60
McDonald's	185.9	92.40
MCI	26.9	50.70

Firm	Spend ($)	Milimp
Levi's	27.0	40.80
Bud Lite	45.6	10.40
ATT/Bell	154.9	88.90
Calvin Klein	5.0	12.00
Wendy's	49.7	29.20
Polaroid	26.9	38.00
Ford	166.2	40.10
Meow Mix	7.6	12.30

A.3 Billionaires

Fortune magazine annually publishes a list of billionaires. The 1992 list included 231 individuals or families. Their wealth (in billions of dollars), age (in years), and geographic location (**A**sia, **E**urope, **M**iddle East, **U**nited States, or **O**ther) are reported. (* means not available.)

Wealth	Age	Region
37.0	50	M
24.0	88	U
14.0	64	A
13.0	63	U
13.0	66	U
11.7	72	E
10.0	71	M
8.2	77	U
8.1	68	U
7.2	66	E
7.0	69	M
6.2	36	O
5.9	49	U
5.3	73	U
5.2	52	E
5.0	77	M
5.0	73	M
4.9	62	A
4.8	54	U
4.7	63	U
4.7	23	U
4.6	70	O
4.6	59	E
4.5	96	E
4.5	84	O
4.5	40	E
4.3	60	U
4.0	77	E
4.0	68	E
4.0	83	E
4.0	68	A
4.0	40	E
4.0	62	M
4.0	69	E
4.0	49	A
3.9	64	A
3.9	83	A
3.8	41	A
3.8	78	A
3.6	80	A
3.5	68	O
3.4	67	U
3.4	71	O
3.4	54	A
3.3	62	E
3.3	69	A
3.3	58	U
3.2	71	U
3.2	55	O
3.0	66	E
3.0	65	E
3.0	50	U
3.0	64	E
3.0	57	A
3.0	86	M
3.0	71	E
3.0	68	E
3.0	68	E
3.0	54	U
2.8	68	A
2.8	76	E
2.8	52	E
2.8	73	O
2.8	46	O
2.7	69	U
2.7	63	E
2.6	42	E
2.6	67	E
2.6	62	O
2.6	66	U
2.6	75	U
2.5	74	E
2.5	73	E
2.5	84	M
2.5	49	A
2.4	60	U
2.4	71	O
2.4	76	A
2.4	67	E
2.3	54	A
2.3	57	U
2.3	54	O
2.3	64	O
2.2	85	E
2.2	45	A
2.2	39	O
2.2	54	E
2.1	68	U
2.1	85	U
2.0	70	M
2.0	102	M
2.0	38	U
2.0	73	A
2.0	91	E
2.0	82	U
2.0	74	M
2.0	81	M
2.0	*	U
2.0	62	E
2.0	62	U
2.0	67	U
2.0	80	O

Wealth	Age	Region
2.0	68	M
2.0	80	U
2.0	*	U
2.0	60	E
2.0	74	O
1.9	48	U
1.9	60	E
1.9	43	E
1.9	64	O
1.9	67	U
1.8	62	A
1.8	90	E
1.8	66	U
1.8	68	A
1.8	60	A
1.8	53	A
1.8	47	E
1.8	86	U
1.8	67	A
1.7	54	U
1.7	77	E
1.7	61	U
1.7	83	E
1.7	61	U
1.7	58	U
1.7	64	U
1.7	53	A
1.7	67	A
1.6	57	E
1.6	62	A
1.6	*	E
1.6	64	O
1.6	69	A
1.6	71	E
1.6	54	U
1.6	78	A
1.5	45	U
1.5	69	U
1.5	59	U
1.5	*	A
1.5	82	O
1.5	68	E
1.5	41	E

Wealth	Age	Region
1.5	60	E
1.5	64	E
1.5	44	E
1.5	7	E
1.5	72	E
1.5	56	E
1.5	60	E
1.4	61	E
1.4	79	O
1.4	42	O
1.4	63	E
1.4	49	E
1.4	56	E
1.4	67	U
1.4	75	E
1.4	43	M
1.4	61	U
1.4	54	O
1.4	47	E
1.4	64	U
1.4	52	A
1.4	73	A
1.3	83	U
1.3	64	E
1.3	71	O
1.3	71	E
1.3	61	M
1.3	83	E
1.3	43	E
1.3	47	U
1.3	79	E
1.3	53	E
1.3	73	U
1.3	72	U
1.3	72	U
1.3	59	A
1.3	77	E
1.3	68	E
1.3	42	E
1.3	61	U
1.2	69	A
1.2	82	O
1.2	*	E

Wealth	Age	Region
1.2	56	U
1.2	42	M
1.2	63	U
1.2	75	U
1.2	*	E
1.2	59	A
1.2	70	E
1.2	46	M
1.2	68	U
1.2	68	A
1.2	69	A
1.2	68	O
1.2	64	A
1.1	53	E
1.1	79	E
1.1	49	E
1.1	47	U
1.1	75	U
1.1	76	M
1.1	66	U
1.1	85	U
1.1	66	O
1.1	70	U
1.1	58	E
1.1	72	E
1.1	52	M
1.0	52	O
1.0	79	E
1.0	69	A
1.0	52	M
1.0	75	E
1.0	62	E
1.0	65	M
1.0	63	U
1.0	87	E
1.0	61	U
1.0	58	O
1.0	60	E
1.0	67	O
1.0	80	E
1.0	63	U
1.0	9	M
1.0	59	E

A.4 Singer Heights

Heights (in centimetres) of singers in the New York Choral Society in 1979 are recorded below.

Soprano	Alto	Tenor	Bass
163	165	175	183
158	157	183	178
168	173	180	183
165	170	168	175
152	170	193	185
155	160	188	180
165	170	180	183
168	168	168	173
165	160	173	173
160	183	170	180
170	157	178	168
165	155	165	173
158	168	183	180
165	163	178	185
173	152	173	185
165	155	185	178
160	168	168	173
165	168	173	178
158	168	170	191

Soprano	Alto	Tenor	Bass
165	157	163	173
168	178		180
158	165		178
165	163		188
160	160		178
165	165		191
168	175		191
165	155		175
157	168		183
165	165		180
168	155		178
165	160		180
155	163		173
165	170		178
168	168		191
165	173		183
157			168
			183
			178
			175

Source: **http://lib.stat.cmu.edu/DASL/Datafiles/Singers.html**

A.5 Crawling Age

The table that follows displays data from a study of the age at which infants learn to crawl. Researchers were interested in whether or not heavy winter clothing inhibited an infant's learning to crawl. The table contains the number of infants born during each month (n), the mean crawling age (in weeks) and standard deviation (SD), and the average monthly temperature (in degrees Celsius) six months after the birth month.

Birth Month	*n*	Crawling Age	SD	Temp
January	32	29.84	7.08	22
February	36	30.52	6.96	22
March	23	29.70	8.33	17
April	26	31.84	6.21	11
May	27	28.58	8.07	14
June	29	31.44	8.10	0
July	21	33.64	6.91	−1
August	45	32.82	7.61	0
September	38	33.83	6.93	3
October	44	33.35	7.29	9
November	49	33.38	7.42	14
December	44	32.32	5.71	19

Source: **http://lib.stat.cmu.edu/DASL/Datafiles/Crawling.html**

A.6 Census Data

Listed below is a selection of census data collected from the colonies in New France, later to become Lower Canada, in 1665, 1765, and 1860.

1665 Census of New France

Region	Families	Population	Males	Females	Married		Widowed & Unmarried	
					Males	Females	Males	Females
Beauport	29	185	117	68	28	28	89	40
Beaupré	89	533	315	218	84	83	231	135
Côte St. Jean, Côte St. François, Côte St. Michel	27	153	99	54	24	26	75	28
Île d'Orléans	96	452	291	161	93	84	198	77
Lauzon	3	13	9	4	3	3	6	1
Montréal	107	625	384	241	105	105	279	136
Notre-Dame des Anges, Rivière St. Charles	24	112	67	45	28	24	39	21
Québec	71	547	360	187	65	53	295	134
Sillery	23	140	93	47	23	21	70	26
Trois-Rivières	69	455	299	156	75	64	224	92

1765 Census of New France

Region	Families	Population	Males	Females	Married		Widowed & Unmarried	
					Males	Females	Males	Females
Beauport	167	891	451	440	167	165	284	275
Île d'Orléans–St. François	71	378	185	193	71	67	114	126
Île d'Orléans–St. Jean	91	524	264	260	91	90	173	170
Île d'Orléans–St. Pierre	88	471	225	246	85	88	140	158
Île d'Orléans–Ste. Famille	83	457	244	213	77	83	167	130
Rivière St. Charles	41	297	146	151	36	41	110	110
St. Charles	204	1073	546	527	204	198	342	329
St. Jean d'Eschaillons	32	183	93	90	32	32	61	58
St. Jean Port	73	393	191	202	70	73	121	129
Trois-Rivières	126	644	309	335	130	153	179	182

1860 Census of Lower Canada

Region	Families	Population	Males	Females	Married		Widowed & Unmarried	
					Males	Females	Males	Females
Beauharnois	2 354	15 697	7 887	7 810	2 352	2 350	5 535	5 460
Chicoutimi	1 492	10 317	5 625	4 692	1 734	1 516	3 891	3 176
Drummond	1 881	12 280	6 342	5 888	2 076	1 878	4 316	4 010
Gaspé, et Île de la Madeleine	2 246	13 988	7 362	6 626	2 337	2 234	5 025	4 392
Hochelaga	2 769	16 415	8 290	8 125	2 632	2 442	5 658	5 683
Islet	2 025	12 300	6 221	6 079	1 913	1 897	4 308	4 182
Jacques Cartier	1 718	11 215	5 741	5 474	1 612	1 556	4 129	3 918
Joliette	3 246	21 100	10 723	10 377	3 486	3 076	7 237	7 301
Kamouraska	2 835	21 055	10 544	10 511	3 090	3 121	7 454	7 390
Laval	1 688	10 501	5 263	5 238	1 518	1 462	3 745	3 776
Lotbinière	2 712	20 004	10 169	9 835	2 896	2 895	7 271	6 940
Lévis	3 235	22 065	11 225	10 840	3 237	3 213	7 988	7 627
Montcalm	2 307	14 754	7 527	7 227	2 132	2 030	5 395	5 197
Montréal	17 570	90 227	43 758	46 469	13 388	12 985	30 370	33 484
Québec City	16 077	49 057	23 691	25 366	7 209	7 169	16 482	18 197
Trois-Rivières	991	6 053	2 932	3 121	882	920	2 050	2 201

A.7 Men's Track Times

These data are the national record times for eight races for men before the 1984 Olympics Games. The record times are listed for 55 countries (in seconds for 100 m, 200 m, and 400 m, and in minutes for the rest).

Country	100 m	200 m	400 m	800 m	1500 m	5 K	10 K	Marathon
Argentina	10.39	20.81	46.84	1.81	3.70	14.04	29.36	137.72
Australia	10.31	20.06	44.84	1.74	3.57	13.28	27.66	128.30
Austria	10.44	20.81	46.82	1.79	3.60	13.26	27.72	135.90
Belgium	10.34	20.68	45.04	1.73	3.60	13.22	27.45	129.95
Bermuda	10.28	20.58	45.91	1.80	3.75	14.68	30.55	146.62
Brazil	10.22	20.43	45.21	1.73	3.66	13.62	28.62	133.13
Burma	10.64	21.52	48.30	1.80	3.85	14.45	30.28	139.95
Canada	10.17	20.22	45.68	1.76	3.63	13.55	28.09	130.15
Chile	10.34	20.80	46.20	1.79	3.71	13.61	29.30	134.03
China	10.51	21.04	47.30	1.81	3.73	13.90	29.13	133.53
Colombia	10.43	21.05	46.10	1.82	3.74	13.49	27.88	131.35
Cook Islands	12.18	23.20	52.94	2.02	4.24	16.70	35.38	164.70
Costa Rica	10.94	21.90	48.66	1.87	3.84	14.03	28.81	136.58
Czechoslovakia	10.35	20.65	45.64	1.76	3.58	13.42	28.19	134.32
Denmark	10.56	20.52	45.89	1.78	3.61	13.50	28.11	130.78
Dominican Republic	10.14	20.65	46.80	1.82	3.82	14.91	31.45	154.12
Finland	10.43	20.69	45.49	1.74	3.61	13.27	27.52	130.87
France	10.11	20.38	45.28	1.73	3.57	13.34	27.97	132.30
Germany (East)	10.12	20.33	44.87	1.73	3.56	13.17	27.42	129.92
Germany (West)	10.16	20.37	44.50	1.73	3.53	13.21	27.61	132.23
Greece	10.22	20.71	46.56	1.78	3.64	14.59	28.45	134.60
Guatemala	10.98	21.82	48.40	1.89	3.80	14.16	30.11	139.33
Hungary	10.26	20.62	46.02	1.77	3.62	13.49	28.44	132.58
India	10.60	21.42	45.73	1.76	3.73	13.77	28.81	131.98
Indonesia	10.59	21.49	47.80	1.84	3.92	14.73	30.79	148.83
Ireland	10.61	20.96	46.30	1.79	3.56	13.32	27.81	132.35
Israel	10.71	21.00	47.80	1.77	3.72	13.66	28.93	137.55
Italy	10.01	19.72	45.26	1.73	3.60	13.23	27.52	131.08
Japan	10.34	20.81	45.86	1.79	3.64	13.41	27.72	128.63
Kenya	10.46	20.66	44.92	1.73	3.55	13.10	27.38	129.75
Korea (North)	10.91	21.94	47.30	1.85	3.77	14.13	29.67	130.87

Country	100 m	200 m	400 m	800 m	1500 m	5 K	10 K	Marathon
Korea (South)	10.34	20.89	46.90	1.79	3.77	13.96	29.23	136.25
Luxembourg	10.35	20.77	47.40	1.82	3.67	13.64	29.08	141.27
Malaysia	10.40	20.92	46.30	1.82	3.80	14.64	31.01	154.10
Mauritius	11.19	22.45	47.70	1.88	3.83	15.06	31.77	152.23
Mexico	10.42	21.30	46.10	1.80	3.65	13.46	27.95	129.20
Netherlands	10.52	20.95	45.10	1.74	3.62	13.36	27.61	129.02
New Zealand	10.51	20.88	46.10	1.74	3.54	13.21	27.70	128.98
Norway	10.55	21.16	46.71	1.76	3.62	13.34	27.69	131.48
Papua New Guinea	10.96	21.78	47.90	1.90	4.01	14.72	31.36	148.22
Philippines	10.78	21.64	46.24	1.81	3.83	14.74	30.64	145.27
Poland	10.16	20.24	45.36	1.76	3.60	13.29	27.89	131.58
Portugal	10.53	21.17	46.70	1.79	3.62	13.13	27.38	128.65
Romania	10.41	20.98	45.87	1.76	3.64	13.25	27.67	132.50
Singapore	10.38	21.28	47.40	1.88	3.89	15.11	31.32	157.77
Spain	10.42	20.77	45.98	1.76	3.55	13.31	27.73	131.57
Sweden	10.25	20.61	45.63	1.77	3.61	13.29	27.94	130.63
Switzerland	10.37	20.46	45.78	1.78	3.55	13.22	27.91	131.20
Taiwan	10.59	21.29	46.80	1.79	3.77	14.07	30.07	139.27
Thailand	10.39	21.09	47.91	1.83	3.84	15.23	32.56	149.90
Turkey	10.71	21.43	47.60	1.79	3.67	13.56	28.58	131.50
United Kingdom	10.11	20.21	44.93	1.70	3.51	13.01	27.51	129.13
USA	9.93	19.75	43.86	1.73	3.53	13.20	27.43	128.22
USSR	10.07	20.00	44.60	1.75	3.59	13.20	27.53	130.55
Western Samoa	10.82	21.86	49.00	2.02	4.24	16.28	34.71	161.83

Source: **http://lib.stat.cmu.edu/DASL/Datafiles/Men'sTrack.html**

A.8 Smoking and Mortality

Government statisticians in England conducted a study of the relationship between smoking and lung cancer. The smoking index is the ratio of the average number of cigarettes smoked per day by men in the particular occupational group to the average number of cigarettes smoked per day by all men. The mortality index is the ratio of the rate of deaths from lung cancer among men in the particular occupational group to the rate of deaths from lung cancer among all men.

Variable Names:

Occupational_Group: Occupational Group
Smoking: Smoking index (100 = average)
Mortality: Lung cancer mortality index (100 = average)

Occupational_Group	Smoking	Mortality
Farmers, foresters, and fishers	77	84
Miners and quarry workers	137	116
Gas, coke, and chemical makers	117	123
Glass and ceramics makers	94	128
Furnace, forge, foundry, and rolling-mill workers	116	155
Electrical and electronics workers	102	101
Engineering and allied trades	111	118
Professionals, technical workers, and artists	66	51
Leather workers	88	104
Textile workers	102	88
Clothing workers	91	104
Food, drink, and tobacco workers	104	129
Woodworkers	93	113

Occupational_Group	Smoking	Mortality
Drivers of stationary engines, cranes, etc.	125	113
Makers of other products	112	96
Service, sport, and recreation workers	100	120
Painters and decorators	110	139
Transport and communications workers	115	128
Labourers not included elsewhere	133	146
Paper and printing workers	107	86
Warehouse workers, storekeepers, packers, and bottlers	105	115
Clerical workers	87	79
Sales workers	91	85
Construction workers	113	144
Administrators and managers	76	60

Source: **http://lib.stat.cmu.edu/DASL/Datafiles/SmokingandCancer.html**

A.9 Triathlon Results

Listed below are the results of the 2001 Subaru Triathlon Series Guelph Lake II Triathlon held on September 1, 2001. The age categories are **A**—Elite Male; **C**—Male 14–19; **D**—Male 20–24; **E**—Male 25–29; **F**—Male 30–34; **G**—Male 35–39; **H**—Male 40–44. **Plc/Total** stands for the athlete's position out of the number of competitors in the age category. **Ovr** stands for the athlete's place over all.

				750 m Swim			30 km Bike				7 km Run				
Pos	Time	Plc/Total	Category	Cat	Ovr	Time	/100 m	Cat	Ovr	Time	km/h	Cat	Ovr	Time	/km
1	1:22:30	1/7	A	1	1	9:29	1:16	2	5	49:08:00	36.6	1	4	23:54:00	3:25
2	1:22:57	1/93	F	1	13	10:40	1:26	1	1	48:28:00	37.2	2	3	23:50:00	3:25
3	1:23:03	2/7	A	5	10	10:32	1:25	1	2	48:30:00	37.1	2	5	24:02:00	3:26
4	1:25:13	3/7	A	4	4	10:11	1:22	3	6	49:27:00	36.4	4	17	25:35:00	3:40
5	1:25:22	2/93	F	3	23	11:20	1:31	5	12	50:19:00	35.8	1	2	23:44:00	3:24
6	1:26:37	4/7	A	2	2	9:47	1:19	6	25	52:05:00	34.6	3	6	24:46:00	3:33
7	1:27:01	1/101	H	2	27	11:29	1:32	1	8	49:31:00	36.4	5	25	26:03:00	3:44
8	1:27:11	3/93	F	2	20	11:17	1:31	2	3	48:33:00	37.1	10	52	27:22:00	3:55
9	1:27:14	4/93	F	8	66	12:29	1:40	3	9	49:36:00	36.3	3	10	25:10:00	3:36
10	1:27:32	5/7	A	3	3	10:08	1:22	5	21	51:31:00	35	5	20	25:54:00	3:42
11	1:27:33	1/86	G	2	21	11:18	1:31	1	4	48:36:00	37	9	65	27:40:00	3:58
12	1:27:36	5/93	F	5	41	11:52	1:35	4	10	49:36:00	36.3	7	28	26:09:00	3:45
13	1:27:42	2/101	H	1	19	11:17	1:31	4	19	51:24:00	35	1	8	25:02:00	3:35
14	1:28:22	1/57	E	1	12	10:39	1:26	1	27	52:17:00	34.4	1	12	25:26:00	3:38
15	1:28:33	6/7	A	6	17	11:14	1:30	4	7	49:30:00	36.4	6	70	27:50:00	3:59
16	1:29:04	1/18	C	8	53	12:10	1:38	2	23	51:34:00	34.9	2	11	25:21:00	3:38
17	1:29:11	2/18	C1	2	18	11:16	1:31	4	64	55:07:00	32.7	1	1	22:49:00	3:16
18	1:29:13	3/101	H	9	77	12:40	1:42	2	14	50:34:00	35.6	4	23	26:00:00	3:43

Appendix B: Tables

B.1 Z-Score Table

To find the proportion of data with a z-score equal to or less than a calculated value, locate the z-score on the left side of the chart and match it with the appropriate second decimal place. For example,

$$P(z \leq -1.15) = 0.1251$$

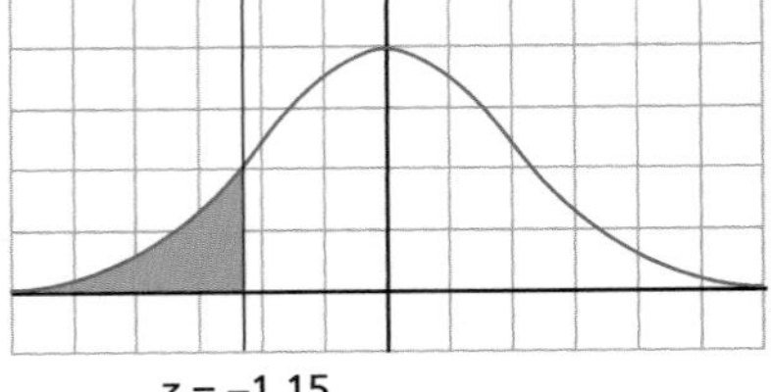

$z = -1.15$

	0.00	0.01	0.02	0.03	0.04	0.05	0.06	0.07	0.08	0.09
−2.9	0.0019	0.0018	0.0018	0.0017	0.0016	0.0016	0.0015	0.0015	0.0014	0.0014
−2.8	0.0026	0.0025	0.0024	0.0023	0.0023	0.0022	0.0021	0.0021	0.0020	0.0019
−2.7	0.0035	0.0034	0.0033	0.0032	0.0031	0.0030	0.0029	0.0028	0.0027	0.0026
−2.6	0.0047	0.0045	0.0044	0.0043	0.0041	0.0040	0.0039	0.0038	0.0037	0.0036
−2.5	0.0062	0.0060	0.0059	0.0057	0.0055	0.0054	0.0052	0.0051	0.0049	0.0048
−2.4	0.0082	0.0080	0.0078	0.0075	0.0073	0.0071	0.0069	0.0068	0.0066	0.0064
−2.3	0.0107	0.0104	0.0102	0.0099	0.0096	0.0094	0.0091	0.0089	0.0087	0.0084
−2.2	0.0139	0.0136	0.0132	0.0129	0.0125	0.0122	0.0119	0.0116	0.0113	0.0110
−2.1	0.0179	0.0174	0.0170	0.0166	0.0162	0.0158	0.0154	0.0150	0.0146	0.0143
−2.0	0.0228	0.0222	0.0217	0.0212	0.0207	0.0202	0.0197	0.0192	0.0188	0.0183
−1.9	0.0287	0.0281	0.0274	0.0268	0.0262	0.0256	0.0250	0.0244	0.0239	0.0233
−1.8	0.0359	0.0351	0.0344	0.0336	0.0329	0.0322	0.0314	0.0307	0.0301	0.0294
−1.7	0.0446	0.0436	0.0427	0.0418	0.0409	0.0401	0.0392	0.0384	0.0375	0.0367
−1.6	0.0548	0.0537	0.0526	0.0516	0.0505	0.0495	0.0485	0.0475	0.0465	0.0455
−1.5	0.0668	0.0655	0.0643	0.0630	0.0618	0.0606	0.0594	0.0582	0.0571	0.0559
−1.4	0.0808	0.0793	0.0778	0.0764	0.0749	0.0735	0.0721	0.0708	0.0694	0.0681
−1.3	0.0968	0.0951	0.0934	0.0918	0.0901	0.0885	0.0869	0.0853	0.0838	0.0823
−1.2	0.1151	0.1131	0.1112	0.1093	0.1075	0.1056	0.1038	0.1020	0.1003	0.0985
−1.1	0.1357	0.1335	0.1314	0.1292	0.1271	0.1251	0.1230	0.1210	0.1190	0.1170
−1.0	0.1587	0.1562	0.1539	0.1515	0.1492	0.1469	0.1446	0.1423	0.1401	0.1379
−0.9	0.1841	0.1814	0.1788	0.1762	0.1736	0.1711	0.1685	0.1660	0.1635	0.1611
−0.8	0.2119	0.2090	0.2061	0.2033	0.2005	0.1977	0.1949	0.1922	0.1894	0.1867
−0.7	0.2420	0.2389	0.2358	0.2327	0.2296	0.2266	0.2236	0.2206	0.2177	0.2148
−0.6	0.2743	0.2709	0.2676	0.2643	0.2611	0.2578	0.2546	0.2514	0.2483	0.2451
−0.5	0.3085	0.3050	0.3015	0.2981	0.2946	0.2912	0.2877	0.2843	0.2810	0.2776
−0.4	0.3446	0.3409	0.3372	0.3336	0.3300	0.3264	0.3228	0.3192	0.3156	0.3121
−0.3	0.3821	0.3783	0.3745	0.3707	0.3669	0.3632	0.3594	0.3557	0.3520	0.3483
−0.2	0.4207	0.4168	0.4129	0.4090	0.4052	0.4013	0.3974	0.3936	0.3897	0.3859
−0.1	0.4602	0.4562	0.4522	0.4483	0.4443	0.4404	0.4364	0.4325	0.4286	0.4247
−0.0	0.5000	0.4960	0.4920	0.4880	0.4840	0.4801	0.4761	0.4721	0.4681	0.4641

Note: A spreadsheet form of this table is available on the textbook CD.

Z-Score Table

To find the proportion of data with a z-score equal to or less than a calculated value, locate the z-score on the left side of the chart and match it with the appropriate second decimal place. For example,

$$P(z \leq -1.15) = 0.1251$$

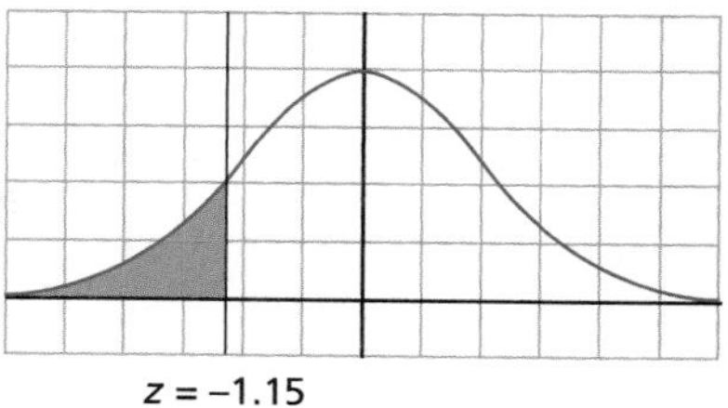

	0.00	0.01	0.02	0.03	0.04	0.05	0.06	0.07	0.08	0.09
0.0	0.5000	0.5040	0.5080	0.5120	0.5160	0.5199	0.5239	0.5279	0.5319	0.5359
0.1	0.5398	0.5438	0.5478	0.5517	0.5557	0.5596	0.5636	0.5675	0.5714	0.5753
0.2	0.5793	0.5832	0.5871	0.5910	0.5948	0.5987	0.6026	0.6064	0.6103	0.6141
0.3	0.6179	0.6217	0.6255	0.6293	0.6331	0.6368	0.6406	0.6443	0.6480	0.6517
0.4	0.6554	0.6591	0.6628	0.6664	0.6700	0.6736	0.6772	0.6808	0.6844	0.6879
0.5	0.6915	0.6950	0.6985	0.7019	0.7054	0.7088	0.7123	0.7157	0.7190	0.7224
0.6	0.7257	0.7291	0.7324	0.7357	0.7389	0.7422	0.7454	0.7486	0.7517	0.7549
0.7	0.7580	0.7611	0.7642	0.7673	0.7704	0.7734	0.7764	0.7794	0.7823	0.7852
0.8	0.7881	0.7910	0.7939	0.7967	0.7995	0.8023	0.8051	0.8078	0.8106	0.8133
0.9	0.8159	0.8186	0.8212	0.8238	0.8264	0.8289	0.8315	0.8340	0.8365	0.8389
1.0	0.8413	0.8438	0.8461	0.8485	0.8508	0.8531	0.8554	0.8577	0.8599	0.8621
1.1	0.8643	0.8665	0.8686	0.8708	0.8729	0.8749	0.8770	0.8790	0.8810	0.8830
1.2	0.8849	0.8869	0.8888	0.8907	0.8925	0.8944	0.8962	0.8980	0.8997	0.9015
1.3	0.9032	0.9049	0.9066	0.9082	0.9099	0.9115	0.9131	0.9147	0.9162	0.9177
1.4	0.9192	0.9207	0.9222	0.9236	0.9251	0.9265	0.9279	0.9292	0.9306	0.9319
1.5	0.9332	0.9345	0.9357	0.9370	0.9382	0.9394	0.9406	0.9418	0.9429	0.9441
1.6	0.9452	0.9463	0.9474	0.9484	0.9495	0.9505	0.9515	0.9525	0.9535	0.9545
1.7	0.9554	0.9564	0.9573	0.9582	0.9591	0.9599	0.9608	0.9616	0.9625	0.9633
1.8	0.9641	0.9649	0.9656	0.9664	0.9671	0.9678	0.9686	0.9693	0.9699	0.9706
1.9	0.9713	0.9719	0.9726	0.9732	0.9738	0.9744	0.9750	0.9756	0.9761	0.9767
2.0	0.9772	0.9778	0.9783	0.9788	0.9793	0.9798	0.9803	0.9808	0.9812	0.9817
2.1	0.9821	0.9826	0.9830	0.9834	0.9838	0.9842	0.9846	0.9850	0.9854	0.9857
2.2	0.9861	0.9864	0.9868	0.9871	0.9875	0.9878	0.9881	0.9884	0.9887	0.9890
2.3	0.9893	0.9896	0.9898	0.9901	0.9904	0.9906	0.9909	0.9911	0.9913	0.9916
2.4	0.9918	0.9920	0.9922	0.9925	0.9927	0.9929	0.9931	0.9932	0.9934	0.9936
2.5	0.9938	0.9940	0.9941	0.9943	0.9945	0.9946	0.9948	0.9949	0.9951	0.9952
2.6	0.9953	0.9955	0.9956	0.9957	0.9959	0.9960	0.9961	0.9962	0.9963	0.9964
2.7	0.9965	0.9966	0.9967	0.9968	0.9969	0.9970	0.9971	0.9972	0.9973	0.9974
2.8	0.9974	0.9975	0.9976	0.9977	0.9977	0.9978	0.9979	0.9979	0.9980	0.9981
2.9	0.9981	0.9982	0.9982	0.9983	0.9984	0.9984	0.9985	0.9985	0.9986	0.9986

Note: A spreadsheet form of this table is available on the textbook CD.

B.2 Random Number Table

00	90556	37303	16868	53589	34379	95887	96973	17864
01	28137	88672	12904	18049	24437	13430	47540	15194
02	51010	48541	58401	45575	00050	44076	80951	12764
03	27146	79380	59119	34417	10507	94520	37050	33195
04	09471	37596	48904	33110	16068	54301	59722	39419
05	06937	52014	20221	62155	17189	20272	03726	21235
06	76703	55469	80031	92790	74086	09831	70653	72818
07	42330	77174	14747	28461	48197	18666	59922	76880
08	14286	31458	30754	37777	74590	81545	82075	88622
09	55339	15957	01051	55382	22965	18593	03136	99255
10	81415	83348	63890	45336	26242	49262	62257	20572
11	63018	86085	23365	11689	36390	97436	54829	00472
12	56703	47117	76919	60611	22130	88657	72046	29157
13	67071	39298	79566	98255	20912	78454	94100	95609
14	92788	76191	51701	17598	77924	99201	12390	12442
15	87424	01941	82159	00658	79348	47689	50578	49560
16	19095	42266	56901	96735	07064	25994	27594	93311
17	84561	00658	30626	82997	63483	11622	76111	07887
18	06892	40229	66054	39827	61818	85321	33272	64160
19	56072	22220	26686	08382	11604	12391	31574	59241
20	15501	58964	15104	14112	47242	35783	28399	39059
21	48163	38864	44783	95837	40156	28217	36555	80736
22	81107	47007	83751	29585	38337	72519	91217	20381
23	14672	85479	51111	70973	93345	71761	45438	55190
24	73210	79314	29412	63650	30103	01569	86577	27335
25	43723	96825	69858	57422	73081	88570	79092	61842
26	76513	24168	72935	56364	76055	20502	75847	49878
27	69537	32262	66053	89384	99121	66874	05340	93318
28	80620	92013	08570	67344	46608	38410	15889	63623
29	23427	39331	71012	69431	18599	52356	52676	47706
30	58194	62339	15949	32382	87751	62464	68011	92785
31	58300	17028	07585	58332	07732	26258	89411	14425
32	54993	74812	71535	43850	43322	73798	26255	12198
33	87922	12979	74064	12979	49389	92121	52425	68214
34	84191	30237	62899	23397	39938	09213	45894	17828
35	06157	70816	40245	65382	09586	51572	69772	63888
36	58501	61189	88182	23039	43550	69405	43015	95838
37	90029	89998	59217	90137	13712	70685	95036	86037
38	43312	39357	40894	04645	33396	41046	54467	99240
39	05058	76661	63523	00707	57996	14116	00631	14049
40	79577	49450	34059	69844	40964	83200	11351	99432

Appendix C: How to Use a TI-83 Plus Calculator

C.1 How to Enter Data in a List

Statistical functions can only be run on data that are entered in a list.

Clear Lists

Before you begin, make sure all the lists are empty by pressing [2nd] [+] [4] [ENTER] to execute the **ClrAllLists** command. Now you are ready to enter new data.

Edit Lists

Press [STAT] [1] to edit a list. The screen should look like this.

Enter Data

Use the arrow keys to select the list you would like to edit ($\mathbf{L_1} - \mathbf{L_6}$). Data can be input using the number keys followed by the [ENTER] key. The data will be stored in memory until they are cleared.

Correcting Errors

Using the arrow keys, place the cursor on top of an incorrect number and enter it correctly. All other entries will stay in their original place. The [DEL] key can also be used to eliminate an entry and to move all following entries back to fill in the gap. To add an entry and move the existing entries down, press [2nd] [DEL] and key in the new number.

Example 1

Clear all lists and enter the following data into $\mathbf{L_2}$: 1, 2, 5, 3, 7, 4, 3, 1, 6, 5.

Solution

[2nd] [+] [4] [ENTER]	*Clear all lists*
[STAT] [1] [▶]	*Edit* $\mathbf{L_2}$
[1] [ENTER] [2] [ENTER] [5] [ENTER]	*Enter data*
[3] [ENTER] [7] [ENTER] [4] [ENTER]	
[3] [ENTER] [1] [ENTER] [6] [ENTER]	
[5] [ENTER]	

Example 2

Change the first number in $\mathbf{L_2}$ to a 7.

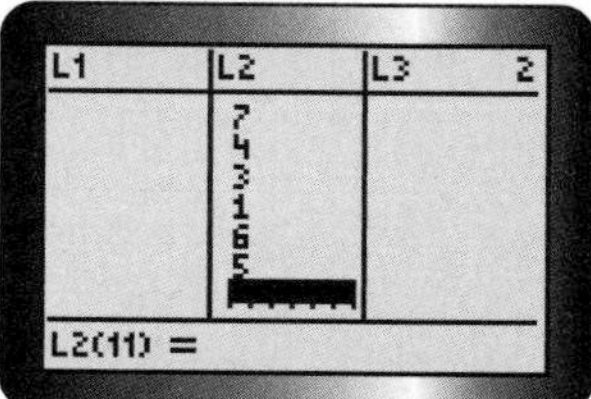

Solution

[▲] [▲] … [▲] ten times	*Select entry*
[7] [ENTER]	*Replace entry*

C.2 How to Perform a Linear Regression

LinReg is a statistical function that takes two lists of variables and relates them to a linear equation $y = ax + b$, with slope a and y-intercept b. The calculator, by default, makes $\mathbf{L_1}$ the X-variable and $\mathbf{L_2}$ the Y-variable; however, you can refer to the manual for more advanced ways to compare two lists.

Enter Data

Following the methods in Appendix C.1, enter two lists of data to be analyzed: one in $\mathbf{L_1}$ and the other in $\mathbf{L_2}$.

Select Command

Press [STAT] and [▶] to select the **CALC** menu.
Then press [4] to select the **4:LinReg (ax + b)** command. Finally, press [ENTER].
The screen display should look something like this.

Correlation Coefficient

Your calculator can be set to find the correlation coefficient when performing a linear regression. Press [2nd] [0] to look at the **CATALOG** menu. Scroll down until you see the **DiagnosticOn** command selected with an arrow; press [ENTER]. The **DiagnosticOn** command will appear on the screen; press [ENTER] to execute it. The calculator will return the message **Done**.

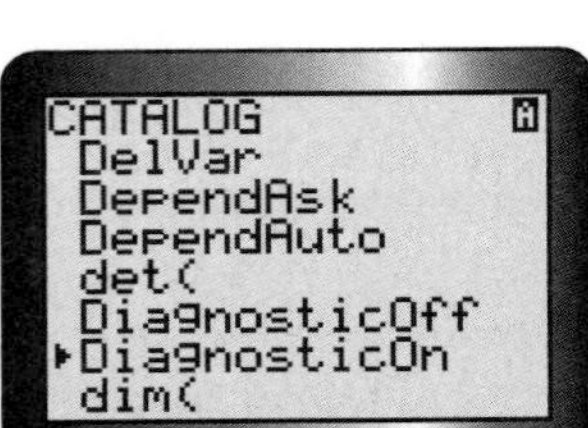

Perform Regression

Now when you perform a linear regression, the calculator will also report the correlation coefficient r, as well as the coefficient of determination r^2 (which is the percent of the data that is accurately described by the regression equation).

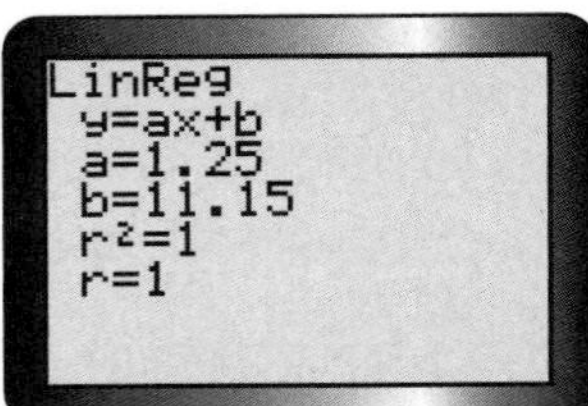

Example

Clear all lists, enter the following information, and perform a linear regression. (Make sure diagnostics are turned on.)

$\mathbf{L_1}$ 1, 3, 5, 7, 9 $\mathbf{L_2}$ 12, 15, 18, 20, 22

Solution

[2nd] [+] [4] [ENTER]	*Clear all lists*
[STAT] [1] [1] [ENTER] [3] [ENTER]	*Edit* $\mathbf{L_1}$
[5] [ENTER] [7] [ENTER] [9] [ENTER] [▶]	
[1] [2] [ENTER] [1] [5] [ENTER] [1] [8] [ENTER]	*Edit* $\mathbf{L_2}$
[2] [0] [ENTER] [2] [2] [ENTER] [2nd] [MODE]	
[STAT] [▶] [4] [ENTER]	*Perform linear regression*

See display screen above for the correct results.

C.3 How to Perform a Quadratic Regression

QuadReg is a statistical function that takes two lists of variables and relates them to the standard quadratic equation $y = ax^2 + bx + c$. As with linear regressions, the calculator makes $\mathbf{L_1}$ the X-variable and $\mathbf{L_2}$ the Y-variable; however, you can refer to the manual for more advanced ways to use QuadReg.

Enter Data

Following the methods in Appendix C.1, enter two lists of data to be analyzed: one in $\mathbf{L_1}$ and the other in $\mathbf{L_2}$.

```
QuadReg
 y=ax²+bx+c
 a=.9821428571
 b=13.52857143
 c=-3.053571429
```

Select Command

Press [STAT] and [▶] to select the **CALC** menu. Then press [5] to select the **QuadReg** command. Finally, press [ENTER]. The screen display, depending on the data being analyzed, should look like this.

Determination Coefficient

Your calculator can be set to find the coefficient of determination when performing a quadratic regression. Press [2nd] [0] to look at the CATALOG menu. Scroll down until you see the **DiagnosticOn** command selected with an arrow; press [ENTER]. The DiagnosticOn command will appear on the screen; press [ENTER] to execute it. The calculator will return the message **Done**.

```
CATALOG
 DelVar
 DependAsk
 DependAuto
 det(
 DiagnosticOff
▶DiagnosticOn
 dim(
```

Perform Regression

Now when you perform a linear regression, the calculator will also report the coefficient of determination r^2 (which is the percent of the data that is accurately described by the regression equation).

```
QuadReg
 y=ax²+bx+c
 a=.9821428571
 b=13.52857143
 c=-3.053571429
 R²=.9998625126
```

Example

Clear all lists, enter the following information, and perform a quadratic regression. (Make sure diagnostics are turned on.)

$\mathbf{L_1}$ 1, 3, 5, 7, 9 $\qquad$ $\mathbf{L_2}$ 12, 45, 90, 140, 198

Solution

Keystrokes	
[2nd] [+] [4] [ENTER]	*Clear all lists*
[STAT] [1] [1] [ENTER] [3] [ENTER]	*Edit* $\mathbf{L_1}$
[5] [ENTER] [7] [ENTER] [9] [ENTER] [▶]	
[1] [2] [ENTER] [4] [5] [ENTER] [9] [0]	*Edit* $\mathbf{L_2}$
[ENTER] [1] [4] [0] [ENTER] [1] [9] [8]	
[ENTER]	
[2nd] [MODE]	
[STAT] [▶] [5] [ENTER]	*Perform quadratic regression*

See display screen above for the correct results.

C.4 How to Construct Scatter Plots

The TI-83 Plus calculator has six different graphing formats for statistical data entered in lists, and a scatter plot is one of them. Up to three stat plots can be displayed at once.

Enter Data
Following the methods in Appendix C.1, enter two lists of data to be analyzed: one in $\mathbf{L_1}$ and the other in $\mathbf{L_2}$.

Define Plot
Press [2nd] [Y=] to access the **STAT PLOT** menu. Press [1] to edit the options for **Plot 1**. Using the arrow keys, move the cursor over the word **On** and press [ENTER] to turn on **Plot 1**. Again, using the arrow keys, move the cursor over the scatter-plot icon and press [ENTER] to select scatter plot.

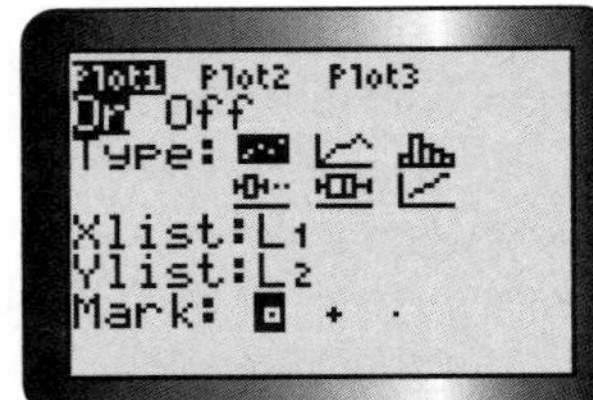

Set Display Options
Press [ZOOM] [9] to automatically adjust the display settings to suit your data set. The calculator will then automatically graph the data set you selected in the **STAT PLOT** menu.

Example

Clear all lists, enter the following information, and create a scatter plot.

$\mathbf{L_1}$ 25.1, 16, 3, 12.7, 8.5, 4.4

$\mathbf{L_2}$ 8, 2, 0.3, 1.4, 0.9, 0.45

Solution

[2nd] [+] [4] [ENTER]	*Clear all lists*
[STAT] [1] [2] [5] [.] [1] [ENTER] [1] [6] [ENTER] [3] [ENTER] [1] [2] [.] [7] [ENTER] [8] [.] [5] [ENTER] [4] [.] [4] [ENTER] [▸]	*Edit* $\mathbf{L_1}$
[8] [ENTER] [2] [ENTER] [.] [3] [ENTER] [1] [.] [4] [ENTER] [.] [9] [ENTER] [.] [4] [5]	*Edit* $\mathbf{L_2}$
[ZOOM] [9] [ENTER]	*Set display options*

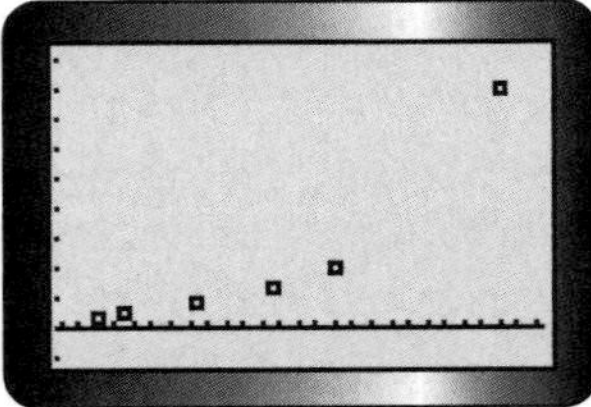

C.5 How to Plot a Line of Best Fit

Once data have been entered into two lists ($\mathbf{L_1}$ and $\mathbf{L_2}$) and you have enabled one of the stat plots, the line of best fit can be displayed on the screen with a scatter plot by storing the linear regression data in one of the Y-variables.

Perform Regression
Press [STAT] [▸] [4] to select **4:LinReg(ax+b)** from the **CALC** menu.

Identify Lists

Press [2nd] [1] [,] [2nd] [2] [,] [VARS] [▸] [1] [1] [ENTER] to identify the lists on which to perform the regression, and the place in which to store the equation. The calculator will then display the results of your linear regression.

Press [ZOOM] [9] to set up the screen dimensions and graph both the scatter plot and the line of best fit.

C.6 How to Create a Histogram

Once data have been entered into one of the lists (L_1), a histogram can be displayed using the STAT PLOT command.

Select Plot1

Press [2nd] [Y=] to access the **STAT PLOTS** menu. Select the first plot by pressing [1] or by using the arrow keys and pressing [ENTER].

Enable Plot1

Select **On** using the cursor and press [ENTER]. Using the arrow keys, select the histogram icon and press [ENTER]. Make sure the **Xlist** is L_1.

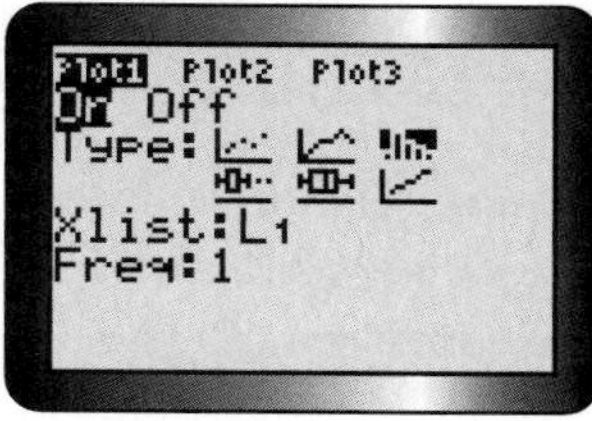

Display Graph

Adjust the display settings by pressing [ZOOM] and set the display to **9: ZoomStat** by pressing [9]. The graph will automatically appear on the screen with the optimal display settings.

Example

Enter the following data into L_1 and display a histogram of the data. Find the number of data in the tallest bar by using the **TRACE** function.

5, 10, 13, 14, 15, 16, 16, 16, 17, 17, 17, 18, 18, 18, 19, 19, 20, 21, 21, 22

Solution

[STAT] [1] [5] [ENTER] [1] [0] [ENTER] [1] [3] [ENTER] [1] [4] [ENTER] [1] [5] [ENTER] [1] [6] [ENTER] [1] [6] [ENTER] [1] [6] [ENTER] [1] [7] [ENTER] [1] [7] [ENTER] [1] [7] [ENTER] [1] [8] [ENTER] [1] [8] [ENTER] [1] [8] [ENTER] [1] [9] [ENTER] [1] [9] [ENTER] [2] [0] [ENTER] [2] [1] [ENTER] [2] [1] [ENTER] [2] [2] [ENTER]	*Enter data*
[2nd] [Y=] [1]	*Select Plot1*
[ENTER] [▾] [▸] [▸] [ENTER]	*Enable Plot1*
[ZOOM] [9]	*Display graph*
[TRACE] [▸] [▸] [▸]	*Explore graph*

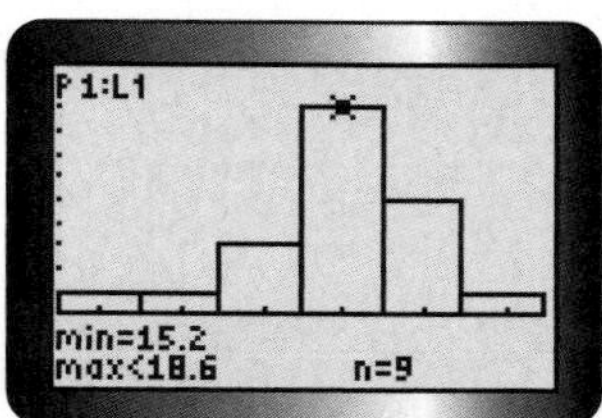

C.7 How to Use the randNorm Command

This command can be used to create a series of random numbers normally distributed about a given mean generated with a given standard deviation. You must supply three arguments: the mean and the standard deviation for the data sample, and the number of pieces of data.

For example, randNorm(0,1,50) will create a list of 50 randomly selected numbers normally distributed about a mean of 0 with a standard deviation of 1.

Select Command
Press [MATH] [▸] [▸] [▸] [6] to select the **6:randNorm(** command.

Enter Arguments
Key in the mean, the standard deviation, and the number of pieces of data, in that order. Press [0] [,] [1] [,] [5] [0] [)] [ENTER] to create the data set mentioned in the example.

Store Results
For you to be able to do any analysis on these results, they must be stored in a list. Press [STO▸] [2nd] [1] to store the results in $\mathbf{L_1}$.

Example

Create a list of 35 random numbers that are normally distributed about the mean 71.1 with a standard deviation of 13.6. (Do not press [ENTER] after the arguments; instead, store directly into $\mathbf{L_1}$.)

Solution

[MATH] [▸] [▸] [▸] [6]	*Select command*
[7] [1] [.] [1] [,] [1] [3] [.] [6] [,] [3] [5] [)]	*Enter arguments*
[STO▸] [2nd] [1] [ENTER]	*Store results*

C.8 How to Use the normalcdf Command

This command will return the proportion of data that lies on a normal distribution between the two z-scores given.

For example, to find the probability of a randomly selected piece of data being one standard deviation or more below the mean, you would evaluate normalcdf(–1E99, –1), using –1E99 as the lower bound and –1 as the upper bound. The probability is approximately 15.9%.

Select Command
Press [2nd] [VARS] [2] to select **2:normalcdf(** from the **DISTR** menu.

Enter Argument
[(-)] [1] [2nd] [,] [9] [9] [,] [(-)] [1] [)] [ENTER]

C.9 How to Use the invnormal Command

This command returns the z-score of the normally distributed piece of data that has the given percent of data less than or equal to itself.

For example, to find the z-score that corresponds to a piece of data that has 65% of the data less than or equal to itself, you would evaluate invnormal(0.65). ($z \doteq 0.385$)

Select Command
Press [2nd] [VARS] [3] to select **3:invnormal(** from the **DISTR** menu.

Enter Argument
[0] [.] [6] [5] [)] [ENTER]

Example

What z-score divides a normal distribution into 25% below and 75% above?

Solution

[2nd] [VARS] [3] *Select command*
[.] [2] [5] [)] [ENTER] *Enter arguments*

C.10 How to Plot Residuals Using RESID

The distance from a point on a scatter plot to the line of best fit is known as the residual value. Refer to Appendices C.1: How to Enter Data in a List, C.4: How to Construct Scatter Plots, and C.5: How to Plot a Line of Best Fit. Once you have done all this, you can calculate each point's distance from the line of best fit and store those values in $\mathbf{L_3}$.

Select $\mathbf{L_3}$
Press [STAT] [1] to edit the lists, and then move the cursor using the arrow keys to the column heading $\mathbf{L_3}$.

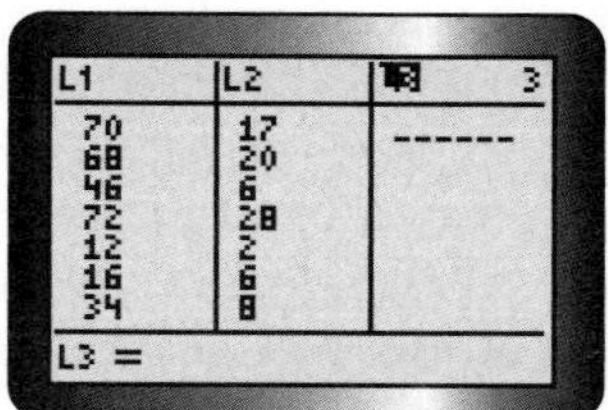

RESID
Press [2nd] [STAT] [7] to select **RESID**, the variable in which residual values are stored, and press [ENTER].

Set Up Plot2
Press [2nd] [Y=] to set up Plot 2. Use the arrow keys to move the cursor over the display **ON** and press [ENTER]. Select the scatter-plot icon and change the **Ylist** to $\mathbf{L_3}$.

Plot Residuals
Press [ZOOM] [9] to set up the display and show the graph with residuals.

C.11 How to Create and Display Random Numbers

randInt is a command that produces a random number within a specified range and can be repeated a specified number of times. Two arguments must be provided: lower bound and upper bound. If no number of trials is specified, the calculator assumes that only one is required.

For example, to find a random integer between 1 and 10, you would execute the command randInt(1,10). To find five random integers between 1 and 10, you would execute the command randInt(1,10, 5).

Select Command
Press [MATH] [▶] [▶] [▶] to use the **PRB** menu and select **5:randInt(** by pressing [5].

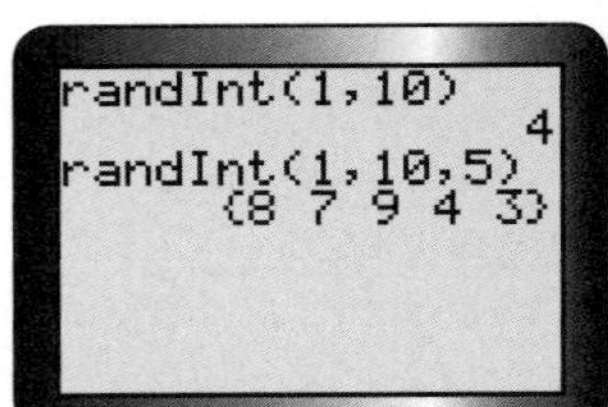

Enter Argument
Enter the lower and upper bounds by keying [1] [,] [1] [0]. If you would like to repeat this command five times, for example, you would also key [,] [5] before entering the closing bracket [)].

C.12 How to Write Programs

The instruction manual for the TI-83 Plus calculator has a number of resources in Chapter 16 and in Appendices A and B that explain in great detail how to program your calculator.

Create Program
Press [PRGM] [▶] [▶] [ENTER] to begin creating a new program. You will be asked to enter the name of your new program. Using the green letter keys on your calculator, enter a name up to eight characters in length and press [ENTER].

Edit Program
Once a program name has been entered, you are automatically sent to the program editor. Commands can be accessed from any of the Advanced Function Keys ([MATH], [APPS], [PRGM], [VARS]). Consult your manual for more on using commands in programs. To return to a program that has already been named, press [PRGM] [▶] to access the **EDIT** menu, pick the program from the list using the arrow keys, and then select it using the [ENTER] key. To exit the program editor, press [2nd] [MODE].

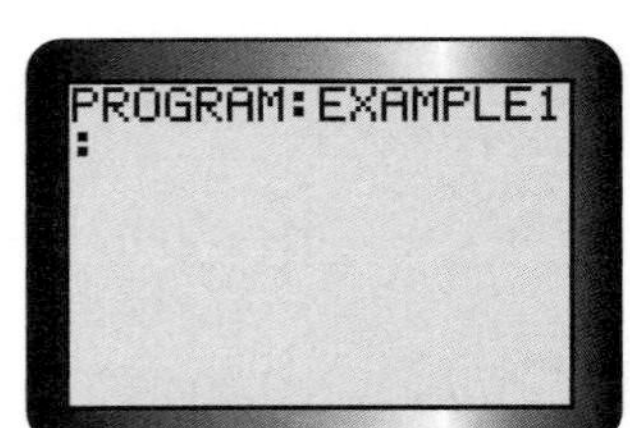

Delete Program
Once a program is no longer needed, you can delete it by pressing [2nd] [+] [2] [7]. Each of the programs currently loaded on your calculator will be listed. Select the program you wish to delete and press the [DEL] key.

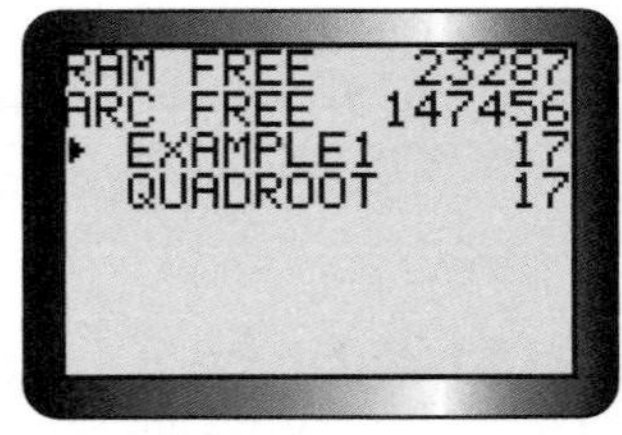

Check the textbook CD for sample programs like the one that follows. These can be loaded into your calculator to make calculations and perform simulations.

Example

Create a program that will take a hockey player's face-off winning percent, number of attempts, and number of successes, and will perform a given number of trials to calculate an experimental probability. Make the program compare this experimental value with the theoretical probability of the same event.

```
:Disp "ENTER WINNING"
:Input "PERCENTAGE", P
:Disp "ENTER NUMBER"
:Input "OF ATTEMPTS", A
:Disp "ENTER NUMBER OF"
:Input "SUCCESSES", S
:Disp "ENTER NUMBER OF"
:Input "TRIALS", T
:T=>X
:0 => B
:Lbl 99
:0 => C
:For (Y, 1, A, 1)
:randInt (0, 99) > W
:If P>W
:C+1=>C
: End
:Disp "WIN", C
:If C=S
:B+1=>B
:If T<1
:Goto 98
:T-1=>T
Goto 99
:Lbl 98
:Disp "EXPERIMENTAL", (B/X)
:Disp "THEORETICAL"
:Disp (A nCr S)*((P/100)^S)*
(((100-P)/100)^(A-S))
:Stop
```

C.13 Using the Prob Sim Application

Probability Simulation (Prob Sim) is a FLASH application for the TI-83 Plus calculator. It can be accessed by pressing the APPS button and selecting it from the list of installed software. If it is not installed on your calculator, you will need to install it from the textbook CD using a TI Graph Link cable and Graph Link software available at the TI Web site: **www.ti.com/calc/graphlink**.

Execute Program

Press APPS and use the arrow keys to select **Prob Sim** from the list of applications. Finally, press ENTER, and then press a key to see the simulation menu.

Select Simulation

Prob Sim can perform six different simulations. Either press the number beside a simulation or select it using the arrow keys.

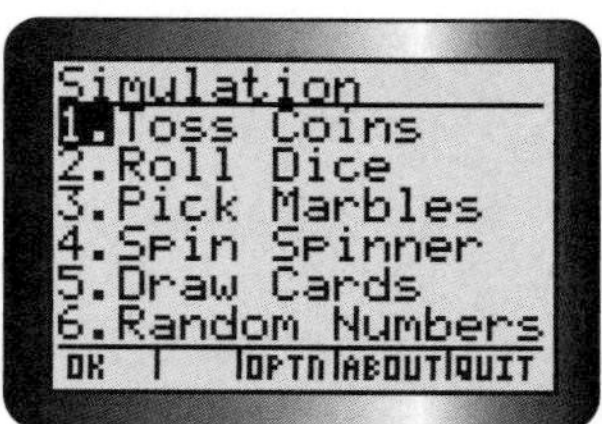

1. **Toss Coins** will simulate two-sided probability of up to three coin tosses at a time for multiple trials. The number of heads can be displayed as a bar graph or in table format, and data can be exported to your Mac or PC using TI Graph Link.
2. **Roll Dice** will simulate up to three dice being tossed for multiple trials. A variety of dice are available (6-, 8-, 10-, 12-, and 20-sided dice). The total of the three rolls is displayed in either a bar graph or in table format, and data can be exported to your Mac or PC using TI Graph Link.

3. **Pick Marbles** is a simulation of up to five types of marbles being randomly selected, with the number of each type or experimental probability of each type being graphed or displayed in a table. The results can also be exported to a Mac or PC.
4. **Spin Spinner** is a simulation of a spinner with up to eight different outcomes. Both frequency and experimental probability can be displayed in a bar graph or table, and the results can be exported to a Mac or PC.
5. **Draw Cards** uses 52- and 32-card deck options to demonstrate a random selection of cards from up to three decks both with and without replacement. All results are recorded in a table, and can be exported to a Mac or PC.
6. **Random Numbers** is a simulator that randomly selects up to six integers at a time and displays the results in a table. The results can also be exported to a Mac or PC.

With each of the simulators, the values for each bar can be displayed by pressing the left or right arrow keys.

C.14 How to Calculate $_nP_r$ and $_nC_r$

Permutations and combinations can be calculated using commands from the PRB menu available with [MATH].

Enter Argument
Both $_nP_r$ and $_nC_r$ require the first argument (the n-value) to be keyed first.

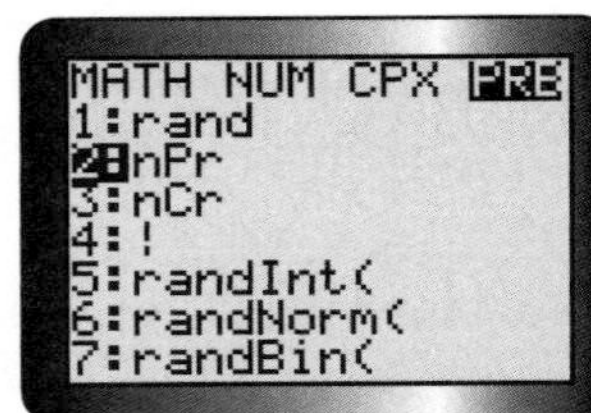

Select Command
Press [MATH] [▸] [▸] [▸] to access the **PRB** menu. $_nP_r$ can be used by pressing [2] and $_nC_r$ can be accessed by pressing [3].

Enter Arguments
The r-value must now be entered. The expression can then be evaluated by pressing [ENTER].

Example

Evaluate the following expressions.

(a) $_6P_3$ **(b)** $_{13}C_7$ **(c)** $_{101}C_{98}$

Solution

(a) [6] *Enter argument*
[MATH] [▸] [▸] [▸] [2] *Select command*
[3] [ENTER] *Enter argument*

(b) [1] [3] *Enter argument*
[MATH] [▸] [▸] [▸] [3] *Select command*
[7] [ENTER] *Enter argument*

(c) [1] [0] [1] *Enter argument*
[MATH] [▸] [▸] [▸] [2] *Select command*
[9] [8] [ENTER] *Enter argument*

6 nPr 3
120
13 nCr 7
1716
101 nCr 98
166650

C.15 How to Enter Matrices

The TI-83 Plus calculator can use up to 10 different matrices at a time. Before a matrix can be used, it must be defined and each individual entry must be keyed in.

Select Matrix
Press [2nd] [x^{-1}] to select the Matrix editor. Use the arrow keys [▲] and [▼] to select the name of the matrix you would like to edit.

Enter Dimension
Press [▶][▶] [ENTER] to select the **EDIT** menu. You can now define the number of rows and columns by entering the number of each, separated by the [ENTER] key.

Enter Numbers
You can now enter the numbers into the matrix by keying them in and pressing [ENTER]. You can also use the arrow keys to navigate the screen and correct errors, if necessary.

Using Matrices
A matrix can now be called by pressing [2nd] [x^{-1}] and pressing [ENTER]. The name of the matrix will then appear on the home screen.

Example

Enter the following matrices into a TI-83 Plus calculator.

(a) $[A] = \begin{bmatrix} 2 & -3 & 1 \\ 0 & 0 & 1 \\ 2 & 5 & -7 \end{bmatrix}$ **(b)** $[B] = \begin{bmatrix} 9 & 3 \\ 1 & 0 \\ -1 & 2 \end{bmatrix}$

Solution

(a) [2nd] [x^{-1}] — *Select matrix*
[▶] [▶] [ENTER] [3] [ENTER] [3] [ENTER] — *Enter dimension*
[2] [ENTER] [-] [3] [ENTER] [1] [ENTER] — *Enter numbers*
[▶][▶][1] [ENTER] [2] [ENTER] [5] [ENTER]
[-] [7] [ENTER]

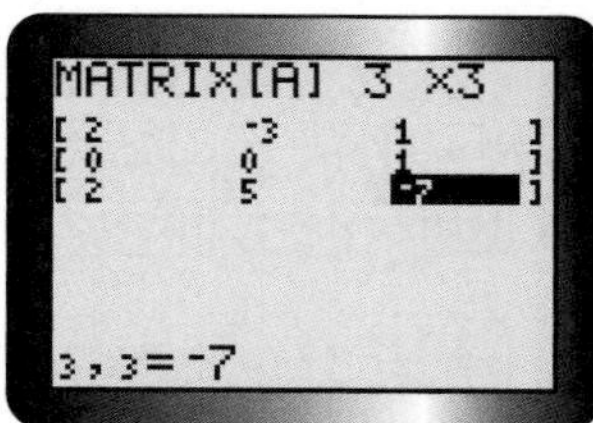

(b) [2nd] [x^{-1}] — *Select matrix*
[▶] [▶] [▼] [ENTER] [3] [ENTER] [2] [ENTER] — *Enter dimension*
[9] [ENTER] [3] [ENTER] [1] [▼] — *Enter numbers*
[-] [1] [ENTER] [2] [ENTER]

C.16 How to Add, Subtract, or Multiply Matrices

Matrices must have compatible dimensions before you can add, subtract, or multiply them using a TI-83 Plus calculator. The names of the matrices are selected from the Matrix editor and displayed on the home screen. If defined, you can find the sum, difference, or product of any two matrices.

Select Matrix Name
Press [2nd] [x^{-1}] to access the Matrix editor. Use the [▲] [▼] arrow keys to select the matrix you want and press [ENTER].

Select Operation
Back on the home screen, you can key whatever operation you wish.

Select Matrix Name
Press [2nd] [x^{-1}] and select the matrix you want using the arrow keys.

Example

Find the following results for the matrices $[A] = \begin{bmatrix} 2 & -3 & 1 \\ 0 & 0 & 1 \\ 2 & 5 & -7 \end{bmatrix}$, $[B] = \begin{bmatrix} 9 & 3 \\ 1 & 0 \\ -1 & 2 \end{bmatrix}$, and $[C] = \begin{bmatrix} 5 & -2 \\ 0 & -3 \\ 4 & -8 \end{bmatrix}$.

(a) [A] * [B] **(b)** [C] + [B]

See Appendix C.15 for how to enter matrices.

Solution

(a) [2nd] [x^{-1}] [ENTER] *Select matrix name*
[*] *Select operation*
[2nd] [x^{-1}] [▼] [ENTER] *Select matrix name*

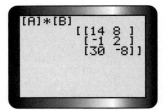

```
[A]*[B]
      [[14 8 ]
       [-1 2 ]
       [30 -8]]
```

(b) [2nd] [x^{-1}] [▼] [ENTER] *Select matrix name*
[+] *Select operation*
[2nd] [x^{-1}] [▼] [▼] [ENTER] *Select matrix name*

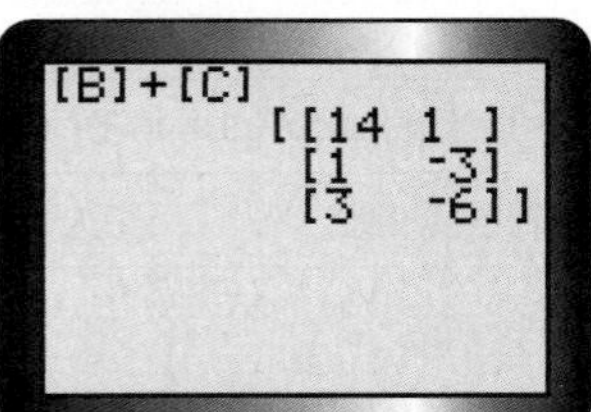

C.17 How to Multiply Matrices by a Scalar

Once a matrix has been entered into memory, it can be recalled from the MATRX menu.

Select Matrix

Press [2nd] [x^{-1}] and select the matrix you need using the arrow keys [▲] [▼]. Then press [ENTER].

Perform Operation

Finally, perform the desired operation and press [ENTER] to discover the result.

Example

Find the result of 15*[B] if $[B] = \begin{bmatrix} 9 & 3 \\ 1 & 0 \\ -1 & 2 \end{bmatrix}$.

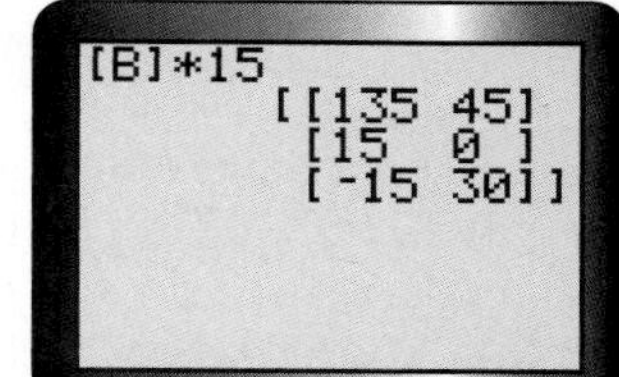

Solution

[2nd] [x^{-1}] [▼] [ENTER] *Select matrix*

[*] [1] [5] *Perform operation*

C.18 How to Export Matrices into Lists

A matrix can have one or more of its columns transferred to a list using the **8:Matr>list(** command.

Select Operation

Press [2nd] [x^{-1}] [▶] to select the **MATH** menu and select the **8:Matr>list(** command by pressing [8].

Enter Arguments

Identify the matrix you would like to transfer by pressing [2nd] [x^{-1}], and selecting it with the [▲] and [▼] arrow keys followed by [ENTER] and [,]. Next, enter one list for each column in the matrix, separated by a comma. When you have entered enough lists, press [)] [ENTER].

Example

Take the matrix $[A] = \begin{bmatrix} 2 & -3 & 1 \\ 0 & 0 & 1 \\ 2 & 5 & -7 \end{bmatrix}$ and export it into lists L_3, L_4, and L_5.

Solution

[2nd] [x^{-1}] [▶] [8] *Select operation*

[2nd] [x^{-1}] [ENTER] [,] [2nd] [3] [,] [2nd] [4] [,] *Enter arguments*

[2nd] [5] [,] [)] [ENTER]

C.19 How to Import Lists into a Matrix

A series of lists can be imported into a matrix; this is true even for a matrix that has not yet been defined. The destination matrix will be given enough rows and columns to accommodate what is being sent to it. If the lists are not the same length, zeros will be added to the short lists until they are all the same length.

Enter Numbers

Press [STAT] [1] and use the arrow keys to enter numbers in the lists.

Select Operation

Press [2nd] [x^{-1}] [▶] [9] to select the **9:List>matr(** command from the **MATH** menu.

Enter Arguments

Enter the list names using [2nd] [1] – [6], separated by commas, and then finally enter a matrix name by pressing [2nd] [x^{-1}] and choosing one from the list.

Example

Enter the following data into lists and then import into a matrix:

L1: 1, 2, 3, 4, 5, 6

L2: 2, 4, 6, 8, 10, 12

L3: 2, 4, 8, 16, 32, 64

Solution

[2nd] [+] [4] [ENTER] — *Clear all lists*

[STAT] [1] [1] [ENTER] [2] [ENTER] [3] [ENTER] [4] [ENTER] [5] [ENTER] [6] [ENTER] [▶] [2] [ENTER] [4] [ENTER] [6] [ENTER] [8] [ENTER] [1] [0] [ENTER] [1] [2] [ENTER] [▶] [2] [ENTER] [▶] [4] [ENTER] [▶] [8] [ENTER] [1] [6] [ENTER] [3] [2] [ENTER] [6] [4] [ENTER] — *Enter numbers*

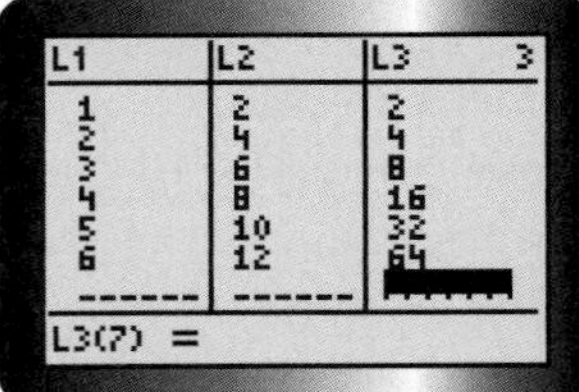

[2nd] [MODE] — *Return to home screen*

[2nd] [x^{-1}] [▶] [9] — *Select operation*

[2nd] [1] [,] [2nd] [2] [,] [2nd] [3] [,] [2nd] [x^{-1}] [1] — *Enter arguments*

Note: A matrix can be viewed by pressing [2nd] [x^{-1}] [▶] [▶] and selecting it from the list.

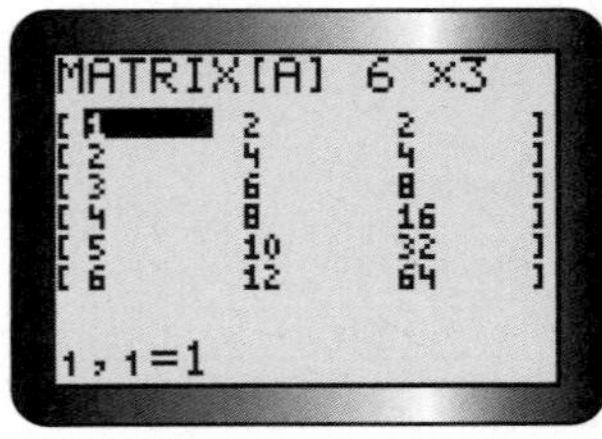

Appendix D: How to Use Fathom™ Software

D.1 Introduction to Fathom™

Fathom™ is an interactive environment in which you can explore statistical properties and create effective statistical simulations. When you run Fathom™, you will first see the empty Fathom™ document with the toolshelf directly below the menu bar.

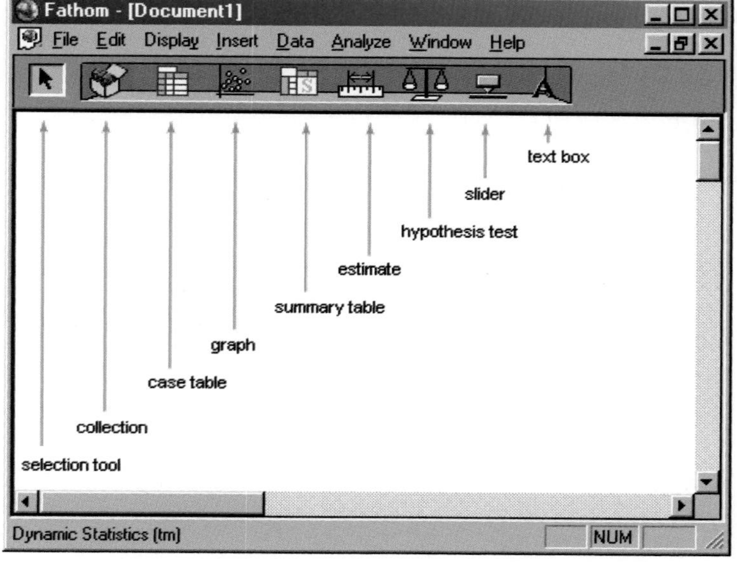

Selection Tool
Used for selecting and deselecting items in the Fathom™ document.

Collection
Used to hold data.

Case Table
Used to display data; similar to a spreadsheet.

Graph
Used to create a display of a data set.

Summary Table
Used to calculate summary statistics.

Estimate
Used to estimate parameters and calculate confidence intervals.

Hypothesis Test
Used to perform hypothesis tests.

Slider
Used to adjust variable parameters.

Text Box
Used to add a text box to the Fathom™ document.

D.2 How to Create a Collection

The writers of Fathom™ wanted to make an icon to represent a gathering of data: a collection from which you can take statistical measures. You can observe the data in a collection in a number of different ways, which you will learn about later in Appendix D.

Get Collection

Drag a collection from the toolshelf and it will become an icon in the Fathom™ document. Double-click on the temporary name **Collection 1** and you can key in a new name for it.

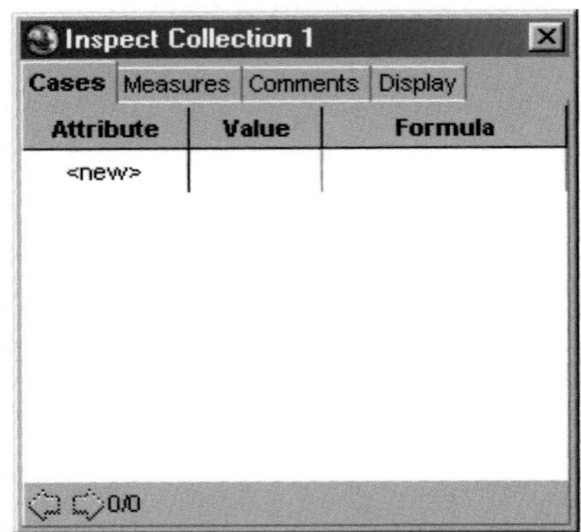

Inspect the Collection

Double-clicking on the icon will bring up the inspector. Four different views are available. With the **Cases** tab, you can see and edit each individual case; however, a case table is a more effective way to do this. Measures can be defined using the **Measures** tab, comments for the collection can be added with the **Comments** tab, and the display settings can be edited using the **Display** tab.

Create Cases

In the bottom menu bar you can see that there are 0 cases to work with. Right-clicking on the icon or the inspector and selecting **New Cases** from the pop-up menu can generate empty cases. Simply key in the number of new cases needed and they will be made part of the collection. Notice that a collection that has cases in it is no longer an empty box; rather, it contains gold balls.

Example

Create a collection called MDM4U with 32 cases that have the attributes Name, Midterm, and Final_Grade.

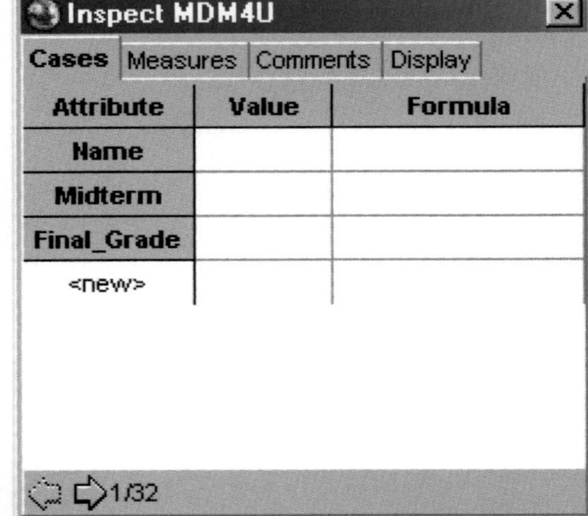

Solution

1. Open a new Fathom™ document, drop a new collection into the Fathom™ document.
2. Double-click on **Collection 1** and key in MDM4U. Press Enter.
3. Double-click on the icon to open the inspector.
4. Click on **<new>** and key in Name. Press Enter.
5. Repeat for Midterm, and Final_Grade, pressing Enter each time.
6. Right-click on the icon and select **New Cases**. Key in 32 in the box and press Enter.

D.3 Setting Up a Case Table

The simplest way to fill a case table with data is to drag it off the toolshelf and drop it into the Fathom™ document. From there, you can input data directly into it.

Get Table
Drag a case table from the toolshelf and drop it into a new Fathom™ document.

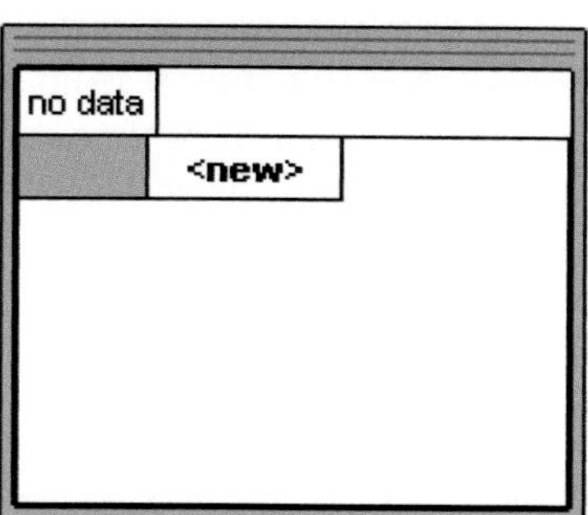

Label Attribute
Once the table is in place, the attribute label will appear as **<new>**. Click on it once and enter the attribute label you would like to use. Attribute names must begin with a letter and contain only letters, digits, or underscores (_). Once the label is in place, the computer will automatically create a collection icon for this case table in the Fathom™ document.

Enter Data
Once the attribute label is in place, you can enter data into the cells below it or enter a new attribute by clicking on **<new>**. As you enter data for different cases, notice how the collection is now full of gold balls. Each gold ball represents one case.

Example

In a new Fathom™ document, create a case table that contains the following data:

Name	Tonya	Sylvie	Rhiannon	Megan
Hand	R	L	R	R
Points	112	78	51	66

Solution

1. Drag and drop a case table from the toolshelf onto a new Fathom™ document.
2. Click on **<new>** and key in Name. Press Enter.
3. Repeat for the Hand and Points, pressing Enter each time.
4. Under Name, key in Tonya; Sylvie; Rhiannon; Megan. Press Enter after each name.
5. Under Hand, key in R; L; R; R. Press Enter after each entry.
6. Under Points, key in 112; 78; 51; 66. Press Enter after each entry.

Collection 1

	Name	Hand	Points	<new>
1	Tonya	R	112	
2	Sylvie	L	78	
3	Rhiannon	R	51	
4	Megan	R	66	

Remember: In a case table, each row represents one case (i.e., one person in the population), while each column represents one attribute (i.e., a characteristic of each element in the population).

D.4 Importing Data from Outside Sources

Data can be imported from other programs as well as from the Internet, and used to form collections of data in a Fathom™ document.

From a Text File

A spreadsheet in tab-delimited form can be imported by clicking **File**, **Import from File,** and then selecting it from the **Select Import File** menu. You can also simply drag the file icon from your desktop and drop it into a Fathom™ document. A collection is automatically created. While the collection is selected, drag a case table from the toolshelf to view and edit the entries.

From an HTML File

In the same way, a file can be imported by selecting **Import from URL** from the **File** menu and then keying the Web address where your table is located. You can also drag the address icon from your Web browser and drop it into a Fathom™ document.

From a Spreadsheet

A series of cells can be converted into a case table in Fathom™ by using the mouse to select them from the spreadsheet, and then copying them to the clipboard by pressing **Ctrl-C**. You can then drag and drop a new collection from the toolshelf into an empty Fathom™ document and click **Edit**, **Paste Cases**.

Example

Import a chart from the Statistics Canada Web site and then create a collection with a case table.

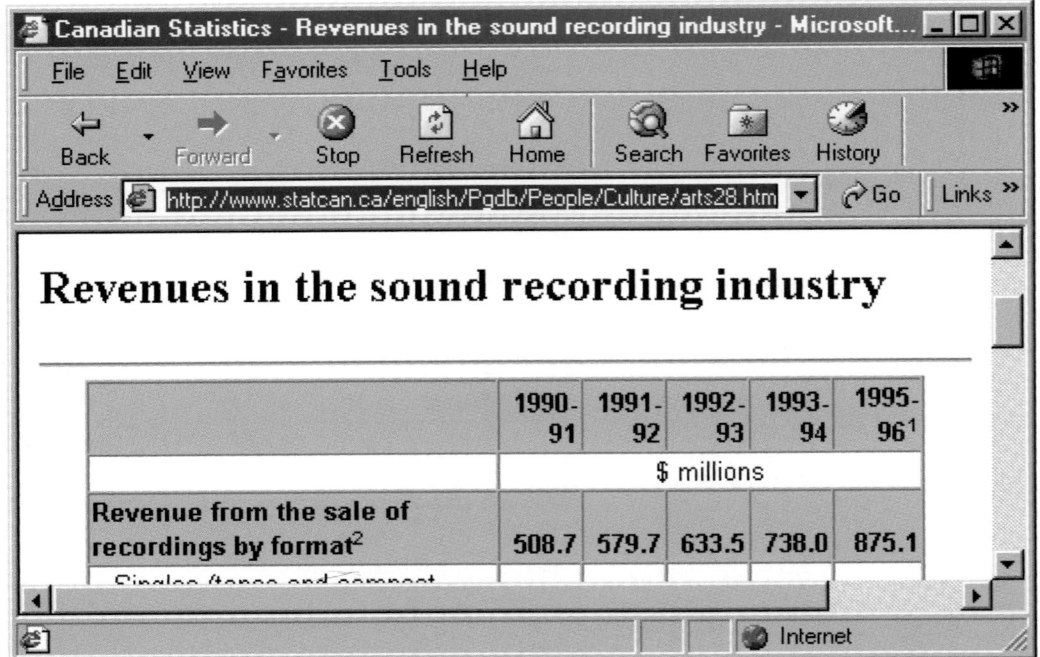

Solution

1. Using the URL **www.statcan.ca/english/Pgdb/People/Culture/arts28.htm**, you can either import this table directly by clicking on **File...Import from URL** and keying this address, or you can drag the icon from the address box of the Web browser and drop it into an empty Fathom™ document. A collection will automatically be formed.
2. While the collection is selected, drag a case table from the toolshelf and drop it into the Fathom™ document.
3. When you import a table from the Internet or from some other source, there are usually some cosmetic corrections to be made that do not have a significant impact on the accuracy of your results. In this example, a number of characters were not interpreted correctly and need to be fixed.

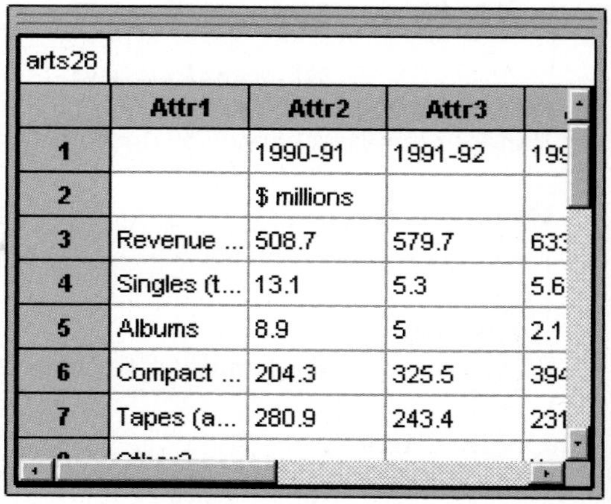

arts28

	Attr1	Attr2	Attr3	
1		1990-91	1991-92	19
2		$ millions		
3	Revenue ...	508.7	579.7	63
4	Singles (t...	13.1	5.3	5.6
5	Albums	8.9	5	2.1
6	Compact ...	204.3	325.5	39
7	Tapes (a...	280.9	243.4	231

Each time you import data, check and correct the following:

1. **Relabel Attributes:** Attribute names must begin with a letter and contain only letters, digits, or underscores (_). Double-click on the attribute label **Attr1** and key a more suitable name. As you can see, case 1 contains the labels for the second column, third column, and so on. These attributes could all be renamed **Sales90_91**, and so on.
2. **Delete Redundant Cases:** To start, cases 1 and 2 contain label information, and once the attributes have been relabelled, you can delete them. Select the row by clicking on the number on the left, and then click **Edit..Delete Case**. Be sure to scroll down the list to see if there are any other unneeded cases.
3. **Check for Incompatible Data Types:** Sometimes text data are left in a column that is supposed to be for a numerical attribute. In this example, both "x" and "-" are used in the sales attributes to represent zero. Each instance must be changed into a 0 to be interpreted properly.

Remember: It is always a good idea to save the HTML original on your computer so that you can compare your results later. From your Web browser, select **Save As** from the **File** menu and give the file an appropriate name.

D.5 How to Create and Display Random Numbers

Random numbers cannot be displayed in Fathom™ unless they are in a case table.

Retrieve Case Table
Drag a new case table and drop it into a new Fathom™ document.

Name Attribute
Click on **<new>** and enter an attribute label. A new collection will automatically be created.

Create Cases
Next, right-click outside the open cell in the chart and select **New Cases** from the pop-up menu. After entering the number of cases, you will be ready to fill them with a random value.

Define Formula
Double-clicking on the collection icon will let you see the inspector. With the **Cases** tab selected, double-click in the Formula column and you will be able to edit a formula for each of the cases in this collection. To have a random number between 0 and 1 in each case, you can either key **random()** in the dialogue box or you can select it from the browsing window. Click on **Functions**, then **Random number**, and then double-click on **random**. It will then be pasted into the formula box. Click OK and you will see that each case in the case table now contains a random number. If you key a number between the brackets, you will then get a positive random number that is less than that.

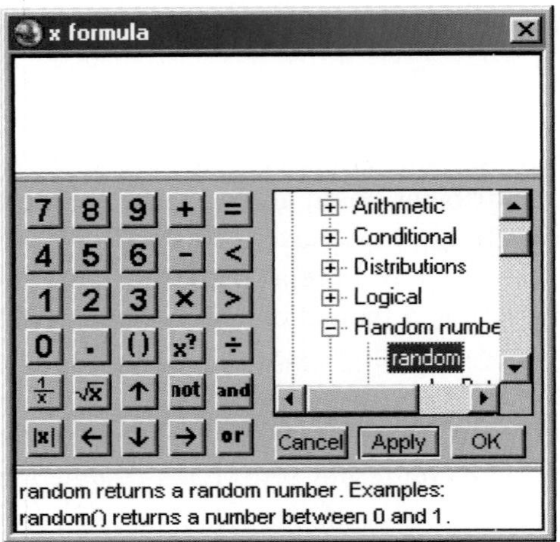

Example

Create a collection that contains 45 random integers, each between 5 and 15.

Solution

1. Drag a new case table off the toolshelf and drop it into a new Fathom™ document. Click on **<new>** and key x as the attribute label.
2. Right-click on the collection icon and select **New Cases** from the pop-up menu. Enter 45 as the number of new cases.
3. Double-click on the collection icon.
4. Double-click in the formula column of the inspector, and type the following formula: **round(random(10)+5)**. Click OK.

D.6 How to Make a Scatter Plot and a Least-Squares Line

A scatter plot is a powerful investigational tool that makes it possible to visually recognize a relationship between two variables.

Create Case Table

To create a scatter plot you need a case table with two attributes recorded for a number of cases. The more data points you have, the more confident you can be of the result. Drag a new case table from the toolshelf and drop it into a new Fathom™ document. Enter labels for the two attributes and then enter the data.

Set Up Graph

Drag a new graph from the toolshelf and drop it into the Fathom™ document. You can now drag one of the attributes to the horizontal axis and drop it there. Drag and drop the second attribute on the vertical axis, and the scatter plot will be complete. The scales can be adjusted by dragging the pointer across them.

Insert Least-Squares Line

Once the scatter plot has been created, select the graph and then select **Least-Squares Line** from the **Graph** menu. A line will now be plotted that closely approximates the trend that the data suggest. A formula for the least-squares line will also be added to the graph.

Example

Create a scatter plot with a least-squares line from the following data:

X 12, 15, 18, 21, 24, 27, 30, 33, 36, 39, 42
Y 2.5, 4.1, 7.4, 8.9, 11.1, 12.2, 15.1, 17.7, 19.5, 21.3, 24.0

Solution

1. Drag a new case table from the toolshelf and drop it into a new Fathom™ document. Click on **<new>**, key in X, and press Enter. Click on **<new>**, key in Y, and press Enter again.
2. Key in the data into each column.
3. Drag a graph off the toolshelf and drop it into the document.
4. Drag the X attribute from the case table and drop it at the bottom of the graph. Drag the Y attribute from the case table and drop it along the left side of the graph.
5. From the **Graph** menu, select **Least-Squares Line**.

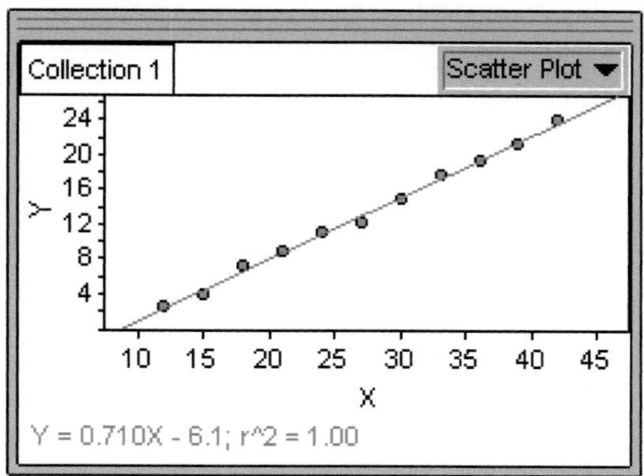

D.7 How To Plot Residuals

When working with a line or function and a scatter plot, you can explore how far off the line a particular data point is by making a residual plot. This graph would represent each point's distance above or below the line.

Create a Scatter Plot

You must have a scatter plot constructed with a line modelling the data (least-squares line, median—median line, etc.). Follow the directions in Appendix D.6 for creating a scatter plot with a least-squares line.

Make Residual Plot

With the graph selected, select **Make Residual Plot** from the **Graph** menu. You may need to rescale the graph to get a good look at the data.

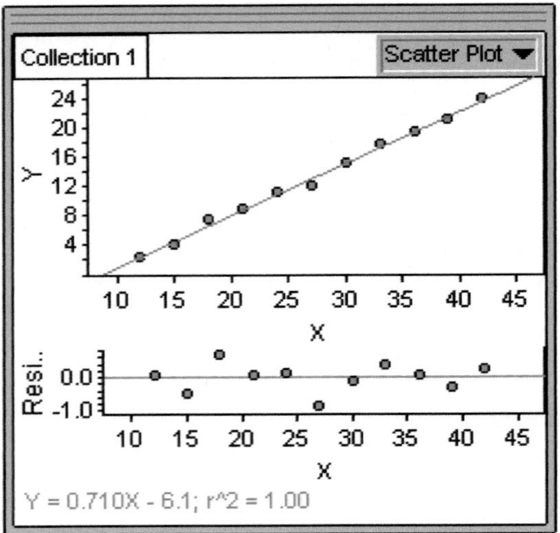

Example

For the data given in the example in Appendix D.6, make a residual plot.

Solution

With the graph selected, select **Make Residual Plot** from the **Graph** menu. Rescale the graph as needed.

D.8 How to Create a Histogram

A histogram is a visual display of the frequency of continuous measurement data (measured by real numbers) and is only able to display one attribute at a time.

Create Case Table

Drag a case table off the toolshelf and drop it into a new Fathom™ document. Define the attribute according to the type of data provided. Remember that an attribute is a characteristic of the population you are studying (e.g., a student's final grade, arm span in centimetres) and only one attribute can be displayed at a time. Be sure to enter raw data and not data that are already sorted into categories.

Set Up Graph

Take a new graph off the toolshelf and drop it into the Fathom™ document. Next, drag the attribute you wish to display onto the horizontal axis and drop it there. Fathom™ will automatically create a histogram or bar chart for the data you have provided.

Example

Create a histogram with bin widths of 10 cm from the given data.
The heights of all the female teachers at Winona Public School (cm): 168, 172, 175, 162, 174, 170, 155, 170, 146, 178, 160, 184, 173, 184, 172, 137, 178, 175

Solution

1. Drag a case table off the toolshelf and drop it into a new Fathom™ document. Click on **<new>** and key in **Height** as a new attribute name.
2. Enter the given data in the attribute named Height.
3. Drag a graph off the toolshelf and drop it into the Fathom™ document.
4. Drag the attribute **Height** from the case table and drop it onto the horizontal axis.
5. Select Histogram from the drop-down menu in the top right.
6. Double-click on the graph and the text window for the graph will appear. Click on the blue text following **Bin width:** and enter **10**. Click on the blue text that follows **starting at:** and enter 130.

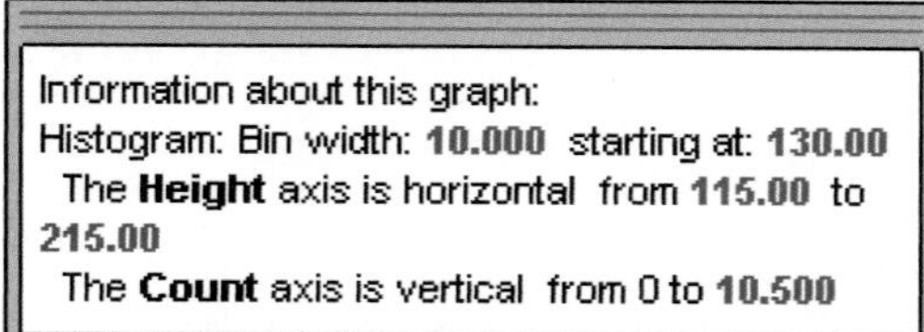

Information about this graph:
Histogram: Bin width: 10.000 starting at: 130.00
The Height axis is horizontal from 115.00 to 215.00
The Count axis is vertical from 0 to 10.500

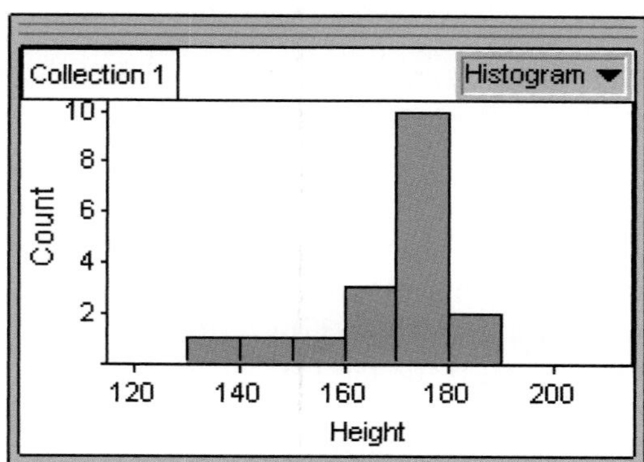

D.9 How to Perform a Simulation

In the Fathom™ environment, you can create a simulation that will allow you to calculate an experimental probability.

Create a Case Table and Collection

Drag a case table off the toolshelf and drop it into a new Fathom™ document. Once you start keying in the case table, a new collection will be created automatically.

Label Attributes

Click on **<new>** and key in the name of an attribute. Label as many as are necessary. Once attributes are labelled, you can create cases and begin simulating data.

Create Cases

Right-click inside the case table and select **New Cases** from the pop-up menu. Key in the number of simulated cases that are necessary. Remember, more is better.

Create Random Numbers
Most simulations require that a body of random data be created. Right-click on the attribute label you want to simulate and select **Edit Formula** from the pop-up menu. The formula can be keyed in directly or selected from the menu on the right. Refer to Appendix D.5 for more on generating random numbers.

Summary Attribute
An additional attribute can be used to summarize whether a case is a success or failure, depending on the simulation. The results can then be analyzed with a graph. Refer to Appendix D.8 for more on creating histograms.

Example
Rory claims that he can roll three dice at once and get numbers greater than 3 on each die. Create a simulation that can estimate the experimental probability of accomplishing this feat.

Solution

1. Drag a case table from the toolshelf and drop it into a new Fathom™ document.
2. Label attributes **Die1**, **Die2**, **Die3**, and **Win** by clicking on **<new>**, keying them in, and pressing Enter.
3. Right-click on the attribute label **Die1** and select **Edit Formula** from the pop-up menu. Key **round(random(5)+1)** into the text box and click OK. Repeat for Die2 and Die3.
4. Right-click on **Win** and select **Edit Formula** from the pop-up menu. Inside the text box, key in **if(Die1>3** [tab] **if(Die2>3** [tab] **if(Die3>3** [tab] **"win"** [tab] **"lose"** [tab] **"lose"** [tab] **"lose"** and click OK (press the tab key for each [tab]).
5. Right-click on the collection icon and select **New Cases**. Key in **100** and click OK.
6. Drag a new graph from the toolshelf and drop it into the Fathom™ document. Drag the Win attribute and place it on the horizontal axis. From this display you can see the results of the simulation.

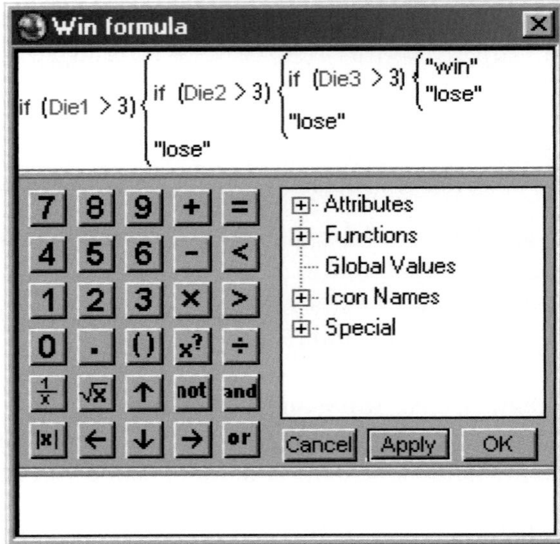

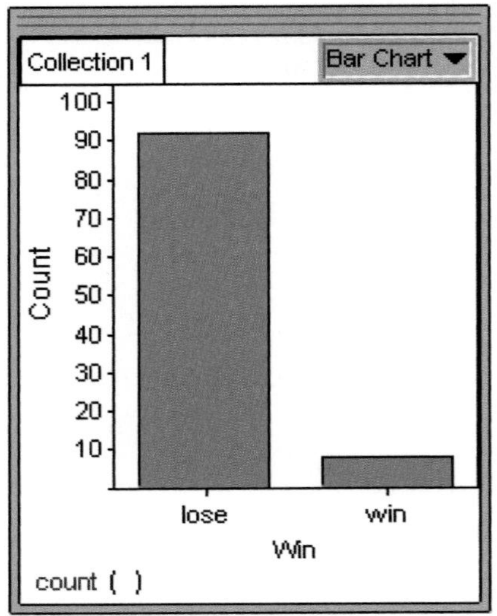

Appendix E: How to Use Spreadsheet Software

E.1 How to Use Formulas in Spreadsheets

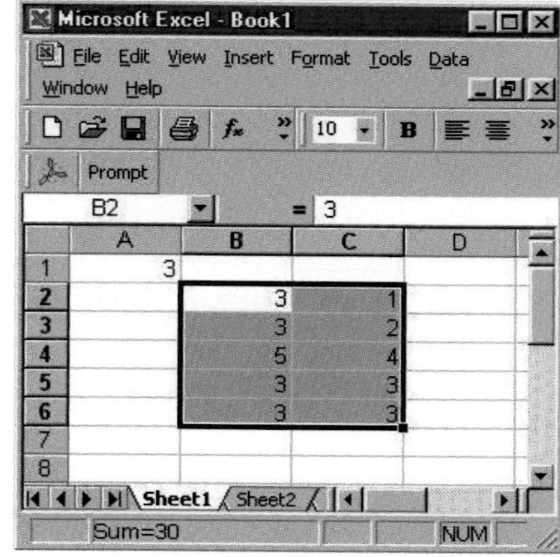

Formulas use data already entered into a spreadsheet to calculate a result. This result will appear in the cell where the formula has been entered. To refer to a group of cells, or an array, you would refer to opposite corners of a block, separating them with a colon (cell references must be separated with two periods in Quattro Pro). For example, in this picture, the cells selected in the box would be referenced as **B2:C6** (**B2..C6** in Quattro Pro).

The first six cells in column B would be referenced using the beginning and ending cells **B1:B6** (**B1..B6** in Quattro Pro). You can also list cells individually, separating them with commas (**B1**, **B2**, **B3**, **B4**, **B5**, **B6**).

The following formulas might be of use to you in this course:

=AVERAGE(A1:A10)	Returns the arithmetic mean of the numbers in cells A1 to A10; in Quattro Pro use **AVG(A1..A10)**.
=COMBIN(n, r)	Returns ${}_nC_r$; in Quattro Pro use **COMB (n, r)**.
=CORREL(A1:G1, A2:G2)	Returns the correlation coefficient between two data sets.
=INT(C12)	Rounds the number in cell **C12** to the nearest integer.
=INTERCEPT(A1:F1, A2:F2)	Returns the y-intercept of the linear regression line through the given y-values **A1** to **F1**, and the given x-values **A2** to **F2**.
=NORMDIST(X, μ, σ, 1)	Returns the normal distribution probability for **X** given the mean μ and standard deviation σ.
=NORMINV(p, μ, σ)	Returns the inverse of the normal cumulative distribution for the mean μ and standard deviation σ.
=PERMUT(n, r)	Returns ${}_nP_r$.
=QUARTILE(C1:C10, n)	Returns minimum (**n**=0), 1st Quartile (**n**=1), Median(**n**=2), 3rd Quartile (**n**=3), or maximum value (**n**=4) for the cells **C1** to **C10**.
=SLOPE(A1:F1, A2:F2)	Returns the slope of the linear regression line through the given y-values **A1** to **F1**, and the given x-values **A2** to **F2**.
=STDEV(B1:B4)	Estimates the standard deviation based on cells **B1**, **B2**, **B3**, and **B4**; in Quattro Pro use **STD(B1..B4)**.
=SUM (A1:A10)	Calculates the sum of the cells **A1** to **A10**.

Many other statistical functions are also available. To learn more about them, use the Help files associated with your spreadsheet software.

E.2 How to Use IF Statements in a Spreadsheet

Logical operators are spreadsheet commands that test a logical condition and return defined values. They are useful in creating simulations of experiments on a spreadsheet.

IF(condition, TRUE_value, FALSE_value) will return the TRUE_value if the condition is true; otherwise, the FALSE_value will be returned. When looking at the spreadsheet, only the value of the expression will be visible (TRUE_value or FALSE_value). To edit the formula, you must click on the cell and make your corrections in the text box.

Example

Create an equation that will return 75 if the sum of cells A1 to A4 is greater than 4. If A1 is less than or equal to 4, then return 50.

Solution

IF(SUM(A1:A4)>4, 75, 50)

E.3 How to Create and Display Random Numbers

The **RAND()** function will display a random real number between 0 and 1. It is useful for creating simulation data. To generate random numbers in another range, multiply RAND() by the difference between the high and low number, and then add the new low number [RAND() * (high number – low number) + low number].

Example

Generate a random number between

(a) 1 and 10

(b) 15 and 60

Solution

(a) While within a spreadsheet, key in the following equation: @RAND*9 + 1.

(b) While within a spreadsheet, key in the following equation: @RAND*45 + 15.

E.4 How to Perform a Simulation

Using the random number generator, you can create a spreadsheet simulator that will allow you to calculate an experimental probability.

Example

Roberto estimates that the probability of rain is 0.25. Create a simulation that calculates the probability of Roberto having a week (5 school days) when it does not rain. Carry out 20 trials.

Solution

1. In a new spreadsheet, make labels for 5 columns (M, T, W, Th, F) for the 5 days of the week, and then make a column to total the number of days without rain.
2. Paste the equation =RAND() into an array that is 5 wide and 20 long. This will represent the simulation of 20 trials of 5 days a week.
3. Count the number of rows that contain 5 days without rain. Divide this number by 20 to calculate the probability.

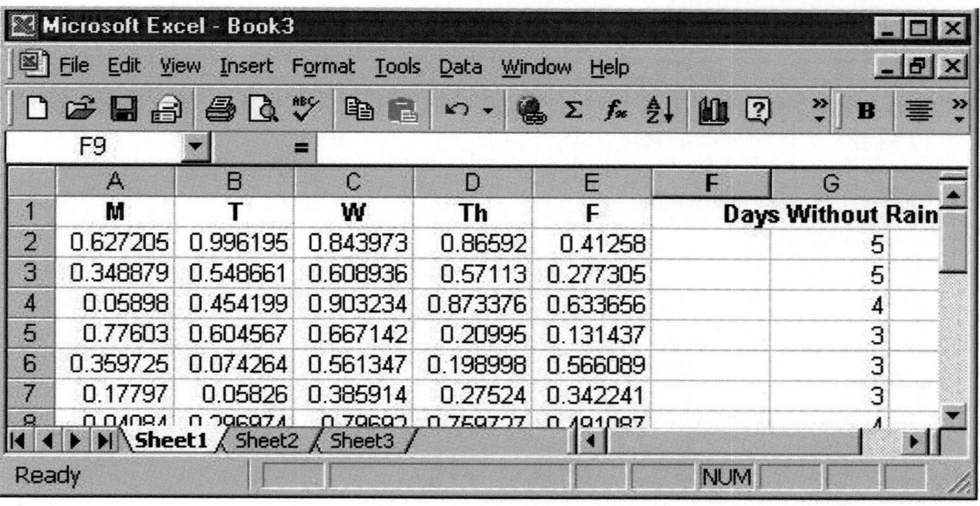

	A	B	C	D	E	F	G
1	M	T	W	Th	F	Days Without Rain	
2	0.627205	0.996195	0.843973	0.86592	0.41258		5
3	0.348879	0.548661	0.608936	0.57113	0.277305		5
4	0.05898	0.454199	0.903234	0.873376	0.633656		4
5	0.77603	0.604567	0.667142	0.20995	0.131437		3
6	0.359725	0.074264	0.561347	0.198998	0.566089		3
7	0.17797	0.05826	0.385914	0.27524	0.342241		3

E.5 How to Create a Histogram

Both Microsoft Excel and Corel Quattro Pro have the ability to define a series of cells and create a histogram from that data.

Enter Data
Key the data into a series of rows or columns. Remember to include the labels with the data, if applicable.

Select the Cells
Using the mouse, select the cells that you want to study in a graphic format. Select **Chart** from the **Insert** menu.

Set Up Parameters
Follow the instructions provided by your software package to complete the process.

Once a chart has been created, it can be copied and pasted into a word-processing document.

Example

Enter the following data into a spreadsheet program, and then create a histogram of the results.

	J	F	M	A	M	J	J	A	S	O	N	D
Temperature (°C)	3	–1	4	8	13	18	21	19	16	13	8	2
Rainfall (mm)	41	55	38	31	30	27	22	25	29	35	41	43

Solution

1. Open a new spreadsheet and enter the data given (including labels).
2. Select all the cells and then click **Insert**, **Chart**.
3. Follow on-line instructions.

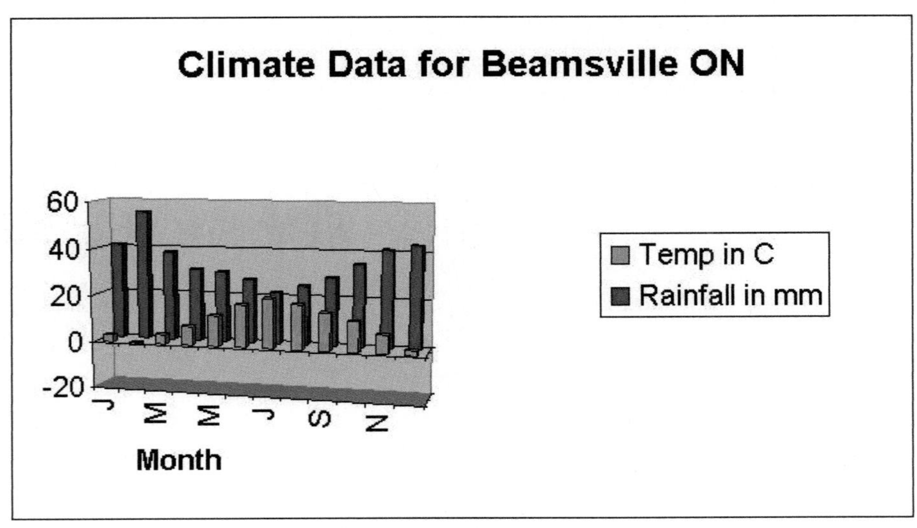

Answers and Indexes

Answers

Chapter 1

1.1 Exercises, page 11

1. **(a)** Each soccer ball represents 2 goals.
   (b) Jared: 14, Phil: 10, Beth: 8, Talia: 16
   (c) *Example*: Sometimes you might have to use part of the symbol and then it is hard to tell the fraction of the symbol drawn.
2. **(a)** Each tick represents 3.5 students.
   (b) Have each tick represent a whole number, say 4 or 5.
   (c) about 542
3. **(a)**

Number of Hours	Tally	Frequency
0	||	2
0.5	𝍸 |	6
1	𝍸 ||||	9
1.5	|	1
2	𝍸	5
2.5		0
3	||	2
3.5		0
4		0
4.5		0
5	|	1

   (b)

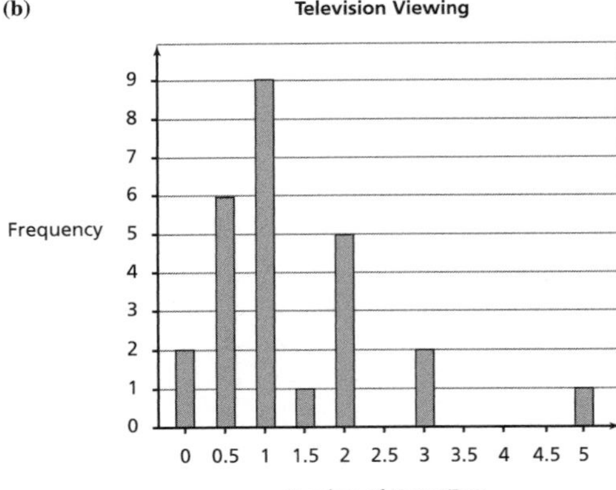

   (d) 3.1 h/day; Most students underestimated their television watching time.
4. **(a)** Label on the vertical axis.
   (b) Both display frequency of the data.
   (c) Histograms display frequencies for continuous intervals, while bar graphs show frequencies for each discrete horizontal-axis value.
   (d) When data are in intervals, not discrete.
5. **(a)** French Language 16.7%, English Fiction 27.8%, English Non-Fiction 44.4%, Reference 5.6%, Spanish Language 5.5%
   (b) French Language $20 875, English Fiction $34 750, English Non-Fiction $55 500, Reference $7000, Spanish Language $6875
6.

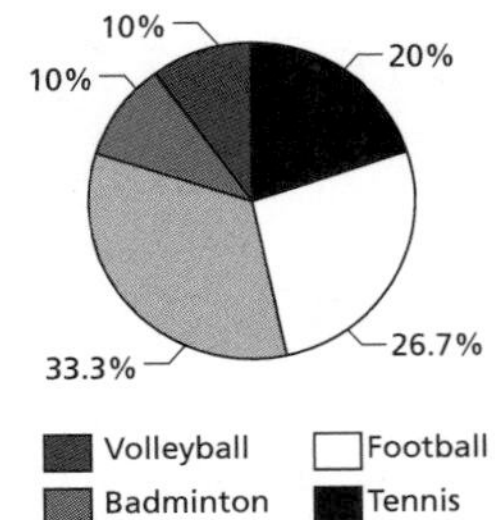

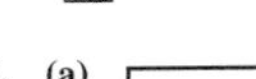

7. **(a)**

Class Interval	Frequency
2:30–2:59	1
3:00–3:29	4
3:30–3:59	8
4:00–4:29	14
4:30–4:59	5
5:00–5:29	2

   (b) 93.3%
   (c) You do not need to check every song's length.
   (d) histogram

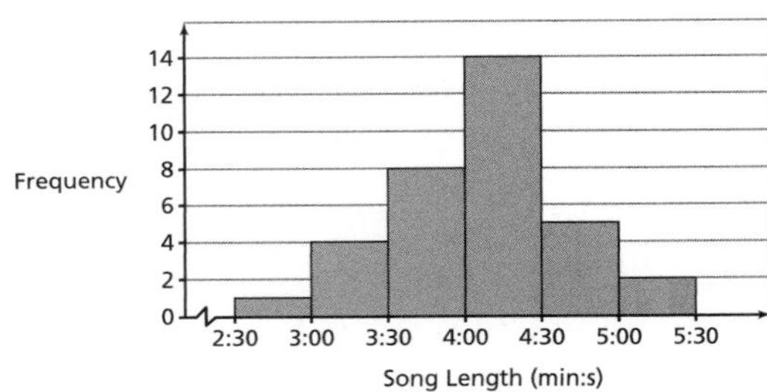

8. **(a)**

Stem	Leaf
1	6
2	1 4 5
3	0 3 3 4
4	8
5	2 3
6	
7	1 1 2 6 6
8	9
9	8
10	2 6 8 9 9
11	0 2 6 8
12	2 2 8

   (b) 16
   (c) 40%

9. **(a)** Preferred Pet

Cat	
Dog	
Bird	
Fish	
Iguana	

Black represents Grade 9 student
White represents Grade 12 student

(b) $\frac{41}{60}$ or 68%

(c) $\frac{24}{30}$ = 80%; A lot more Grade 9 students have pets other than cats and dogs.

10. **(a)** pie chart **(b)** bar graph **(c)** circle graph **(d)** bar or pie graph **(e)** bar graph

12. **(a)** Blood Types in Canada

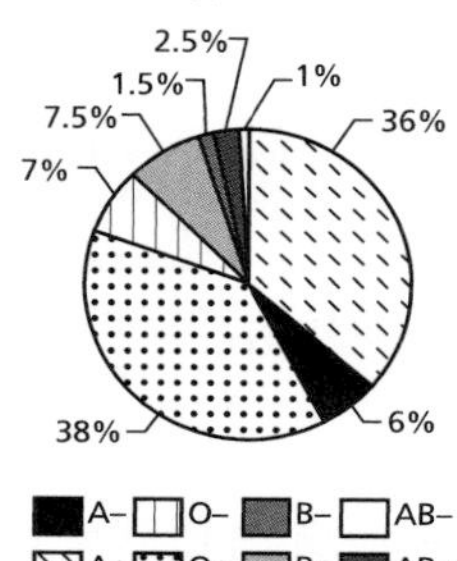

(b) 315

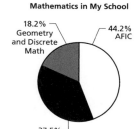

14. **(a)** Answers will vary; for example: AFIC: 80, Data Management: 68, Geometry: 33

Mathematics in My School

18.2% Geometry and Discrete Math
44.2% AFIC
37.5% Data Management

(b) Answers may vary. Circle graph is easier to compare.

(c) More students are enrolled in AFIC than either of the other Grade 12 courses.

1.2 Exercises, page 20

1. no
2. yes
3. no
4. Males care less.
5. no
6. more females; 8 female, 4 male
7. no
8. more males

11. **(a)** Yes; If $\frac{4}{11}$ of the May Go group attend, you are above 55%.

(b) The student council should report that only 31 of the 85 students polled said they will not go.

12. **(a)** No, you do not know if those who enjoy mathematics are the ones who will complete university.

(b) Combine the graphs and give proportions of level of enjoyment of mathematics within the level of education.

13. **(a)** Proportion of infant deaths has been decreasing since 1948.

14. **(a)** The temperatures at the South Pole have remained basically the same from 1957 to 1987.

15. **(a)** 83% of people answered less than 6 questions correctly; 55% answered less than 4 questions correctly.

(c) The higher the level of education a person has, the greater their chance of answering a question correctly.

1.3 Exercises, page 37

1. **(a)** Time of Revolution and Distance from Sun

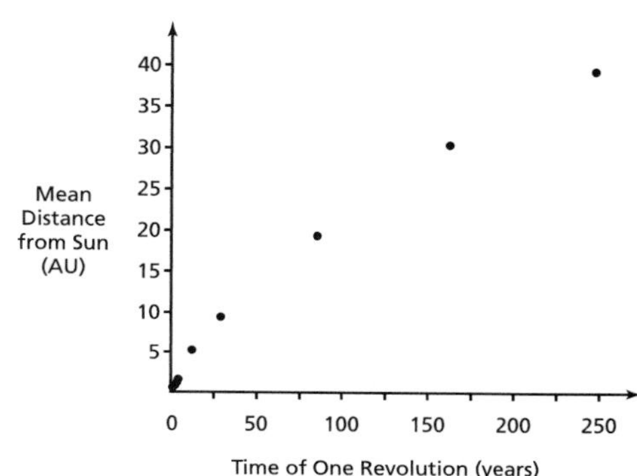

(b) Total Cost of Photos

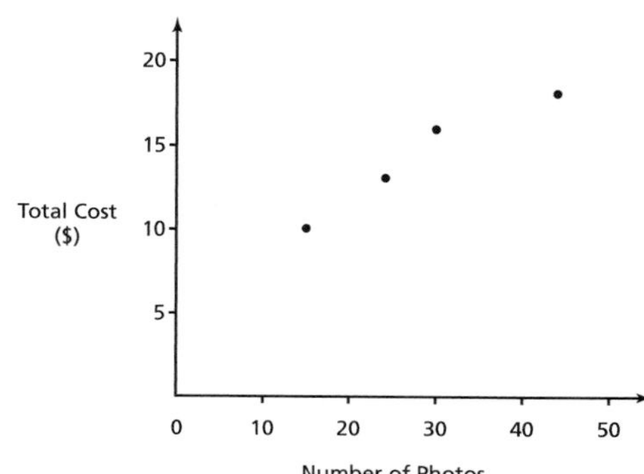

(c) Average Speed and Number of Seats on Airplanes

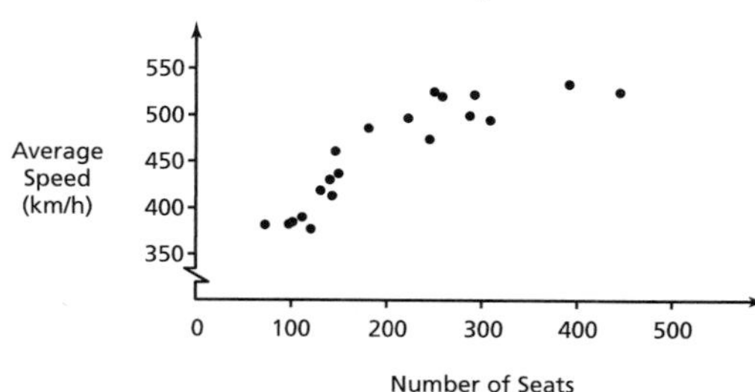

(d)

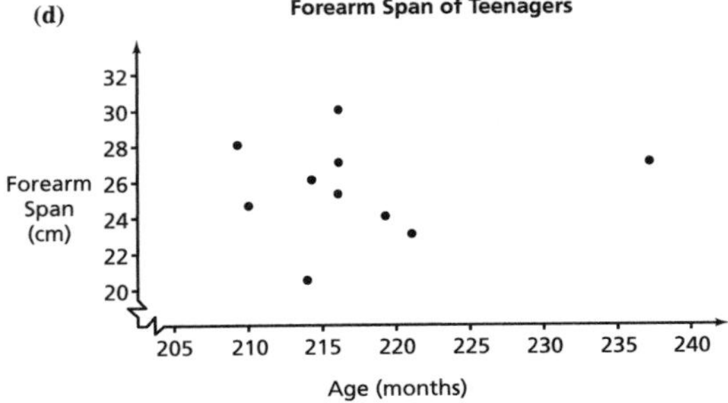

2. **(a)** no trend **(b)** no trend
(c) weak positive correlation **(d)** strong positive correlation

3. **(a)**

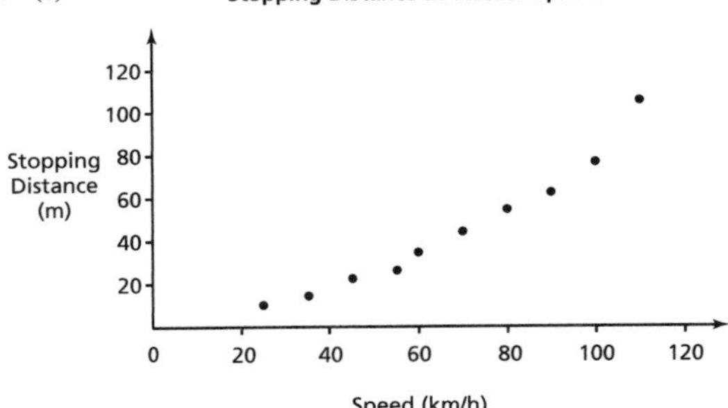

(b) strong positive trend, non-linear; The faster you go, the longer it will take to stop. Stopping distance increases.

(c) exponential or parabolic, with exponential slightly better

4. **(a)**

Amount Collected for Charity from Students

Amount Collected ($)

3000 2900 2800 2700 2600 2500 2400 2300 2200 2100 2000

120 125 130 135 140 145 150 155

Number of Students

(b) weak negative trend; The more students, the less money that was collected.

5. **(a)**

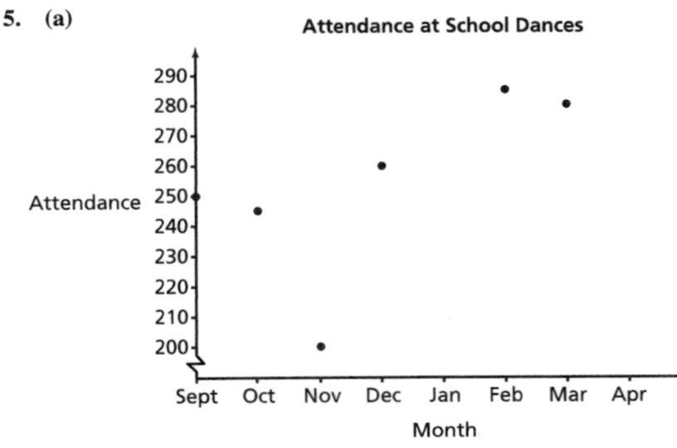

(b) There is a weak positive correlation; attendance seems to increase with time.

6. $y = -7.4x + 136.5$, about 70

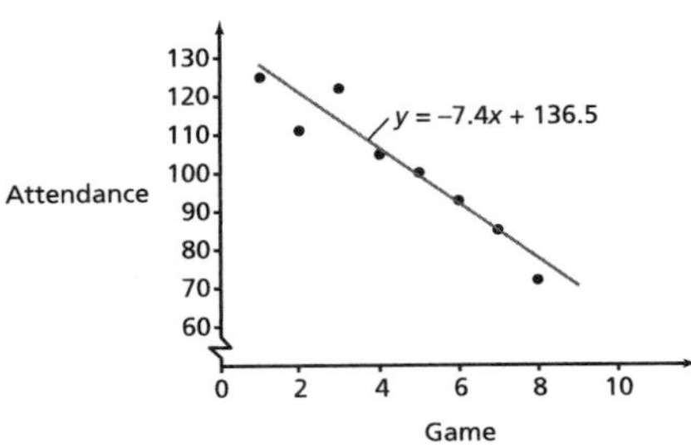

7. $y = 0.345x + 6.115$, about 16

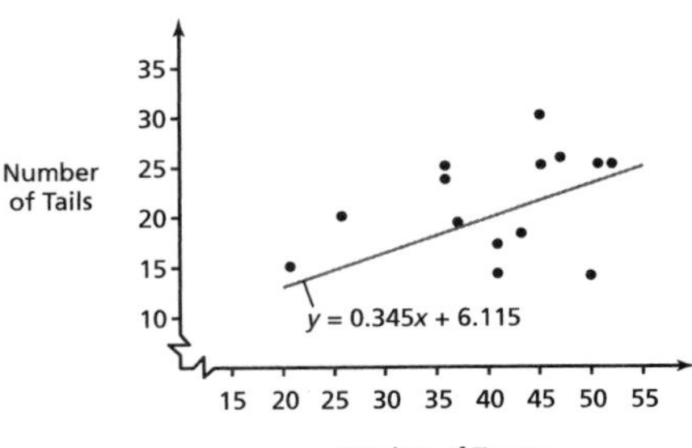

8. $y = 0.0219x - 36.555$, about 5.93

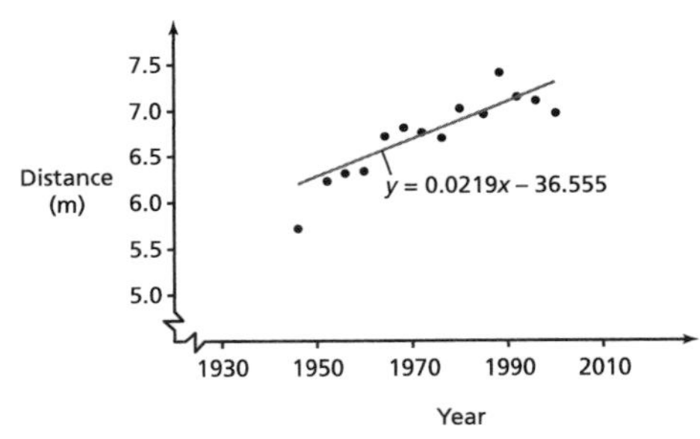

9. $y = -203.57x + 2482.98$, about 1 more

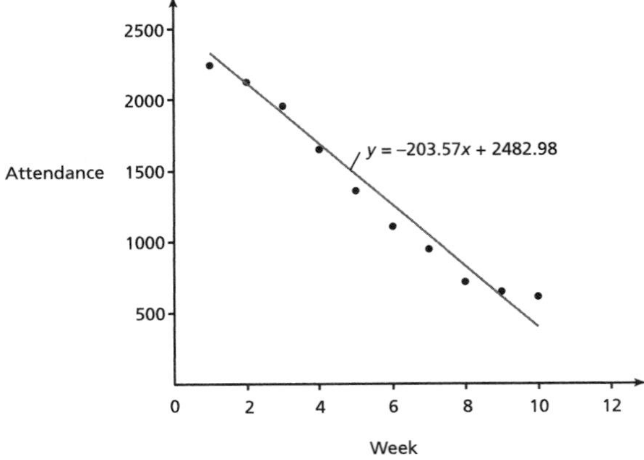

1.4 Exercises, page 51

1. (a) strong positive correlation
   (b) moderate negative correlation
   (c) weak positive correlation
   (d) no correlation
2. (a) negative correlation (b) positive correlation
   (c) negative correlation (d) positive correlation
3. (a) $y = 17.457x + 23.857$; $R^2 = 0.9848$
   (b) $y = -0.8919x + 55.541$; $R^2 = 0.7451$
   (c) $y = 4.7143x + 55.048$; $R^2 = 0.8589$
4. (a) 0.9924 (b) −0.8632 (c) 0.9268
5. Each of these residual plots suggests that a quadratic regression would be more appropriate.

(a)

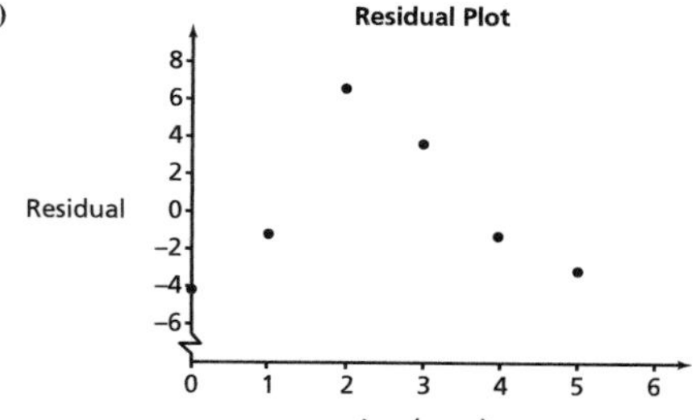

(b)

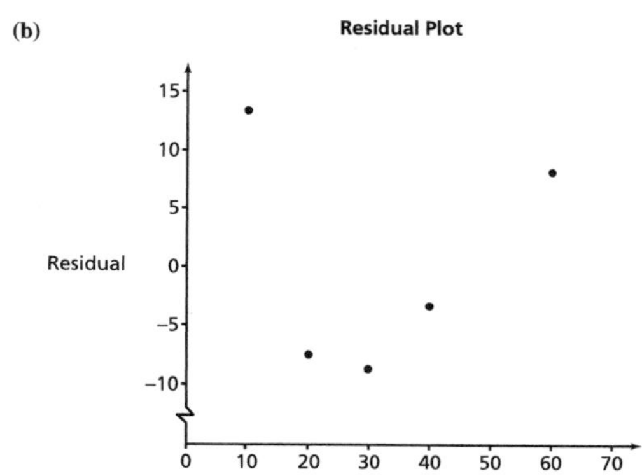

(c)

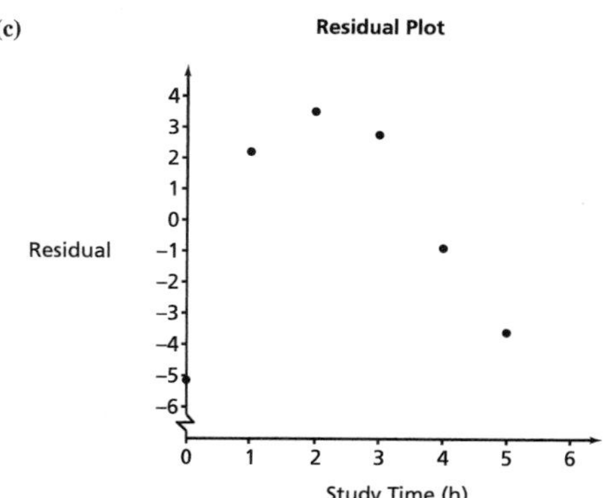

6. (a)

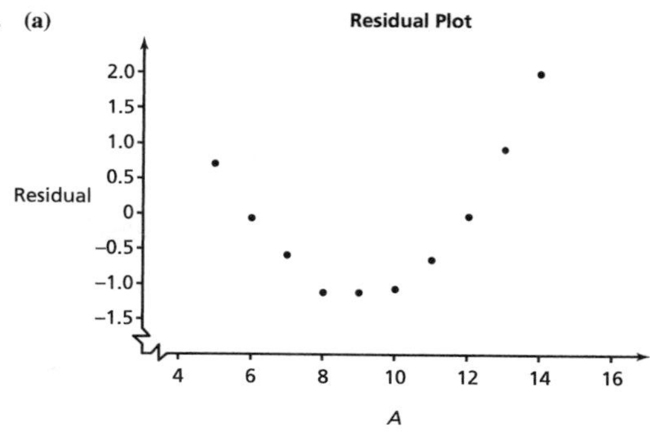

(b)

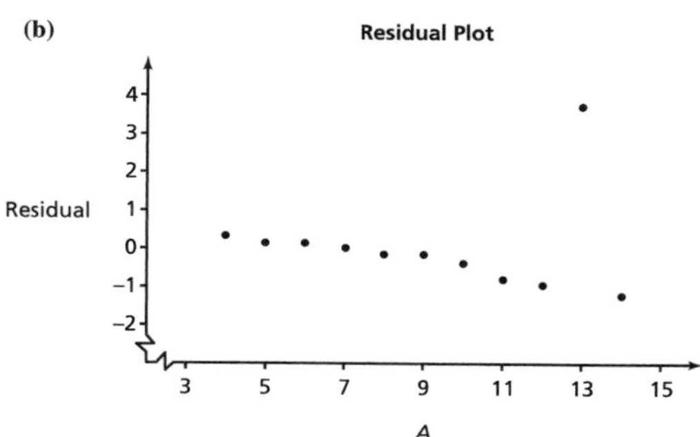

(c)

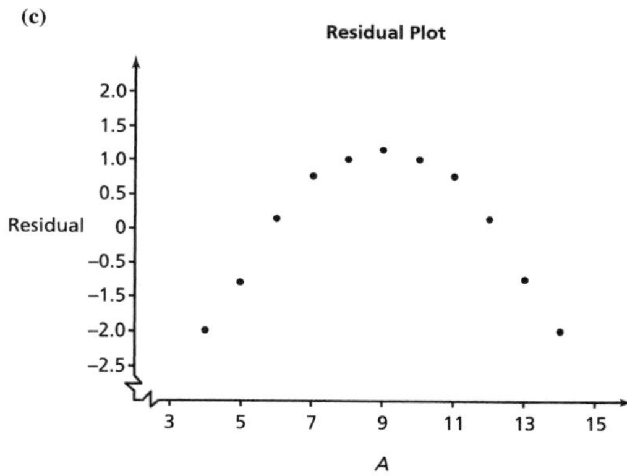

7. (a) Answers may vary; for example:

(i)

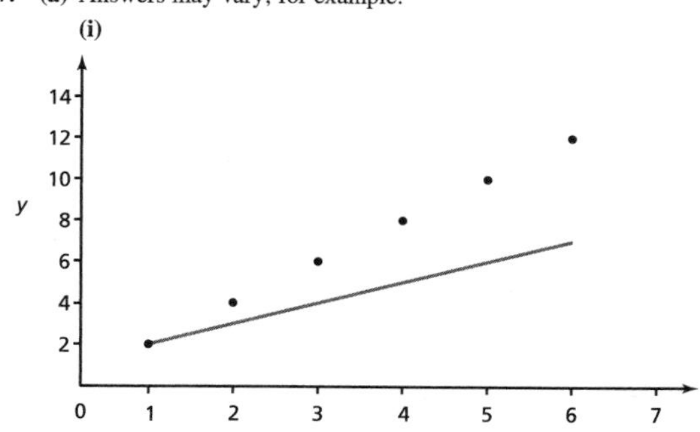

(ii)

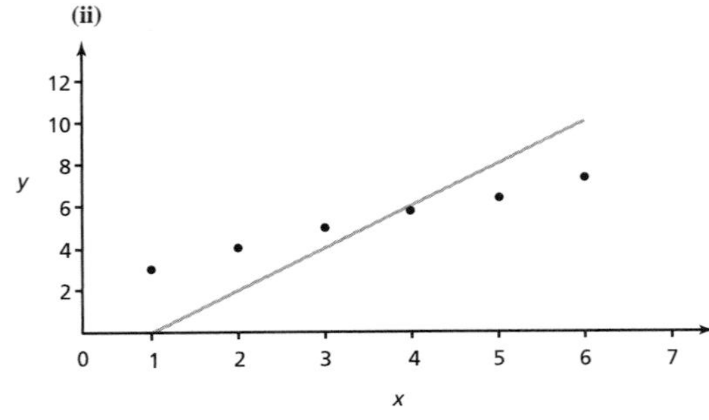

(b) **(i)** The line of best fit is too low (all the actual values are higher than the line of best fit).
(ii) The slope of the line of best fit is the wrong sign.

(c) The residual plot would be all zeros.

(d) The residual plot should have small values, both positive and negative.

8. **(a)** 25% **(b)** 72.25% **(c)** 43.56%
(d) 81% **(e)** 1% **(f)** 10.24%

9. **(a)** A medium to low number, 0.66 or less
(b) Answers may vary; for example: 0.36, 0.67, 0.23, 0.14, –0.56 or about $\frac{1}{5}$ or 20%

10. **(a)** No. People who get heart disease are more likely to be ill and thus, taking medicine (maybe aspirin).
(b) No. Depression and anger might be one of the many causes of illness. A good and cheerful attitude helps you to stay healthy, but it does not prevent you from becoming ill.
(c) No. Must take into account other possibilities, such as the chemistry of the water. Why did the pine needles fall into the water in the first place? Were the trees dying?

12. **(a)** Between 1896 and 1996, the winning distance has been increasing at an almost steady rate and it has more than doubled.
(b)

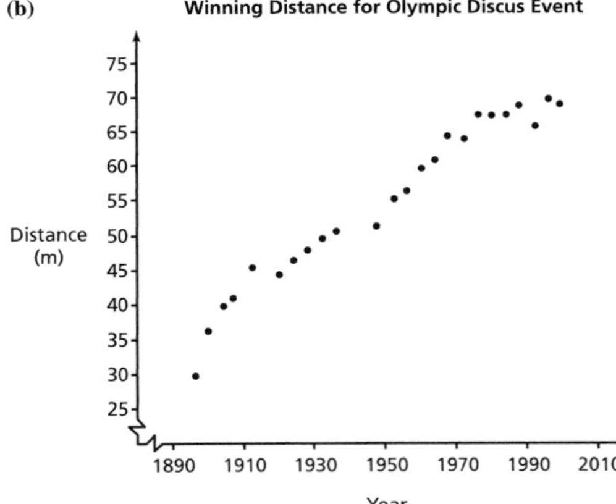

13. **(a)** Population: $y = 393\ 329.7092x - 753\ 176\ 520.4$,
Births: $y = -12\ 412.35x + 24\ 813\ 089$,
Deaths: $y = 1645.078\ 462x - 3\ 084\ 404.065$,
Infant Deaths: $y = -430.860\ 769\ 2x + 856\ 494.4277$;
Population: 22 862 996, Births: 323 522, Deaths: 161 336, Infant Deaths: 6426
Note: The line of best fit for Deaths starts at 1960 and the earlier data were ignored.
(b) Population: $y = 338\ 693.0495x - 646\ 153\ 909$;
Births: $y = -1212.606\ 458x + 2\ 786\ 924.049$,
Note: This is not very significant, $r = -0.437\ 580$;
Deaths: $y = 1809.539\ 083x - 3\ 407\ 250.213$;
Infant Deaths: $y = -330.585\ 923\ 2x + 659\ 798.1764$
(c) Only Births does not have a line of best fit with a high significance.

1.5 Exercises, page 60

1. **(a)** same data, different scales
(b) The same, from \$35 000 to \$42 000 (by \$7000) over 12 months (1 year)
(c) The first graph shows a large profit growth over the year. The second graph shows very little profit over the year.

2. **(a)** They are identical, except in size.
(b) The area has increased by a factor of four (10 squares to 40 squares).
(c) A factor of 2
(d) Because the area of the second house is so much larger than the first house, it appears that the size of homes has increased tremendously.

3. It seems that the price in 1980 is 2.5 times the price in 1975, but really it is only 1.5 times. The price in 1990 seems 4 times the price in 1975, but really it is only 2 times. Also, it does not look like a steady increase in the price, although it is a steady increase. Change the vertical scale (cost) so that it has regular intervals.

5. " Near a 20-year low" could mean 19 years and a few months. "18-year low" might not have included 1999, since it was not over yet.

6. **(a)** Misleading; 4 out of 5 of all dentists? Or, 4 out of 5 dentists that they asked.
(b) Misleading; Maybe the store in Bruce Mines has mostly that company's product.
(c) Misleading; They probably mean 75% of the ones that go to university obtain a degree, or that 75% of graduates go to university.
(d) Misleading; What do they mean by closer ties? Maybe 53% of the Canadians agreed.
(e) Misleading. This could mean that other countries are doing better. We could even be doing better, but other countries' improvements were better over the year.

9. **(i)** **(a)** Yes, the horizontal scale (time) is not properly spaced.
(ii) **(a)** Yes; the vertical scale (percent) is not properly spaced. The differences look larger.
(iii) **(a)** Yes; the vertical scale (percent) is not properly spaced. The differences look larger.
(iv) **(a)** Yes. Choose a better format for answers. Choose a larger sample than Business Leaders.

12. **(a)**

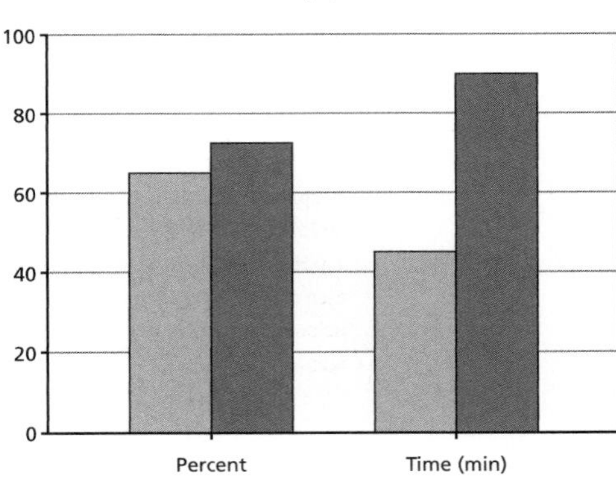

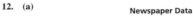

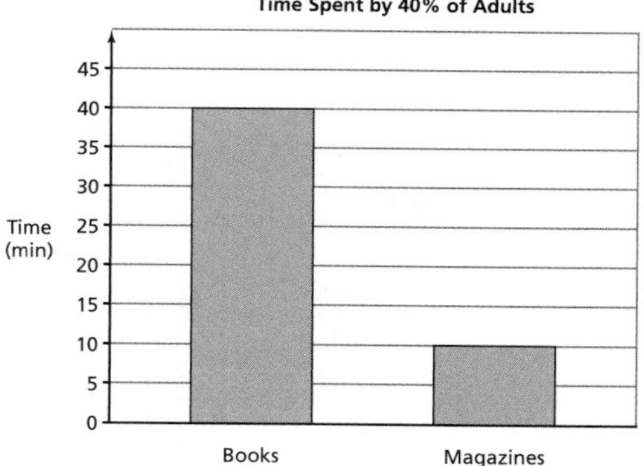

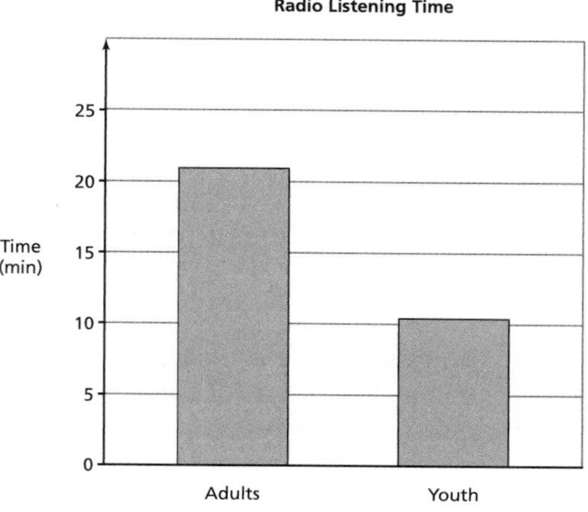

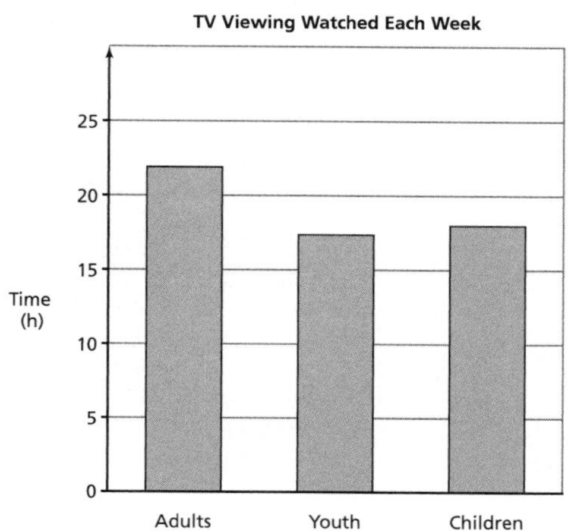

(b) Newspapers: There are more weekend readers who read double the time that weekday readers read. Books and Magazines: 40% of adults read books four times longer than they read magazines. Radio: Adults listen to the radio twice as much as youths. Television: Adults watch more television than youths and children.

Chapter 1 Wrap-Up, page 68

1. **(a)**

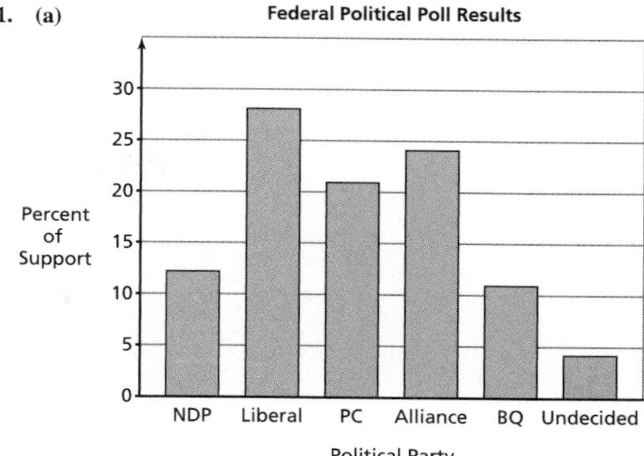

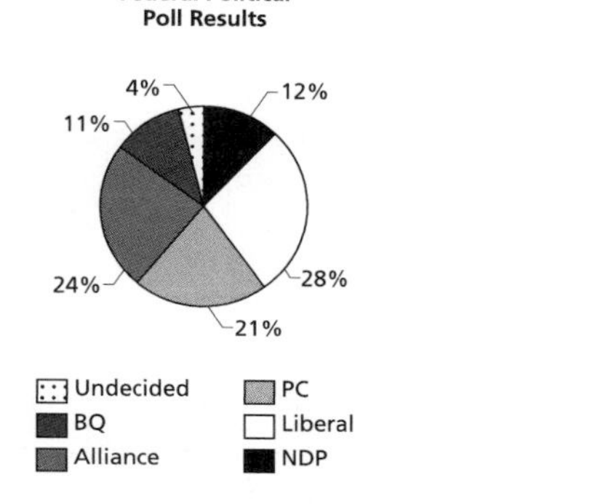

(b) Bar graph is easier because you can clearly see which bars are higher.

2. bar graph

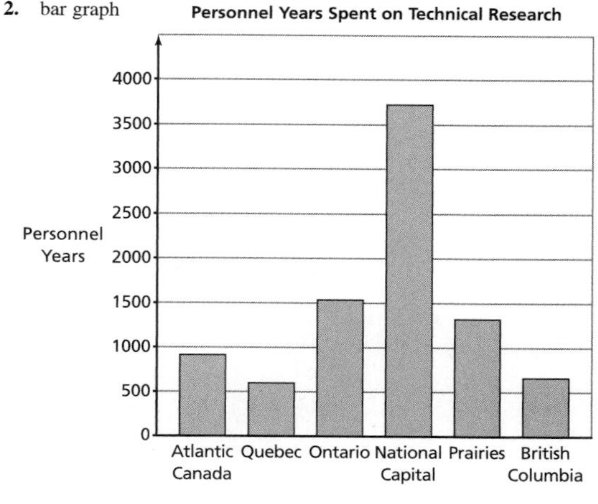

3. (a)

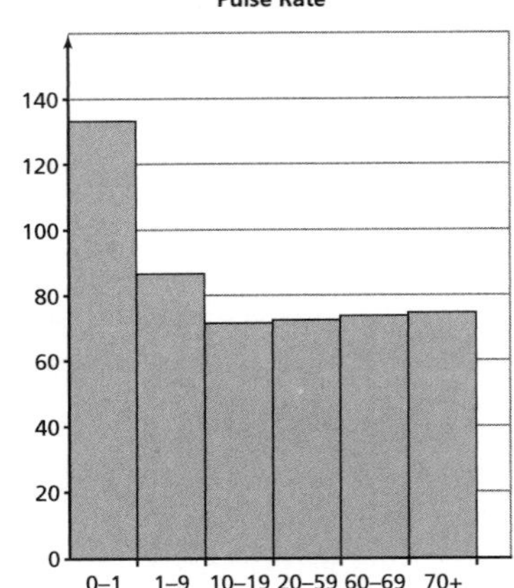

(b)

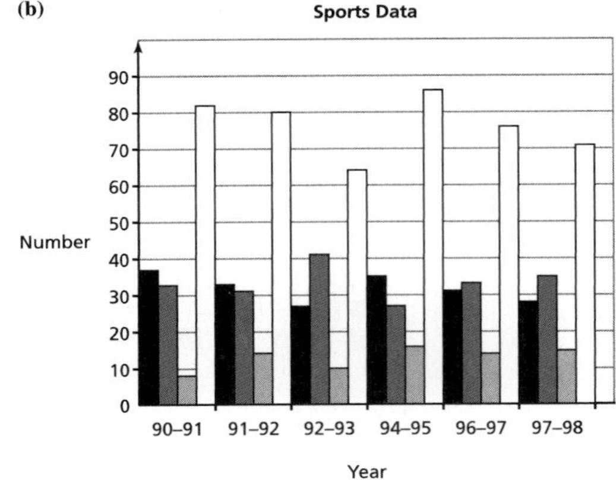

(c)

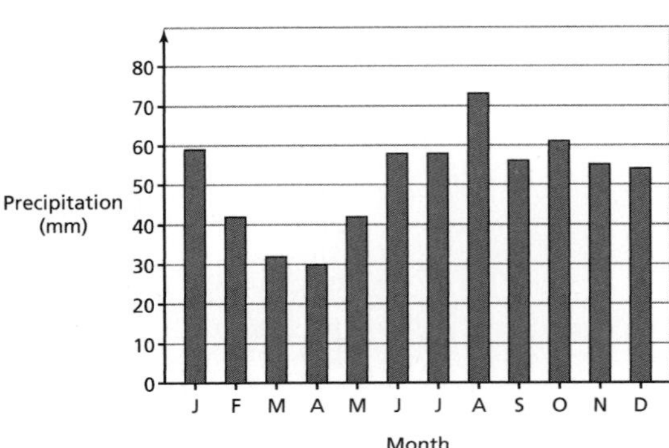

4. **(a)** no
   (b) You need the average consumption from other countries.
   (c), (d) The daily average water consumption, excluding water used by agriculture and industry, is higher in North America than in Switzerland, U.K., Nigeria, West Germany, Belgium, and India combined, which the writer misidentified.
   (e) Research the consumption from other countries.
5. **(a)** $y = 3.2485x + 4.1394$
   (b) Answers may vary, e.g.: Mass $= \frac{10}{3} \times \text{age} + \frac{11}{3}$
   (c) Answers may vary, e.g.: 57 kg
   (d) Mass = 3.2485 × age + 4.1394. Mass of a 16-year-old boy: 56.12 kg; $r = 0.962\ 374$, confident
6. **(a)**

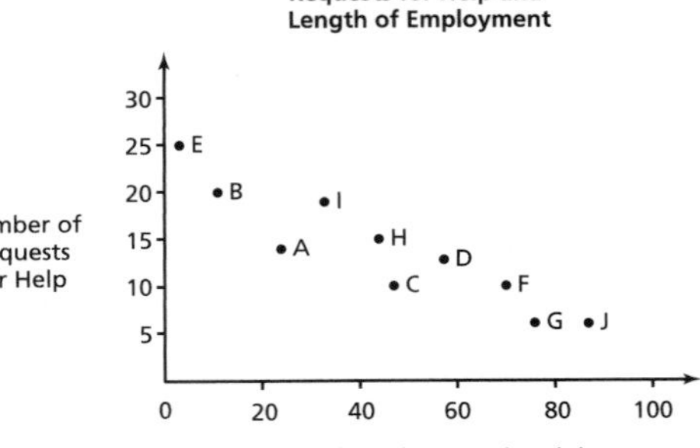

   (b) less often
7. **(a)** $y = -0.0335x + 8.4679$
   (b) Strong negative correlation; Yes, this is expected. A car will operate more efficiently at a moderately quick speed.
8. **(c)** Answers will vary; for example: $y = 0.411\ 429x + 0.642\ 857$
   (d) 25; 21 using line of best fit. Close because answers are close each time, but different.
9. **(a)** Average wage per hour implies making the same income across Canada, but pay is very different when you work less hours.
   (b) No, this impression is not accurate.
   (c) Add another graph showing total yearly income across Canada.

Chapter 1 Test, page 71

1. **(a)** Yes, students think Math teachers are nerds. No, because kids were asked to draw mathematicians, not math teachers.
   (b) There is a misconception that mathematicians (and intelligent people, in general) are nerds.
2. **(a)**

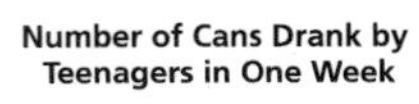

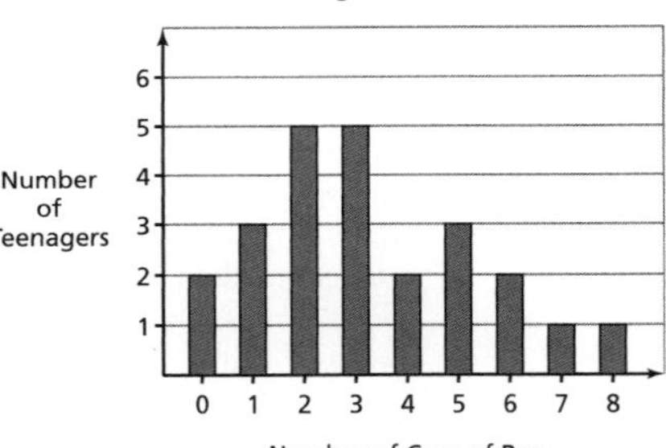

   (b) A frequency table would be quicker.
3. **(a)** $y = 0.1357x + 0.7714$
   (b) Mass = 0.135 724 85 × age + 0.7714
   (c) 2.13 kg
   (d) strong positive correlation
4. **(a)** no correlation
   (b) strong correlation; more rainfall helps vegetation grow
   (c) strong correlation; more mass means higher fuel consumption
5. **(a)**

4	5 8 9
5	1 2 4 5 5 6 7 7 8 9
6	0 1 2 2 3 7 8
7	1 5

   (b) 6 games
   (c) 18.2%
   (d) In only 9% of the games did the team score more than 68 points. It is not very likely.

6. **(a)** $y = 96.019x + 670.53$
   (b) Mass of heart = 96.019 × mass of the cat + 670.53 using TI-83 Plus calculator or computer spreadsheet software
   (c) The mass of the heart increases as the mass of a cat increases.
   (d) No, because it is not a good fit.
7. No, because it appears that taxes have quadrupled.
8. **(a)** Using a vertical scale from 0 to $1000 would make the differences between Carrie and Musinta seem smaller.
   (b) Using a vertical scale from $390 to $710 would make her sales figures seem to be increasing more than they are.
9. **(a)** 16.8% **(b)** 67.2%
   (c) 86.5% **(d)** 19.4%
   (e) 25.0% **(f)** 100%
10. **(a)** The picture for January 1984 is many times smaller than the one for February 1983, but unemployment only dropped from 10.5% to 8.0%.
    (b) No, this impression is not accurate.
    (c) Extending the vertical to 0 will fix the inaccuracy.

Chapter 2

2.1 Exercises, page 81

1. **(a)** preparing for a camping trip: packing, shopping list, drive, sleeping bag, sunscreen; things done on the camping trip: unpack, canoe, relax, swim, sleep, eat, bug bite, picnic
   (b) things you do in a car: steer, shift, push, pull, turn; parts of a car: pedal, wheel, brake, tire, dial, seat, switch, window, radio
   (c) parts of a computer: hard drive, mouse, CD-ROM, keyboard, cable, monitor; things to do with a computer: type, click, download, read, play, record, save, load, plug-in
   (d) things to do in the backyard: dig, plant, prune, water, clip, harvest, garden; things you use in the backyard: seeds, hose, hoe, shovel, fertilizer
   (e) things you do before work: wake up, shower, breakfast, drive; things you do during the day at work: copier, phone, meeting, fax, lunch, break
   (f) actions in a hockey game: slashing, face off, skate, shoot, save; objects related to hockey: ref, blue line, puck, fans, goalie, forward, defence, net
4. **(a)** estimation of height and distance, person's height; person's age, actual height, actual distance
   (b) females' estimate of size of crowd, males' estimate of size of crowd, actual size of crowd
   (c) quality of a person's clothing, mid-term average
   (d) mid-term average in all subjects, favourite subject
5. Answers may vary; for example: **(a)** estimation of height and distance 1, person's height 1, person's age 1, actual height 1, actual distance 1 (depends on the object)
   (b) females' estimate of size of crowd 1, males' estimate of size of crowd 1, actual size of crowd 8
   (c) quality of a person's clothing 6, mid-term average 1
   (d) mid-term average in all subjects 1, favourite subject 1

2.2 Exercises, page 89

1. **(a)** quantitative **(b)** qualitative **(c)** qualitative
   (d) quantitative (but could be qualitative)
   (e) qualitative **(f)** qualitative **(g)** quantitative
   (h) quantitative **(i)** quantitative **(j)** qualitative
2. **(a)** discrete (but could be continuous)
   (d) continuous **(g)** continuous **(h)** discrete **(i)** discrete
3. **(a)** weather conditions: qualitative; absenteeism: quantitative, discrete (but could be continuous); population: Grade 9 students in our school
   (b) profiles: qualitative; population: people who buy used cars in Canada
   (c) amount of television: quantitative (measured in minutes); discrete; physical fitness: quantitative, continuous; population: adult females
   (d) average number of breakfast meals eaten: quantitative, discrete; grades: quantitative, continuous; population: Grade 9 students
   (e) number of female students with speeding tickets: quantitative, discrete; number of male students with speeding tickets: quantitative, discrete; population: teenagers who have been issued speeding tickets
   (f) home conditions: qualitative; population: school-aged children
   (g) time of day: quantitative, discrete; number of available parking spaces: quantitative, discrete; population: shoppers who drive to the local mall
   (h) amount spent on clothes: quantitative, discrete; amount of money student earns: quantitative, discrete; population: students at our school
4. **(a)** sample, longitudinal **(b)** sample, cross-sectional
   (c) sample, longitudinal (could be cross-sectional)
   (d) sample, longitudinal **(e)** sample, cross-sectional
   (f) sample, cross-sectional (could be longitudinal)
   (g) sample, longitudinal **(h)** sample, cross-sectional
5. **(a)** **(i)** school environment club
   (ii), (iii), (iv) quantity for each T-shirt size: quantitative; discrete
   (b) **(i)** electors in a district
   (ii) level of support: qualitative
   (c) **(i)** plants on 45 hectares of land
   (ii) plant species: qualitative; number of species / ha: quantitative; discrete
   (d) **(i)** native community on Manitoulin Island
   (ii) family structure during the last century: qualitative
   (e) **(i)** present and former staff and students, parents and interested community members
   (ii) new names for the school: qualitative
   (f) **(i)** teenagers today and 20 years ago
   (ii) economic situation of teenagers today: qualitative; economic situation of teenagers 20 years ago: qualitative
6. **(a)** **(i)** census **(ii)** cross-sectional
   (b) **(i)** sample **(ii)** cross-sectional
   (c) **(i)** census **(ii)** cross-sectional
   (d) **(i)** sample **(ii)** longitudinal
   (e) **(i)** sample **(ii)** cross-sectional
   (f) **(i)** sample **(ii)** longitudinal
9. **(i)** **(a)** cross-sectional **(b)** longitudinal
   (c) longitudinal **(d)** cross-sectional
   (e) longitudinal **(f)** cross-sectional
   (ii) The population in each case is very large so a census would be difficult to obtain.
10. **(a)** all the integrated circuits at a manufacturing plant
    (b) integrated circuits selected by the quality-control officer

2.3 Exercises, page 99

1. (a) cluster random sampling
   (b) simple random sampling
   (c) systematic random sampling
   (d) multi-stage random sampling
   (e) stratified random sampling
2. Cluster: Arrange the class in groups of three and randomly select two groups. Stratified: Divide the class into females and males and randomly select 3 students of each gender. Systematic: Randomly pick the first student, then pick every fourth student until you have selected six.
3. (a) Quick and easy, but the sample may not end up representative of the population by chance.
   (b) Straight forward, but the sample may not end up representative of the population by chance.
   (c) Each stratum is represented, but the sample may not end up representative of the population by chance.
   (d) All members of the chosen groups are represented, but not all groups are represented.
   (e) Higher chance of representation of each group than simple random sampling, but the sample may not end up representative of the population by chance.
4. Answers may vary; for example:
   (a) 30, 76, 157, 410, 19, 394
   (b) 3, 44, 85, 126, 167, 208, 249, 290, 331, 372
   (c) 5, 34, 89, 122, 156, 199, 222, 267, 290, 322, 333, 389
   (d) 202, 213, 229, 233, 244, 256, 278, 281, 290, 295
5. (a) simple (b) cluster (c) systematic
   (d) multi-stage (e) stratified
6. (c) Make the males and females into strata and perform a stratified random sample.
7. In stratified random sampling, the population is divided into groups (strata) and a representative simple random sample is taken from each stratum, while a systematic random sample takes every nth individual in the population, where n is the sampling interval. $n = \frac{\text{population size}}{\text{sample size}}$. For example: Sample 5 students from a class of 24. There are 15 males. Stratified: Divide the class into 9 females and 15 males. Take two random females and three random males. Systematic: Arrange the students in alphabetical order and take every fourth student.
8. Choose a random number of classes, then choose a random number of students from each of these classes.
9. Answers may vary; for example:
   (a) Shuffle the cards and select the first 13 cards in the deck.
   (b) Shuffle the cards and select every fourth card.
   (c) Separate the cards into 4 piles by suit. Randomly pick one suit. Take top 3 cards from each pile and one other card.
   (d) Separate the cards into 4 suits. Randomly pick one suit.
   (e) Separate the cards into 2 piles of the same colour in each pile. Randomly select 13 cards from one pile.
10. Answers may vary; for example:
    (a) B774, X315, X322, P035, L506, L501, P032, X320, B777, P039, B771, L507
    (b) L503, L506, X315, X318, X321, B772, B775, B778, P034, P037
    (c) L504, L503, L501, X316, X318, X315, B771, B774, B773, P032, P033, P034
11. No, because not every model would be represented.
12. (a) simple random sampling
    (b) stratified random sampling
    (c) systematic random sampling or simple random sampling
    (d) multi-stage random sampling
    (e) stratified random sampling
13. Quota sampling: Set the number of women, men, high income, medium income, and low income from each state or region. This is not random.
14. The longer the sample is, the more representative of the population it becomes.

2.4 Exercises, page 105

1. (a) What do you think of the quantity of homework assigned so far in the course?
   (b) Describe your degree of preference to the type of music listed below.
   (c) What are your plans for post-secondary school?
   (d) What is your favourite type (genre) of television program?
   (e) How confident are you in your swimming ability?
2. (a) Answers may vary; for example: What do you think about the quantity of homework assigned so far in this course?
   A) too much B) appropriate C) not enough
   D) no opinion
   (b) Rank the following types of music in order of preference (1 means hate; 5 means love).
   (c) After high school, I plan to attend: A) college B) university C) apprenticeship D) other
   (d) My favourite type (genre) of television show is A) comedy B) real-life C) science fiction D) educational E) news F) other
   (e) How confident are you in your swimming ability? A) very B) somewhat C) a little D) not at all E) no opinion
3. (a) What do you think of your timetabled courses this semester? Check all that apply. ❑ interesting ❑ challenging ❑ useful
   (b) Student council will attempt to have the following activities. Rank them from 1 for most important to 5 for least important.
   ____ more dances ____ more lunch time sports
   ____ more music before school ____ more assemblies
   ____ more university tours
   (c) Rate the television programs on this list from 1 to 5 (1 meaning very satisfied and 5 meaning not very satisfied).
4. (i) (a) (ii) (a) (iii) (c) (iv) (c)
5.

Criterion	(a)	(b)	(c)	(d)	(e)	(f)
Simple	N	Y	Y	N	Y	Y
Specific	Y	Y	Y	Y	Y	Y
Readable	N	Y	Y	Y	Y	Y
Avoids jargon	Y	Y	Y	N	N	N
Avoids abbreviations	Y	Y	N	Y	Y	Y
Avoids negatives	Y	Y	Y	Y	Y	N
Avoids being leading	Y	Y	Y	N	N	Y
Avoids insensitivity	Y	Y	Y	N	N	Y

   (a) List adjectives that describe the state of the environment. What is the extent of pollution in Ontario?
   (c) Should the Ontario Municipal Board be funded to initiate waste audits across the province? Yes No
   (d) Should mining companies be forced to decrease the amount of sulfur dioxide being emitted at smelters? Please comment.
   (e) On a 5-point scale, do you agree that all corporations should pay higher taxes?
   (f) Should forestry companies be able to cut down all trees in certain areas? Explain.
6. Open questions allow a wide degree of possibilities, which might be difficult to interpret. Closed questions are easy to analyze, but the options may bias the results.

7. (i) (a) Information where there is only a limited number of answers
(b) More than one answer or ranking or unlimited number of choices
(ii) (a) Stating preference of each choice in the list
(b) Specific questions with only one answer
(iii) (a) Information with more than one answer
(b) Ranking or answers that are not given
(iv) (a) Evaluating something or expressing an opinion about it
(b) Ranking, more than one answer, information other than a rating

8. (a) open, information (b) open, information
(c) open (d) closed, ranking
(e) open, information (f) closed, checklist
(g) open, ranking

10. (a) Rate the quality of cafeteria food at your school with a number from 1 to 5 (1 means horrible, 5 means great).
(b) Rank the following musical styles from most favourite (1) to least favourite (6): __ alternative __ folk __ hip hop __ pop __ jazz __ rock
(c) Check the activities that you would like to see offered at a school fundraiser. ❑ lucky draw ❑ drama ❑ singing contest ❑ magic show

12. (a) closed, information (b) open
(c) closed, ranking (d) closed, information
(e) open (f) closed, information

2.5 Exercises, page 113

1. (a) non-response (b) sampling
(c) response (d) sampling
2. (a), (b), and (c)
3. (a) and (c)
4. Response bias. Have the company name blocked from Call Display. (Could also be considered non-response bias)
5. Which store did you visit? How much money did you spend?
6. Make each question have the option of being open. Provide a space for other: __
9. Non-response: The alumnus may not reply. Household: Since only 60% of associations provided lists, there might be misrepresentation.
10. (a) non-response, household
11. (a) (i) Response bias. Information about rising youth crime should not be given.
(ii) What do you feel should be the top enforcement priority for the local police force?
(b) (i) Response bias. Baseball, fastball, softball, and two-pitch are almost the same, so are ice hockey, shinny, and ball hockey.
(ii) Rank the following: ___ baseball ___ hockey ___ cricket ___ basketball ___ lacrosse
(c) (i) Response bias. Scrumptious is larger than Bland; use of bold text
(ii) You should have ordered Scrumptious Really Good Decent Bland (same font size)
12. The entire questionnaire generates a response bias and should be rewritten (except Question 1).

2.6 Exercises, page 123

1. (a) Sites about Thomas Engine trains
(b) Information on Gandalf found on members.tripod.com Web sites
(c) Information on sharks but not related to hockey
(d) Sites in the .ca domain with words like Canada, Canadian, etc.
(e) Information on hot dogs or ketchup or mustard
(f) Sites about Slim Whitman or Slim Witman
2. (a) A Web directory is a commercial service that provides keyword searches that link to sites. A search engine is a Web site that performs searches of the whole Internet.
(b) (i) Web directory
(ii) search engine
(iii) search engine
(iv) Web directory
3. (a) (Sale | Sell) & "CD burners"
(b) Stat* & software
(c) Literature +domain:ca
(d) "Your school" +domain:ca
(e) education +site:gov.on.ca
(f) download +"independent recording artist" +domain:ca
4. (a) "Ralph Waldo Emerson" +quotes
(b) "Mount Logan" +(altitude OR height)
(c) RCMP +history
(d) "Emily Carr" +site:canoe.ca
5. (a) "New York City" +theater
(b) Kosovo +refugees
(c) music –classical
(d) ("Toronto Blue Jays") +("Montreal Expos") +player +stat*
(e) mathematician +canad*
(f) drug* +illicit –heroin –cocaine

2.7 Exercises, page 130

1. (a) spreadsheet (b) database (c) spreadsheet
(d) database (e) spreadsheet (f) table
2. Bolt width (mm), Frequency: 35–39.9, 2; 40–44.9, 4; 45–49.9, 6; 50–54.9, 7; 55–59.9, 7, 60–64.9, 6
4. 1950: 2.6, 1955: 2.8, 1960: 3.0, 1965: 3.4, 1970: 3.8, 1975: 4.1, 1980: 4.5, 1985: 4.9, 1990: 5.3, 1995: 5.8, 2000: 6.1, 2005: 6.5, 2010: 6.8, 2015: 7.2, 2020: 7.6, 2025: 7.8, 2030: 8.2, 2035: 8.5, 2040: 8.8, 2045: 8.9, 2050: 9.1
5. (a) Graph (iv) (b) Graph (vi) (c) Graph (v)
(d) Graph (ii) (e) Graph (iii) (f) Graph (i)
6. (155, 52), (175, 67), (185, 72), (195, 77), (205, 79), (215, 83)
7. (b) mean for $x = 13.4$; mean for $y = 7.1$; median for $x = 13.6$; median for $y = 7.1$

13. (a), (b)

Sol	High	Low	Average
1	−29.10°C	−85.40°C	−60.64°C
2	−26.86°C	−85.84°C	−59.34°C
3	−28.02°C	−85.38°C	−61.55°C

14. (a), (b)

Sol	High	Low	Average
1	248°K	185°K	216.5°K
2	248°K	184°K	216°K
3	249°K	185°K	217°K
4	248°K	185°K	216.5°K
5	249°K	186°K	217.5°K

15. (a), (b)

Sol	High	Low	Average
1	6.99 mb	6.68 mb	6.835 mb
2	6.96 mb	6.77 mb	6.865 mb
3	6.97 mb	6.77 mb	6.87 mb
4	6.96 mb	6.77 mb	6.865 mb
5	6.96 mb	6.68 mb	6.82 mb

$\text{average} = \frac{\text{high} + \text{low}}{2}$

Chapter 2 Wrap-Up, page 136

2. (a) teenagers in your community
   (b), (c) smoking habits, qualitative; taxation levels, quantitative
   (d) continuous
3. simple, systematic, stratified, multi-stage, random sampling
4. (a) simple (b) stratified (c) systematic
5. (a) sample (b) census (c) sample
6. (a) Perspective buyers at a local car dealership

Chapter 2 Test, page 138

1. (a) room temperature, humidity, sunlight
2. (a) stratified (b) systematic (c) multi-stage
   (d) systematic (e) cluster

Chapter 3

3.1 Exercises, page 146

1. (a) left-skewed
   (b) mound-shaped, symmetric
   (c) left-skewed
   (d) U-shaped, bimodal, symmetric
   (e) uniform, symmetric
   (f) right-skewed
2. (a) year on a penny (b) top 100 films
   (c) bowling scores (d) electric bill
   (e) cheap seats at the stadium (f) gestation period of animals
3. If the bin is too narrow, it will show spaces.
4. Answers may vary. For example:
   (a) 2 (b) 0.2 (c) 20 (d) 1
5. Answers may vary. For example:
   (a) 4.5–6.5, 6.5–8.5, 8.5–10.5, 10.5–12.5, 12.5–14.5
   (b) 0.115–0.315, 0.315–0.515, 0.515–0.715, 0.715–0.915, 0.915–1.115
   (c) 111.5–131.5, 131.5–151.5, 151.5–171.5, 171.5–191.5, 191.5–211.5
   (d) −3.05 to −2.05, −2.05 to −1.05, −1.05 to −0.05, −0.05 to 0.95, 0.95 to 1.95
6. Answers may vary. For example:

(a)

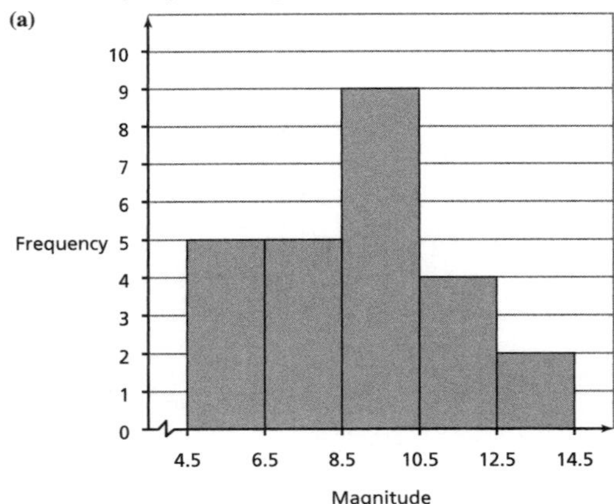

(b)

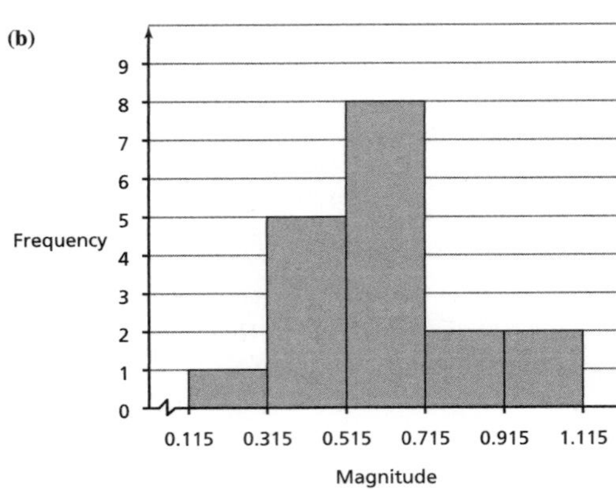

(c)

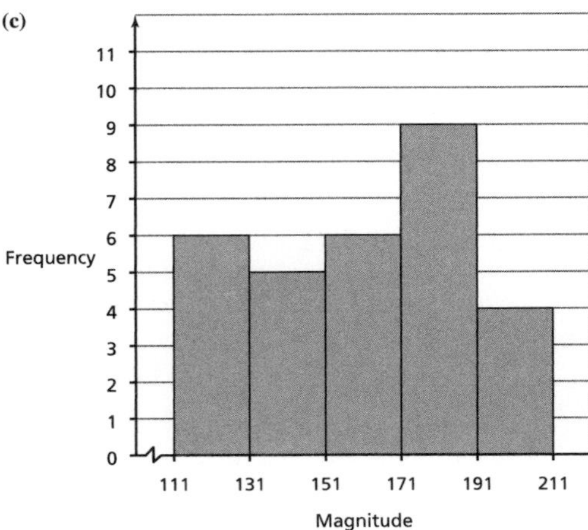

(d)

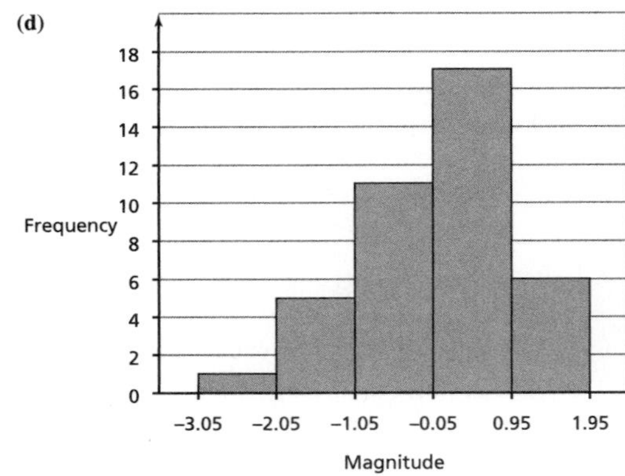

7. **(a)**

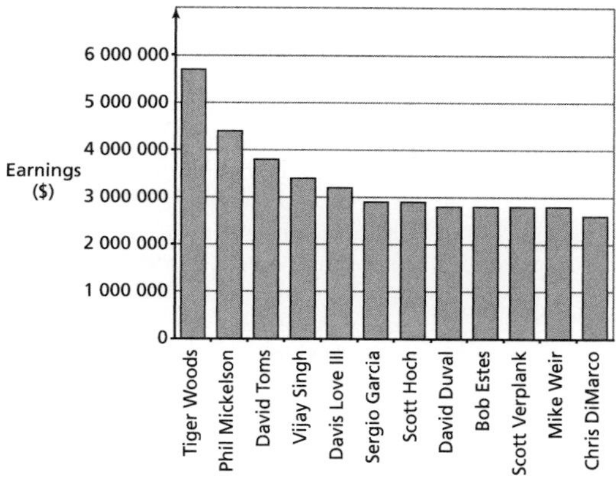

(b)

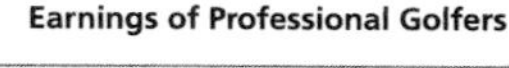

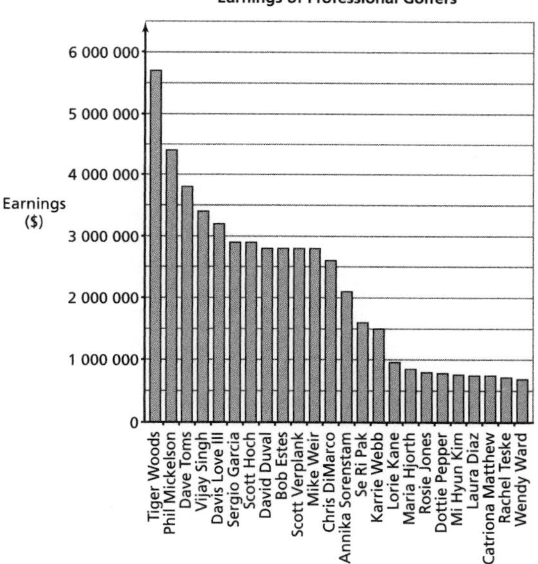

8. **(a)** 12.1%, 22.3%, 19.6%, 16%, 12.2%, 8.4%, 5.3%, 4.1%

(c)

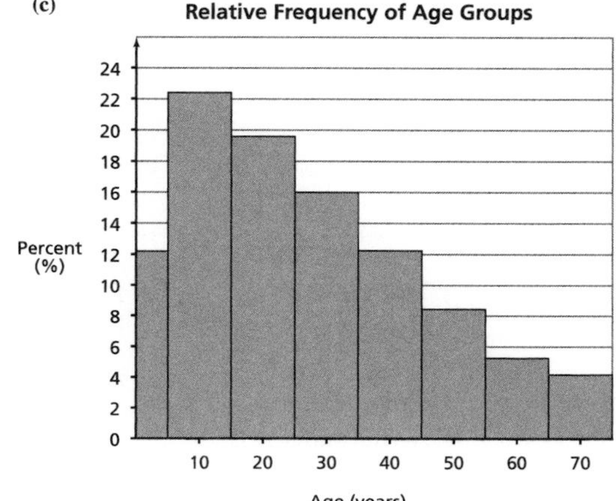

(e) right-skewed

(f) Smaller bin widths make comparison difficult.

9. **(a)** 30

(b) There are very few larger amounts, which makes the graph right-skewed.

11.

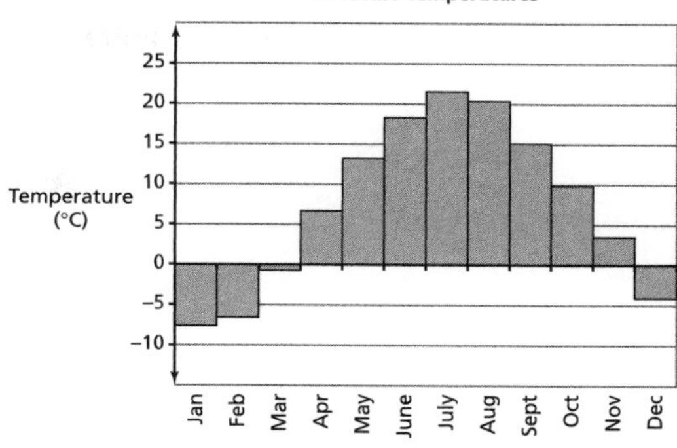

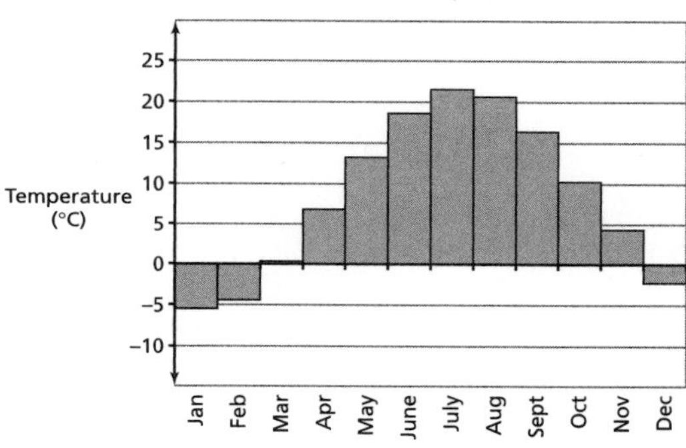

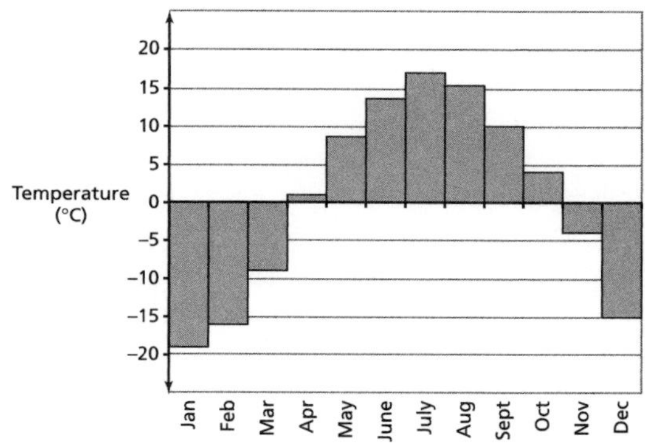

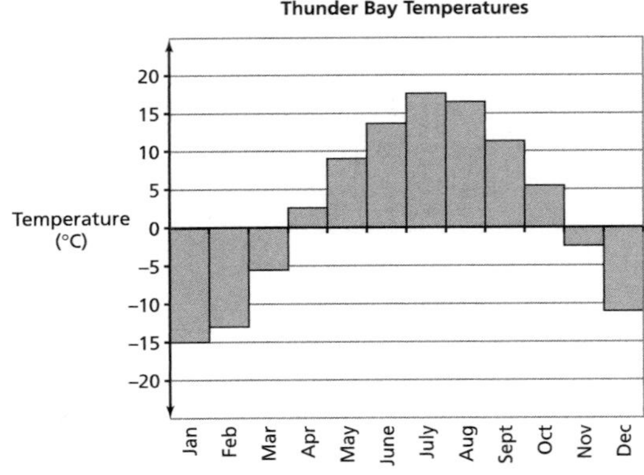

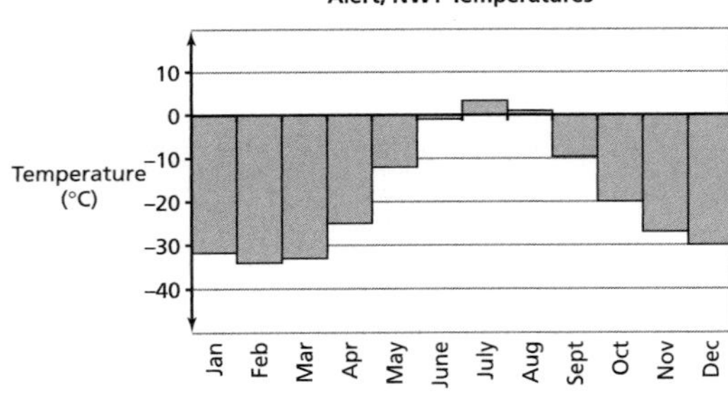

13. Hamilton: 21.7°C – (–5.5°C) or 26.2°C

3.2 Exercises, page 158

1. **(a)** mean: 72, median: 69, mode: none
   (b) mean: $755, median: $687.50, mode: $625
   (c) mean: 2.7, median: 3, mode: 3
   (d) mean: 5.8 min, median: 6.5 min, mode: 5.0 min and 7.0 min
   (e) mean: 11.56, median: 12, mode: 15
   (f) mean: $8704.50; median: $0; mode: $0
2. Answers may vary. Example:
   (a) median **(b)** median **(c)** mode
   (d) median **(e)** median **(f)** mean or mode
3. **(a)** skewed right **(b)** skewed right **(c)** symmetric
   (d) skewed left **(e)** skewed left **(f)** skewed right
4. **(a)** 7.18, 7, 8
   (b) mean and median; they are equal and take into account the other sizes; mode = most popular size
5. **(a)** (ii) **(b)** (iii) **(c)** (i) **(d)** (iv)
6. **(a)** No; there could be many low sales, but one very high outlier.
   (b) No; it depends on the number of people in each class.
   (c) No; the maximum value could have been 20, but it did not have to be 20.
   (d) No; the median does not show what the values to the left and right are. It is only the middle value. The other numbers could be very high or very low.
   (e) Yes; since each salary is raised by 10%, that is the same as raising the mean by 10%.
   (f) Yes; the middle salary is still the median; therefore, it is $33 000 after the raise.
   (g) This is possible if the data are strongly skewed and there are some high outliers.
   (h) No; the store could have sold 20 pop, 20 rock, and 30 classical, for example.
7. **(a)** Compact: mean: 29 mi/gal, median: 30 mi/gal; Luxury: mean: 18 mi/gal, median: 16 mi/gal; Family: mean: 21 mi/gal, median: 21 mi/gal
   (b) Compact: mean and median: right side because largest frequencies are to the right; Luxury: mean and median: left side because largest frequencies are to the left; Family: mean and median: right side because largest frequencies are to the right and centre
8. **(a)** 5, 10, 10, 10, 15
   (b) 5, 5, 5, 100, 100
   (c) –10, –10, 15, 15, 15
9. Calgary: 3.6; Ottawa: 5.6
10. Find the number of students in each class. Multiply each mean by the number of students in its class, add these two numbers, and divide the sum by the total number of students in the two classes.
11. mean: 6.78, median: 7, mode: 7
12. mean: 1980–1989; median: 1980–1989; modal interval: 1990–1999
13. **(a)** at least 58.3% **(b)** 75%
    (c) Not possible; you would need 108.3%.
14. **(a)** **(i)** 5, 5, 10, 10, 15, 15
    (ii) 3, 5, 5, 12, 15, 15, 15
    (b) The median is the middle value and it does not take into account what the other values are. The mean weighs every number the same. Thus, it is influenced by outliers.
15. **(a)** **(i)** $\frac{a+b+c+d}{4}$ **(ii)** $\frac{b+c}{2}$
    (b) **(i)** $\frac{k(a+b+c+d)}{4}$ **(ii)** $\frac{k(b+c)}{2}$
    (c) **(i)** $\frac{a+b+c+d}{4} + p$ or $\frac{a+b+c+d+4p}{4}$ **(ii)** $\frac{b+c+2p}{2}$

3.3 Exercises, page 168

1. **(a)** 75.9, 37.3 **(b)** 38.6 **(c)** 63.95
   (d) 25% **(e)** 17.7
2. **(a)** range: 8, Q1: 3, Q2: 6, Q3: 7, IQR: 4
   (b) range: 80, Q1: 16, Q2: 40, Q3: 68, IQR: 52
   (c) range: 30, Q1: 7, Q2: 13.5, Q3: 16, IQR: 9
   (d) range: 28, Q1: 5, Q2: 6, Q3: 9, IQR: 4
3. **(a)** 0.37 **(b)** 2.87 **(c)** 0.70 **(d)** 2.65
4. **(a)** (iii) **(b)** (ii) **(c)** (iv) **(d)** (i)
5. Q1: $30 000, Q2: $32 000, Q3: $34 000, IQR: $4000, σ: $2665
6. Yes, if all the numbers are the same.
7. **(a)** Class A: mean: 71.9, standard deviation: 6.01; Class B: mean: 71, standard deviation: 3.98; Class C: mean: 70.4, standard deviation: 5.68; Class D: mean: 76.9, standard deviation: 1.91; lowest pulse rate: Class C; most consistent pulse rate: Class D
   (b) Class A: median: 73, IQR: 12; Class B: median: 70, IQR: 6; Class C: median: 69, IQR: 8; Class D: median: 76, IQR: 2; No, because the low IQR means consistent results, as the standard deviation showed. The lowest median is in Class C, showing the low pulse rate as the mean showed.
8. **(a)** June and July have the biggest difference between high and low temperatures.
   (b) mean temperature: 4.8°C, mean high temperature: 10.6°C, mean low temperature: 1.4°C
   (c) range: 31.5°C, high: 32.7°C, low: 30.2°C; IQR: 22.2°C, high: 22.55°C, low: 19.95°C; standard deviation: 11.76, high: 11.48, low: 10.36
   (d) temperature: 6, high: 6, low: 6
9. No. She is more consistent. Her standard deviation now is 1.8 and before it was 3.9.
10. **(a)** range: 7, standard deviation: 2.22, IQR: 3
    (b) They would double.
    (c) They would all stay the same.
11. Prince Edward Island; Its standard deviation of 1.1 is the lowest.

12. $\frac{\sum(x-\bar{x})^2}{n} = \frac{\sum(x^2-2x\bar{x}+\bar{x}^2)}{n} = \frac{\sum x^2 - \sum(2x\bar{x}) + \sum\bar{x}^2}{n}$

$= \frac{\sum x^2}{n} - \frac{2\bar{x}\sum x}{n} + \frac{n\bar{x}^2}{n} = \frac{\sum x^2}{n} - 2\bar{x}^2 + \bar{x}^2 = \frac{\sum x^2 - n\bar{x}^2}{n}$

13. Yes. If one student's mark is a lot lower on one test and a lot higher on another test, the average could be the same, but the standard deviation would be higher. The other student could have almost the same mark every test and have a low standard deviation.
14. Yes. Answers may vary; for example: 162, 167, 168, 169, 170, 171.5 and 163, 165, 167, 168, 169, 172.5

3.4 Exercises, page 176

1. **(a)** yes
   (b) No, 68% of the values fall within 1 standard deviation.
   (c) yes **(d)** yes **(e)** depends on $\bar{x}$ **(f)** yes
2. The standard deviation can be analyzed mathematically and it takes into account all of the data values.
3. **(a)** **(i)** mean: 45.19, median: 45.5, standard deviation: 1.70
   (ii)

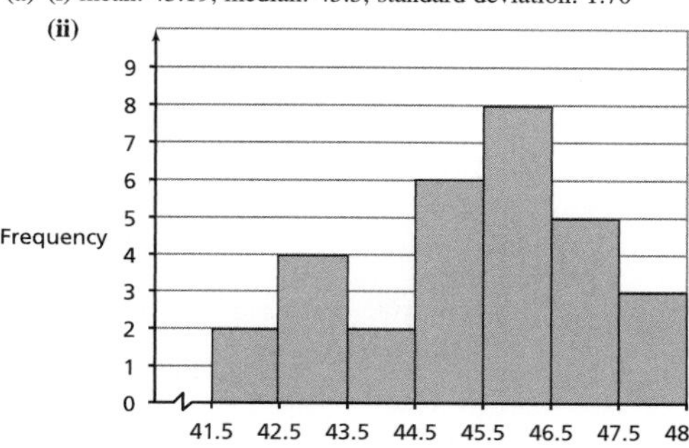

   (b) **(i)** mean: 8.62, median: 8, standard deviation: 2.85
   (ii)

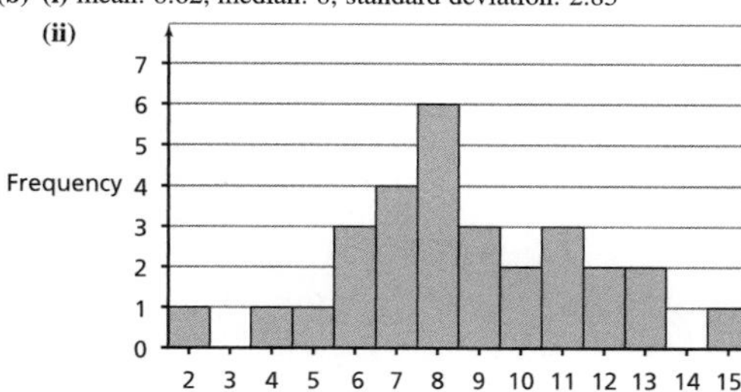

4. **(a)** (c)
5. **(a)** 12 **(c)** 16.3
6. 135; standard deviation = 15
7. **(a)** Yes, for normal distributions, since 99.7% of the data are within 3σ of the mean; 6σ = 99.7% of the data, which is very close to 100% of the data.
   (b) **(a)** 1.07 **(b)** 2.17
8. 180.7 cm and taller
9. **(a)** 9.6 oz to 10.8 oz
   (c) No. There is a 0.15% chance of the cup overflowing, which is not significant.
10. 6.9 years
11. **(a)** might be symmetrical and bell-shaped
    (b) varies
    (c) more symmetrical, more bell-shaped
12. **(a)** Kate: mean: 103.4, standard deviation: 19.86; Bernie: mean: 104.2, standard deviation: 15.37
    (b) Kate: 60%; Bernie: 80%
    (c) Kate: 163; Bernie: 150
13. **(a)** No, that is more than 3 standard deviations from the mean.
14. **(a)** No, that is more than 3 standard deviations from the mean.
    (b) at most 83

3.5 Exercises, page 186

1. **(a)** **(i)** −0.4 **(ii)** 0.6 **(iii)** 2.0 **(iv)** −2.6
   (b) **(i)** −2.4 **(ii)** 0.7 **(iii)** 2.8 **(iv)** −1.1
   (c) **(i)** −0.5 **(ii)** −2.3 **(iii)** 1.7 **(iv)** −2.0
   (d) **(i)** 0.6 **(ii)** −2.8 **(iii)** 1.6 **(iv)** 0.0
2. **(a)** No. The area is 1. **(b)** Yes.
   (c) No. They are all exactly equal to 0.
   (d) Yes. (or N(0, 1^2))
3. 760
4. **(a)** 67th percentile **(b)** 99th percentile
   (c) 20th percentile **(d)** 3rd percentile
5. **(a)** −0.13 **(b)** 0.61 **(c)** −1.48 **(d)** 2.05
6. **(a)** 60 **(b)** 40 **(c)** 75 **(d)** 45
   (e) 31.9 **(f)** 52 **(g)** 66.2 **(h)** 27.6
7. **(a)** **(i)** 0.17 **(ii)** 2.57
   (b) 74.2%; 25.7% **(c)** (z = 1.28) 185 points
8. 0.38%
9. **(a)** 0.38% **(b)** 37.8% **(c)** 5.30
10. **(a)** 94th percentile **(b)** 640.8
11. **(a)** 428.4g **(b)** 0.35%
12. **(a)** 12 **(b)** 0 **(c)** 68
13. No. There is only a 0.37% chance that the temperature could be over 30°C on any given day.
14. 63.6, 78.4
15. mean = 1.95 m; standard deviation = 0.82 m

3.6 Exercises, page 193

1. **(a)** **(i)** 29.38 **(ii)** 24.22 **(iii)** 22.03 **(iv)** 20.41 **(v)** 21.63
   (b) (iv), (v), (iii), (ii), (i)
   (c) No relationship
2. **(a)** 45 **(b)** 68 **(c)** 58 **(d)** 80
3. **(a)** 1.80 m **(b)** 2.00 m **(c)** 1.94 m **(d)** 1.66 m
4. Bush: 0.387, Cruz Jr.: 0.530, Delgado: 0.540, Gonzalez: 0.388, Stewart: 0.463, Team Total: 0.430
7. **(a)** Index = cost $\times \frac{1000}{\text{speed}} \times \frac{100}{\text{seats}}$
   (b) L1011–100/200: $2424, B767–300: $2525, B747–100: $2773, B757–200: $3092, B747–400: $3219, DC–10–10: $3654, B767–200: $3832, DC–10–30: $4410, A300–600: $4447
8. **(a)** Index = 2 × adult + 2 × child + parking + 2 × cap + 4 × drink + 4 × hot dog
   (b) Montreal: $79.76, Florida: $91.89, Detroit: $98.04, Colorado: $123.60, Toronto: $125.81, Ottawa: $127.22, Atlanta: $131.60, Baltimore: $132.05, New York: $143.11, Boston: $156.12

9. **(a)**

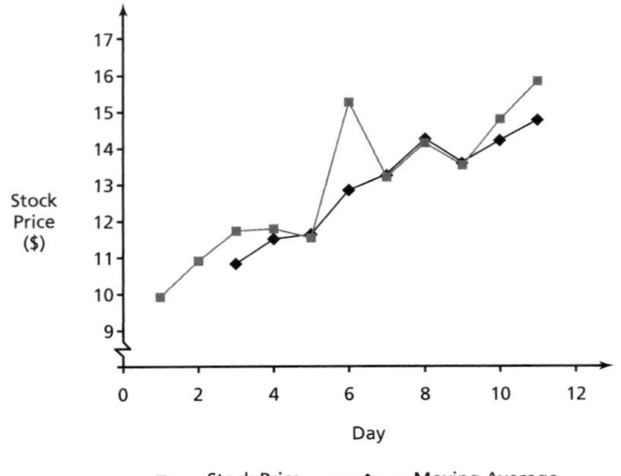

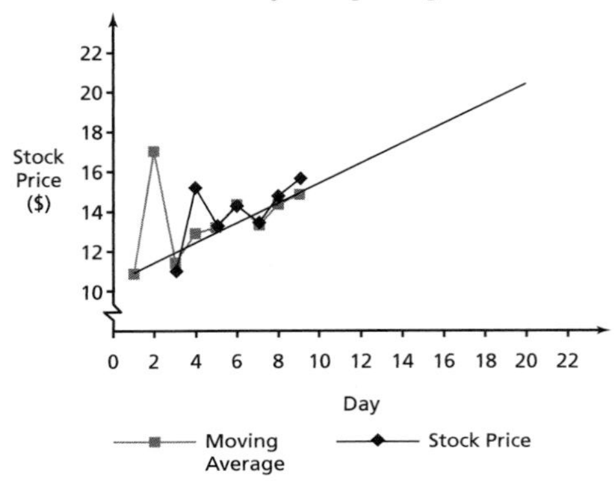

(b) Another 11 days

(c) On most days

(d) Increase the 3-day moving average

11. **(b)**

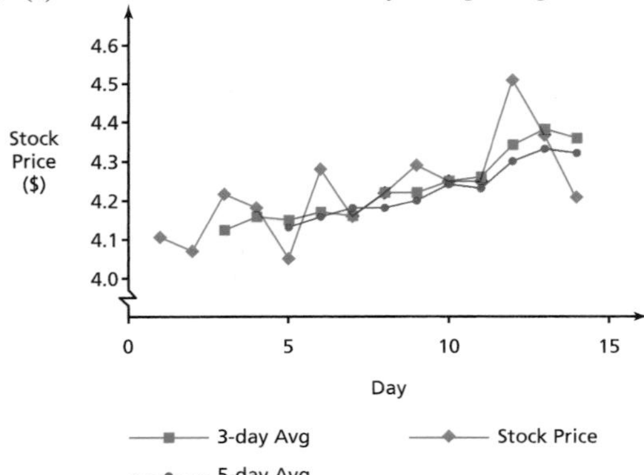

(c) The 5-day moving average is lower.

Chapter 3 Wrap-Up, page 199

1. Answers may vary. For example:
(a) 3 **(b)** 2 **(c)** 20

2. Answers may vary. For example:

(a)

Class	Tally	Frequency
3.5–6.5	|	1
6.5–9.5	||	2
9.5–12.5	卌 |	6
12.5–15.5	卌 卌 卌	15
15.5–18.5	||||	4
18.5–21.5	|	1

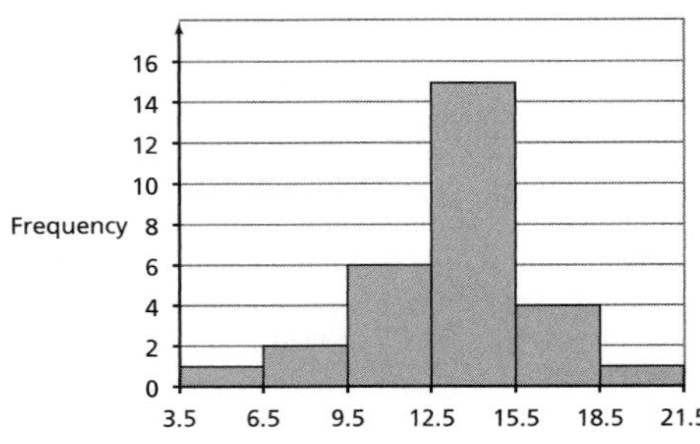

(b)

Class	Tally	Frequency
0.05–2.05	卌	5
2.05–4.05	卌	5
4.05–6.05	卌 |||	8
6.05–8.05	卌	5
8.05–10.05	卌	5
10.05–12.05	||	2

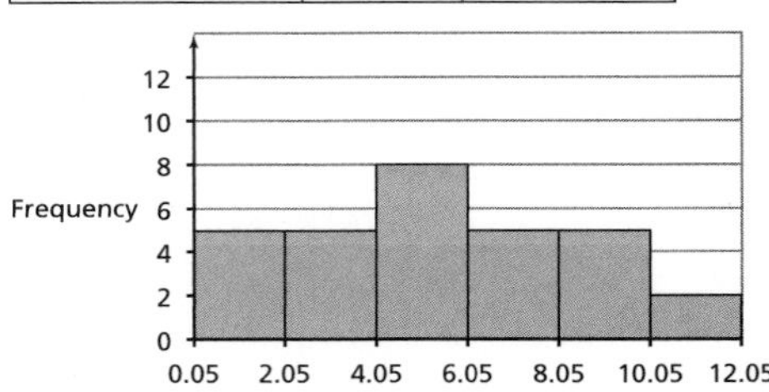

(c)

Class	Tally	Frequency
88.5–108.5	|||	3
108.5–128.5	卌	5
128.5–148.5	卌 卌 |	11
148.5–168.5	卌 卌	10
168.5–188.5		0
188.5–208.5	|	1

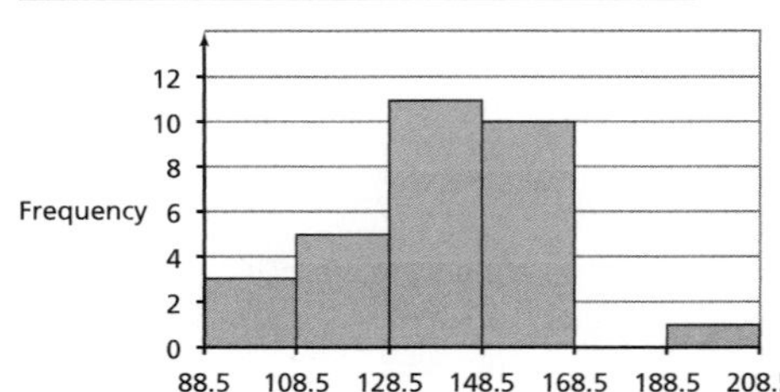

3. **(a)** mean: 13.3, median: 14, mode: 14; median
(b) mean: 5.2, median: 4.9, mode: 4.7; median
(c) mean: 140.7, median: 143, mode: 145; median

4. **(a)** mean: 7.82, median: 5–9, modal interval: 0–4
(b) median

5. **(a)** Antonia ($\bar{x} = 12.9$, $\sigma = 2.29$), Jamil ($\bar{x} = 12.4$, $\sigma = 2.8$); Antonia is more effective.
   (b) Antonia
6. **(a)** 84.9% **(b)** 26.4%

Chapter 3 Test, page 200

1.

2. **(a)** Min: mean: 146.18, median: 140, mode: NA; Jan: mean: 219.64, median: 222, mode: NA; Gigi: mean: 189.45, median: 177, mode: NA
   (b) Min: Q1 = 130, Q2 = 140, Q3 = 174, IQR = 44, standard deviation: 25.07; Jan: Q1 = 203; Q2 = 222, Q3 = 243, IQR = 40, standard deviation: 27.95; Gigi: Q1 = 160, Q2 = 177, Q3 = 212, IQR = 52, standard deviation: 28.27
   (c) Min: 6, 11, 11; Jan: 7, 10, 11; Gigi: 9, 11, 11
3. Marnie can assume donations will be within 3 standard deviations of the mean; \$30–\$120
4. 21.19%
5. 6.11 years
6.

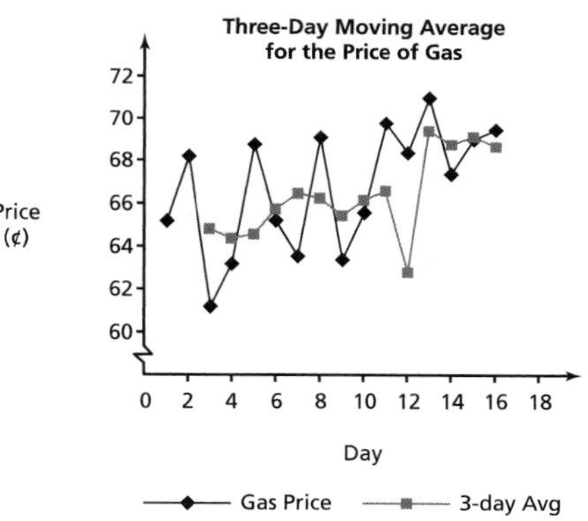

7. Sakic (178.0), Weight (133.2), Thornton (129.4), Iginla (114.4), Kariya (104.0)

Chapter 4

4.1 Exercises, page 209

1. **(a)** Toss a coin 10 times and record the number of times 7 or more heads occurs. Answers may vary; for example, 0.172.
   (b) Roll a die and record the number of times 1 occurs. Answers may vary; for example, 0.167.
2. **(a)** Answers may vary; for example, 0.0769.
   (b) **(i)** the particular card chosen
   (ii) Answers may vary; for example, 50.
   (iii) drawing a queen from the deck
3. **(b)** **(i)** Answers may vary; for example, 10; 5; 0.5; 20, 11; 0.55; 30, 15, 0.5, …, 100, 50, 0.5

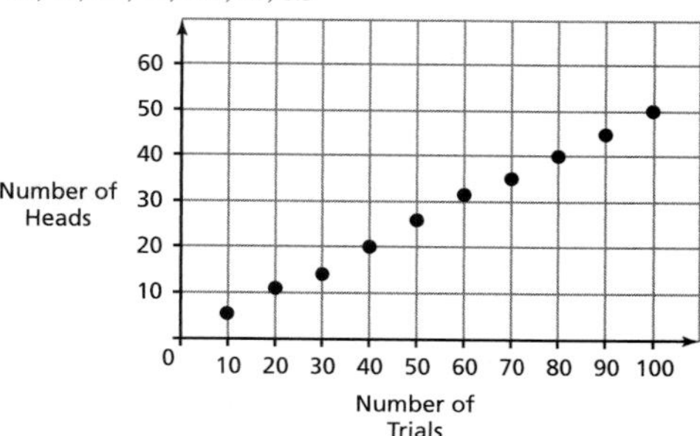

   (ii) tossing a coin
   (iii) the coin turns up heads
   (iv) The probability gets closer to 0.5.
4. **(a)** Answers may vary; for example, 0.501. Answer depends on the length of the shaft of the tack, roundness of the top, and diameter of the shaft.
   (b) 0.499 **(c)** 251
5. **(a)** Toss 10 coins and record the number of times at least 5 heads occurs and the total number of trials.
   (c) Answers may vary; for example, 0.6230.
6. **(a)** Answers may vary; for example, 0.5.
   (b) Answers may vary; for example, 0.0619.
7. **(a)** Answers may vary; for example, 0.0769.
   (b) Answers may vary; for example, 0.0010.
8. Make a spinner with 5 equal sectors of angle 72°, labelled A, B, C, D, E. Spin 5 times, recording the outcome and compare to the correct given answers.
9. **(a)** Let 0 represent a head and let 1 represent a tail.
   (b) $\frac{1}{9}$
   (c) Increase the number of trials in the experiment.
   (d) Let 0 represent a male and let 1 represent a female.
   (e) You can do more trials if needed.
10. Make a spinner with sector angles 72° and 288°. The larger sector represents a field goal. Answers may vary; for example, 0.0102.
11. Make a spinner with sector angles 36° and 324°. The smaller sector represents a defective keyboard. Answers may vary; for example, 0.0204.
12. **(a)** Make a spinner with sector angles 108° and 252°. The larger sector represents a seat belt wearer. Answers may vary; for example, 0.0306.
    (b) no
13. Roll a die and record how many rolls it takes to get all 6 numbers. Create a spreadsheet of random integers 1 to 6. How many rows until you have all numbers 1 to 6? Answers may vary; for example, 23.
14. Create a spreadsheet of 3 random integers 1 to 3. Let 1 represent a green light. How many rows have no 1? Answers may vary; for example, 0.1406.

4.2 Exercises, page 218

1. **(a)** 7 of diamonds
   (b) ace of spades, ace of hearts, ace of clubs, ace of diamonds
   (c) 2, 3, 4, 5, 6, 7, 8, 9, 10 of clubs
   (d) 2, 4, 6, 8, 10 of clubs, diamonds, hearts, or spades
2. **(a)** only (a)
   (b) (a) $\frac{1}{52}$ (b) $\frac{1}{13}$ (c) $\frac{9}{52}$ (d) $\frac{5}{13}$
3. **(a)** 5 **(b)** $\frac{3}{5}$ **(c)** $\frac{2}{5}$ **(d)** 0

4. (a) $\frac{1}{27}$ (b) $\frac{1}{54}$ (c) $\frac{2}{27}$
(d) $\frac{1}{2}$ (e) $\frac{2}{3}$ (f) $\frac{1}{18}$

5. (a) $\frac{1}{2}$ (b) $\frac{1}{6}$ (c) $\frac{1}{2}$ (d) $\frac{1}{26}$ (e) $\frac{10}{13}$

6. (a) $\frac{1}{2}$ (b) $\frac{1}{4}$ (c) $\frac{1}{4}$

7. (a) $\frac{1}{4}$ (b) $\frac{3}{4}$

8. (a) $\frac{1}{11}$ (b) $\frac{2}{11}$ (c) $\frac{4}{11}$

9. (a) $\frac{1}{5}$ (b) $\frac{1}{5}$
(c) Odd; there are 38 odd and only 37 even numbers.

10. (a) $\frac{1}{8}$ (b) $\frac{7}{8}$ (c) $\frac{3}{8}$

11. $\frac{59}{360}$

12. (a) 36 (b) $\frac{1}{6}$ (c) $\frac{5}{6}$

13. $\frac{1}{10}$

14. 6

15. People do not choose randomly. The outside numbers are chosen less often and the higher number 3 is selected more often from the two numbers left.

4.3 Exercises, page 228

1. (a) {6, 9} (b) {2, 5, 6, 9, 10, 12}
(c) {9, 10} (d) {2, 4, 6, 9, 10, 12}
(e) ∅ (f) {9}

2. (a) 0; mutually exclusive
(b) 0.75; not mutually exclusive
(c) 0.6; mutually exclusive

3. (a) 0 (b) 0.5 (c) 0.5

4. $\frac{11}{12}$

5. $\frac{6}{7}$

6. (a)

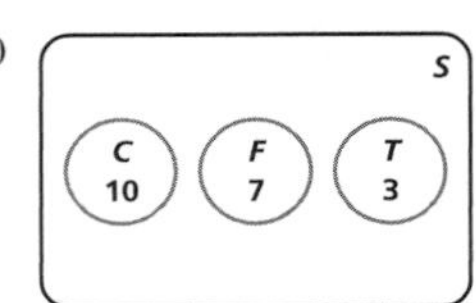

(b) (i) $\frac{1}{2}$ (ii) $\frac{3}{20}$ (iii) $\frac{13}{20}$

7. 0.8

8. (a)

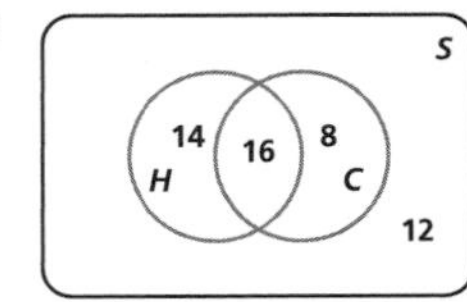

(b (i) $\frac{7}{25}$ (ii) $\frac{19}{25}$ (iii) $\frac{13}{25}$

9. $\frac{2}{13}$

10. $\frac{4}{13}$

11. $\frac{23}{36}$

12. 0.5

14. (a) $\frac{7}{45}$ (b) $\frac{8}{9}$ (c) $\frac{26}{45}$

15. $\frac{9}{52}$

4.4 Exercises, page 235

1. (a) $\frac{12}{19}$ (b) $\frac{3}{8}$

2. $\frac{2}{9}$

3. $\frac{1}{3}$

4. $\frac{1}{17}$

5. (a) $\frac{61}{250}$ (b) $\frac{11}{750}$

6. $\frac{3}{28}$

7. 0.48

8. (a) $\frac{29}{50}$ (b) $\frac{23}{50}$ (c) $\frac{1}{50}$ (d) $\frac{7}{50}$

9. (a) $\frac{4}{1431}$ (b) $\frac{2}{159}$ (c) $\frac{2}{477}$
(d) $\frac{13}{53}$ (e) $\frac{16}{477}$ (f) $\frac{52}{477}$

10. (a) 1, 2; 1, 3; 1, 4; 2, 3; 2, 4; 3, 4
(b) (i) $\frac{5}{6}$ (ii) $\frac{1}{6}$ (iii) $\frac{1}{6}$ (iv) $\frac{1}{3}$ (v) $\frac{2}{3}$

11. (a) $\frac{1}{2}$ (b) $\frac{3}{5}$

12. (a) Region *C* satisfies both *A* and *B* conditions, so events are not mutually exclusive.

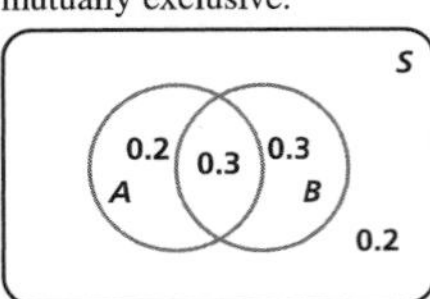

(b) You get the same answers for the probabilities, so the condition has no influence.

13. (a) 0.8 (b) 0.7 (c) 0.56 (d) 0.44

14. (a) 0.32 (b) 0.21

15. $\frac{1}{2}$

16. (a) 2% (b) 8%

4.5 Exercises, page 245

1. 24

2. (a)

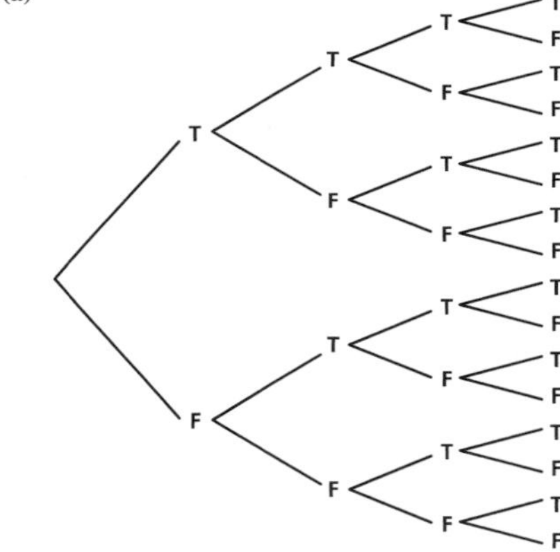

(b) $\frac{1}{16}$ (c) $\frac{1}{4}$

3. (a) 7D 7D (b) AS 7D
(c) 2C2C, 2C3C, 2C4C, … , 10C9C, 10C10C
(d) AS2C, AS4C, AS6C, …, AD8C, AD10C

4. (a) 36
(b) 1 red, 1 white is the only outcome
(c) 1 red, 2 white; 2 red, 1 white
(d), (e) 2: (1, 1); $\frac{1}{36}$
3: (1, 2), (2, 1); $\frac{1}{18}$
4: (1, 3), (2, 2), (3, 1); $\frac{1}{12}$
5: (1, 4), (2, 3), (3, 2), (4, 1); $\frac{1}{9}$

6: (1, 5), (2, 4), (3, 3), (4, 2), (5, 1); $\frac{5}{36}$

7: (1, 6), (2, 5), (3, 4), (4, 3), (5, 2), (6, 1); $\frac{1}{6}$

8: (2, 6), (3, 5), (4, 4), (5, 3), (6, 2); $\frac{5}{36}$

9: (3, 6), (4, 5), (5, 4), (6, 3); $\frac{1}{9}$

10: (4, 6), (5, 5), (6, 4); $\frac{1}{12}$

11: (5, 6), (6, 5); $\frac{1}{18}$

12: (6, 6); $\frac{1}{36}$

5. **(a)** 240 **(b)** (card number and suit, die number)
(c) **(i)** $\frac{1}{4}$ **(ii)** $\frac{1}{4}$ **(iii)** $\frac{1}{20}$ **(iv)** $\frac{1}{10}$ **(v)** $\frac{1}{10}$

6. **(a)** $\frac{2}{729}$ **(b)** $\frac{1}{81}$ **(c)** $\frac{4}{729}$
(d) $\frac{1}{4}$ **(e)** $\frac{32}{729}$ **(f)** $\frac{35}{324}$

7. Two-engine plane is safer, $\frac{3}{4}$ vs. $\frac{11}{16}$.

8. **(a)** $\frac{1}{2}$ **(b)** $\frac{2}{9}$ **(c)** $\frac{1}{42}$ **(d)** $\frac{5}{84}$

9. **(a)** $\frac{1}{4}$ **(b)** $\frac{79}{200}$ **(c)** $\frac{121}{200}$

10. **(a)** $\frac{1}{8}$ **(b)** $\frac{1}{2}$ **(c)** $\frac{7}{8}$

11. **(a)** 1000 **(b)** $\frac{1}{10}$ **(c)** $\frac{1}{5}$

12. **(a)** 17 576 000 **(b)** $\frac{1}{26}$ **(c)** $\frac{1}{17\,576\,000}$

13. **(a)** **(i)** $\frac{128}{625}$ **(ii)** $\frac{1}{3125}$ **(iii)** $\frac{64}{3125}$ **(iv)** $\frac{2944}{3125}$

4.6 Exercises, page 255

1. **(a)** 120 **(b)** 60 **(c)** 29 030 400
(d) 5 **(e)** 720 **(f)** 6006

2. **(a)** n **(b)** $3n$ **(c)** $n - r$

3. **(a)** 5! **(b)** $\frac{8!}{5!}$ **(c)** $\frac{30!}{27!3!}$ **(d)** $\frac{12!}{10!}$

4. **(a)** 3 628 800 **(b)** 362 880 **(c)** 40 320

5. 2730

6. **(a)** 720 **(b)** 360

7. 415 800

8. **(a)** Each side is 360.
(b) **(i)** $n = 5$ **(ii)** $n = 10$ **(iii)** $n = 18$ **(iv)** $n = 19$

9. **(a)** 9360
(b) **(i)** $\frac{10}{39}$ **(ii)** $\frac{19}{156}$ **(iii)** $\frac{6}{65}$ **(iv)** $\frac{19}{780}$ **(v)** $\frac{7}{1170}$

10. **(a)** 9600
(b) **(i)** $\frac{1}{4}$ **(ii)** $\frac{1}{8}$ **(iii)** $\frac{9}{100}$ **(iv)** $\frac{1}{40}$ **(v)** $\frac{1}{150}$

11. **(a)** $\frac{1}{1\,000\,000}$ **(b)** $\frac{1}{10\,000}$

12. **(a)** $\frac{1}{22}$ **(b)** $\frac{1}{44}$ **(c)** $\frac{2}{33}$

13. $\frac{1}{10!}$

14. **(a)** 2 159 206 336 **(b)** 456 976 000 **(c)** 77 907 188 096

15. $n = 6$

4.7 Exercises, page 262

1. **(a)** 56 **(b)** 35 **(c)** 12
(d) 10 **(e)** 120 **(f)** 1

2. 924

3. 3150

4. **(a)** $\binom{18}{2} = 153$ **(b)** $\binom{10}{2} = 45$ **(c)** $\frac{5}{17}$

5. 752 538 150

7. **(a)** 126 **(b)** 40 **(c)** 20
(d) 1 **(e)** 121 **(f)** 45
(g) **(b)** $\frac{20}{63}$ **(c)** $\frac{10}{63}$ **(d)** $\frac{1}{126}$ **(e)** $\frac{121}{126}$ **(f)** $\frac{5}{14}$

8. **(a)** 1260 **(b)** $\frac{2}{9}$

9. **(a)** $\frac{11}{850}$ **(b)** $\frac{2}{17}$ **(c)** $\frac{1}{5525}$ **(d)** $\frac{11}{1105}$

10. **(a)** $\frac{9}{38}$ **(b)** $\frac{69}{190}$ **(c)** $\frac{121}{190}$

11. 1:13 983 815

12. **(a)** $\frac{1}{2}, \frac{1}{2}$ **(b)** 1:1, 1:1

13. **(a)** 5:6 **(b)** 6:5

14. 4:1

15. 2:3

16. **(a)** probability of unfavourable outcome:probability of favourable outcome
(b) $\frac{1}{101}$

17. **(a)** Both involve selections of different objects. In permutations, order is important and in combinations, order is not important.
(b) ${}_nC_r$ is the number of ways r objects can be selected from n different objects if order is not important. ${}_nP_r$ is the number of ways r objects can be selected from n different objects if order is important. ${}_nC_r = \frac{{}_nP_r}{r!}$

18. **(a)** $\frac{145}{11\,792}$ **(b)** $\frac{20}{469}$ **(c)** $\frac{1}{9\,657\,648}$

19. No, 135 games need to be played in 10 cities.

Chapter 4 Wrap-Up, page 268

1. **(a)** 24 **(b)** 0 **(c)** 1
(d) 1 **(e)** 1 **(f)** 153

2. **(a)**

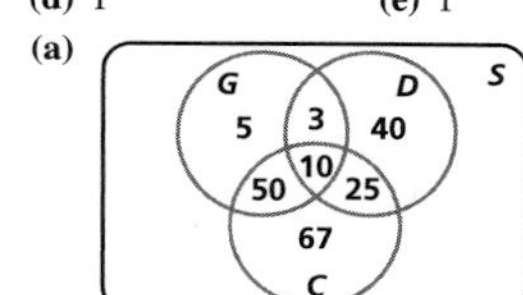

(b) 152

3. **(a)**

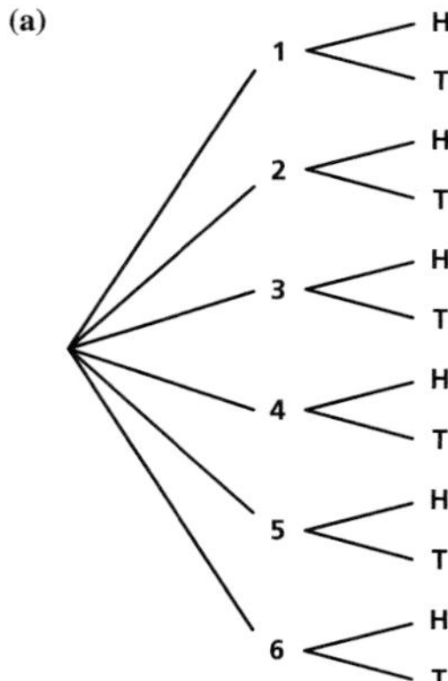

(b) 6 **(c)** 3

4. Use a spreadsheet to generate about 30 random integers from 1 to 12. Count the number of terms until you arrive at your birth month. Repeat. Answers may vary; for example, 10 after repeating 20 times.

5. **(a)** $\frac{1}{2}$ **(b)** $\frac{1}{4}$ **(c)** $\frac{91}{216}$ **(d)** $\frac{6}{4165}$
(e) $\frac{11}{663}$ **(f)** $\frac{1}{143}$ **(g)** $\frac{1}{120}$

6. **(a)** 1 860 480 **(b)** 362 880 **(c)** 10 897 286 400
(d) 60 **(e)** 1320 **(f)** 50 400
(g) 369 600 **(h)** 12 **(i)** 80 640
(j) 8 042 346 130 104 **(k)** 1013

7. no, dependent, $P(A \mid B) \neq P(A \mid B')$

8. **(a)** 0.0915 **(b)** 0.3917

9. Answers may vary; for example:
   (a) Selecting a number that is either even or odd
   (b) Rolling a die and drawing a card from a deck of 52 cards
   (c) Selecting an even number and selecting a multiple of 5
   (d) Drawing a card and then drawing another card without replacement

10. (a) $\frac{4}{5}$ (b) $\frac{1}{2}$ (c) $\frac{2}{3}$ (d) $\frac{3}{10}$ (e) 1:1

11. (a) $\frac{1}{2730}$ (b) $\frac{1}{455}$

Chapter 4 Test, page 270

1. (a)

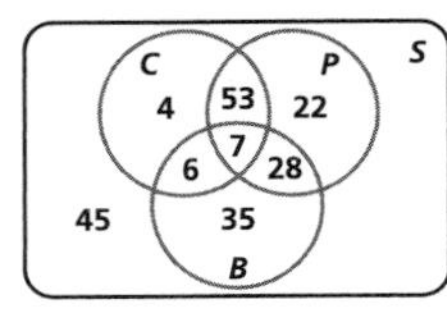

(b) 45 (c) $\frac{19}{50}$ (d) $\frac{3}{5}$

2. (a)

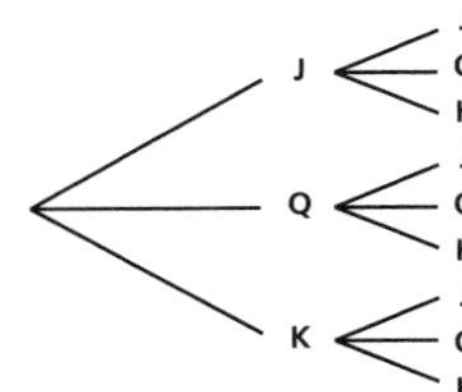

(b) 3 (c) $\frac{1}{3}$

3. $\frac{1}{20\,825}$

4. 1001

6. $\frac{1}{14}$

7. (a) (i) $\frac{80}{243}$ (ii) $\frac{304}{729}$
   (b) (i) $\frac{5}{14}$ (ii) $\frac{17}{42}$

8. 0.5687

Chapter 5

5.1 Exercises, page 277

1. (a) There can only be 0, 1, or 2 heads.
   (b) 0 heads: $\frac{1}{4}$, 1 head: $\frac{1}{2}$, 2 heads: $\frac{1}{4}$
   (c) 1

2. (a), (c), (e)

3. A probability distribution gives the probability of each outcome. Therefore, they must add to 1.

4. (a), (c) Probabilities add to 1.

5. 3.5

6. 4.5

7. (a) $\frac{5}{18}$ (b) $\frac{1}{9}$ (c) $\frac{5}{6}$ (d) $\frac{7}{18}$

8. 1: $\frac{1}{8}$, 2: $\frac{1}{8}$, 3: $\frac{1}{8}$, 4: $\frac{1}{8}$, 5: $\frac{1}{8}$, 6: $\frac{1}{8}$, 7: $\frac{1}{8}$, 8: $\frac{1}{8}$

9. 2: $\frac{1}{64}$, 3: $\frac{1}{32}$, 4: $\frac{3}{64}$, 5: $\frac{1}{16}$, 6: $\frac{5}{64}$, 7: $\frac{3}{32}$, 8: $\frac{7}{64}$, 9: $\frac{1}{8}$, 10: $\frac{7}{64}$, 11: $\frac{3}{32}$, 12: $\frac{5}{64}$, 13: $\frac{1}{16}$, 14: $\frac{3}{64}$, 15: $\frac{1}{32}$, 16: $\frac{1}{64}$

10. (a) 0: $\frac{2}{5}$, 1: $\frac{8}{15}$, 2: $\frac{1}{15}$
   (b) Answers may vary; for example, 0: $\frac{9}{25}$, 1: $\frac{29}{50}$, 2: $\frac{3}{50}$.
   (c) 0: $\frac{2}{5}$, 1: $\frac{53}{100}$, 2: $\frac{7}{100}$ (d) 0.67

11. (a) Answers may vary; for example, 0: 0.68, 1: 0.3, 2: 0.02.
   (b) Answers may vary; for example, 0: 0.65, 1: 0.3, 2: 0.05.
   (c) 0: 0.64, 1: 0.32, 2: 0.04 (d) 0.4

12. Yes, submit the bid. The expected return is $15 000.

13. (a) Answers may vary; for example, 0: 0, 1: 0, 2: 0, 3: 0, 4: 0, 5: 0, 6: 0.05, 7: 0.05, 8: 0.1, 9: 0.1, 10: 0.22, 11: 0.15, 12: 0.12, 13: 0.08, 14: 0.05, 15: 0.08, 16: 0, 17: 0, 18: 0, 19: 0, 20: 0
   (b) Answers may vary; for example, 0: 0, 1: 0, 2: 0, 3: 0, 4: 0, 5: 0, 6: 0.03, 7: 0.07, 8: 0.14, 9: 0.17, 10: 0.2, 11: 0.16, 12: 0.12, 13: 0.06, 14: 0.03, 15: 0.02, 16: 0, 17: 0, 18: 0, 19: 0, 20: 0
   (c) Answers may vary; for example, 0: 0, 1: 0, 2: 0, 3: 0, 4: 0, 5: 0.01, 6: 0.04, 7: 0.07, 8: 0.12, 9: 0.16, 10: 0.18, 11: 0.16, 12: 0.12, 13: 0.07, 14: 0.04, 15: 0.01, 16: 0, 17: 0, 18: 0, 19: 0, 20: 0
   (d) 0.021

14. $30

5.2 Exercises, page 289

1. (a) $\binom{11}{3}$ (b) $\binom{21}{19}$ (c) $\binom{16}{14}$ (d) $\binom{n+1}{r-1}$

2. (a) $\binom{10}{8}$ (b) $\binom{20}{2}$ (c) $\binom{15}{1}$ (d) $\binom{100}{2}$
   (e) $\binom{7}{0}$ (f) $\binom{20}{20}$ (g) $\binom{25}{24}$ (h) $\binom{100}{7}$

3. (a) $x^6 + 6x^5y + 15x^4y^2 + 20x^3y^3 + 15x^2y^4 + 6xy^5 + y^6$
   (b) $a^5 + 5a^4b + 10a^3b^2 + 10a^2b^3 + 5ab^4 + b^5$
   (c) $1^4 + 4(1)^3(-2) + 6(1)^2(-2)^2 + 4(1)(-2)^3 + (-2)^4$
   (d) $\left(\frac{2}{3}\right)^5 + 5\left(\frac{2}{3}\right)^4\left(\frac{1}{3}\right) + 10\left(\frac{2}{3}\right)^3\left(\frac{1}{3}\right)^2 + 10\left(\frac{2}{3}\right)^2\left(\frac{1}{3}\right)^3 + 5\left(\frac{2}{3}\right)\left(\frac{1}{3}\right)^4 + \left(\frac{1}{3}\right)^5$

4. (a) 6 (b) 2 (c) 2 (d) 3

5. $(a + b)^7$

6. 8

7. 204

8. (a) 10 (b) 10 (c) 23

9. (a) All equal 0 except row 1. (b) All equal 0. (c) 0, $n \neq 0$

10. (a) 10, 15, 21 (b) third diagonal ($r = 2$)
   (c) $\binom{n+1}{n-1}$ or $\binom{n+1}{2}$ (d) 5050

11. 8

12. 462

13. (a) $a^4 + 8a^3b + 24a^2b^2 + 32ab^3 + 16b^4$
   (b) $x^6 - 6x^5y + 15x^4y^2 - 20x^3y^3 + 15x^2y^4 - 6xy^5 + y^6$
   (c) $c^4 + 4c^2 + 6 + 4c^{-2} + c^{-4}$
   (d) $d^5 - 5d^3 + 10d - 10d^{-1} + 5d^{-3} - d^{-5}$

14. (a) $t_{r+1} = \binom{10}{r}x^{10-r}y^r$ (b) $t_{r+1} = (-1)^r\binom{10}{r}x^{10-r}y^r$
   (c) $t_{r+1} = \binom{8}{r}z^{8-2r}$ (d) $t_{r+1} = \binom{9}{r}w^{18-3r}$

15. (a) $84x^{10}$ (b) $70c^4d^4$ (c) $-160\,380x^{-6}$
   (d) does not exist (e) $\frac{1215}{4096}$

17. The identities are the same with n replaced by $n - 1$.

18. The identities are the same with r replaced by $r - 1$.

19. $a = 3$, $b = 2$, $n = 8$

5.3 Exercises, page 299

1. (a) (i) 10 (ii) $\frac{1}{2}$ (iii) 6
   (b) (i) 7 (ii) $\frac{1}{3}$ (iii) 3

2. 1

3. $\binom{n}{k}2^{-n}$

4. It is the sum of the probabilities of all the possible outcomes, which always adds to 1.

5. (b) There are 4 dice, so the probability of a 1 is multiplied by the 4 ways of getting a 1.
(c) $\left(\frac{1}{2}\right)^4 = \frac{1}{16}$ (d) $\frac{3}{8}$
(e) 0: $\frac{1}{16}$, 1: $\frac{1}{4}$, 2: $\frac{3}{8}$, 3: $\frac{1}{4}$, 4: $\frac{1}{16}$ (f) $\frac{1}{16}$

7. (a) 0.243 (b) 3 (c) 0.595
8. (a) $\frac{15}{64}$ or 0.234 (b) $\frac{57}{64}$ or 0.891 (c) $\frac{1}{64}$ or 0.016
9. (a) 0.132 (b) 0.168 (c) 3.5 (d) 0.002
10. (a) (i) 0.138 (ii) 0.562 (iii) 0.034
(b) 2.8
11. (a) 0.013 (b) 0.350
(c) (a) 1 (b) 3
12. 0.008
13. 0.271
14. 0.037

5.4 Exercises, page 311

1. (a) 0.25 (b) 0.375 (c) 0.25
(d) 0.063 (has been rounded off)
(e) 0.063 (has been rounded off)
2. (a) 0.323 011 (b) 0.290 710 (c) 0.155 045
(d) 0.054 266 (e) 0.013 024 (f) 0.002 171
3. (a) 0.410 (b) 0.819
4. 0.026 424
5. (a) 0.120 (b) approximation: 0.251, exact: 0.252
6. (a) 0.091 (b) approximation: 0.201, exact: 0.203
7. (a) 0.132
(b) approximation: 0.433, exact: 0.417
(c) approximation: 0.034, exact: 0.024
8. approximation: 0.019, exact: 0.016
9. Ten or more doubles are more likely.
10. (a) (i) approximation: 0.556, exact: 0.556
(ii) approximation: 0.000, exact: 0.0001
(b) (i) approximation: 0.898, exact: 0.899
(ii) approximation: 0.005, exact: 0.006
11. 0.500
12. approximation: 0.0392, exact: 0.0281
13. (a) exact: 0.204; exact: 0.006
(b) 6
14. not likely
15. not likely

5.5 Exercises, page 321

1. (a) 7: $\frac{15}{61}$, 8: $\frac{19}{61}$, 9: $\frac{12}{61}$, 10: $\frac{7}{61}$, 11: $\frac{5}{61}$, 12: $\frac{2}{61}$, 13: $\frac{1}{61}$
(b) 1: $\frac{1}{48}$, 2: $\frac{7}{48}$, 3: $\frac{11}{48}$, 4: $\frac{13}{48}$, 5: $\frac{9}{48}$, 6: $\frac{5}{48}$, 7: $\frac{2}{48}$, 8: $\frac{0}{48}$
(c) 3: $\frac{1}{42}$, 4: $\frac{1}{42}$, 5: $\frac{5}{42}$, 6: $\frac{8}{42}$, 7: $\frac{15}{42}$, 8: $\frac{12}{42}$
(d) 10: $\frac{2}{38}$, 11: $\frac{7}{38}$, 12: $\frac{10}{38}$, 13: $\frac{6}{38}$, 14: $\frac{8}{38}$, 15: $\frac{5}{38}$
2. Answers may vary; for example:

X	1	2	3	4	5	6	7	8	9	10
Frequency	8	5	6	6	2	2	3	4	2	12

3. 1: $\frac{8}{50}$, 2: $\frac{5}{50}$, 3: $\frac{6}{50}$, 4: $\frac{6}{50}$, 5: $\frac{2}{50}$, 6: $\frac{2}{50}$, 7: $\frac{3}{50}$, 8: $\frac{4}{50}$, 9: $\frac{2}{50}$, 10: $\frac{12}{50}$
6. (a) 0: $\frac{44}{61}$, 1: $\frac{8}{61}$, 2: $\frac{4}{61}$, 3: $\frac{2}{61}$, 4: $\frac{1}{61}$, 5: $\frac{0}{61}$, 6: $\frac{1}{61}$, 7: $\frac{1}{61}$
(b) 0.195 (c) $\frac{39}{61}$ or 0.639
7. (a)

X	1	2	3	4
Frequency	3	6	9	7

(b) 1: $\frac{3}{25}$, 2: $\frac{6}{25}$, 3: $\frac{9}{25}$, 4: $\frac{7}{25}$ (c) 2.8
8. Answers may vary; for example, $\frac{8}{20}$ or 0.40.
9. Answers may vary; for example, $\frac{7}{20}$ or 0.35.
10. P(18 tails) ≐ 0.0002, so the coin is likely biased.
11. P(miss 4 of 5) = 0.0064; the coach should be concerned.
12. P(guess 7 of 10) ≐ 0.117; no
13. (a) 0.0702
(b) The probability changes as each jellybean is drawn.
(c) 0: 0.583 752, 1: 0.339 391, 2: 0.070 219, 3: 0.006 384, 4: 0.000 251, 5: 0.000 003
(e) 0.5
14. (a) 0 (b) 0 (c) 1
15. Answers may vary; for example: 14
16. 23

Chapter 5 Wrap-Up, page 324

1. (a) Let X be winnings ($).
(b) $E(X)$ = $1.75

X	0	2	5
P(X)	$\frac{1}{2}$	$\frac{1}{4}$	$\frac{1}{4}$

(c) No, since in a fair game the expected winnings would be the same as the cost of playing.
2. (a) 0.96 (b) 2.22
3. (a) 330 (b) 8
4. (a) $243x^5 + 1620x^4y + 4320x^3y^2 + 5760x^2y^3 + 3840xy^4 + 1024y^5$
(b) $64x^{18} - 576x^{17} + 2160x^{16} - 4320x^{15} + 4860x^{14} - 2916x^{13} + 729x^{12}$
(c) $125 - \frac{150}{x} + \frac{60}{x^2} - \frac{8}{x^3}$
(d) $x^4 + 4x^{3.5} + 6x^3 + 4x^{2.5} + x^2$
5. (a) 9 (b) 20 412 (c) $-1512x^{12}$
6. (a) $\frac{74}{21}$ (b) 20 349
7. (a) 0.246 (b) 0.044 (c) 0.044 (d) 0.989
8. (a)

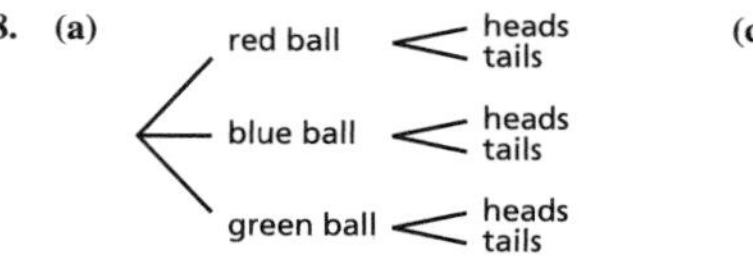

(c) $\frac{3}{10}$
(d) Yes, since the experiment consists of only one trial.
9. 0.407
10. (a) 0.058 (b) 0.016 (c) 0.188 (d) 0.000 001
11. (a) 0.001 (b) 0.570
12. (a) 0.330 (b) 0.4
13. (a) 0.396
(b) No, because the probabilities change every time a marble is drawn.
(c) 0: 0.008, 1: 0.110, 2: 0.371, 3: 0.396, 4: 0.115
(e) 2.5
14. (a) 0.002

Chapter 5 Test, page 326

1. (a) Time in minutes if transaction times with tellers during a 2-h period
(b) 1: $\frac{2}{5}$, 2: $\frac{6}{25}$, 3: $\frac{9}{50}$, 4: $\frac{1}{10}$, 5: $\frac{3}{50}$, 6: $\frac{1}{50}$ (c) 2.24 min
2. (a) 0.06 (b) 0.724 (c) 0.419
3. (b) 0.659
4. Bernoulli trials are for two outcomes only; the probability of each outcome remains the same from trial to trial; the trials are independent of each other.
5. $2^9\binom{15}{9}x^{7.5}$
6. 27
7. $a^3 + b^3 + c^3 + 3a^2b + 3a^2c + 3ab^2 + 3ac^2 + 3b^2c + 3bc^2 + 6abc$
8. Theoretically, simulations are never perfect.

Chapter 6

6.1 Exercises, page 333

4. Diamond shapes represent decisions that are to be made.

6.2 Exercises, page 343

3. Cause-and-effect diagrams list all the possible causes of a single outcome. Tree diagrams begin at a single point and list all possible outcomes.

4. **(a)** tree diagram

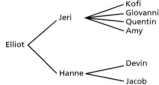

Elliot
Jeri
Kofi
Giovanni
Quentin
Amy
Hanne
Devin
Jacob

(b) directed graph

5.

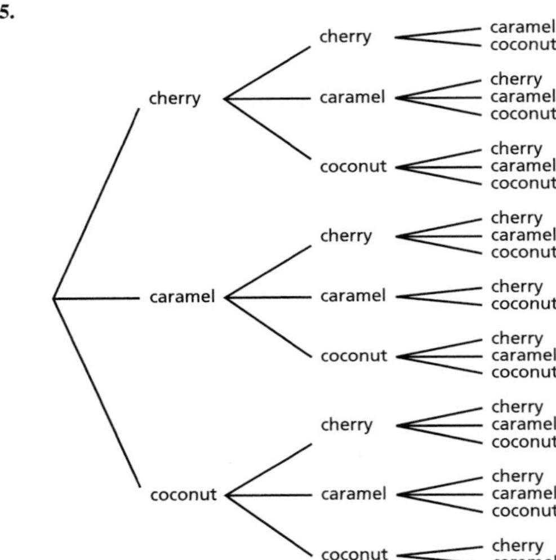

8.

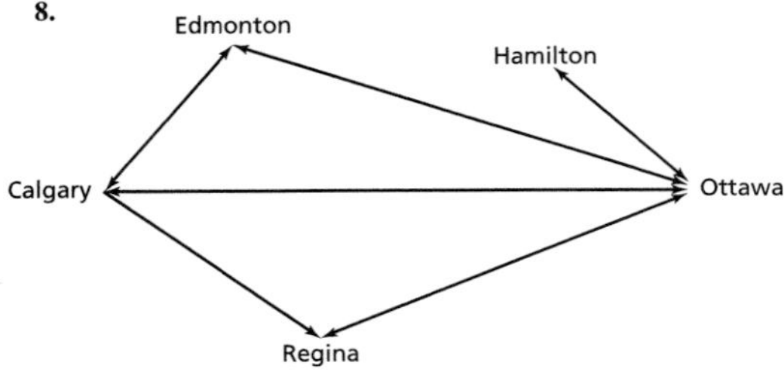

6.3 Exercises, page 353

1. **(a)** 0 **(b)** 8 **(c)** 7 **(d)** 3
(e) A: 3×3, B: 2×4
(f) row 1: 15, row 2: 13, row 3: 20
(g) column 1: 12, column 2: 30, column 3: 56, column 4: 90

2. **(a)** $\begin{bmatrix} 6 & 12 & 27 \\ 9 & 30 & 0 \\ 12 & 33 & 15 \end{bmatrix}$ **(b)** $\begin{bmatrix} 0.2 & 0.5 \\ 0.5 & 0.1 \end{bmatrix}$ **(c)** $\begin{bmatrix} 3 & 6 & 12 \\ 3 & 15 & -1 \\ 5 & 19 & 9 \end{bmatrix}$

(d) not possible **(e)** $\begin{bmatrix} 1 & 5 \\ 5 & 4 \end{bmatrix}$

(f) $\begin{bmatrix} 2 & -3 & -14 & -9 \\ -6 & -16 & -43 & -77 \end{bmatrix}$ **(g)** $\begin{bmatrix} 5 & 10 \\ 10 & -1 \end{bmatrix}$

(h) $\begin{bmatrix} 22 & 5 & -42 & -9 \\ 6 & 20 & -19 & -61 \end{bmatrix}$

3. Matrices A and B have different dimensions, and matrices A and C have the same dimensions.

4. **(a)** a_{11} **(b)** a_{21} **(c)** a_{23} **(d)** a_{22} **(e)** a_{32}

5. Games: 657, Goals: 270, Assists: 645, Points: 915, Penalties in Minutes: 953

6. **(a)** $\begin{bmatrix} 212.0 & 212.9 \\ 66.0 & 66.0 \\ 425.6 & 429.7 \\ 333.8 & 336.6 \\ 3497.1 & 3501.7 \\ 5958.6 & 5955.7 \\ 558.7 & 562.9 \\ 468.9 & 468.0 \\ 1638.9 & 1641.3 \\ 1934.1 & 1920.6 \end{bmatrix}$ **(b)** 5958.6 for Ontario

(c) e_{92}

7. **(a)** 16 590
(b) 1986: 19 654 320, 1991: 21 304 745, 1996: 22 628 910
(c) 1991: $79 288 750 000, 1996: $98 973 000 000, Total: $178 261 750 000

8. **(a)** **(i)** **(b)**

Sport	Total (1000s)	% Males	% Females
Golf	1801	11.1	3.9
Hockey (ice)	1500	12.0	0.5
Baseball	1339	8.0	3.1
Swimming	1120	3.6	5.6
Basketball	787	4.6	1.9
Volleyball	744	3.3	2.8
Soccer	739	4.6	1.5
Tennis	658	3.6	1.8
Skiing, downhill/alpine	657	2.9	2.6
Cycling	608	3.0	2.0
Skiing, cross-country/nordic	512	1.7	2.5
Weightlifting	434	2.5	1.1
Badminton	403	1.7	1.7
Football	387	2.9	0.3
Curling	312	1.5	1.1
Bowling, 10 pin	282	1.1	1.2
Softball	210	1.0	0.7
Bowling, 5 pin	200	0.7	1.0

(ii) 8 328 000
(iii) 4 365 000

9. **(a)** 1998 **(b)** 2000
(c) Scotch Pine: 576, Douglas Fir: 207, Blue Spruce: 303

10. **(a)** $\begin{bmatrix} 39 & 25 & 33 \\ 32 & 28 & 28 \\ 28 & 16 & 15 \\ 16 & 25 & 17 \\ 14 & 17 & 26 \\ 13 & 14 & 11 \\ 13 & 8 & 13 \\ 12 & 9 & 4 \\ 11 & 11 & 7 \\ 11 & 10 & 7 \end{bmatrix}$ **(b)** United States

6.4 Exercises, page 369

1. **(a)** B is a 1×3 matrix and C is a 3×3 matrix. BC is possible because the number of columns in B is equal to the number of rows in C. CB is not possible because the number of columns in B is not equal to the number of rows in C.
   (b) 1×1 matrix
   (c) $10 \times 1 + 20 \times 2 + 30 \times 3 = [140]$
   (d) $BC = [200 \;\; 400 \;\; 600]$
2. XY: 5×5; YX: 3×3
3. **(a)** $[140]$ **(b)** $\begin{bmatrix} 2 & 4 & 6 \\ 1 & 3 & 5 \end{bmatrix}$
4. **(a)** $\begin{bmatrix} 0 & 1 & 1 & 1 & 0 \\ 0 & 0 & 0 & 0 & 1 \\ 0 & 0 & 0 & 1 & 0 \\ 0 & 0 & 0 & 0 & 0 \\ 0 & 0 & 0 & 1 & 0 \end{bmatrix}$ **(b)** $\begin{bmatrix} 0 & 1 & 1 & 1 & 0 \\ 0 & 0 & 0 & 0 & 1 \\ 0 & 0 & 0 & 1 & 0 \\ 1 & 0 & 0 & 0 & 1 \\ 0 & 0 & 0 & 1 & 0 \end{bmatrix}$
5. 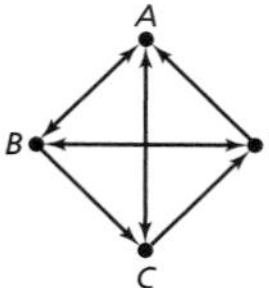

6. **(a)** Both equal $\begin{bmatrix} -2 & -2 \\ 16 & 16 \end{bmatrix}$.
   (b) $A \times B = \begin{bmatrix} -1 & -1 \\ 6 & 10 \end{bmatrix}$; $B \times A = \begin{bmatrix} 2 & 6 \\ 3 & 7 \end{bmatrix}$
   (c) Both equal $\begin{bmatrix} -6 & -6 \\ -6 & -6 \end{bmatrix}$. **(d)** Both equal $\begin{bmatrix} 6 & 6 \\ 10 & 10 \end{bmatrix}$.
7. **(a)** Both equal $\begin{bmatrix} 4 & 4 & 4 \\ 8 & 8 & 8 \\ 8 & 8 & 8 \end{bmatrix}$.
   (b) $A \times B = \begin{bmatrix} 3 & 1 & 0 \\ 3 & 2 & 3 \\ 1 & 5 & 2 \end{bmatrix}$; $B \times A = \begin{bmatrix} 0 & 2 & 4 \\ 1 & 4 & 3 \\ 3 & 0 & 3 \end{bmatrix}$
   (c) Both equal $\begin{bmatrix} 0 & 0 & 0 \\ 2 & 2 & 2 \\ 2 & 2 & 2 \end{bmatrix}$. **(d)** Both equal $\begin{bmatrix} 4 & 4 & 4 \\ 6 & 6 & 6 \\ 6 & 6 & 6 \end{bmatrix}$.
8. Both equal $\begin{bmatrix} 6 & 0 \\ 3 & 0 \end{bmatrix}$.
9. Answers may vary. Both are equal if $A = \begin{bmatrix} 1 & 0 \\ 0 & 1 \end{bmatrix}$ and $B = \begin{bmatrix} -1 & 0 \\ 0 & 1 \end{bmatrix}$.
10. Kiddie: \$9.58, Adult: \$14.17
11. Descartes: frame pieces: 50, glass sections: 14; Gauss: frame pieces: 70, glass sections: 20; Fermat: frame pieces: 94, glass sections: 28
12. Monday: \$81 875, Tuesday: \$89 625, Wednesday: \$95 750, Thursday: \$120 625, Friday: \$126 875, Saturday: \$116 000, Sunday: \$84 000
13. **(a)** A: \$23, B: \$44, C: \$86, D: \$107
    (b) Descartes: \$310, Gauss: \$440, Fermat: \$608
14. **(a)** yes **(b)** yes **(c)** 3
15. **(a)** 3 **(b)** not possible
16. **(a)** cottage: \$2.68, white: \$3.23, buttermilk: \$2.24
    (b) \$580

6.5 Exercises, page 379

1. **(a)** Turn on computer. Turn on monitor. Enter password. Turn on printer. Click on Shortcut. Click Print. Exit program. Turn off printer. Click Start. Click Shut Down. Turn off computer. Turn off monitor.
   (b) Get two slices of bread. Push down toaster switch. Get plate from cupboard. Get knife from drawer. Get peanut butter from shelf. Spread peanut butter on bread. Eat peanut butter on toast.
   (c) Drive to school. Park the car. Go to first class. Go to second class. Eat lunch. Go to third class. Go to fourth class. Go to after-school practice. Drive home
   (d) Turn on CD player. Turn on stereo receiver. Select CD. Press play. Adjust volume.
3. Sequential tasks are dependent on each other and must be performed in order. Parallel tasks are independent and may be performed simultaneously. Sequential examples: turn on car; drive. Wet hair; shampoo. Parallel examples: walk and talk. Drive and listen to the radio.
5. **(i)** **(a)** A: 0, B: 5, C: 10, D: 17, E: 36, F: 36, G: 43, H: 56, Finish: 63
   (b) A: 0, B: 3, D: 3, C: 9, E: 9, F: 21, G: 40, H: 40, J: 40, K: 57, Finish: 65
   (c) A: 0, B: 1, G: 2, C: 11, H: 6, D: 16, I: 14, K: 10, E: 19, J: 17, F: 25, End: 32
   (d) G: 0; A: 2; H: 4; B: 6; I: 6; C: 8; J: 12; D: 12; E: 20; End: 22
   (e) A: 0, B: 6, C: 12, F: 32, E: 23, D: 19, G: 33, I: 41, H: 35, End: 54
   (ii) **(a)** A-B-C-D-E-G-H **(b)** A-D-E-F-J-K
   (c) A-G-C-D-E-F **(d)** G-A-B-C-D-E
   (e) A-C-E-G-I or A-C-E-F-G-I
   (iii) **(a)** 63 d **(b)** 65 d **(c)** 32 d
   (d) 22 d **(e)** 54 d
6. **(a)** 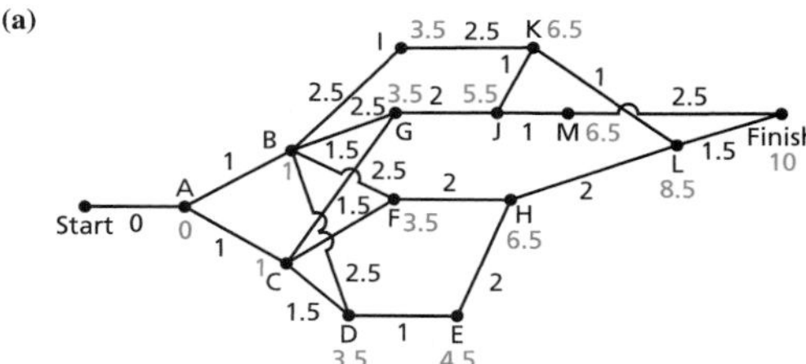

   (b) 10 months
7. 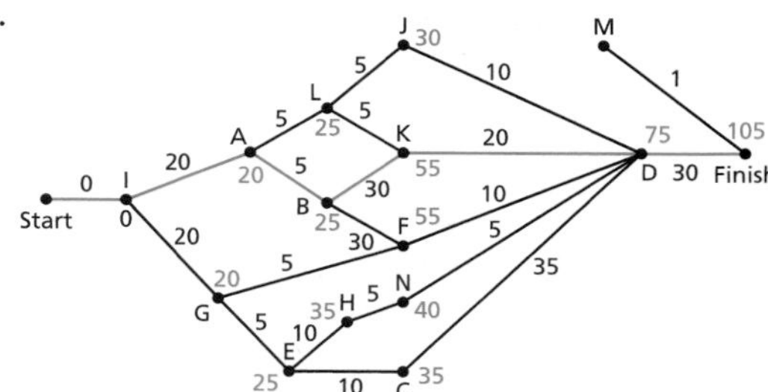

Critical Path: I-A-B-K-D; 105 min

9. (a)

	Duration (min)	Prerequisite(s)
A. Fry beef	10	—
B. Chop $\frac{1}{2}$ onion	1	—
C. Chop 1 green pepper	2	—
D. Add oil, onion, garlic, sauce, corn, green pepper, sugar, salt, chili	5	A, B, C
E. Bake in oven	45	D, F, H, I
F. Combine cornmeal and milk	10	—
G. Mix flour, salt, baking powder, sugar	2	—
H. Add vegetable shortening, egg, milk	5	G
I. Preheat oven to 375°	9	—
J. Cool dish	15	E

(b)

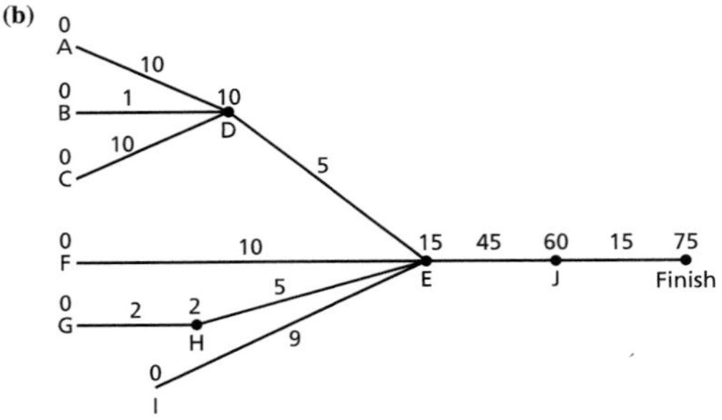

(c) 75 min

Chapter 6 Wrap-Up, page 385

3. Not possible to cross each bridge just once.

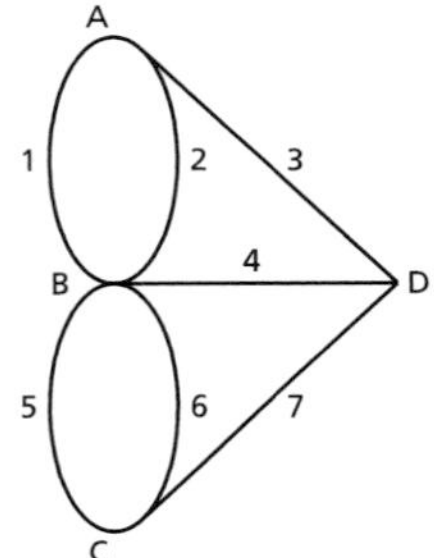

4. (a) A: 1×3, B: 3×1, C: 3×3

(b) $\begin{bmatrix} 2 & 2 & 4 \\ 4 & 6 & 1 \\ 1 & 1 & 4 \end{bmatrix}$ **(c)** $\begin{bmatrix} 0 & 2 & 4 \\ 4 & 4 & 1 \\ -1 & 1 & 2 \end{bmatrix}$ **(d)** $\begin{bmatrix} 2 & 4 & 8 \\ 8 & 10 & 2 \\ 0 & 2 & 6 \end{bmatrix}$

(e) $\begin{bmatrix} 3 \\ -6 \\ -30 \end{bmatrix}$ **(f)** $[9 \quad 17 \quad 21]$

(g) $B \times C$ does not exist. $C \times B = \begin{bmatrix} 43 \\ 16 \\ 32 \end{bmatrix}$

(h) When two matrices $m \times n$ and $k \times j$ are multiplied, we must have that $n = k$ (inner dimensions match). For $A \times C$, $3 = 3$, so this is okay. For $C \times A$, $3 \neq 1$, so this is NOT okay.

(i) Both equal $[15 \quad 19 \quad 26]$.

5. 1-3-5-8-10-11; earliest completion time: 36 d

6. (a)

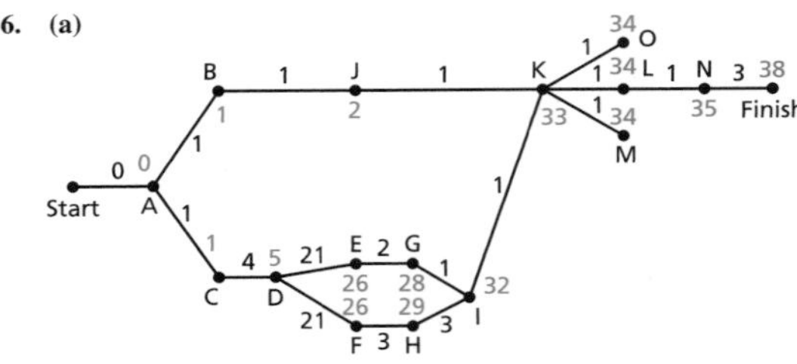

(b) A-C-D-F-H-I-J-K-L-N **(c)** 38 d

Chapter 6 Test, page 387

2. (a) A: 1×3, B: 3×1, C: 3×3

(b) $\begin{bmatrix} 4 & 2 & 4 \\ 7 & 1 & 1 \\ 6 & 1 & 7 \end{bmatrix}$ **(c)** $\begin{bmatrix} 0 & 2 & 4 \\ 1 & -1 & 1 \\ 4 & 1 & -1 \end{bmatrix}$ **(d)** $\begin{bmatrix} 4 & 4 & 8 \\ 8 & 0 & 2 \\ 10 & 2 & 6 \end{bmatrix}$

(e) $\begin{bmatrix} 6 \\ -9 \\ 21 \end{bmatrix}$ **(f)** $[17 \quad -3 \quad -1]$

(g) $B \times C$ does not exist. $C \times B = \begin{bmatrix} -26 \\ -15 \\ -28 \end{bmatrix}$

(h) Inside dimensions must be the same to multiply two matrices. For $A \times C$, $(1 \times 3) \times (3 \times 3)$ is okay. For $C \times A$, $(3 \times 3) \times (1 \times 3)$ is NOT okay.

(i) Both equal $[14 \quad -3 \quad 19]$.

3. (a)

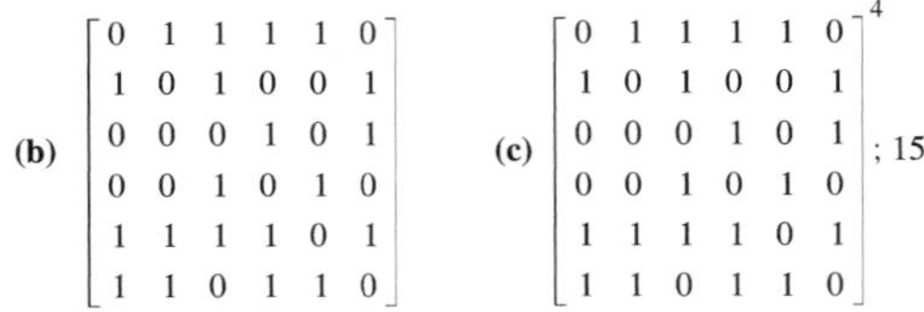

(b) $\begin{bmatrix} 0 & 1 & 1 & 1 & 1 & 0 \\ 1 & 0 & 1 & 0 & 0 & 1 \\ 0 & 0 & 0 & 1 & 0 & 1 \\ 0 & 0 & 1 & 0 & 1 & 0 \\ 1 & 1 & 1 & 1 & 0 & 1 \\ 1 & 1 & 0 & 1 & 1 & 0 \end{bmatrix}$ **(c)** $\begin{bmatrix} 0 & 1 & 1 & 1 & 1 & 0 \\ 1 & 0 & 1 & 0 & 0 & 1 \\ 0 & 0 & 0 & 1 & 0 & 1 \\ 0 & 0 & 1 & 0 & 1 & 0 \\ 1 & 1 & 1 & 1 & 0 & 1 \\ 1 & 1 & 0 & 1 & 1 & 0 \end{bmatrix}^4$; 15

4. A-B-H-K-L-M-E-J-G: EST: 59 d

Task	Duration (d)	Prerequisite Task(s)
Start	0	
A	2	Start
B	5	A
C	7	B, H
D	4	C
E	12	D, I, M
F	4	E
G	7	F, J
H	7	B
I	10	H
J	5	E
K	7	H
L	9	K
M	5	H, L

Index

Data Index

Technology Index

MATHEMATICS OF DATA MANAGEMENT TEXT CREDITS

Statistics Canada information is used with the permission of the Minister of Industry, as Minister responsible for Statistics Canada. Information on the availability of the wide range of data from Statistics Canada's Regional Offices, its World Wide Web site at **http://www.statcan.ca**, and its toll-free access number 1–800–263–1136.

Page 6 Pictograph of number of participants (aged 15 and older) in the five most popular sports activities in Canada adapted from the Statistics Canada Web site, The General Social Survey, 1998, **www.statcan.ca/english/Pgdb/People/Culture/arts16.htm**, February, 2002.

Page 7 Data regarding the television viewing habits of Canadians adapted from the Statistics Canada Web site, 'Television viewing time,' Catalogue no. 87F0006XPB, **www.statcan.ca/english/Pgdb/People/Culture/arts22a.htm**, February 2002.

Page 15 Chart, composition of Canadian families, adapted from the Statistics Canada publication "Data Products: The Nation 1996 Census of Population," Catalogue 93F0020XCB, September 1999.

Page 24 Graphs, 'Live Births in Canada 1948–1997' and 'Infant Deaths During Birth in Canada 1948–1997.' Data have been extracted from **Fathom Dynamic Statistics™**, Key Curriculum Press, 1150 65th St., Emeryville, CA 94608, 1–800–995–MATH.

Page 25 Graphs, 'South Pole Temperature, 1957' and 'South Pole Temperature, 1987.' Data have been extracted from **Fathom Dynamic Statistics™**, Key Curriculum Press, 1150 65th St., Emeryville, CA 94608, 1–800–995–MATH / Table 1: Citizenship Test Report Card reprinted by permission of COMPAS Inc.

Page 26 Table 2: Correct Response in Percent by Education reprinted by permission of COMPAS Inc.

Page 32 Table, 'Canadian Tuition Consumer Price Index 1975–2000' adapted from the Statistics Canada Web site, **www.statcan.ca/english/Subjects/Cpi/cpi-en.htm**, February 2002.

Page 37 Number of available seats and average speed of a variety of planes. Data have been extracted from **Fathom Dynamic Statistics™**, Key Curriculum Press, 1150 65th St., Emeryville, CA 94608, 1–800–995–MATH.

Page 40 Table, winning women's Olympic long-jump distance, from the British Broadcasting Corporation (BBC).

Pages 42–43 Scatter plots, 'Canadian Tuition CPI,' adapted from the Statistics Canada Web site, **www.statcan.ca/english/Subjects/Cpi/cpi-en.htm**, February 2002.

Page 54 Table, winning distance for the Olympic men's discus event, from the British Broadcasting Corporation (BBC) / Table. Data have been extracted from **Fathom Dynamic Statistics™**, Key Curriculum Press, 1150 65th St., Emeryville, CA 94608, 1–800–995–MATH.

Page 55 Table. Data have been extracted from **Fathom Dynamic Statistics™**, Key Curriculum Press, 1150 65th St., Emeryville, CA 94608, 1–800–995–MATH / Table, 'Retail Merchandising in Canada' adapted from the Statistics Canada Web site, **www.statcan.ca/english/IPS/Data/63c0016.htm**, February 2002.

Page 58 Article, 'York Region: A Great Place to Do Business: Survey.' Reprinted with permission from *The Liberal*, Richmond Hill.

Page 61 Newspaper headline 'Boom pushes jobless rate to 18-year low' reprinted with permission from *The Globe and Mail* / Newspaper headline 'Golden Era: Jobless rate at 19-year low' reprinted with permission from *The National Post* / Newspaper headline 'Jobless rate sinks to near 20-year low' from *The Kingston Whig-Standard*, December 4, 1999.

Page 62 Chart, 'DaimlerChrysler Share Price,' R.O.B. Magazine, Oct. 2001, p. 57. Reprinted with permission from *The Globe and Mail* / Graph, 'Central Bank Interest Rate Targets.' Reprinted with permission from Phillips, Hager & North Investment Management Ltd.

Page 63 Graph, 'Performance During Recessions: S&P 500 U.S. Corporate Profits.' Reprinted with permission from Phillips, Hager & North Investment Management Ltd. / Graph, 'Canadian Business Leaders on the Economy and the Military,' adapted from *The National Post*, October 29, 2001, A2, Source: COMPAS Inc. Reprinted with permission from *The National Post* and COMPAS Inc.

Page 69 Chart, average water consumption per day adapted from World Resources 2000–2001, World Resources Institute.

Page 70 Chart, 'Average Wage/Hour for Canada & Provinces, 1998.' Reprinted by permission of XPLANE Corp. (**XPLANE.com**).

Page 72 Graphic, 'Drop in U.S. Unemployment' adapted from the Fort Worth Star-Telegram, February 4, 1984. Reprinted by permission of the Fort Worth Star-Telegram.

Page 83 Tables, 'Guideline for Daily Nutritional Requirement' and 'Dishes' adapted from Reader's Digest, *The How-To Book of Healthy Cooking Good Food That's Good For You* (Pleasantville, New York: The Reader's Digest Association, Inc. 1995), pp. 9, 61, 106, 133, 159. Copyright © 1995, The Reader's Digest Association, Inc. and its licensors. All rights reserved.

Page 110 Adapted from *Statistics* by David Freedman, Robert Pisoni and Roger Purves, W.W. Norton & Company, Inc. (1978).

Page 129 Table, university volleyball statistics adapted from the Brock University website (**http://www.pec.brocku.ca/~jcurrie/stats.html**). Reproduced with permission from Brock University, Brock Badgers Women's Volleyball Team.

Page 130 Graph, 'World Population 1950–2050' from the U.S. Bureau of the Census, World Population: 1950–2050, **http://www.census.gov/ipc/www/img/worldpop.gif** (accessed February 14, 2002).

Page 133 Chart, Viking Lander Mars data, July 1976 from Project "Live From Earth and Mars" (**http://www-k12.atmos.washington.edu/k12/resources/mars_data-information/data.html**). Reprinted by permission of Project "Live From Earth and Mars," Dept. of Atmospheric Sciences, University of Washington—J.E. Tillman.

Page 134 Graphs, Viking Lander 1 from Project "Live From Earth and Mars" (**http://www-k12.atmos.washington.edu/k12/resources/mars_data-information/data.html**). Reprinted by permission of Project "Live From Earth and Mars," Dept. of Atmospheric Sciences, University of Washington—J.E. Tillman.

Page 140 Excerpt from "The University Crunch" from Maclean's Guide to Canadian Universities and Colleges 2001. Reprinted by permission of *Maclean's* magazine.

Page 141 Data, Richter Scale from the United States Geological Survey, National Earthquake Information Center.

Page 147 Charts, PGA and LPGA information from CNN Sports Illustrated (**CNNSI.com**). Copyright © 2001 CNN/Sports Illustrated. An AOL Time Warner Company. All Rights Reserved.

Page 148 Chart, temperatures of various Canadian cities adapted from the Climate Station Catalogue, Meteorological Service of Canada, Environment Canada (**http://www.msc-smc.ec.gc.ca/climate/station_catalogue/index_e.cfm**). Reproduced with the permission of the Minister of Public Works and Government Services Canada, 2002.

Page 160 Graphs, highway fuel efficiency for three types of cars. Data have been extracted from **Fathom Dynamic Statistics™**, Key Curriculum Press, 1150 65th St., Emeryville, CA 94608, 1–800–995–MATH.

Page 161 Charts, temperatures for Calgary & Ottawa adapted from the Climate Station Catalogue, Meteorological Service of Canada, Environment Canada (**http://www.msc-smc.ec.gc.ca/climate/station_catalogue/index_e.cfm**). Reproduced with the permission of the Minister of Public Works and Government Services Canada, 2002.

Page 170 Table, Ottawa monthly temperature averages adapted from the Climate Station Catalogue, Meteorological Service of Canada, Environment Canada (**http://www.msc-smc.ec.gc.ca/climate/station_catalogue/index_e.cfm**). Reproduced with the permission of the Minister of Public Works and Government Services Canada, 2002.

Page 171 Table, 'Canada Assistance Plan Payments ($ millions)' from Human Resources Development Canada. Reproduced with the permission of the Minister of Public Works and Government Services Canada, 2002.

Page 191 Table, Consumer Price Index August 2000 to July 2001 adapted from the Statistics Canada Web site, **www.statcan.ca/english/Subjects/Cpi/cpi-en.htm**, February 2002.

Page 194 Table, operating cost, seating capacity, and speed for various types of planes. Data have been extracted from **Fathom Dynamic Statistics™**, Key Curriculum Press, 1150 65th St., Emeryville, CA 94608, 1–800–995–MATH.

Page 272 Article: 'Disappearance of toads, frogs has some scientists worried,' by Charles Petit, Chronicle Science Writer, San Francisco Chronicle, April 20, 1992. © SAN FRANCISCO CHRONICLE. Reprinted by permission.

Page 347 Table, breakdown by grade of student enrolment in Ontario schools, 1998–99 from the Ontario Ministry of Education (**http://www.edu.gov.on.ca/eng/general/elemsec/quickfacts/1998-99/**). © Queen's Printer for Ontario, 2002. Reproduced with permission.

Page 353 Table, Regular season data for Bobby Orr. Reproduced by permission of Orr Fan (**http://www.orrfan.com/stats.htm**) © H. Holman.

Page 354 Table, number of people employed in September and October of 2001 adapted from Statistics Canada, *The Daily*, Friday, November 2, 2001, **www.statcan.ca/Daily/English/011102/td011102.htm** / Table, number of Canadians 15 years of age or older by their highest degree or certificate, adapted from the Statistics Canada Web site, 1996 Census Nation tables, **www.statcan.ca/english/Pgdb/People/Education/educ42.htm**, February 2002.

Page 355 Table, number of Canadians involved in a variety of sports activities adapted from the Statistics Canada Web site, The General Social Survey, 1998, **www.statcan.ca/english/Pgdb/People/Culture/arts16.htm**, February, 2002.

Page 356 Table, results from the 2000 Summer Olympic Games in Sydney, Australia from the British Broadcasting Corporation (BBC).

MATHEMATICS OF DATA MANAGEMENT PHOTO CREDITS

Cover Dominique Sarraute/Image Bank

Chapter 1 Page 6: CORBIS/MAGMA; Page 13: EyeWire/RET_009; Page 25: EyeWire/E001328; Page 26: CP Picture Archive/Kevin Frayer; Page 37: PhotoDisc/ST000396; Page 40: CP Picture Archive/Doug Mills; Page 62: CORBIS/MAGMA

Chapter 2 Page 74: Dick Hemingway; Page 75: (top left) © Comstock Images/KS9566, (bottom left) © Comstock Images/KS9385; Page 78: PhotoDisc/LS011048; Page 80: CORBIS/MAGMA; Page 82: CP Picture Archive/Hans Deryk; Page 84: Dick Hemingway; Page 90: Dick Hemingway; Page 92: Dick Hemingway; Page 94: CP Picture Archive/Byron Rollins; Page 102: Dick Hemingway; Page 107: Bluestone Productions/SuperStock; Page 109: Dick Hemingway; Page 110: © Bettmann/CORBIS/MAGMA; Page 118: Dick Hemingway; Page 122: PhotoDisc/ED001366; Page 126: Dick Hemingway; Page 135: Dick Hemingway

Chapter 3 Page 140: EyeWire/ETE_032; Page 141: Edward R. Tufte, *The Visual Display of Quantitative Information*, Graphics Press, 1983; Page 143: (left) Dick Hemingway, (right) Anne Bradley/Nelson; Page 150: EyeWire/ETE_032; Page 151: PhotoDisc/ED001308; Page 154: © Myrleen Ferguson/PhotoEdit/PictureQuest; Page 157: Dick Hemingway; Page 162: EyeWire/ETE_032; Page 167: CP Picture Archive/Jim Fox; Page 172: (top left) Copyright 1996 Geotyme Enterprises. Unauthorized use prohibited. Reproduced by permission of Bohdan Petyhyrycz, (top right) Copyright 1996 Geotyme Enterprises. Unauthorized use prohibited. Reproduced by permission of Bohdan Petyhyrycz, (bottom left) EyeWire/ETE_032; Page 175: CORBIS/MAGMA; Page 179: EyeWire/ETE_032; Page 188: EyeWire/ETE_032; Page 190: CP Picture Archive/Julie Jacobson; Page 193: CP Picture Archive/Aaron Harris; Page 196: EyeWire/ETE_032

Chapter 4 Page 203: © Comstock Images/KS14429; Page 206: Anne Bradley/Nelson; Page 209: Anne Bradley/Nelson; Page 211: CP Picture Archive/Ryan Remiorz; Page 214: North Wind Picture Archives; Page 217: Anne Bradley/Nelson; Page 219: © Bob Rowan; Progressive Image/CORBIS/MAGMA; Page 221: Reprinted with permission from The Master and Fellows of Gonville and Caius College, Cambridge; Page 228: CORBIS/MAGMA; Page 231: Jaume Gaul/Firstlight.ca; Page 233: Lee Canfield/SuperStock; Page 235: PhotoDisc/TR000757; Page 237: Ron Watts/Firstlight.ca; Page 239: CP Picture Archive/Mike Derer; Page 244: CP Picture Archive/Jonathan Hayward; Page 246: Anne Bradley/Nelson; Page 251: Anne Bradley/Nelson; Page 256: Anne Bradley/Nelson; Page 264: PhotoDisc/SP000240

Chapter 5 Page 272: Corel; Page 273: EyeWire/MPE_001; Page 277: PhotoDisc/BU002476; Page 278: (top left) Dick Hemingway, (bottom left) PhotoDisc/BU003803; Page 280: Corel; Page 283: Chu Shih-Chieh's *Precious Mirror of the Four Elements*, published in 1303; Page 284: © Archivo Iconografico, S.A./CORBIS/MAGMA; Page 302: Corel; Page 323: Corel

Chapter 6 Page 328: CORBIS/MAGMA; Page 337: CORBIS/MAGMA; Page 338: (top left) EyeWire/ETE_053, (bottom left) CORBIS/MAGMA; Page 344: CP Picture Archive/Paul Henry; Page 346: CORBIS/MAGMA; Page 358: CORBIS/MAGMA; Page 363: (top) The Thamesville Maize, home of Ken & Ingrid Dieleman, **www.cornfieldmaze.com**. Photo taken by: Austin Wright, (bottom left) CORBIS/MAGMA; Page 371: PhotoDisc/AA029223; Page 380: CP Picture Archive/Ray Smith; Page 382: CORBIS/MAGMA; Page 383: PhotoDisc/ED000236